Framework MATHS 7

TEACHER'S BOOK

David Capewell Formerly Westfield School, Sheffield
Marguerite Comyns Queen Mary's High School, Walsall
Gillian Flinton All Saints Catholic High School, Sheffield
Geoff Fowler Maths Strategy Manager, Birmingham
Kam Grewal-Joy Mathematics Consultant
Derek Huby Mathematics Consultant, West Sussex
Peter Johnson Wellfield High School, Leyland, Lancashire
Penny Jones Waverley School, Birmingham
Jayne Kranat Langley Park School for Girls, Bromley
Ian Molyneux St. Bedes RC High School, Ormskirk
Peter Mullarkey Netherhall School, Maryport, Cumbria
Nina Patel Ifield Community College, West Sussex

Great Clarendon Street, Oxford OX2 6DP

Oxford University Press is a department of the University of Oxford.
It furthers the University's objective of excellence in research, scholarship, and education by publishing worldwide in

Oxford New York

Auckland Cape Town Dar es Salaam Hong Kong Karachi
Kuala Lumpur Madrid Melbourne Mexico City Nairobi
New Delhi Shanghai Taipei Toronto

With offices in

Argentina Austria Brazil Chile Czech Republic France Greece
Guatemala Hungary Italy Japan Poland Portugal Singapore
South Korea Switzerland Thailand Turkey Ukraine Vietnam

Oxford is a registered trade mark of Oxford University Press in the UK and in certain other countries

First published 2002

British Library Cataloguing in Publication Data

Data available

ISBN-13: 978-0-19-914846-2
ISBN-10: 0-19-914846-5

10 9 8 7

Typeset by Mathematical Composition Setters Ltd.

Printed and bound by Bell and Bain, UK.

Acknowledgements
The photograph on the cover is reproduced courtesy of Pictor International (UK).

The publishers and authors would like to thank the following for permission to use photographs and other copyright material: Corbis UK, pages 1, 12, 165 and 235, Robert Harding, pages 12, 18 and 230, Empics, page 29, Anthony Blake Photo Library, pages 39 and 68, Pictor International UK, page 157.

Figurative artwork by Jeff Anderson.

The authors would like to thank
Sarah Caton, Karen Greenway, Lyn Lynam, David Shiers and Karl Warsi for their help in compiling this book.

About this book

This book has been written specifically to help you implement the Framework for Teaching Mathematics with students who have gained a Level 2 or 3 at the end of KS2. The content is based on the Year 5 and 6 teaching objectives from the Primary Framework but ensures access to Year 7 objectives. To make the most of the material contained in this book it is strongly recommended that your students use the corresponding Student Book as shown on the back cover.

The authors are experienced teachers and maths consultants, who have been incorporating the approaches of the Framework into their teaching for many years and so are well qualified to help you successfully introduce the objectives in your classroom.

The book is made up of units which follow the support tier of the medium-term plans that complement the Framework document, following the pitch, pace and progression.
The units are:

Each unit comprises double page spreads which should take a lesson to teach. These are shown on the full contents list.

References are made to resource material available on CD-ROM. There is more information about the CD-ROM on the back cover.

How to use this book

This book is organised into double page spreads that correspond to a 50–60 minute lesson. The left-hand page gives suggestions for an engaging three-part lesson.

The **mental starter** is designed to be inclusive, that is all students should be able to participate most of the time. It usually provides a lead-in to the concepts of the main lesson.

An overview of the **teaching objectives** covered in each unit is provided on the first page of a unit so you can include references in your scheme of work.

Useful resources are listed here including CD-ROM references. These are also listed at the beginning of each unit so you can be fully prepared in advance.

The **introductory activity** will help you bring the associated student book to life as it provides engaging questions that will help students discuss the mathematical ideas.

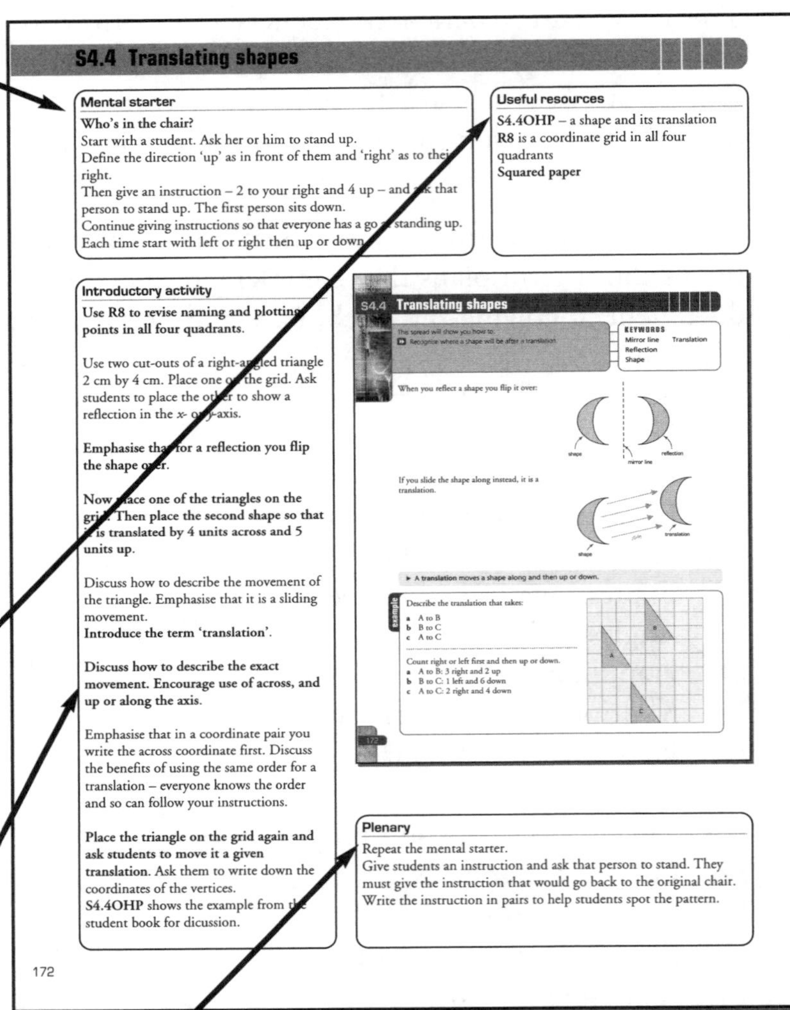

The **plenary** is a vital part of the three-part lesson, suggesting a way of rounding up the learning and helping to overcome any difficulties students may have faced.

The right-hand page of each spread corresponds to the student book exercise and will help you to make the most of the material provided.

Further activities are suggested that extend the questions provided, meaning you are unlikely to run out of work for students to do.

The exercises contain three levels of **differentiation**: lead-in, focus and challenge. These three levels are highlighted to make it easier for you differentiate within ability groups and to manage the learning environment effectively.
Relevant Springboard 7 activities are listed in the appropriate place so you can easily integrate them into the scheme.

Further activities

Students create their own diagrams as in question 2 but using all four quadrants and challenge a partner to translate the shape a given distance and direction.

Challenge students to consider the coordinates of the vertices of the object and the image following a translation and to generalise if possible.

Differentiation

Support questions:
- Question 1 involves recognising translations.
- Question 2 focuses on plotting points and translating shapes.
- The further activity focuses on translating shapes in all four quadrants.

Core tier: focuses on rotation.

Exercise S4.4

1 Describe these translations.
The first one is done for you.

a A→B $\begin{pmatrix}\text{6 right}\\ \text{1 up}\end{pmatrix}$
b D→B
c G→D
d E→F
e H→I
f I→H
g A→F
h F→D
i F→G
j A→D
k B→C

2 On squared paper draw: the x-axis from $x = 0$ to $x = 13$
the y-axis from $y = 0$ to $y = 13$
Plot each shape on the same grid.
- Name each shape.
- Translate each shape.
- Write down the coordinates of the translated shape.

A (3, 12) (6, 13) (6, 11) (3, 12) Translate A $\begin{pmatrix}\text{1 to the left}\\ \text{5 down}\end{pmatrix}$

B (0, 9) (0, 11) (6, 11) (6, 9) (0, 9) Translate B $\begin{pmatrix}\text{5 to the right}\\ \text{3 down}\end{pmatrix}$

C (0, 6) (1, 6) (1, 8) (0, 6) Translate C $\begin{pmatrix}\text{4 to the right}\\ \text{0 up}\end{pmatrix}$

D (0, 2) (1, 2) (1, 3) (2, 3) (2, 1) (0, 1) (0, 2) Translate D $\begin{pmatrix}\text{4 to the right}\\ \text{3 up}\end{pmatrix}$

E (3, 2) (5, 3) (3, 1) (3, 2) Translate E $\begin{pmatrix}\text{8 to the right}\\ \text{6 up}\end{pmatrix}$

F (5, 1) (5, 2) (6, 2) (6, 3) (7, 3) (7, 1) (5, 1) Translate F $\begin{pmatrix}\text{4 to the right}\\ \text{3 up}\end{pmatrix}$

173

Exercise commentary

The questions assess Primary Framework Page 107.
Problem solving
The further activity assesses Primary Framework Page 81.
Group work
The further activity is suitable for pair work.
Misconceptions
Students plot (y, x) instead of (x, y).
Emphasise that x comes before y in the alphabet and similarly a for across comes before u for up so plot x then y.
The common error with translations is to translate by the wrong amount, typically getting vertices mixed up.
Encourage students to focus on one particular vertex to decide where to place the shape. If necessary they can then repeat with another vertex.
Tracing the shapes and moving the paper can help students to spot errors.
Links
2-D shapes: Primary Framework Page 103.

Homework

S4.4HW provides practice in translating shapes.

Answers

1 b 4 right and 5 up c 3 right and 4 up d 4 right e 4 right and 1 up
f 4 left and 1 down g 8 right and 4 down h 6 left
i 9 left and 4 down j 2 right and 4 down k Not a translation
2 A Isosceles triangle; (2, 7), (5, 8), (5, 6), (2, 7)
B Rectangle; (5, 6), (5, 8), (11, 8), (11, 6), (5, 6)
C Right-angled triangle; (4, 6), (5, 6), (5, 8), (4, 6)
D Hexagon; (4, 5), (5, 5), (5, 6), (6, 6), (6, 4), (4, 4), (4, 5)
E Scalene triangle; (11, 8), (13, 9), (11, 7), (11, 8)
F Hexagon; (9, 4), (9, 5), (10, 5), (10, 6), (11, 6), (11, 4), (9, 4)

173

The **exercise commentary** shows the Primary Framework coverage and there is an overview on the first page of each unit.

Problem solving is integrated throughout and the opportunities in each exercise are clearly highlighted here so you can make the most of them.

Opportunities for **group work** are highlighted so that you can vary the ways students learn.

Common **misconceptions** are highlighted and there are suggestions for helping students overcome difficulties. This is designed to avoid longer term problems arising.

Links to other subject areas are clearly highlighted to help you design your own scheme of work. Helping students make links with other subject areas can contribute to a whole-school numeracy policy.

The **answers** to the exercises are given so that you have all the information you need.

Homework sheets from the CD-ROM are described so you can quickly choose which ones to use.

Contents

Mental starters

Objectives covered in this unit:

- Count on and back in steps.
- Recall multiplication facts to 10 × 10 and derive associated division facts.

Resources needed

* means class set needed

Essential:

R7 (OHP) – Function machines

A1.3OHP – Sequence patterns

Useful:

R17 – 100 square

R19 (OHP) – ruler

A1.1OHP – Sequence descriptions

A1.2ICT* – Generating sequences in Excel

Bags of sugar

A1 Sequences and functions

This unit will show you how to:

- Recognise and extend number sequences.
- Make general statements about odd or even numbers.
- Recognise multiples up to 10 × 10.
- Understand and use the relationships between the four operations.
- Develop from explaining a generalised relationship in words to expressing it in a formula using symbols.
- Solve mathematical problems or puzzles, recognise and explain patterns and relationships, generalise and predict.

Many natural patterns grow according to a sequence.

Before you start

You should know how to ...	Check in
1 Count on or back in steps of any size.	1 **a** Count on from 2 in steps of 3: 2, _, _, _, _ **b** Count back from 20 in steps of 4: 20, _, _, _, _
2 Use × and ÷ facts for 2, 5, 10 tables.	2 Write down the answer to each question: **a** 2 × 10 = __ **b** 18 ÷ 2 = _ **c** 4 × 5 = __ **d** 35 ÷ 5 = __ **e** 40 ÷ 4 = __ **f** 60 ÷ 10 = _ **g** 3 × 10 = __ **h** 40 ÷ 5 = _
3 Use a 10 × 10 multiplication grid.	3 Use a multiplication grid to work out the answer to each question: **a** 24 ÷ 6 = _ **b** 35 ÷ 7 = __ **c** 5 × __ = 35 **d** _ × 6 = 36 **e** __ ÷ 4 = 36 **f** 72 ÷ 9 = _ **g** 8 × __ = 48 **h** 7 × __ = 56

1

Unit commentary

Aim of the unit

This unit aims to consolidate students' ability to extend number sequences from rules, patterns and function machines, and it introduces the idea of using letters to stand for numbers.

Introduction

Discuss what students understand by the term sequence: numbers that grow according to a pattern or rule, and identify sequences they already know.

Emphasise that there are many naturally occurring sequences: spirals, sunflowers, pineapples etc.

Framework references

This unit focuses on:

- Year 6 teaching objectives pages: 17, 19, 53, 55, 59
- Problem solving objectives pages: 79, 81

The unit provides access to:

- Year 7 teaching objectives pages: 112, 144, 146, 148, 150, 160, 162

Check in activity

Ask questions based on the multiplication grid printed at the end of the book.

Start with straightforward multiplication questions:

- Work out 3 × 8, 6 × 7 etc.

Develop to giving the answer and asking for the question:

- The answer is 54, what is the question?

Discuss possibilities.

Differentiation

Core tier focuses on generating sequences using a term-to-term rule and recognising algebraic conventions.

Springboard 7

Pages 50, 51, 52.

Mental starter

Count on

- Choose a number to start with, say 7.
- Go around the class, with each student adding 3: 7, 10, 13, ...
- Use different start numbers and step sizes.

Useful resources

A1.1OHP contains some different numerical sequences for discussion.

Introductory activity

Write down the sequence of even numbers and ask if students can see the pattern.
Encourage them to describe the pattern in words, using accurate language.

Define 'sequence' and 'term.'
Discuss everyday things that follow sequences, for example house numbers along a street.
Ask students if they know how their street is numbered.

Emphasise the importance of using a rule to describe a sequence, and to generate terms.
A1.1OHP contains various numerical sequences for discussion.

Ask students to generate a variety of sequences.

- Always start at 10, and then ask individuals to perform an operation on it, for example 'add 4'.
- Go around the class, keeping the rule simple but building up the pace and confidence.

Refer back to the mental starter.

Emphasise the importance of stating the first term as well as the rule.
Give some examples of incomplete instructions, for example 'start at 3 and then subtract'.
Ask students to write down the sequence and then discuss why they are not all the same.

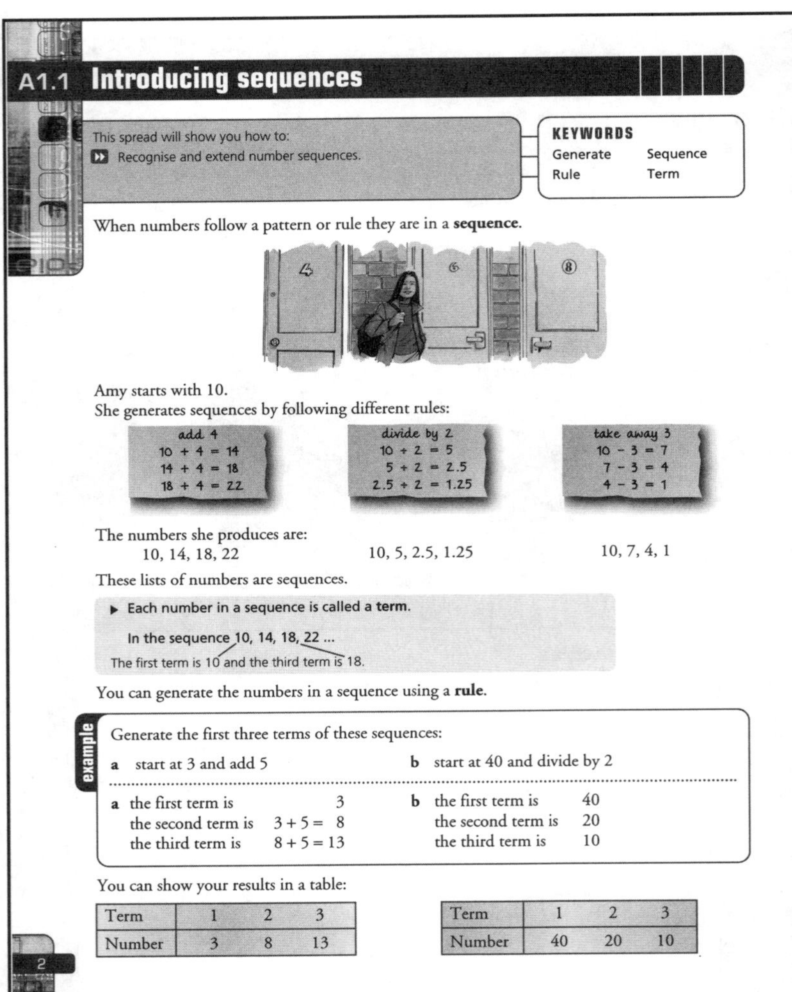

A1.1 Introducing sequences

This spread will show you how to:
- Recognise and extend number sequences.

KEYWORDS
Generate, Sequence, Rule, Term

When numbers follow a pattern or rule they are in a **sequence**.

Amy starts with 10.
She generates sequences by following different rules:

add 4	divide by 2	take away 3
10 + 4 = 14	10 ÷ 2 = 5	10 − 3 = 7
14 + 4 = 18	5 ÷ 2 = 2.5	7 − 3 = 4
18 + 4 = 22	2.5 ÷ 2 = 1.25	4 − 3 = 1

The numbers she produces are:
10, 14, 18, 22   10, 5, 2.5, 1.25   10, 7, 4, 1

These lists of numbers are sequences.

- Each number in a sequence is called a **term**.

In the sequence 10, 14, 18, 22 ...
The first term is 10 and the third term is 18.

You can generate the numbers in a sequence using a **rule**.

example

Generate the first three terms of these sequences:

a start at 3 and add 5 **b** start at 40 and divide by 2

a the first term is 3
the second term is 3 + 5 = 8
the third term is 8 + 5 = 13

b the first term is 40
the second term is 20
the third term is 10

You can show your results in a table:

Term	1	2	3
Number	3	8	13

Term	1	2	3
Number	40	20	10

2

Plenary

Repeat the Count on mental starter, but this time ask students to volunteer the start number and the difference.

Further activities

Ask students to make up sequences of their own for partners to describe as in question 1.

Confident students can be challenged to make up a sequence that has a negative third term.

Differentiation

Support questions:

- Question 1 is a straightforward question about describing arithmetic sequences – weak students may need help with subtractions in parts d and e.
- In questions 2 and 3 students extend number sequences using any of the four rules. Springboard 7, page 51.
- Question 4 extends students' understanding of arithmetic sequences through an investigation. Springboard 7, page 50.

Core tier: focuses on describing sequences using a rule.

Exercise A1.1

1 Describe these sequences in words:
Copy and complete the sentences.

- **a** 2, 4, 6, 8, ... Start at _____ and _____ _____.
- **b** 3, 5, 7, 9, ... Start at _____ and _____ _____.
- **c** 5, 10, 15, 20, ... Start at _____ and _____ _____.
- **d** 20, 18, 16, 14, ... Start at _____ and _____ _____.
- **e** 30, 27, 24, 21, ... Start at _____ and _____ _____.

2 Write down the first five terms of these sequences:

- **a** The first term is 2. The rule is +7.
- **b** The first term is 100. The rule is −10.
- **c** The first term is 12. The rule is double.
- **d** The first term is 25. The rule is +4.
- **e** The first term is 80. The rule is ÷2.
- **f** The first term is 4. The rule is ×3.
- **g** The first term is 200. The rule is ÷2.
- **h** The first term is 1. The rule is ×3.
- **i** The first term is 2. The rule is ×5.
- **j** The first term is 5. The rule is ×10.

3 Amy starts with 16 and generates sequences using the following rules:

a add 3 **b** multiply by 2 **c** divide by 2

For each of these sequences write down the first five terms. Show your results in a table like this:

Term	1	2	3	4	5
a	16				
b	16				
c	16				

4 **Investigation**
The house numbers on Joe's street are arranged like this:

2	4	6	8	10	12
11	9	7	5	3	1

Joe lives at number 7.

- **a** What number house is opposite Joe's?
- **b** Describe the sequence of house numbers on the side opposite Joe's house.

The street is extended and the houses are renumbered like this:

- **c** What number does Joe live opposite now?
- **d** What number does Jack live at if he lives opposite number 11? Investigate further.

Exercise commentary

The questions assess the objectives on Primary Framework Page 17.

Problem solving
Question 4 assesses the objective from Primary Framework Page 79 and question 1 assesses Page 81.

Group work
Students may work in pairs in questions 1 and 2 and in particular discuss how to extend the sequences in 2e and 2g further.

Misconceptions
A common mistake is to assume that sequences cannot be continued into fractions, decimals and negatives.
Discuss questions 1d, 1e, 2b, 2e, 2g and 3c as a group. Use a number line to illustrate that subtractions can continue beyond zero and to illustrate that divisions divide the distance between two points and can continue indefinitely.

Links
Mental methods: Primary Framework Pages 39, 41, 59, 61.
Negative numbers: Page 15.

Homework

A1.1HW requires students to complete the first few terms of a sequence.

Answers

1 **a** Start at 2 and add 2. **b** Start at 3 and add 2. **c** Start at 5 and add 5.
d Start at 20 and subtract 2. **e** Start at 30 and subtract 3.

2 **a** 2, 9, 16, 23, 30 **b** 100, 90, 80, 70, 60 **c** 12, 24, 48, 96, 192
d 25, 29, 33, 37, 41 **e** 80, 40, 20, 10, 5 **f** 4, 12, 36, 108, 324
g 200, 100, 50, 25, 12.5 **h** 1, 3, 9, 27, 81 **i** 2, 10, 50, 250, 1250
j 5, 50, 500, 5000, 50 000

3 **a** 16, 19, 22, 25, 28 **b** 16, 32, 64, 128, 256 **c** 16, 8, 4, 2, 1

4 **a** 6 **b** Start at 2 and add 2. **c** 14 **d** 10

A1.2 Sequences and rules

Mental starter

Count down

- Give students a start number, say 50.
- Students count down in 2s: 50, 48, 46, ...
- Repeat with different start numbers and step sizes.

Useful resources

R17 contains a 100 square for the class to identify sequences.

Introductory activity

Reiterate that the rule to describe a sequence should give the start number and the way to find the next number.
Give an example of an incomplete instruction, for example 'start at 3 and then subtract', and discuss why it is insufficient.
Students can write down the sequence and then compare sequences to show they are different.

Recap the words 'sequence' and 'term'.
Write these sequences on the board:
2, 6, 10, 14, 18, ..., ...
17, 14, 11, 8, ..., ...
and ask students to describe them.

Ask students what the next three terms of each sequence will be.
You could ask for individual responses or a whole-class response using (**R1**) digit cards.

Encourage students to find and describe sequences in the numbers 1 to 100.
Use a '100 square' (**R17**) and ask students to identify patterns within it, for example in the leading diagonal
1, 12, 23, 34, ...
Ask groups of students to identify patterns, and then they can describe their pattern for the rest of the class to solve.

Encourage precise language, in particular the use of the words 'sequence', 'rule' and 'term'.

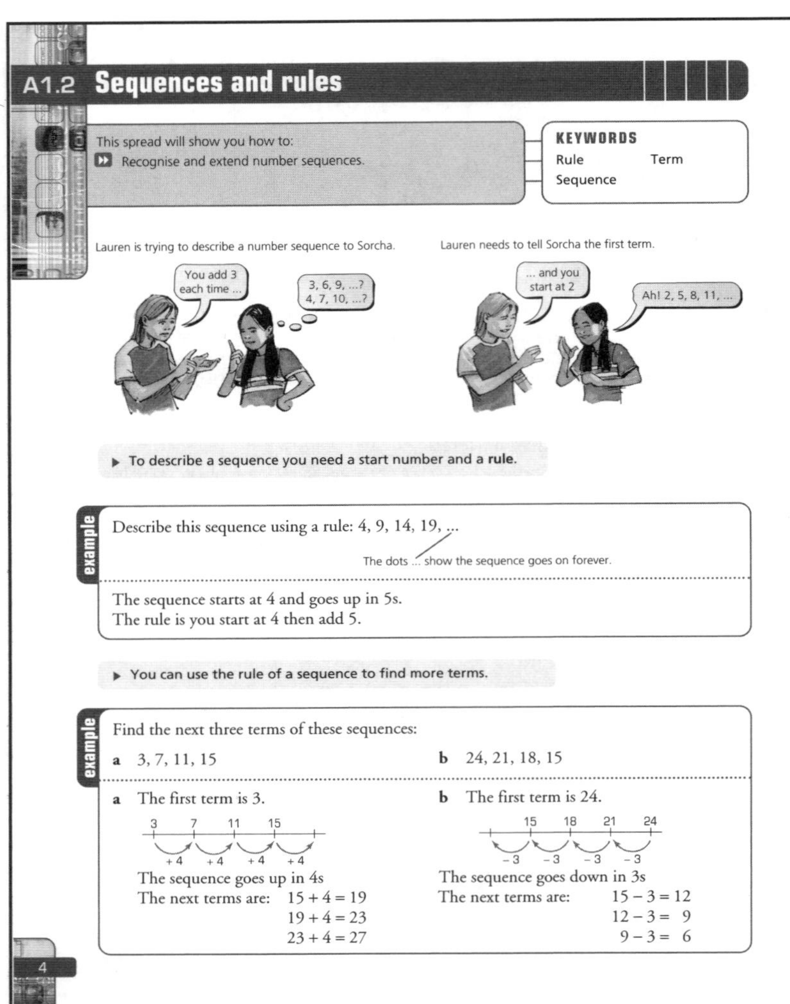

A1.2 **Sequences and rules**

This spread will show you how to:
- Recognise and extend number sequences.

KEYWORDS
Rule
Term
Sequence

Lauren is trying to describe a number sequence to Sorcha.

Lauren needs to tell Sorcha the first term.

- To describe a sequence you need a start number and a **rule**.

example

Describe this sequence using a rule: 4, 9, 14, 19, ...

The dots ... show the sequence goes on forever.

The sequence starts at 4 and goes up in 5s.
The rule is you start at 4 then add 5.

- You can use the rule of a sequence to find more terms.

example

Find the next three terms of these sequences:

a 3, 7, 11, 15

b 24, 21, 18, 15

a The first term is 3.

The sequence goes up in 4s
The next terms are: $15 + 4 = 19$
$19 + 4 = 23$
$23 + 4 = 27$

b The first term is 24.

The sequence goes down in 3s
The next terms are: $15 - 3 = 12$
$12 - 3 = 9$
$9 - 3 = 6$

4

Plenary

- Explore the Fibonacci sequence; you could give the first few terms: 1, 1, 2, 3, 5, ... and see if the class can guess the next term.
- You could do this with digit cards, so individuals have a chance to work it out for themselves.
- Give students the first two terms of a variation, for example 2 and 5, and ask for the 6th and 7th terms.

Further activities

In **A1.2ICT**, students use spreadsheets to generate simple integer sequences using a term-to-term rule.

Alternatively

Ask students to investigate question 1f to find a rule for each of the times tables. Confident students can be challenged to make up a sequence that has two rules, for example: ×3 and +1.

Differentiation

Support questions:

- Questions 1 and 2 are straightforward questions about describing arithmetic sequences.
- In questions 3 and 4 students generate number sequences using any of the four rules.
- Question 5 requires a good understanding of how sequences are generated as students will find more than one rule. Springboard 7, page 51.

Core tier: focuses on generating terms of a sequence using a rule.

Exercise A1.2

1 Copy and complete these statements for each of these sequences:

- The first term is ____
- The rule is ____ ____
- The next three terms are ____, ____, ____

a 2, 5, 8, 11 b 2, 3, 4, 5
c 20, 18, 16, 14, 12 d 5, 7, 9, 11, 13
e 2, 10, 18, 26 f 3, 6, 9, 12, 15
g 30, 26, 22, 18, 14 h 20, 40, 60, 80
i 7, 21, 63, 189 j 0, 6, 12, 18, 24

You may need a calculator for part i.

2 Describe these sequences in words.
Use your rule to find the next two terms.
a 25, 21, 17, 13 ...
b 3, 10, 17, 24 ...
c 16, 19, 22, 25 ...
d 5, 10, 20, 40 ...

3 Write down the first five terms of these sequences:
a start at 4, each term is 2 bigger than the one before it
b the first term is 7, and each term is 4 larger
c the first term is 19, and each term is 3 smaller
d the first term is 6, and each term is 1.5 larger
e the second term is 13, and each term is 7 larger

4 a Make up a sequence where the second term is 5. Describe it in words.
Here is an example: 3, 5, 7, 9, 11.
b Make up a sequence where the second term is 3. Describe it in words.
c Make up a sequence where the second term is 2. Describe it in words.
d Make up a sequence where the third term is 5. Describe it in words.

5 A sequence starts: 1, 2,

The sequence could be: 1, 2, 3, 4, 5, ...
The first term is 1 and the rule is + 1.

The sequence could also be: 1, 2, 4, 8, 16, ...
The first term is 1 and the rule is × 2.

Find two different ways to continue each of these sequences.
Describe each of your rules.
a 2, 4, __, __, __ or 2, 4, __, __, __
b 1, 3, __, __, __ or 1, 3, __, __, __
c 5, 10, __, __, __ or 5, 10, __, __, __

5

Exercise commentary

The questions assess the objectives on Primary Framework Page 17.

Problem solving

Question 5 assesses the objective from Primary Framework Page 79 and questions 1 and 2 assess Page 81.

Group work

The language used in question 3 could be discussed as a group before students attempt the questions.
Students will benefit from working in pairs on question 5.

Misconceptions

Students will often just look at the first two terms to determine the rule.
Questions 1e, 1f, 1h and 1j in particular will highlight this, and question 5 will encourage students to see why you need to use all the terms.
Emphasise the need to check the rule works with all the given terms.
In question 4 many students will assume they are given the first term.
Discuss 4b as a group to highlight this.

Links

Mental methods: Primary Framework Pages 38–41, 58–61.
Negative numbers: Page 15.

Homework

A1.2HW requires students to describe sequences in words, and to describe missing terms.

Answers

1 **a** 2; add 3; 14, 17, 20 **b** 2; add 1; 6, 7, 8 **c** 20; subtract 2; 10, 8, 6
d 5; add 2; 15, 17, 19 **e** 2; add 8; 34, 42, 50 **f** 3; add 3; 18, 21, 24
g 30; subtract 4; 10, 6, 2 **h** 20; add 20; 100, 120, 140
i 7; times 3; 567, 1701, 5103 **j** 0; add 6; 30, 36, 42
2 **a** Start at 25 then subtract 4; 9, 5. **b** Start at 3 then add 7; 31, 38.
c Start at 16 then add 3; 28, 31. **d** Start at 5 then double; 80, 160.
3 **a** 4, 6, 8, 10, 12 **b** 7, 11, 15, 19, 23 **c** 19, 16, 13, 10, 7
d 6, 7.5, 9, 10.5, 12 **e** 6, 13, 20, 27, 34

A1.3 Sequences in diagrams

Mental starter

Multiply

- Give students a start number: 1.
- Ask them to multiply by a step number: 2.
- Repeat to generate the first five terms of a sequence: 1, 2, 4, 8, 16.
- Repeat with other step numbers.

Useful resources

A1.3OHP contains a sequence of square patterns for class discussion.
Multilink cubes for group work.

Introductory activity

Recap briefly what students should know about sequences.
Ask students to describe the sequence: 1, 2, 4, 8, 16, … using the terminology they have learned, and say what the next three terms will be.

Briefly explain these common sequences: even numbers and odd numbers.
Discuss why even numbers are called even and odd numbers are called odd.
Use the bench example in the student book to help.

Show the first sequence on **A1.3OHP**.

Discuss how the sequence develops, using words.
Two blocks are added each time.
Discuss how to describe the sequence: use a start number and a rule. Repeat with the other sequences on **A1.3OHP**.

Show how multilink cubes can be used to generate simple sequences.
You could refer to the examples in the student book.

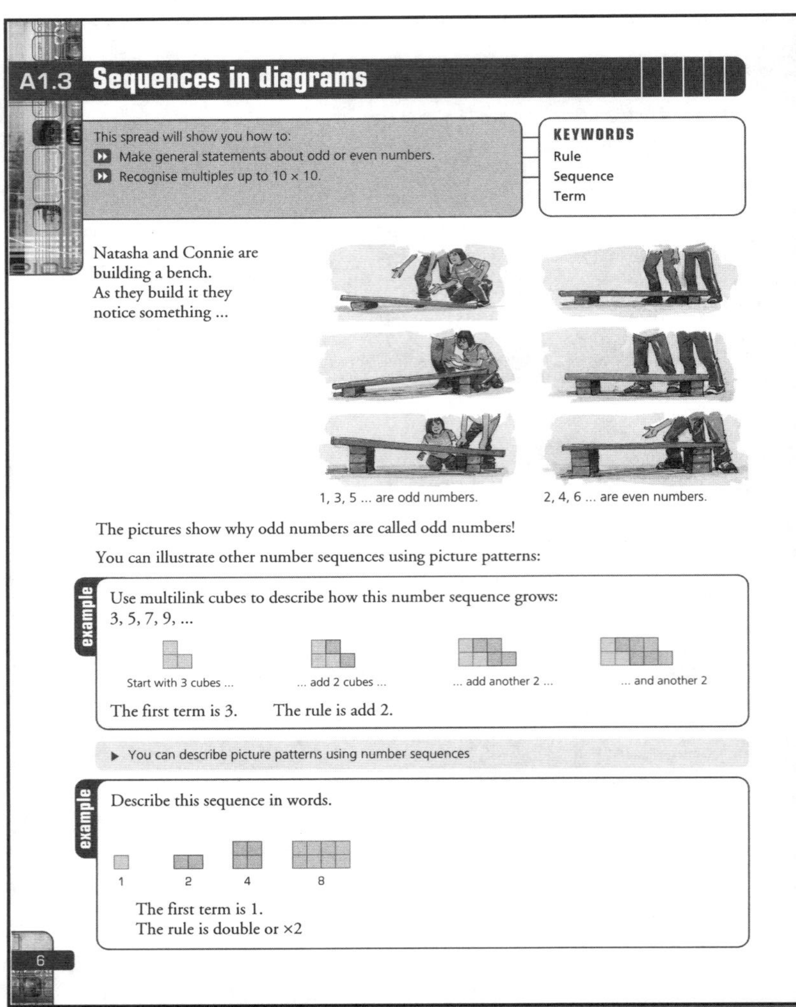

A1.3 Sequences in diagrams

This spread will show you how to:
- Make general statements about odd or even numbers.
- Recognise multiples up to 10 × 10.

KEYWORDS
Rule
Sequence
Term

Natasha and Connie are building a bench.
As they build it they notice something …

1, 3, 5 … are odd numbers.
2, 4, 6 … are even numbers.

The pictures show why odd numbers are called odd numbers!

You can illustrate other number sequences using picture patterns:

example

Use multilink cubes to describe how this number sequence grows:
3, 5, 7, 9, …

Start with 3 cubes … … add 2 cubes … … add another 2 … … and another 2

The first term is 3. The rule is add 2.

- You can describe picture patterns using number sequences

example

Describe this sequence in words.

1 2 4 8

The first term is 1.
The rule is double or ×2

6

Plenary

Discuss the exercise, particularly question 4.
Ask students to describe the multilink patterns that they made to represent the different types of sequence.

Further activities

Students can work out the number of squares in the 10th pattern in question 1. They can try to describe how to find the rule for any pattern.

In question 4 students can draw a pattern for the 'three times table +1' and then compare it with the three times table.

Differentiation

Support questions:

- Question 1 is a straightforward question about describing picture patterns – weak students may use multilink cubes.
- In question 2 students predict terms of a sequence and in question 3 they need to spot patterns in a table.
- Question 4 requires students to generate patterns to describe sequences.

Core tier: focuses on uniquely describing a sequence of patterns.

Exercise A1.3

1 Describe these sequences in words.
Use the rules to find the next two numbers in each sequence.

a

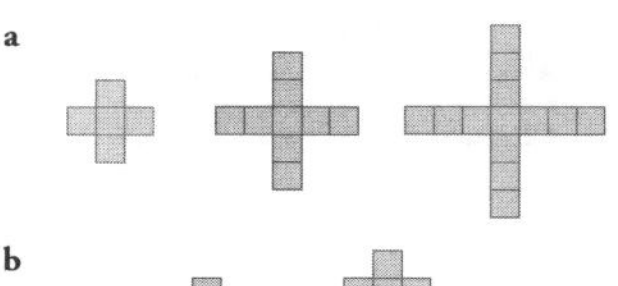

b

2 **a** How many matches are in the third term of this sequence?

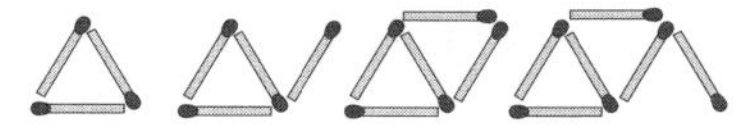

b Draw the next two patterns in the sequence.
c How many matches will be in the 8th pattern?

3 Look at the pattern in this grid.

7	9	11	
10			
	15	17	
16			

Fill in the empty squares.

4 You need a set of multilink cubes.
This pattern describes the sequence of even numbers:

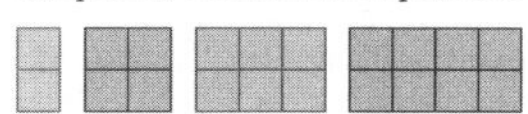

Design a pattern to describe each of these sequences:

a odd numbers
b three times table
c five times table

For each sequence, sketch the first four patterns.

Exercise commentary

The questions assess the objectives on Primary Framework Pages 17–19.

Problem solving
The exercise assesses the objective from Primary Framework Page 79.

Group work
Question 1 could form the basis of a group discussion: what are the differences between the sequences?

Misconceptions
In question 1a, some students will count the middle square twice, once horizontally and once vertically.
Encourage the use of multilink cubes or counters to try to overcome this and discuss counting strategies as a group.
In question 3 many students will find the rule for the first column and then apply it throughout the table.
Encourage the use of checking procedures to help overcome this.

Links
Mental methods: Primary Framework Pages 41, 59, 61.

Homework

A1.3HW provides practice at developing a sequence of patterns and predicting terms.

Answers

1 **a** The first term is 5. The rule is add 4. The next two terms are 17 and 21.
b The first term is 1. The rule is square the term number. The next two terms are 16 and 25.

2 **a** 5 **b** 7 matches, 8 matches **c** 10

3 7, 9, 11, 13; 10, 12, 14, 16; 13, 15, 17, 19; 16, 18, 20, 22

Mental starter

- Give the class the instruction 'multiply by 7'.
- Go around the class, giving numbers for students to apply the instruction to (no bigger than 12).
- Give the instruction 'divide by 8.'
- Repeat the exercise, but with multiples of 8 up to 96.
- Don't use any particular order; try to keep it brisk.

Useful resources

R7 contains some blank function machines for class discussion.

R19 shows a ruler marked in mm and cm.

Introductory activity

Discuss how to convert hours to minutes.

How many minutes

- in an hour?
- in two hours?

How did you work that out?

What's the rule: ×60.

Emphasise that the rule ×60 is a function as it links two measures: minutes and hours.

Write the function as:

no. of hours × 60 = no. of mins.

Introduce function machines.

Start with a simple function, such as 'multiply by 2'.

Ask the class what the output would be for various inputs.

List the outputs and inputs in a table.

Explore the sequence formed by the output numbers.

Use what the class have learned from the previous lessons to describe the sequence as a rule, such as:

The outputs form the sequence of even numbers.

Ensure that the rule offered describes the sequence uniquely, and emphasise the importance of specifying the start number.

Move on to other function machines.

Use the blank function machines on **R7**, and ask students for some simple functions to put into them.

Work out the outputs for simple inputs.

Introduce some simple two-stage function machines.

Review the initial example:

input (hours) ⟶ ×60 ⟶ output (mins)

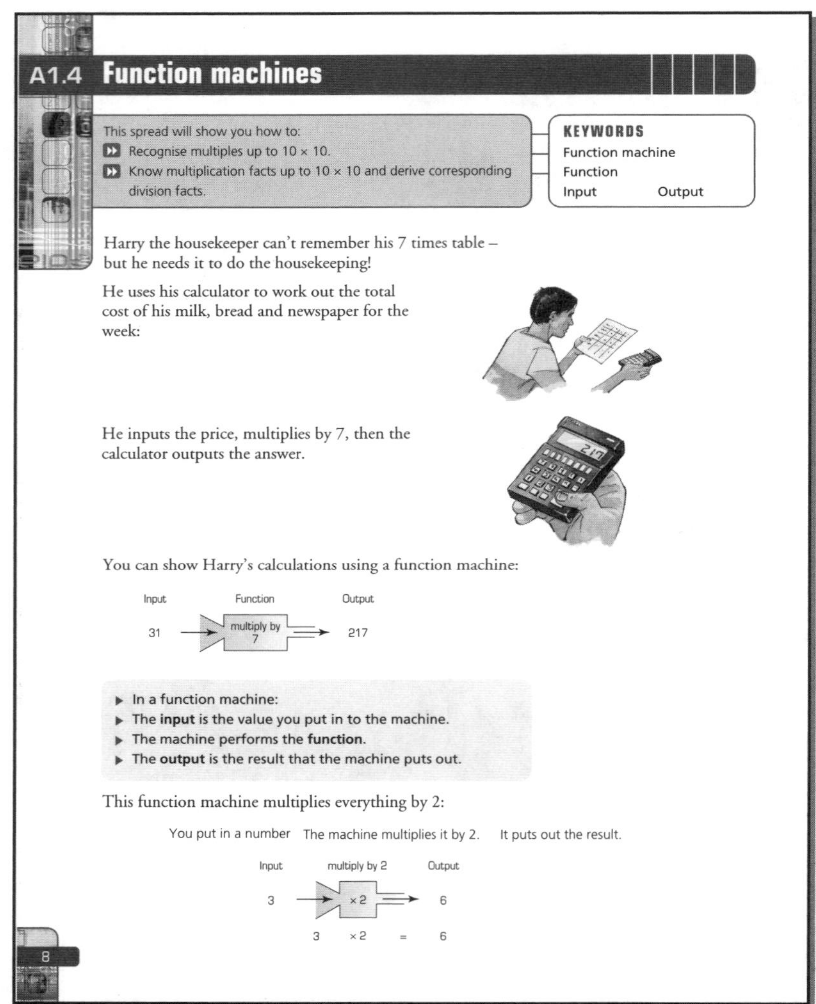

A1.4 Function machines

This spread will show you how to:

- Recognise multiples up to 10 × 10.
- Know multiplication facts up to 10 × 10 and derive corresponding division facts.

KEYWORDS
Function machine
Function
Input
Output

Harry the housekeeper can't remember his 7 times table – but he needs it to do the housekeeping!

He uses his calculator to work out the total cost of his milk, bread and newspaper for the week:

He inputs the price, multiplies by 7, then the calculator outputs the answer.

You can show Harry's calculations using a function machine:

- In a function machine:
- The **input** is the value you put in to the machine.
- The machine performs the **function**.
- The **output** is the result that the machine puts out.

This function machine multiplies everything by 2:

8

Plenary

- Hold up a ruler, or use **R19**, and discuss millimetre and centimetre conversions with the class.
- Draw a function machine on the board to show how to convert cm to mm (× 10).
- Give the class various values in cm, and ask them what the output numbers will be.

Further activities

Students could make up function machines for each other to solve as in question 1. They could give the output and ask for the input.

More able students may devise function machines with three stages for partners to solve.

Differentiation

Support questions:

- Question 1 introduces function machines – weak students may need help recording answers.
- In question 2 students use more than one input in the same machine making recording more complex.
- Questions 3 and 4 use two-stage machines which can cause difficulty.

Core tier: focuses on two-stage function machines.

Exercise A1.4

1 For these function machines, find the outputs for each of the inputs.

2 For these function machines, find the outputs for each of the inputs 1, 2 and 3.

Hint: Input 1, then 2, then 3.

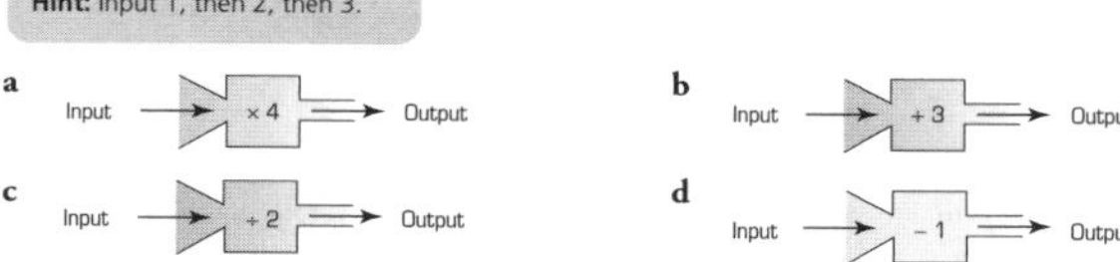

3 These function machines contain two operations.
Follow the example to find the outputs for the given inputs.

Example

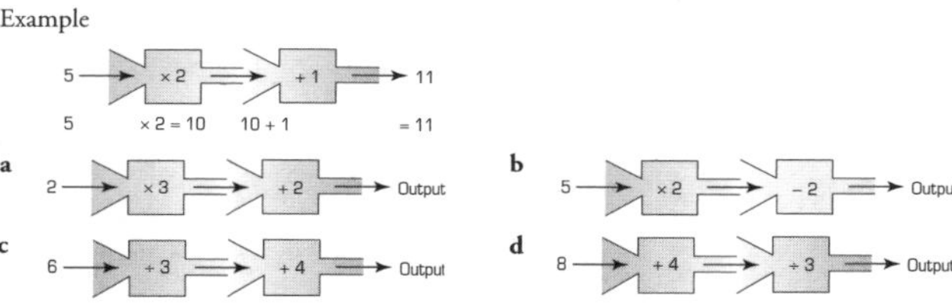

4 Investigation

a Input the values 1, 2 and 3 and work out the outputs for this function machine.

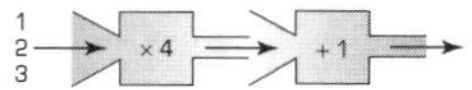

b Reverse the order of the functions (add 1 first).
Work out the outputs.
Are they the same as in (a)?

c *If you change the order of the operations you get a different output.*
Investigate this statement for the functions in question 3.

Exercise commentary

The questions assess the objectives on Primary Framework Pages 19 and 59.

Problem solving

Question 4 assesses the objective from Primary Framework Page 79.

Group work

Much of this work would benefit from class discussion before students undertake the work, in particular it is important to discuss recording in questions 2 and 3. Question 4 is suitable for paired work, as are the further activities.

Misconceptions

Many students will find recording results difficult, hence the need for class discussion.

In question 3 some students think there will be two outputs for each input – one for each machine.

Encourage a systematic approach to using two-stage machines – it may help to demonstrate the process using students as the machines at the front of the class.

Links

Function machines: Secondary Framework Page 60.

Homework

A1.4HW provides practice at using simple function machines.

Answers

1 **a** 7 **b** 15 **c** 8 **d** 48
2 **a** 4, 8, 12 **b** 4, 5, 6 **c** 0.5, 1, 1.5 **d** 0, 1, 2
3 **a** 8 **b** 8 **c** 6 **d** 4
4 **a** 5, 9, 13 **b** 8, 12, 16; no

A1.5 Finding the function

Mental starter

Back to the start

- Give students a rule: add 2.
- Give them an answer: 12
- Ask for the start: 10

Expect the answer 14. Refer back to sequences, describing 12 as the second term if that helps.
Repeat for other rules, keeping the answers simple.

Useful resources

R7 contains blank function machines.

Introductory activity

Recap vocabulary:
input, output, and function.
Draw a simple function, such as × 4, and give an input, perhaps 3. Ask for the output.

Explore simple functions with the input missing.
Draw a simple function machine or use **R7**, and give the function (a simple addition) and the output. Ask what the input could be.
Refer back to the mental starter.

Develop the problem by varying the function: use +, −, × and ÷, but keep them as single operations.

Draw a single function machine with inputs and outputs given, and ask what the function could be.
For example:

The function could be × 3, or + 4.
Discuss what information would help you decide which is the correct function.

Add another pair of values:

The function is × 3.

Repeat for other functions including − and ÷.

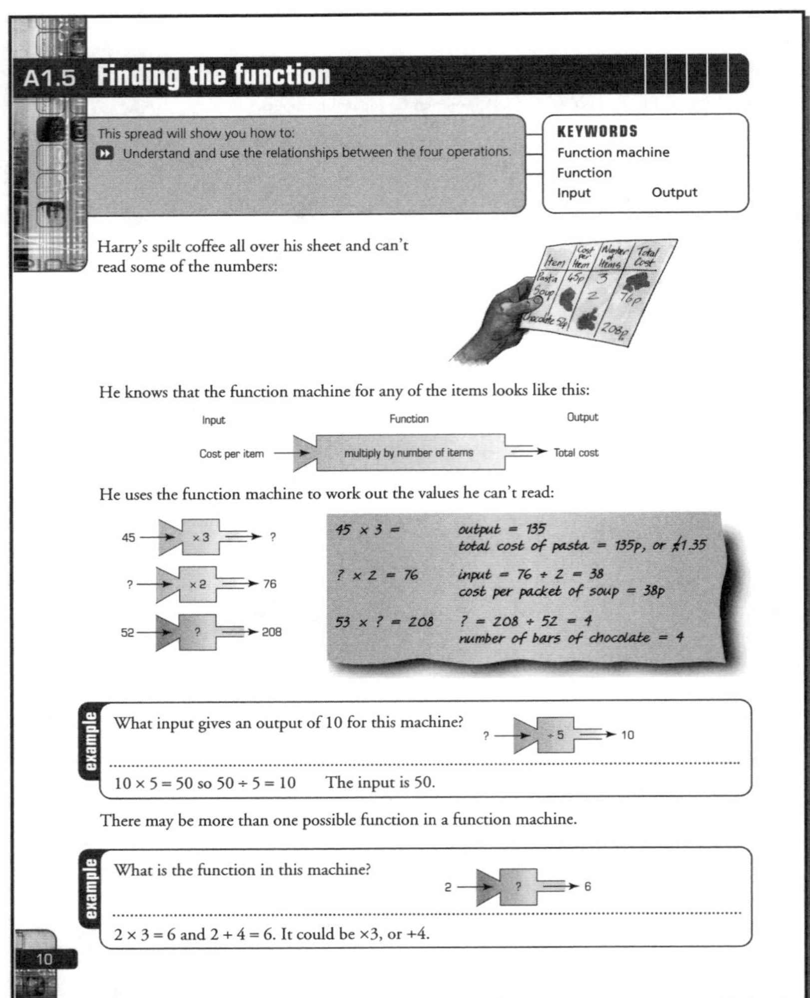

A1.5 Finding the function

This spread will show you how to:
- Understand and use the relationships between the four operations.

KEYWORDS
Function machine
Function
Input Output

Harry's spilt coffee all over his sheet and can't read some of the numbers:

He knows that the function machine for any of the items looks like this:

Input — Function — Output
Cost per item → multiply by number of items → Total cost

He uses the function machine to work out the values he can't read:

45 → ×3 → ?
? → ×2 → 76
52 → ? → 208

45 × 3 = output = 135
total cost of pasta = 135p, or £1.35
? × 2 = 76 input = 76 ÷ 2 = 38
cost per packet of soup = 38p
53 × ? = 208 ? = 208 ÷ 52 = 4
number of bars of chocolate = 4

example
What input gives an output of 10 for this machine? ? → ÷5 → 10

10 × 5 = 50 so 50 ÷ 5 = 10 The input is 50.

There may be more than one possible function in a function machine.

example
What is the function in this machine? 2 → ? → 6

2 × 3 = 6 and 2 + 4 = 6. It could be ×3, or +4.

10

Plenary

Discuss question 1 of the exercise – this will link to more formal algebra.
In particular ask how students found the inputs, and try to encourage verbally expressed rules (for example, you subtract to find the input when the function is +).
If time allows, discuss question 4.

Further activities

Students could make up function machines for each other to solve as in questions 1 and 2.

Able students could play the game question 3 using two- or three-stage function machines.

Differentiation

Support questions:

- Question 1 introduces working backwards – weak students may benefit from using 'think of a number' type sentences.
- Questions 2 and 3 involve finding the function with a one-stage machine and so involve more than one input and output.
- Question 4 uses two-stage machines which can cause difficulty although the question is similar to question 4 in Exercise A1.4.

Core tier: focuses on using a mapping diagram to find a function.

Exercise A1.5

1 For each of these function machines, work out the inputs for the given output.

a 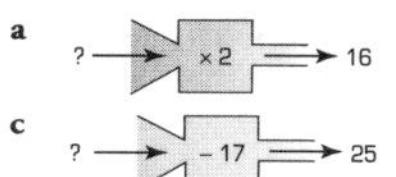

b 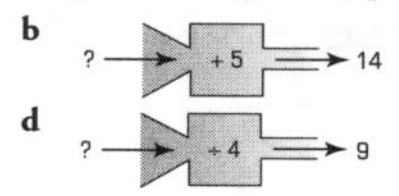

c ? → − 17 → 25

d ? → ÷ 4 → 9

2 In this function machine, the input has been multiplied by 3:

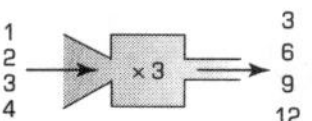

Find the function for each of these machines.

a 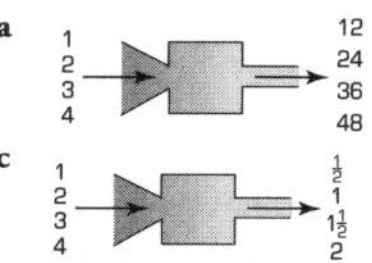

b 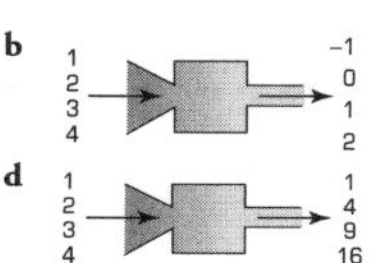

c 1, 2, 3, 4 → $\frac{1}{2}$, 1, $1\frac{1}{2}$, 2

d 1, 2, 3, 4 → 1, 4, 9, 16

3 **Function Guessing Game**

- Player 1 thinks of a function.
- Player 2 writes down an input number, for example: 1
- Player 1 works out the output, and writes it down like this: 1 → 5
- Player 2 thinks of another number, for example: 3. Player 1 writes the output.
- Continue like this:

... until Player 2 guesses the function correctly. In this case, the function is 'add 4'.

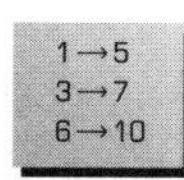

- Swap roles. Player 2 now thinks of a function.
- The winner is the player who has guessed the functions the quickest.

4 **Investigation**

a Write down the outputs for this function machine.

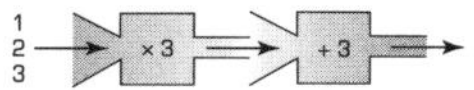

b Write down the outputs for this function machine:

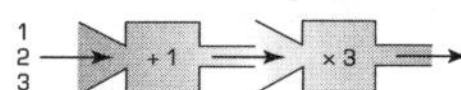

c What do you notice?
Can you find another pair of functions that give the same outputs?

Exercise commentary

The questions assess the objectives on Primary Framework Pages 45–47, 53–55.

Problem solving

Questions 3 and 4 assess the objective from Primary Framework Page 79.

Group work

Question 3 is suitable for paired work.
Question 4 could be discussed in pairs or small groups.

Misconceptions

Many students will assume that one input and output is sufficient to determine the rule.
Emphasise the use of checking procedures to ensure the rule works with all the input, output pairs.
Using more than one input as in question 4 may cause difficulty.
The use of a table or mapping diagram to record results may help.

Links

Mental methods: Primary Framework Pages 61, 63, 65.
Using checking procedures: Primary Framework Page 73.
Function machines: Secondary Framework Pages 60 and 62.

Homework

A1.5HW provides practice at finding missing functions in the context of single-stage function machines.

Answers

1 **a** 8 **b** 9 **c** 42 **d** 36
2 **a** × 12 **b** −2 **c** ÷2 **d** Square
4 **a** 6, 9, 12 **b** 6, 9, 12 **c** Same outputs

Mental starter

Operations!

- Give students a start number: 2.
- Give them a finish number: 8.
- Ask how to get from one to another using either +, −, ×, ÷.
- Students find as many ways as possible using only one operation. (+6, ×4).

Useful resources

R7 contains blank function machines.

Bags of sugar or similar for demonstration.

Introductory activity

Introduce the term 'variable'.
Recap function machines, and define inputs and outputs as variables.

Discuss a simple example of a function machine, for example 'add 3', and use mapping notation:

$1 \longrightarrow 4$
$2 \longrightarrow 5$
$3 \longrightarrow 6$

Explain that a generalisation can be useful in showing the rule.
$n \longrightarrow n + 3$

Discuss the definition of algebra. Define 'algebra' in simple terms.

Emphasise need to use basic conventions of algebra.
Discuss need to order a sentence properly:
YOU ARE HERE
and if you change the order you change the meaning.
Explain the basic convention:

- you write numbers then letters in multiplications:
  $5s$ not $s5$

Emphasise that it is better to leave out the multiplication sign × so you don't confuse it with the letter x.

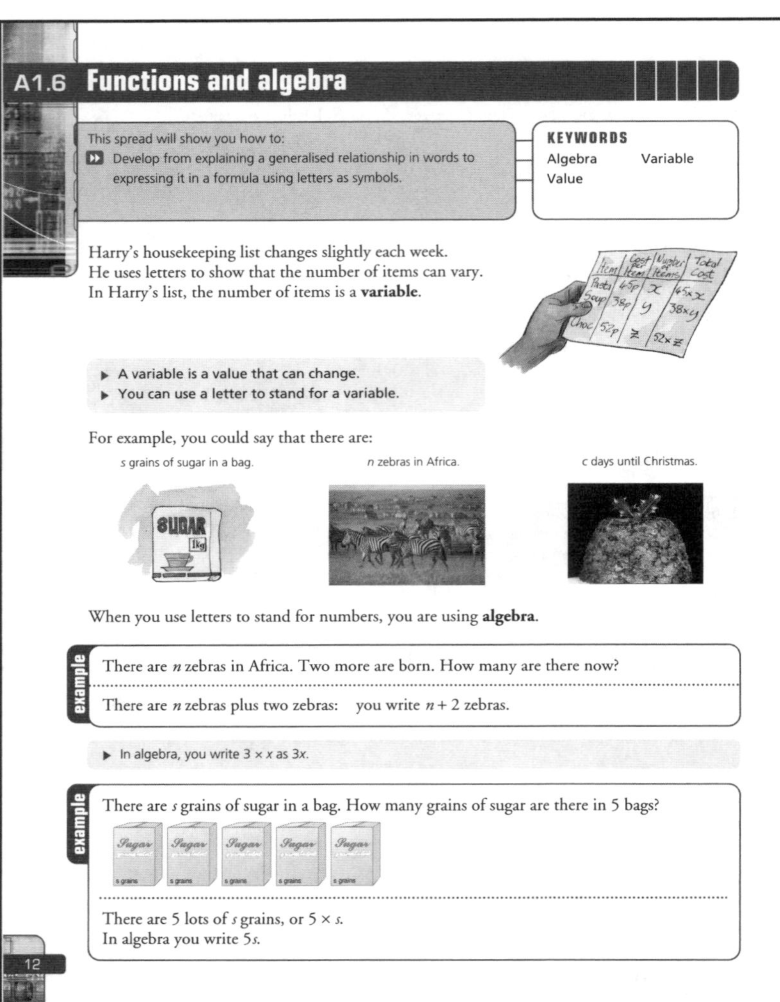

A1.6 Functions and algebra

This spread will show you how to:

- Develop from explaining a generalised relationship in words to expressing it in a formula using letters as symbols.

KEYWORDS
Algebra
Variable
Value

Harry's housekeeping list changes slightly each week.
He uses letters to show that the number of items can vary.
In Harry's list, the number of items is a **variable**.

- A variable is a value that can change.
- You can use a letter to stand for a variable.

For example, you could say that there are:

s grains of sugar in a bag. *n* zebras in Africa. *c* days until Christmas.

When you use letters to stand for numbers, you are using **algebra**.

example: There are n zebras in Africa. Two more are born. How many are there now?

There are n zebras plus two zebras: you write $n + 2$ zebras.

- In algebra, you write $3 \times x$ as $3x$.

example: There are s grains of sugar in a bag. How many grains of sugar are there in 5 bags?

There are 5 lots of s grains, or $5 \times s$.
In algebra you write $5s$.

12

Plenary

Discuss question 4, linking function machines to algebra.
If students are confident you could write a few more up on the board or use **R7**.

Further activities

Students could make up problems for each other to solve as in question 1.

Able students could discuss questions involving divisions such as describing how to share a bill or a prize between groups.

Differentiation

Support questions:

- Question 1 introduces the idea of using a letter to stand for an unknown.
- Questions 2, 3a, 3b and 3c involve writing multiplications using algebra – many students will find 2b difficult.
- Questions 3d, 3e, 3f and 4 focus on using algebra to describe each of the four rules.

Core tier: focuses on forming algebraic expressions from function machines.

Exercise A1.6

1 Write a sentence using a suitable letter to represent each of these variables.

a The number of hairs on a cat.
b The number of words in a newspaper.
c The number of skateboards in America.
d The number of trees in a forest.
e The number of mobile phones in the UK.

> For example:
> The number of cars in the world.
> There are c cars in the world.

2 Look at Harry's housekeeping list in the example on page 12.
You could write the total cost of pasta as $45x$.

a Write the weekly cost of chocolate without multiplication signs.
b Write the total weekly cost of all three items using algebra.

3 Lake Smalldrop contains p fish, q boats, and r ducks.
In Lake Bigwater, there is five times the amount of everything.
How many:

a fish **b** boats **c** ducks
are there in Lake Bigwater?

Lake Median contains 20 less ducks, 100 less fish and 5 less boats than Lake Bigwater.

Using algebra, write how many
d fish, **e** boats **f** ducks
there are on Lake Median.

4 Write the outputs for these function machines using algebra.

For example

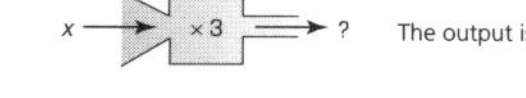

The output is 3x. You write $x \to 3x$.

a

b $x \to$ ÷4 $\to$?

c $x \to$ −5 $\to$?

d $x \to$ +8 $\to$?

Exercise commentary

The questions assess the objectives on Primary Framework Page 81.

Problem solving

Questions 2 and 3 assess the objective from Primary Framework Page 79.

Group work

Question 1 could be discussed as a group as students use different letters.

Misconceptions

Most students find the transition from using numbers and words to using symbols confusing and so it is important to concentrate on setting up good practice from the outset.

Encourage the use of letters to stand for the number of items rather than the item itself – n hairs rather than h for hair or c for cat.

Many students will confuse × and + at this stage.

Question 4 is designed to pick up any confusion – it may help for students to read the machines out loud: x times 4.

Links

Using letters to stand for numbers: Secondary Framework Page 112.

Homework

A1.6HW provides practice at writing a sentence using a letter symbol to stand for the unknown amount.

Answers

1 **a** There are h hairs on a cat.
b There are w words in a newspaper.
c There are s skateboards in America.
d There are t trees in a forest.
e There are m mobile phones in the UK.

2 **a** $52z$ **b** $45x + 38y + 52z$

3 **a** $5p$ **b** $5q$ **c** $5r$ **d** $5p - 100$ **e** $5q - 5$ **f** $5r - 20$

4 **a** $x \longrightarrow 4x$ **b** $x \longrightarrow \frac{x}{4}$ **c** $x \longrightarrow x - 5$ **d** $x \longrightarrow x + 8$

Summary

The unit provides access to the Year 7 key teaching objective:

- Use letter symbols to represent unknown numbers or variables (Secondary Framework Page 112).

Check out commentary

1 Most students will successfully continue the sequences although part **b** may cause difficulty as students tend to add rather than multiply.
Encourage students to check back through their terms once they've written a word description.
Students may continue the sequences correctly but describe the sequence incorrectly, forgetting the first term.
Encourage students to describe their rule to a partner to help overcome this.

2 Students tend to use a letter to stand for an object rather than the number of objects which can lead to later difficulties.
Encourage the use of n or x.
There are lots of opportunities to build on this work throughout the material so keeping a note of any difficulties will help you pick up on them later.

3 There are many potential difficulties here – some students will write the sequence as the pattern numbers 1, 2, 3 rather than counting the squares.
Encourage students to put the terms in a table which may help.
When predicting many students will either add 5 to the 5th term or double the 5th term rather than adding on successive differences.
Encourage students to draw the pattern to verify whether their rule works.

Plenary activity

Write the sequence: 1, 3, 6, 10, ...
Discuss how to describe the sequence in words.
Discuss strategies for predicting the 20th term.
Challenge students to draw the sequence using diagrams.

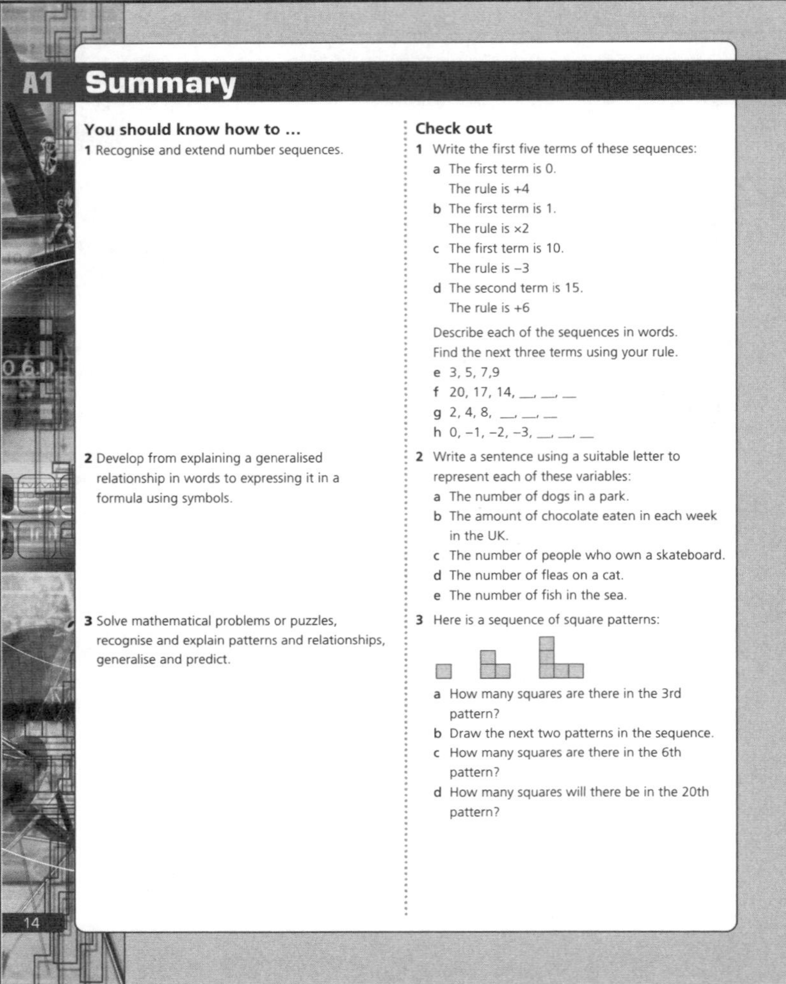

A1 Summary

You should know how to ...

Check out

1 Recognise and extend number sequences.

1 Write the first five terms of these sequences:
a The first term is 0.
The rule is +4
b The first term is 1.
The rule is ×2
c The first term is 10.
The rule is −3
d The second term is 15.
The rule is +6

Describe each of the sequences in words.
Find the next three terms using your rule.
e 3, 5, 7,9
f 20, 17, 14, __, __, __
g 2, 4, 8, __, __, __
h 0, −1, −2, −3, __, __, __

2 Develop from explaining a generalised relationship in words to expressing it in a formula using symbols.

2 Write a sentence using a suitable letter to represent each of these variables:
a The number of dogs in a park.
b The amount of chocolate eaten in each week in the UK.
c The number of people who own a skateboard.
d The number of fleas on a cat.
e The number of fish in the sea.

3 Solve mathematical problems or puzzles, recognise and explain patterns and relationships, generalise and predict.

3 Here is a sequence of square patterns:
a How many squares are there in the 3rd pattern?
b Draw the next two patterns in the sequence.
c How many squares are there in the 6th pattern?
d How many squares will there be in the 20th pattern?

14

Development

Using symbols for unknowns is developed in A2.
Using sequences is developed in A3 to include graphs.

Links

Students will have lots of opportunities to use symbols for unknowns throughout the book and in particular in number and shape. Encourage students to use the proper conventions whenever the opportunity arises.

Mental starters

Objectives covered in this unit:

- Count on and back in steps.
- Round whole numbers to the nearest 10 or 100.
- Know addition and subtraction facts to 20 and whole number complements to 100.
- Find two decimals with a sum of 1.

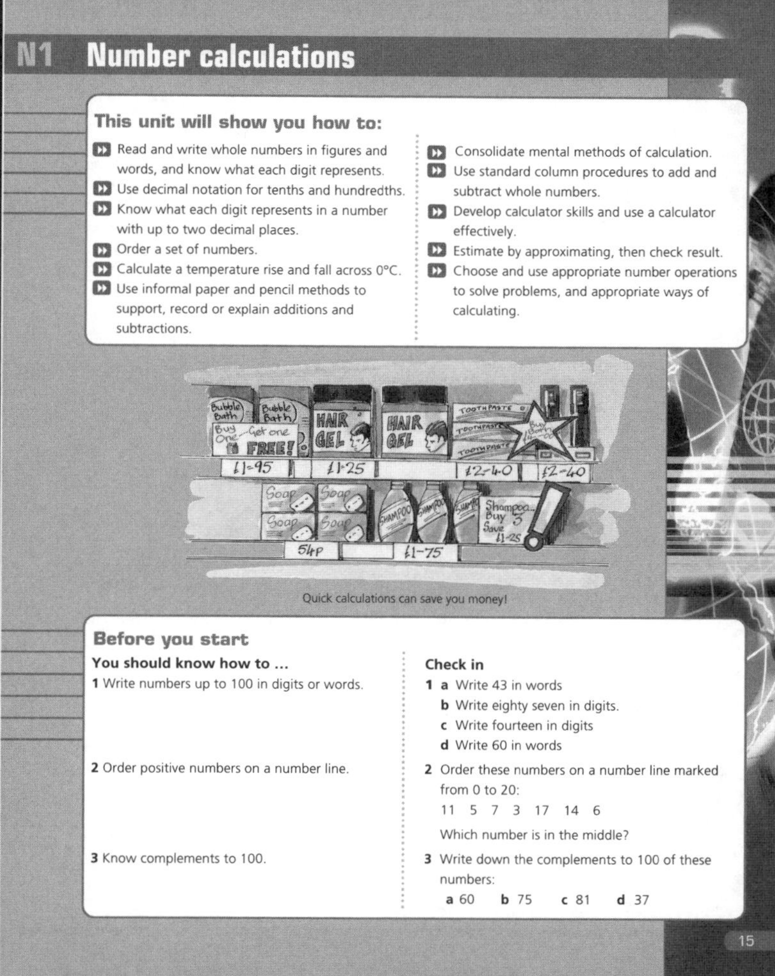

N1 Number calculations

This unit will show you how to:

- Read and write whole numbers in figures and words, and know what each digit represents.
- Use decimal notation for tenths and hundredths.
- Know what each digit represents in a number with up to two decimal places.
- Order a set of numbers.
- Calculate a temperature rise and fall across 0°C.
- Use informal paper and pencil methods to support, record or explain additions and subtractions.
- Consolidate mental methods of calculation.
- Use standard column procedures to add and subtract whole numbers.
- Develop calculator skills and use a calculator effectively.
- Estimate by approximating, then check result.
- Choose and use appropriate number operations to solve problems, and appropriate ways of calculating.

Quick calculations can save you money!

Before you start

You should know how to ...	Check in
1 Write numbers up to 100 in digits or words.	1 **a** Write 43 in words **b** Write eighty seven in digits. **c** Write fourteen in digits **d** Write 60 in words
2 Order positive numbers on a number line.	2 Order these numbers on a number line marked from 0 to 20: 11 5 7 3 17 14 6 Which number is in the middle?
3 Know complements to 100.	3 Write down the complements to 100 of these numbers: **a** 60 **b** 75 **c** 81 **d** 37

15

Check in activity

Practise complements to 20.
Students hold up digit cards to show responses.
Now choose 10 students and ask them to hold up number cards to show: 43, 91, 26, 52, 75, 17, 83, 69, 4, 38.
They arrange themselves in order of size.
Challenge other students to give the complements to 100 of each of the numbers and then to arrange the answers in size order.
Discuss what they notice.

Resources needed

* means class set needed

Essential:
R1* – Digit cards
R4 (OHP) – Place value table
R5* – Number ladders
R6* (OHP) – Number lines
N1.2OHP – Thermometers

Useful:
N1.5OHP – Addition and subtraction examples
N1.1ICT* – Place value in Excel

Unit commentary

Aim of the unit

This unit aims to consolidate students' ability to add and subtract numbers using a range of strategies including negative and decimal numbers.

Introduction

Discuss the cost of items in the picture in the student book:

- Which is more expensive: the soap or the hair gel?
- By how much?
- How much change would you expect from £5 if you buy both?

Emphasise that the unit is about adding and subtracting with different types of numbers.

Framework references

This unit focuses on:

- Year 6 teaching objectives pages: 3, 15, 29, 41, 43, 49, 51, 71, 73
- Problem solving objectives pages: 79, 83, 85, 87, 89

The unit provides access to:

- Year 7 teaching objectives pages: 2–10, 48, 50, 88, 90, 102, 104, 108

Differentiation

Core tier focuses on choosing appropriate methods when calculating with numbers up to 2 dp and includes subtracting negative numbers.

Springboard 7

Pages 55–57, 60, 61, 69, 70, 76–78, 81–85, 87–90, 93, 223–229, 300–304.

N1.1 Place value and ordering

Mental starter

Guess the number

- You pick a number between 0 and 100 and students have to guess the number you are thinking of – they take turns to ask questions.
- Use a number line to zoom in on the unknown number.

R6 has number lines marked in 10 sections.

You could write 1–100 on one and gradually zoom in on the others.

Useful resources

R6 has number lines marked in 10 sections which can be used throughout. You may also want to copy it to give to students to use.

R4 has a place value table.

Introductory activity

Check by asking questions that students can:

- Read/write numbers to 1000
- Order a set of whole numbers
- Know what the digits represent in decimals – tenths and hundredths.

Write the number 25.16 on the board and use it to emphasise the place value of a digit. Ask:

- What is the most significant/important digit?
- What does the 2 stand for?
- What does the 6 stand for?

Encourage students to place numbers on a number line. Use **R6** or draw a number line 1 m long and gradually zoom in.

- Ask students to place 32.6.
- Start with a number line marked from 0–100.
- Then mark in 30 and 40. Then mark in the 32 and 33. Then 32.6.

Repeat with 5.47 starting from 0–10.

Discuss how to order numbers.

Give students four numbers to order: 5.47, 5.8, 4.91, 5.

Ask students to place them on a number line.

Discuss what the end marks should be: 0–10, then 4–5 and 5–6.

Encourage students to discuss their reasons for any placements.

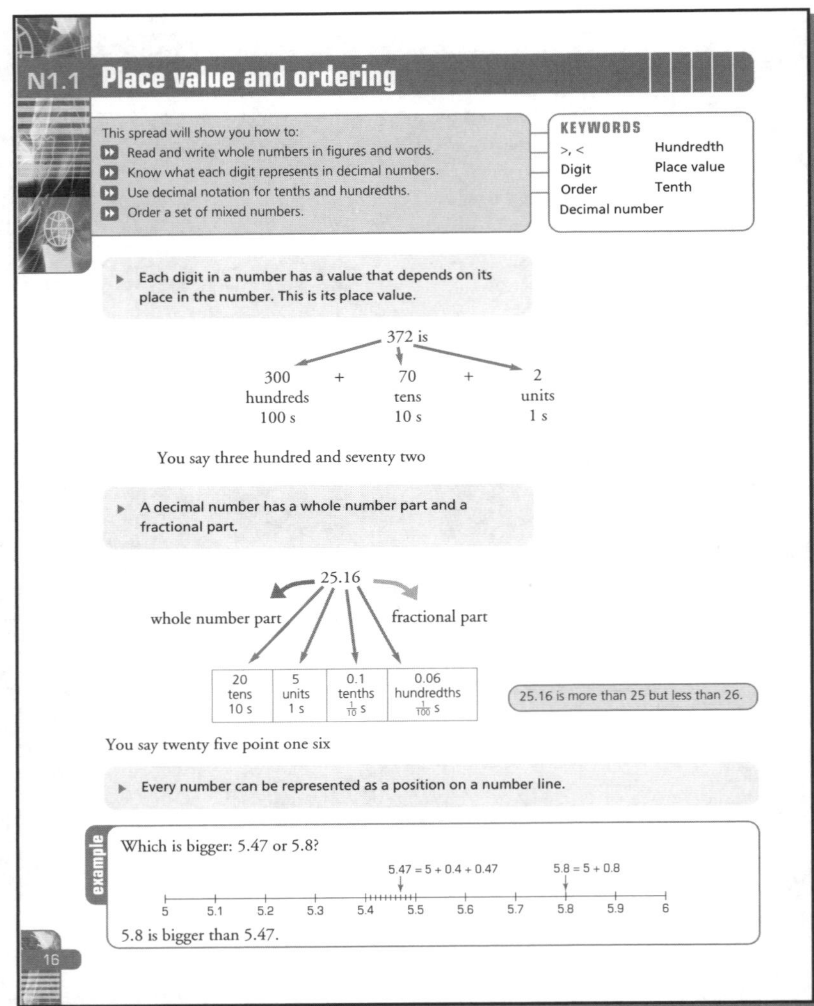

N1.1 Place value and ordering

This spread will show you how to:
- Read and write whole numbers in figures and words.
- Know what each digit represents in decimal numbers.
- Use decimal notation for tenths and hundredths.
- Order a set of mixed numbers.

KEYWORDS
>, < Hundredth
Digit Place value
Order Tenth
Decimal number

- Each digit in a number has a value that depends on its place in the number. This is its place value.

372 is

300	+	70	+	2
hundreds		tens		units
100 s		10 s		1 s

You say three hundred and seventy two

- A decimal number has a whole number part and a fractional part.

25.16

whole number part / fractional part

20	5	0.1	0.06
tens	units	tenths	hundredths
10 s	1 s	$\frac{1}{10}$ s	$\frac{1}{100}$ s

25.16 is more than 25 but less than 26.

You say twenty five point one six

- Every number can be represented as a position on a number line.

example

Which is bigger: 5.47 or 5.8?

5.47 = 5 + 0.4 + 0.47   5.8 = 5 + 0.8

5 5.1 5.2 5.3 5.4 5.5 5.6 5.7 5.8 5.9 6

5.8 is bigger than 5.47.

16

Plenary

Play the game in the mental starter but use numbers with 1 decimal place.

Start with numbers between 0 and 10 and then go up to 100 if students can cope.

Encourage language such as greater than, smaller than, nearest...

Use 2 decimal places if appropriate.

Further activities

In N1.1ICT, students construct a spreadsheet to investigate place value in decimals.

Alternatively

Challenge students to use any of the digits from 0 to 9 once each and a decimal point to find two numbers to add to:
287.9, 841.3 and 533.8

Differentiation

Support questions:

- Questions 1 and 2 are straightforward questions from the Year 5 objectives. Springboard 7, pages 60, 69, 300.
- Questions 3–7 focus on ordering decimals. Springboard 7, pages 61, 70, 301, 302.
- Question 8 presents a challenge: ordering numbers in the context of measures. Springboard 7, pages 303, 304.

Core tier: focuses on problems involving decimals to 2 or 3 dp.

Exercise N1.1

1 Write these numbers using digits:
a eighty five **b** six hundred and thirty nine
c nine hundred and five point three **d** nought point eight seven
e five point seven eight **f** thirty nine point nought one

2 Use words to write these numbers as you would say them:
a 73 **b** 1092 **c** 34.01
d 325 **e** 0.57 **f** 109.63

3 For each set of numbers A, B and C:

A	35	33	36	38	39
B	3.2	3.4	3.8	3.5	3.7
C	3.12	3.24	3.42	3.06	3.7

a Write down the biggest number.
b Write down the smallest number.
c Write the numbers in size order starting with the smallest.

4 Copy and complete these pairs of numbers, using one of the signs:

> means greater than, < means less than

to show which number is bigger.
The first two are done for you.

a	4.2	>	2.1	**b**	3.6	<	5.2	**c**	5.8		5.7
d	12.23		12.56	**e**	8.32		8.09	**f**	0.3		0.25
g	0.57		0.06	**h**	9.25		9.6	**i**	13.06		12.91

5 Using the digits 4 0 5 9 make:
a the largest number **b** the smallest number
c the number nearest to 5000 **d** the number nearest to 10 000

6 What number lies halfway between:
a 13 and 15 **b** 2 and 3 **c** 0.4 and 0.42?

7 These are the results of the 100 metres race at Superspeed School:

Amy	13.3 s
Belinda	14.1 s
Claudia	13.4 s
Danni	13.1 s
Elle	14.0 s

Put the runners in order from fastest to slowest.

8 Put these amounts in order from smallest to largest:
a £4.27, £4.31, 428p, 440p **b** 1.82 m, 1.9 m, 185 cm, 1 m 88 cm

17

Exercise commentary

The questions assess the objectives on Primary Framework Pages 3 and 29.

Problem solving

Question 5 assesses the objective from Primary Framework Page 79, question 7 assesses Page 87 and question 8 assesses Page 85.

Group work

Question 5 is suitable for work in pairs – students discuss the biggest/smallest.

Misconceptions

In questions 1 and 2 some students will miss out the 0s.

Encourage students to say numbers out loud before writing them and use of a place value table.

Students think 9.25 > 9.6 as 25 > 6.

Encourage the use of a number line so that students can see the importance of the place value – a place value table can also help.

In question 4 some students get the signs the wrong way round.

Discuss strategies for remembering as a group so that good ideas are shared.

Links

Comparing and ordering whole numbers: Primary Framework Page 9.

Homework

N1.1HW provides practice in writing numbers in figures and words, and in ordering numbers.

Answers

1 **a** 85 **b** 639 **c** 905.3 **d** 0.87 **e** 5.78 **f** 39.01
2 **a** Seventy-three **b** One thousand and ninety-two
c Thirty-four point nought one **d** Three hundred and twenty-five
e Nought point five seven **f** One hundred and nine point six three
3 **a** A: 39, B: 3.8, C: 3.7 **b** A: 33, B: 3.2, C: 3.06
c A: 33, 35, 36, 38, 39; B: 3.2, 3.4, 3.5, 3.7, 3.8; C: 3.06, 3.12, 3.24, 3.42, 3.7
4 **c** 5.8 > 5.7 **d** 12.23 < 12.56 **e** 8.32 > 8.09 **f** 0.3 > 0.25 **g** 0.57 > 0.06
h 9.25 < 9.6 **i** 13.06 > 12.91
5 **a** 9540 **b** 4059 **c** 5049 **d** 9540 6 **a** 14 **b** 2.5 **c** 0.41 7 D, A, C, E, B
8 **a** £4.27, 428p, £4.31, 440p **b** 1.82 m, 185 cm, 1 m 88 cm, 1.9 m

N1.2 Negative numbers

Mental starter

Number ladders

- Pupils have a ladder with 10 spaces (**R5** or students draw their own).
- Read out a list of numbers and students write each number in turn on a rung. Start with numbers from 0 – 10 and go on to numbers between 3 and 4.
- Numbers written down must be in ascending order – whenever a number cannot be written in it is consigned to the 'rubbish dump'.
- The first pupil to write 10 numbers onto their ladder is the winner.

Useful resources

R5 has ladders marked in 10 sections which you can copy for students.
N1.2OHP has a thermometer marked from $^{-}20$°C to 30°C.
R6 has number lines.

Introductory activity

Discuss temperatures.
Ask what today's temperature is roughly.
Ask what temperature it usually is when it's snowing.

Introduce the thermometer and the fact that below freezing temperatures are shown with a negative sign.

Explain that a thermometer is a number line but you usually use a horizontal number line to save space.
N1.2OHP has both a vertical and a horizontal number line marked from $^{-}20$ to 30.

Ask students to place numbers on the thermometer.
Ask them to explain their reasoning.

Explain that a number line can be used to compare the sizes of positive and negative numbers.
Ask questions such as:
- Which is larger, $^{-}5$ or $^{-}2$?
- Which is colder, $^{-}14$°C or 8°C?

Use a number line to show how to move when adding or subtracting integers in context:
- Use the example in the student book and illustrate it on **N1.2OHP**.
- Make up similar questions.
- Ask students to make up their own questions for the rest of the class.

Always ask them to explain their reasoning.

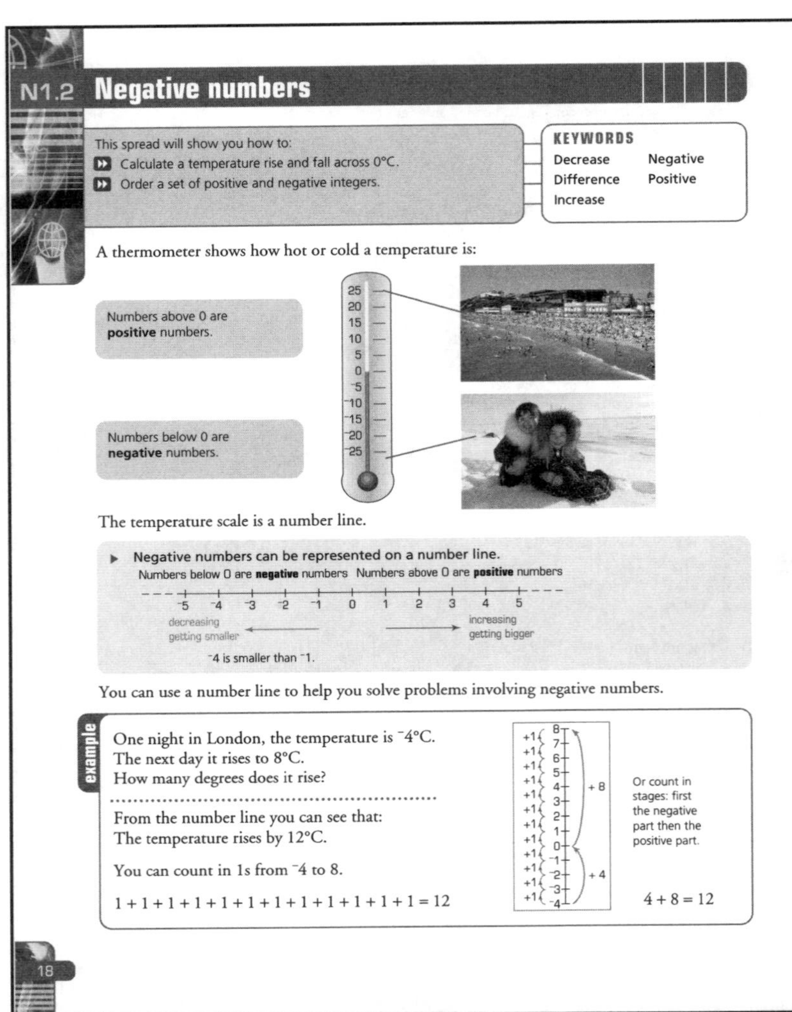

N1.2 **Negative numbers**

This spread will show you how to:
- Calculate a temperature rise and fall across 0°C.
- Order a set of positive and negative integers.

KEYWORDS
Decrease, Difference, Increase, Negative, Positive

A thermometer shows how hot or cold a temperature is:

The temperature scale is a number line.

- **Negative numbers can be represented on a number line.**

$^{-}4$ is smaller than $^{-}1$.

You can use a number line to help you solve problems involving negative numbers.

example

One night in London, the temperature is $^{-}4$°C.
The next day it rises to 8°C.
How many degrees does it rise?

From the number line you can see that:
The temperature rises by 12°C.

You can count in 1s from $^{-}4$ to 8.

1 + 1 + 1 + 1 + 1 + 1 + 1 + 1 + 1 + 1 + 1 + 1 = 12

Or count in stages: first the negative part then the positive part.

4 + 8 = 12

18

Plenary

Play number ladders again as in the mental starter.
This time include negative numbers.
After the game, ask students to explain how they decided where on the ladder to place the numbers.
Use numbers between $^{-}20$ and 30 so you can illustrate their answers on **N1.2OHP**.
Ask them to think more about when they might use negative numbers for the next lesson.

Further activities

Challenge students to make a negative number (say −12) in as many ways as they can, for example:
−14 + 2, −10 − 2, 10 − 22 ...

Use the weather data from a recent newspaper or from the internet and ask students to find the difference between the max and min temperatures.

Differentiation

Support questions:

- Questions 1–3 are straightforward questions about reading and writing negative numbers. Springboard 7, page 76.
- Questions 4 and 5 focus on ordering negative numbers. Springboard 7, page 77.
- Question 6 focuses on calculating temperature changes.

Core tier: focuses on ordering and calculating with negative numbers, including fractions and decimals.

Exercise N1.2

1 Here are six thermometers each showing different temperatures:

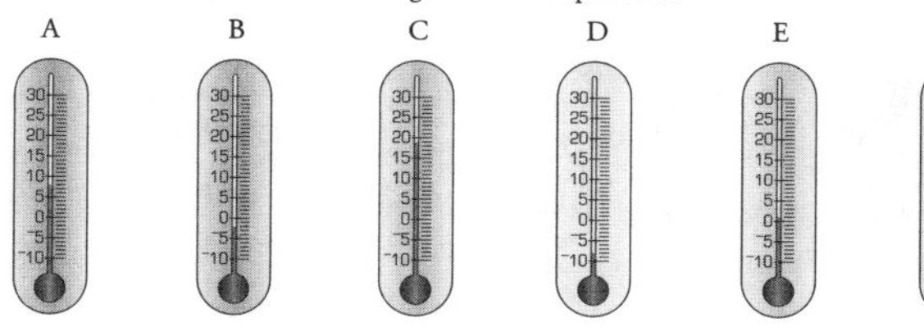

a Which thermometer shows the hottest temperature?
b Which thermometer shows the coldest temperature?
c What is the temperature on thermometer B?
d Which thermometers show less than 0 °C?

2 Write these numbers in words:
a 3603 **b** 21 335 **c** 10 070 **d** −12.5

3 Write these numbers in figures:
a seventy three **b** minus two hundred and thirty
c three thousand, six hundred and two **d** minus eleven point three

4 **a** Write this list of numbers in order of size, smallest first:
−3, 4, 2, −1, 1
b Draw a number line from −4 to 4 and label the numbers on it.

5 From this list of numbers
9 −3 −5 0 −1 7
write down:
a all the positive numbers
b all the negative numbers
c the numbers in order of size, starting with the smallest

5 Copy and complete these tables.

a

Start	Increase	Finish
3 °C	Rises by 6 °C	9 °C
8 °C	Rises by 5 °C	
5 °C	Rises by 12 °C	
−8 °C	Rises by 7 °C	
−3 °C	Rises by 6 °C	

b

Start	Decrease	Finish
18 °C	Falls by 7 °C	
13 °C	Falls by 6 °C	
−1 °C	Falls by 5 °C	
2 °C	Falls by 9 °C	−7 °C
−6 °C	Falls by 6 °C	

Exercise commentary

The questions assess the objectives on Primary Framework Page 15.

Problem solving

The further activity assesses Page 79.

Group work

The further activity is suitable for work in pairs – students can discuss pairs of numbers and therefore increase the range of answers.

Misconceptions

Students commonly think −5 is bigger than −2.
Encourage the use of a number line so that students can see the relative sizes.
Emphasise that one direction shows numbers getting bigger and the other shows numbers getting smaller.
It can also help to present the numbers in context such as using temperatures – the use of real weather data can help.

Links

Comparing and ordering whole numbers: Primary Framework Page 9.
Read and write whole numbers in figures and words: Page 3.

Homework

N1.2HW is based on designing a centigrade thermometer.

Answers

1 **a** F **b** D **c** −2 °C **d** B and D
2 **a** Three thousand, six hundred and three
b Twenty-one thousand, three hundred and thirty-five
c Ten thousand and seventy **d** Minus twelve point five
3 **a** 73 **b** −230 **c** 3602 **d** −11.3
4 **a** −3, −1, 1, 2, 4
5 **a** 7, 9 **b** −1, −3, −5 **c** −5, −3, −1, 0, 7, 9
6 **a** 13 °C, 17 °C, −1 °C, 3 °C **b** 11 °C, 7 °C, −6 °C, −12 °C

N1.3 Negative numbers – addition and subtraction

Mental starter

Following on game

- Choose a student and give them a starting temperature: e.g. 20°C.
- The next student must reduce the temperature: e.g. by 4°C.
- Change the reduction or start again until everyone has had a turn.
- Include addition: Start at $^{-}20$°C and go up 4, for example.

Use a range of temperatures such as $^{-}20$°C to 30°C so students can explain their reasoning using **N1.2OHP**.

Useful resources

N1.2OHP has a thermometer marked from $^{-}20$°C to 30°C.

Introductory activity

Ask students when/where they have seen negative numbers.
Ensure they have a good range of ideas as in the examples.

Use the mental starter activity to explain that the number line can help add to and subtract from a negative number.

Using a number line, ask students to show how to move when adding or subtracting integers in context:

- Use the example in the student book and illustrate it on **N1.2OHP**.

Discuss how to calculate with negative numbers not in context.

- Ask students to say what $^{-}1$°C – 8°C makes.
- Ask them to explain their reasoning.
- Ask them to explain the calculation in context – one evening it was $^{-}1$°C and the temperature dropped by 8°C.
- Repeat with the other examples.
- Ask students to make up their own questions for the rest of the class.

Encourage the use of the horizontal number line as using less space.
Emphasise that if you are adding you move right (or up) and if you are subtracting you move left (or down).

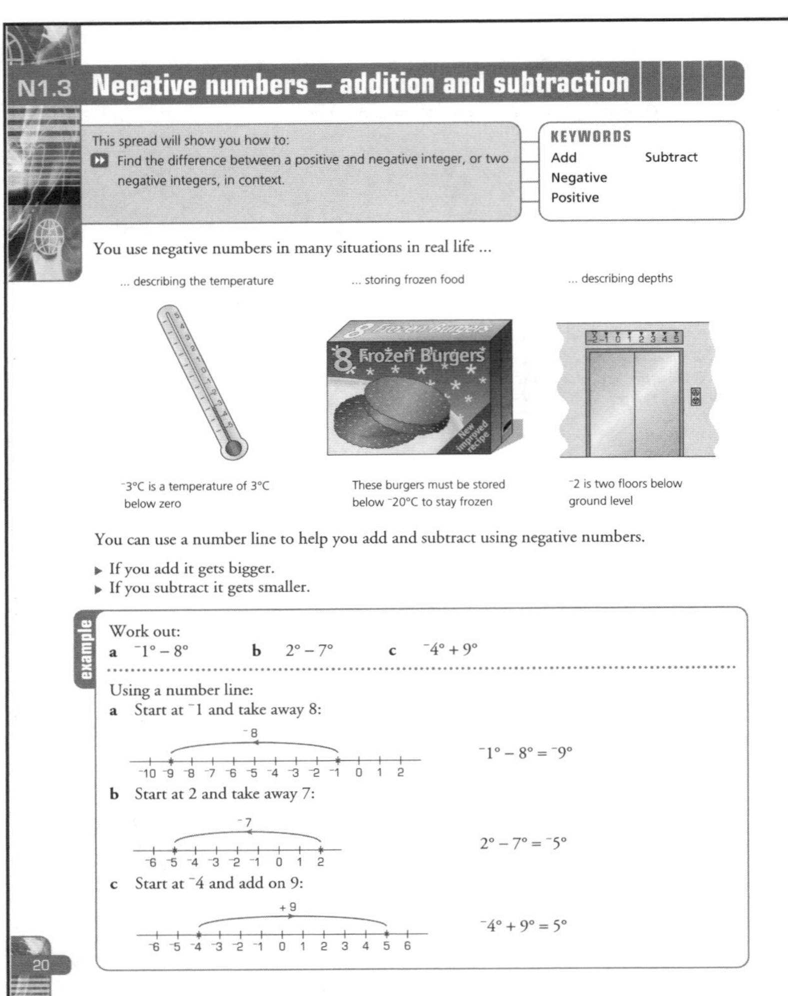

N1.3 Negative numbers – addition and subtraction

This spread will show you how to:

- Find the difference between a positive and negative integer, or two negative integers, in context.

KEYWORDS
Add
Negative
Positive
Subtract

You use negative numbers in many situations in real life ...

... describing the temperature

$^{-}3$°C is a temperature of 3°C below zero

... storing frozen food

These burgers must be stored below $^{-}20$°C to stay frozen

... describing depths

$^{-}2$ is two floors below ground level

You can use a number line to help you add and subtract using negative numbers.

- If you add it gets bigger.
- If you subtract it gets smaller.

example

Work out:
a $^{-}1° - 8°$ **b** $2° - 7°$ **c** $^{-}4° + 9°$

Using a number line:

a Start at $^{-}1$ and take away 8:

$^{-}1° - 8° = {}^{-}9°$

b Start at 2 and take away 7:

$2° - 7° = {}^{-}5°$

c Start at $^{-}4$ and add on 9:

$^{-}4° + 9° = 5°$

20

Plenary

Write a mixture of ten positive and negative integers (between $^{-}20$ and 30) on the board and ask:

- What's the highest/lowest number?
- Rearrange the numbers in size order.
- Find three numbers which add to...
- Find two numbers with a difference of...

Discuss the answers with the students, using **N1.2OHP** to indicate the positions, and identify any patterns.

Further activities

Students make up their own number sequences involving negative numbers and ask partners to describe the sequence using the first term and the rule.

Differentiation

Support questions:

- Question 1 focuses on adding and subtracting using negative numbers in context. Springboard 7, page 78.
- Questions 2–5 focus on finding differences and continuing number patterns.
- Question 6 focuses on continuing number sequences involving negative numbers.

Core tier: focuses on addition and subtraction of negative numbers without context.

Exercise N1.3

1 Write an addition or a subtraction and solve each of these problems:
- **a** The temperature is $^{-}3$ degrees. It rises by 5 degrees. What is the new temperature?
- **b** The temperature is 4 degrees. It falls by 6 degrees. What is the new temperature?
- **c** The temperature is $^{-}7$ degrees. It rises by 8 degrees. What is the new temperature?
- **d** The temperature is 12 degrees. It falls by 15 degrees. What is the new temperature?

2 Calculate the following. You should be able to do some of these questions mentally.

a $7 - 11$	**b** $30 + 46$	**c** $^{-}20 + 30$
d $^{-}18 - 20$	**e** $11 - 20$	**f** $^{-}38 - 70$
g $^{-}160 + 29$	**h** $^{-}30 - 75$	**i** $^{-}185 + 260$

3 Copy and complete this table:

1st term	Rule	2nd term	3rd term	4th term
15	Subtract 5	10	5	0
6	Subtract 4			
$^{-}9$	Add 3			
$^{-}3$	Subtract 5			

4 The table shows the temperatures in eight cities one night.

City	Temp °C	City	Temp °C
London	5	Paris	7
Madrid	2	Rome	2

City	Temp °C	City	Temp °C
Moscow	$^{-}8$	Sydney	15
New York	12	Warsaw	$^{-}12$

How many degrees ...
- **a** warmer than London was Sydney?
- **b** colder than Paris was Rome?
- **c** difference was there between New York and Moscow?
- **d** difference was there between Madrid and Warsaw?

5 Extend this pattern:

$2 + 2 = 4$
$2 + 1 = 3$
$2 + 0 = 2$
$2 + {}^{-}1 = 1$
$2 + {}^{-}2 = 0$
$2 + {}^{-}3 = {}^{-}1$

6 Write down the next three numbers in each of these sequences:
- **a** 2, 7, 12, 17, 22, _, _, _
- **b** 25, 21, 17, 13, 9, _, _, _
- **c** $^{-}15$, $^{-}13$, $^{-}11$, $^{-}9$, $^{-}7$, _, _, _
- **d** 6, 3, 0, $^{-}3$, $^{-}6$, _, _, _
- **e** $^{-}30$, $^{-}22$, $^{-}14$, $^{-}6$, _, _, _
- **f** 23, 12, 1, $^{-}10$, $^{-}21$, _, _, _

Exercise commentary

The questions assess the objectives on Primary Framework Page 15.

Problem solving

Questions 4 and 6 assess Primary Framework Page 81.

Group work

The exercise is most suited to individual work. The further activity is suitable for work in pairs.

Misconceptions

In question 2, students find calculations involving borrowing difficult and using negative numbers makes a written method hard to use.
Encourage the use of a number line and emphasise the method of partitioning.
In sequences students find going past zero confusing.
Emphasise the use of a number line and encourage students to count in 1s past the zero until they can recognise the patterns.

Links

Extending sequences: Primary Framework Page 17.

Homework

N1.3HW is based on changes of height relative to sea level.
It provides practice at subtracting with negative numbers.

Answers

1 **a** 2 degrees **b** $^{-}2$ degrees **c** 1 degree **d** $^{-}3$ degrees
2 **a** $^{-}4$ **b** 76 **c** 10 **d** $^{-}38$ **e** $^{-}9$ **f** $^{-}108$ **g** $^{-}131$ **h** $^{-}105$ **i** 75
3 6, 2, $^{-}2$, $^{-}6$; $^{-}9$, $^{-}6$, $^{-}3$, 0; $^{-}3$, $^{-}8$, $^{-}13$, $^{-}18$
4 **a** 10 °C **b** 5 °C **c** 20 °C **d** 14 °C
5 **a** $2 + {}^{-}4 = {}^{-}2$; $2 + {}^{-}5 = {}^{-}3$; etc.
6 **a** 27, 32, 37 **b** 5, 1, $^{-}3$ **c** $^{-}5$, $^{-}3$, $^{-}1$ **d** $^{-}9$, $^{-}12$, $^{-}15$ **e** 2, 10, 18 **f** $^{-}32$, $^{-}43$, $^{-}54$

Mental starter

Give a series of quick-fire questions that students must either recall or do mentally very quickly:

- Complements to 100.
- Single digit calculations: 30 + 40

Students answer by holding up number cards – you can give them 2 sets of **R1** digit cards each.

Useful resources

Two class sets of **R1** digit cards for the mental starter.

Introductory activity

Discuss why/when you need to work things out mentally, for example to check you get the correct change.

Discuss what makes a good strategy – for example: quick, easy to use.

Highlight that there are lots of strategies that they are already using – ask students to explain how they worked out a sum from the mental starter.

Pick up on anyone using the idea of partitioning and explain it further by asking how to work out 253 + 325. Emphasise that you can change the numbers around to add the smaller one.

- Remind students of the notion of the most significant digit and discuss why you might add that first – gets closer to the answer!
- Draw a number line on the board to illustrate the examples and encourage students to do the same until they understand the method.

Pick up on any use of the compensation method. Illustrate it by:

- Asking students how they would add on 98 or subtract 94.

Encourage the use of 'nearly 100' and discuss how much more or less than 100. Show examples on a number line. Ask students to do the rounding and then move to that number on the number line. Then ask how to compensate.

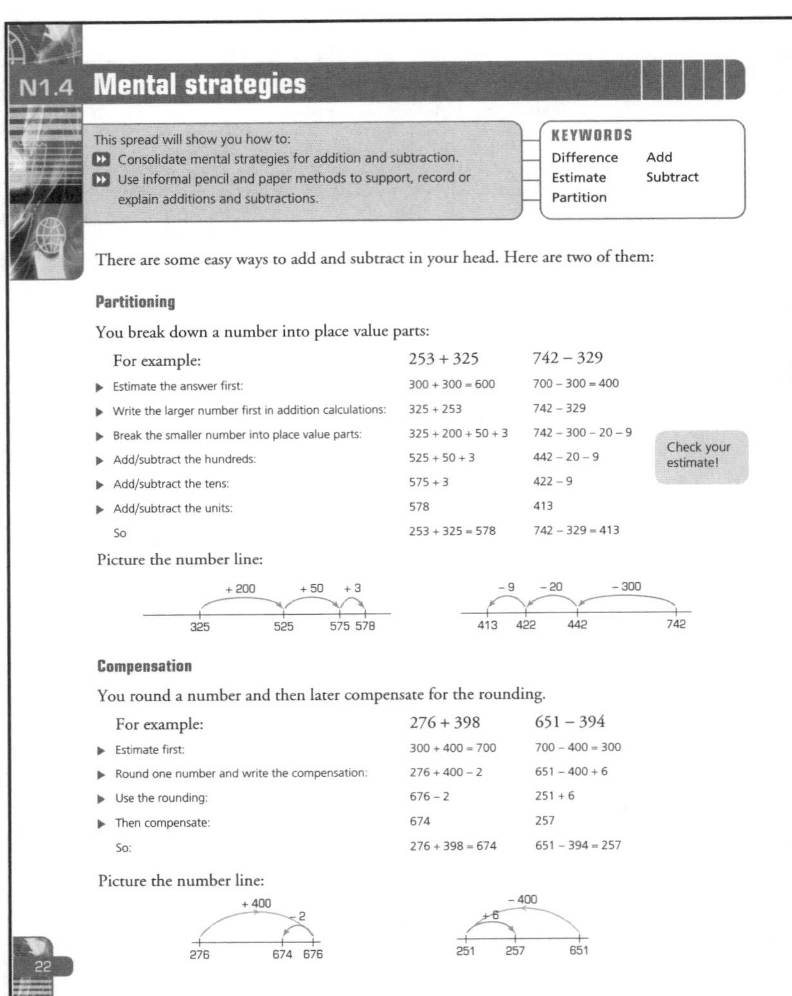

N1.4 Mental strategies

This spread will show you how to:
- Consolidate mental strategies for addition and subtraction.
- Use informal pencil and paper methods to support, record or explain additions and subtractions.

KEYWORDS
Difference, Add, Estimate, Subtract, Partition

There are some easy ways to add and subtract in your head. Here are two of them:

Partitioning

You break down a number into place value parts:

For example:	253 + 325	742 – 329
▸ Estimate the answer first:	300 + 300 = 600	700 – 300 = 400
▸ Write the larger number first in addition calculations:	325 + 253	742 – 329
▸ Break the smaller number into place value parts:	325 + 200 + 50 + 3	742 – 300 – 20 – 9
▸ Add/subtract the hundreds:	525 + 50 + 3	442 – 20 – 9
▸ Add/subtract the tens:	575 + 3	422 – 9
▸ Add/subtract the units:	578	413
So	253 + 325 = 578	742 – 329 = 413

Check your estimate!

Picture the number line:

Compensation

You round a number and then later compensate for the rounding.

For example:	276 + 398	651 – 394
▸ Estimate first:	300 + 400 = 700	700 – 400 = 300
▸ Round one number and write the compensation:	276 + 400 – 2	651 – 400 + 6
▸ Use the rounding:	676 – 2	251 + 6
▸ Then compensate:	674	257
So:	276 + 398 = 674	651 – 394 = 257

Picture the number line:

22

Plenary

Go through question 7 asking students:

- Which method is the best one to use?
- Why?
- Ask them to talk through their working.

Introduce the homework, which is about designing a poster to explain the methods.

Further activities

Students can make up sentences for questions 3, 6 and 7.

Students make up their own problems as in question 7 and challenge each other to solve them as quickly as possible.

Students could go back over questions 1–6 as appropriate, use the other method to solve the problems, then discuss which method is easier to use.

Differentiation

Support questions:

- Question 1 focuses on adding without carries. Springboard 7, pages 55–57, 327.
- Questions 2–6 focus on using the methods of partitioning and compensation. Springboard 7, pages 58, 59, 92, 328, 329.
- Questions 6 and 7 focus on choosing the most appropriate method to use. Springboard 7, pages 93, 330.

Core tier: focuses on mental methods of solving decimal problems.

Exercise N1.4

Use **partitioning** to answer questions 1–3.

1 Add together these money amounts in your head.

a 23p and 5p | b 53p and 4p | c 32p and 13p | d 43p and 23p
e 36p and 32p | f 25p and 63p | g £41 and £44 | h £71 and £28

2 Find the difference between these money amounts:

a 26p and 5p | b 39p and 7p | c 36p and 13p | d 46p and 24p
e 65p and 35p | f 59p and 43p | g £87 and £24 | h £67 and £36

3 Work out these – they get harder as you go through!

a 123 + 52 | b 323 + 46 | c 158 − 32 | d 356 − 23
e 26 + 321 | f 454 − 323 | g 125 + 132 | h 304 + 234
i 875 − 832 | j 5.2 + 3.4 | k 7.2 + 2.5 | l 3.8 − 2.4
m 8.8 − 3.5 | n 12.2 + 5.3 | o 18.6 − 5.4 | p 2.26 + 0.33

Use **compensation** to answer questions 4–6

4 Add these distances together:

a 34 cm and 19 cm | b 45 cm and 17 cm
c 68 m and 28 m | d 46 m and 39 m
e 35 m and 57 m | f 67 m and 27 m

5 Find the difference between these money amounts:

a 53p and 19p | b 74p and 18p
c 56p and 28p | d 78p and 29p
e £45 and £27 | f £63 and £37

6 Work out these – they get harder as you go through!

a 35 + 19 | b 123 + 29 | c 235 + 98 | d 81 − 28
e 252 − 97 | f 528 + 195 | g 267 + 297 | h 453 − 297
i 238 + 187 | j 466 + 285 | k 483 − 286 | l 732 − 589

7 In these questions you must choose which mental method to use.
The best method uses fewer steps so you can do the calculation quicker!

a 45 + 93 | b 65 − 48 | c 163 − 88 | d 235 + 207
e 187 + 235 | f 354 − 123 | g 4.8 − 2.9 | h 3.4 + 5.5
i 8.3 − 6.8 | j 5.3 + 3.8 | k 12.4 + 5.8 | l 13.6 + 12.8
m 7.23 + 2.34 | n 2.65 + 4.27 | o 8.82 − 3.98 | p 22.3 − 15.9

23

Exercise commentary

The questions assess the objectives on Primary Framework Pages 41, 49 and 51.

Problem solving

Question 7 assesses Primary Framework Page 74.

Group work

The exercise is most suited to individual work. The further activities are suitable for work in pairs.

Misconceptions

In partitioning, students lose track of the parts they have to work with.

Encourage the use of jottings to support working and emphasise the need to be consistent and structured, starting with the largest part.

In compensation, students forget to carry or borrow, writing 252 − 97 as 252 − 100 − 3.

Encourage the use of a number line and emphasise the need to approximate first: 252 − 97 is more than 252 − 100.

Links

Measures: Primary Framework Page 91, and approximation: Page 13.

Homework

N1.4HW requires students to design a poster to explain either partitioning or compensation.

Answers

1 a 28p b 57p c 45p d 66p e 68p f 88p g £85 h £99
2 a 21p b 32p c 23p d 22p e 30p f 16p g £63 h £31
3 a 175 b 369 c 126 d 333 e 347 f 131 g 257 h 538 i 43 j 8.6 k 9.7 l 1.4 m 5.3 n 17.5 o 13.2 p 2.59
4 a 53 cm b 62 cm c 96 m d 85 m e 92 m f 94 m
5 a 34p b 56p c 28p d 49p e £18 f £26
6 a 54 b 152 c 333 d 53 e 155 f 723 g 564 h 156 i 425 j 751 k 197 l 143
7 a 138 b 17 c 75 d 442 e 422 f 231 g 1.9 h 8.9 i 1.5 j 9.1 k 18.2 l 26.4 m 9.57 n 6.92 o 4.84 p 6.4

Mental starter

Complements to 1

- Give students a decimal with 1 dp: 0.2
- Ask for the complements to 1: 0.8
- Include 2 dp: 0.12 and 0.88
- Include two-digit numbers between 0 and 10 and their complements to 10: 1.2 and 8.8

Useful resources

N1.5OHP has questions from the example for class discussion.
R4 place value table may be useful.

Introductory activity

Discuss why some calculations are too difficult to do mentally.
The student book suggests you can use estimation when the calculation is difficult – this is covered in N1.6 and is not used here.

Emphasise that it is important to line up the units first as they hold the other digits in their correct places.

Discuss how to add and subtract in columns.
Ask students to explain their methods.
Students must be careful to:

- Line up the units.
- Add from the right to the left.
- Add from the top to the bottom.
- 'Borrow' and 'carry' as necessary.

N1.5OHP contains questions from the example that can lead to discussion.

Introduce the idea of adding and subtracting decimals as following the same methods. It is important that students realise they can 'fill in the blanks' after the decimal point and a good way to introduce this is through the context of money:

- What does £3.6 mean?

Ask students how they could check they had done a subtraction question correctly. Emphasise that you can add the numbers together.

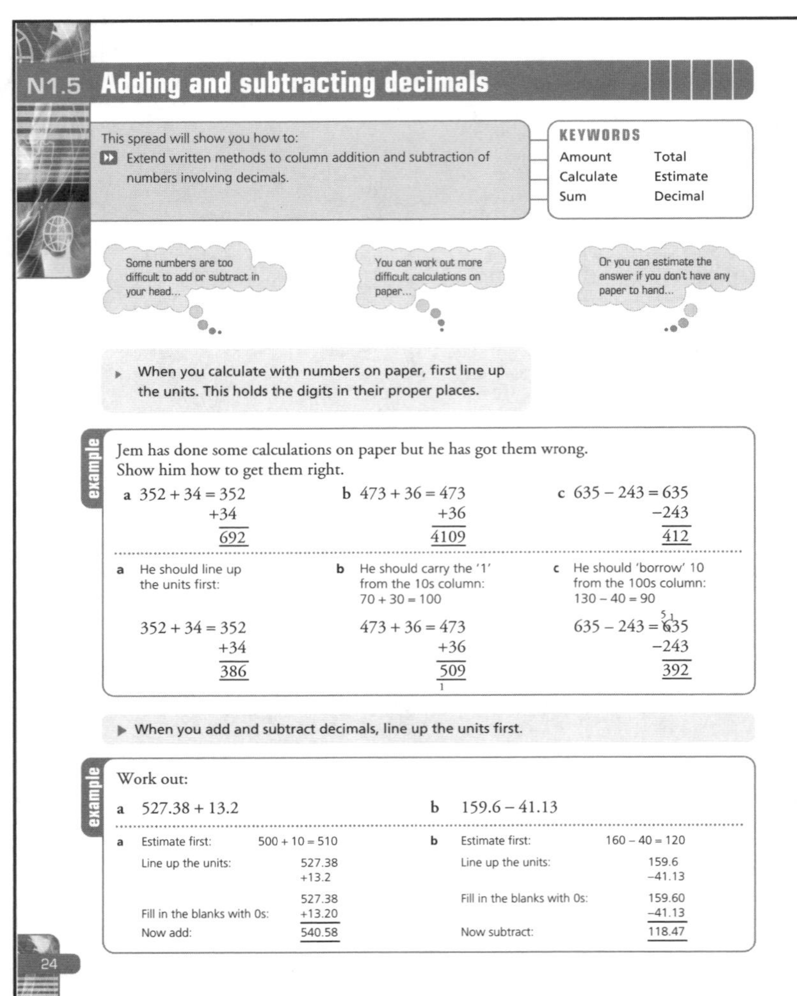

N1.5 **Adding and subtracting decimals**

This spread will show you how to:

- Extend written methods to column addition and subtraction of numbers involving decimals.

KEYWORDS

Amount, Total, Calculate, Estimate, Sum, Decimal

- **When you calculate with numbers on paper, first line up the units. This holds the digits in their proper places.**

example

Jem has done some calculations on paper but he has got them wrong.
Show him how to get them right.

a $352 + 34 = 352$ / $+34$ / $\underline{692}$

b $473 + 36 = 473$ / $+36$ / $\underline{4109}$

c $635 - 243 = 635$ / -243 / $\underline{412}$

a He should line up the units first:
$352 + 34 = 352$ / $+34$ / $\underline{386}$

b He should carry the '1' from the 10s column: $70 + 30 = 100$
$473 + 36 = 473$ / $+36$ / $\underline{509}$ (carry 1)

c He should 'borrow' 10 from the 100s column: $130 - 40 = 90$
$635 - 243 = \overset{5}{\cancel{6}}\,{}^{1}35$ / -243 / $\underline{392}$

- **When you add and subtract decimals, line up the units first.**

example

Work out:

a $527.38 + 13.2$

b $159.6 - 41.13$

a Estimate first: $500 + 10 = 510$
Line up the units: 527.38 / +13.2
Fill in the blanks with 0s: 527.38 / +13.20
Now add: 540.58

b Estimate first: $160 - 40 = 120$
Line up the units: 159.6 / −41.13
Fill in the blanks with 0s: 159.60 / −41.13
Now subtract: 118.47

24

Plenary

Go over the second row of question 6, concentrating on whether students know the methods.
To introduce the homework sheet, discuss what's gone wrong in these questions:

$$\begin{array}{r} 51.6 \\ -38.7 \\ \hline 27.1 \end{array} \qquad \begin{array}{r} 5.26 \\ +21.63 \\ \hline 74.23 \end{array}$$

Further activities

Students can make up sentences for question 1.

Students can explain methods in question 11.

String challenge
Give students 4 or 5 lengths of string and ask them to measure them in cm and then add lengths and find differences. Able students can list all the lengths that can be made.

Differentiation

Support questions:

- Questions 1–3 are whole number problems without carries. Springboard 7, page 81.
- Questions 4–9 focus on decimal problems with carries. Springboard 7, pages 82–84, 223–226.
- Questions 10 and 11 are harder problems for students with a good grasp of written and mental methods. Springboard 7, pages 85, 227–229.

Core tier: focuses on mental methods of adding and subtracting decimals with up to 2 dp.

Exercise N1.5

Show all your working out in this exercise.

1 Calculate

a 364 + 34	**b** 127 + 52	**c** 831 + 63	**d** 243 + 335
e 137 + 532	**f** 253 + 146	**g** 387 − 32	**h** 265 − 54
i 558 − 41	**j** 385 − 214	**k** 957 − 725	**l** 837 − 216

2 Jerry has £243 and Jenny has £354.
How much do they have altogether?

3 George is 195 cm tall. His son is 132 cm tall.
How much taller is George than his son?

4 What do the three sides of this triangle add up to?

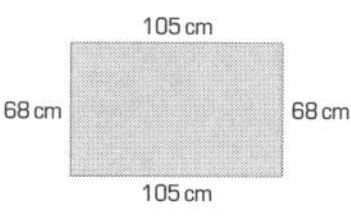

5 Total each of these money amounts:

a £173 and £216	**b** £203 and £562	**c** £185 and £253
d £32.35 and £61.42	**e** £53.07 and £15.21	**f** £25.52 and £14.37
g £18.53 and £18.32	**h** £25.63 and £22.83	

6 Work out these money problems:

a £369–£153	**b** £583–£441	**c** £983–£229	**d** £28.65–£13.52
e £65.49–£32.25	**f** £83.97–£51.46	**g** £63.62–£21.25	**h** £89.53–£36.61

7 Will buys a saucepan costing £23.49 and a book costing £12.75.
How much does he spend altogether?

8 Tracey went shopping with £35.53 in her purse.
She spends £18.26 on clothes.
How much does she have left?

9 What is the sum of the four sides of this rectangle?

10 Calculate:

a 1342 + 356	**b** 8496 − 253	**c** 206 + 955	**d** 37.2 + 62.5
e 85.9 − 42.6	**f** 832.4 + 35.8	**g** 962 − 757	**h** 23.67 − 1.52
i 63.2 − 28.5	**j** 175.2 + 257.4	**k** 3.861 + 2.135	**l** 38.65 − 12.3
m 97.6 − 32.35	**n** 62.42 − 35.8		

11 Make a number as close to 2000 as possible by adding two of these numbers:
832 1257 952 1038

25

Exercise commentary

The questions assess the objectives on Primary Framework Pages 49 and 51.

Problem solving
The exercise assesses Primary Framework Page 74, question 11 assesses Page 79 and questions 5–8 assess Page 85.
The further activities assess Page 75 and Page 77.

Group work
The exercise is most suited to individual work. Students can discuss strategies in question 11 and work on the string challenge together.

Misconceptions
Students fail to line up the units, particularly when using decimals.
Encourage students to approximate before calculating to help them realise a mistake has been made and make use of place value tables.
Students struggling with written methods should be encouraged to revert to mental methods with jottings, developing written methods gradually.

Links
Measures: Primary Framework Page 91, and approximation: Page 13.

Homework

N1.5HW provides practice in adding and subtracting in columns, including decimals.

Answers

1 **a** 398 **b** 179 **c** 894 **d** 578 **e** 669 **f** 399 **g** 355 **h** 211 **i** 517 **j** 171 **k** 232 **l** 621
2 £597 **3** 63 cm **4** 839 mm
5 **a** £389 **b** £765 **c** £438 **d** £93.77 **e** £68.28 **f** £39.89 **g** £36.85 **h** £48.46
6 **a** £216 **b** £142 **c** £754 **d** £15.13 **e** £33.24 **f** £32.51 **g** £42.37 **h** £52.92
7 £36.24 **8** £17.27 **9** 346 cm
10 **a** 1698 **b** 8243 **c** 1161 **d** 99.7 **e** 43.3 **f** 868.2 **g** 205 **h** 22.15 **i** 34.7 **j** 432.6 **k** 5.996 **l** 26.35 **m** 65.25 **n** 26.62
12 952 + 1038 = 1990

N1.6 Using a calculator

Mental starter

Round about

- Give students a two-digit number: 43.
- Ask whether it is nearer:
  0 or 1000?
  0 or 100?
  0 or 50?
  40 or 50?
- Repeat for other two-digit numbers.

Useful resources

R6 has number lines.

Introductory activity

Discuss what they've learnt so far this unit – that faced with a calculation you would:

- do the question mentally or
- do it on paper.

Discuss when they might choose to use a calculator – there are four suggestions in the text.

Discuss also the dangers of using a calculator:

- you may press the wrong button
- you don't always have one to hand
- you should estimate anyway and so you're often half way there so using a calculator could take longer.

Stress the importance of making an approximation first – this means rounding the numbers.
Refer to the mental starter.
Use the number lines from **R6** and gradually zoom out:

- Ask students to place 367.4 on a blank number line.
- Highlight the need for a sensible start and end point to the line.
- This should lead to the nearest 100, 10 and whole number.

Ask students to explain their reasoning each time.

Students should work through the various examples given in the student book to become familiar with their own calculators.

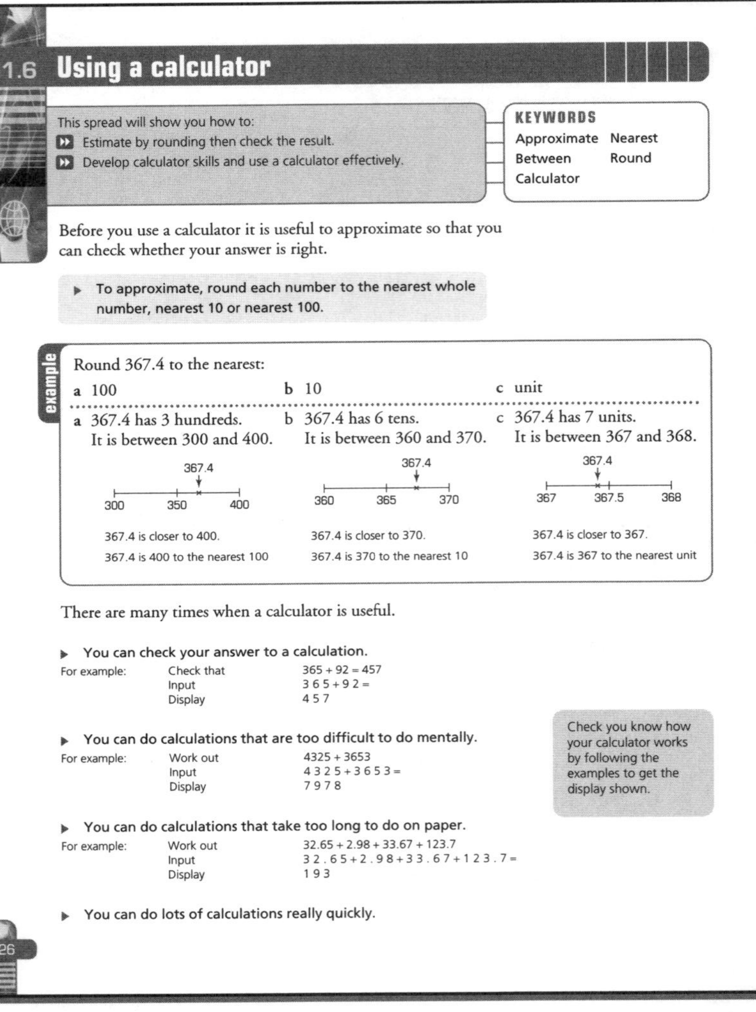

N1.6 **Using a calculator**

This spread will show you how to:
- Estimate by rounding then check the result.
- Develop calculator skills and use a calculator effectively.

KEYWORDS
Approximate Nearest
Between Round
Calculator

Before you use a calculator it is useful to approximate so that you can check whether your answer is right.

- To approximate, round each number to the nearest whole number, nearest 10 or nearest 100.

example

Round 367.4 to the nearest:
a 100 **b** 10 **c** unit

a 367.4 has 3 hundreds.
It is between 300 and 400.
367.4
300 350 400
367.4 is closer to 400.
367.4 is 400 to the nearest 100

b 367.4 has 6 tens.
It is between 360 and 370.
367.4
360 365 370
367.4 is closer to 370.
367.4 is 370 to the nearest 10

c 367.4 has 7 units.
It is between 367 and 368.
367.4
367 367.5 368
367.4 is closer to 367.
367.4 is 367 to the nearest unit

There are many times when a calculator is useful.

- You can check your answer to a calculation.
For example: Check that 365 + 92 = 457
Input 3 6 5 + 9 2 =
Display 4 5 7

- You can do calculations that are too difficult to do mentally.
For example: Work out 4325 + 3653
Input 4 3 2 5 + 3 6 5 3 =
Display 7 9 7 8

- You can do calculations that take too long to do on paper.
For example: Work out 32.65 + 2.98 + 33.67 + 123.7
Input 3 2 . 6 5 + 2 . 9 8 + 3 3 . 6 7 + 1 2 3 . 7 =
Display 1 9 3

- You can do lots of calculations really quickly.

Check you know how your calculator works by following the examples to get the display shown.

26

Plenary

Rounding

- Give students a number: 100, 200, 300, 400 or 500
- Shout out numbers such as 320, 512, … .

Students whose number is closest have to stand up.
Summarise the learning from the unit.
Estimate an answer **then** decide whether to:
do it mentally, or use a written method or calculator.

Further activities

Students can make up sentences to describe the calculations in question 1.

Challenge students to perform calculations involving negative numbers using their calculators:
⁻235 + 152 etc.

Differentiation

Support questions:

- Question 1 involves only whole numbers. Springboard 7, pages 87, 88.
- Questions 2–4 focus on decimal problems and multi-step problems. Springboard 7, page 89.
- Question 5 presents a complex question in context and question 6 requires a good understanding of place value. Springboard 7, page 90.

Core tier: focuses on inputting negative numbers and brackets.

Exercise N1.6

Remember to approximate before calculating.

1 Work out the answers to these calculations on paper.
Check your answers using a calculator.
a 325 + 124 **b** 857 – 235 **c** 258 + 735
d 1354 + 3235 **e** 9268 – 3154 **f** 10 012 – 2573

2 Work out the answers to these money problems on paper.
Check your answers using a calculator.
a £12.32 + £13.55 **b** £16.25 + £23.20 **c** £29.75 – £15.26
d £43.52 – £32.38 **e** £52.63 + £9.21 **f** £41.07 + £15.93

3 Use a calculator to work out:
a 3463 + 2761 + 1926 **b** 5732 + 3581 – 926 **c** 632 + 35.7 + 92.8

4 From this list of numbers
57 93 64 82
use your calculator to work out:
a Which two numbers add to 150? **b** Which two numbers add to 157?
c Which three numbers add to 214? **d** Which two numbers have a difference of 18?

5 Solve these problems using a mental or written method, using a calculator where appropriate.
a A shirt costs £15, a tie costs £13 and a book costs £6.50.
Is £34.80 enough to pay for all these items? Explain your answer.
b These are the weights of ingredients in a recipe:

flour	200 g	1 egg	24.5 g
sugar	100 g	1 litre milk	230 g
vanilla	0.6 g		

What is the total weight of the ingredients?
How many grams less than 1 kilogram is this?

1 kg = 1000 g

6 **Make me zero**
- The first player enters a number into the calculator.
- Players take it in turns to subtract a number from this, but only one digit can be changed at a time.
For example, 3.62 – 0.6 = 3.02 is allowed because only the 6 has changed.
- The display must never show a negative number.
- The winner is the player who makes the display on the calculator zero.

Example:

Player	Button	Display
1		83.62
2	–80	3.62
1	–0.6	3.02
2	–3	0.02
1	–0.01	0.01
2	–0.01	0

Player 2 wins.

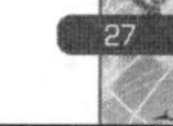

Exercise commentary

The questions assess the objectives on Primary Framework Pages 49, 51, 71 and 73.

Problem solving
Questions 1, 2 and 5 assess Primary Framework Page 74, question 4 assesses Page 79, questions 2 and 5a assess Page 85 and question 5b assesses Page 87.

Group work
Question 6 is suitable for pair work.

Misconceptions
Students just use the calculator without considering the most appropriate and efficient method.
Emphasise the need to estimate and then encourage students to consider whether they can write down the answer from there.
Students fail to line up the units, particularly when using decimals.
Emphasise the importance of approximating before calculating to highlight any errors.

Links
Measures: Primary Framework Page 91, and approximation: Page 13, and decimal place value: Page 29.

Homework

N1.6HW provides practice at solving addition and subtraction problems using a calculator.

Answers

1 **a** 449 **b** 622 **c** 993 **d** 4589 **e** 6114 **f** 7439
2 **a** £25.87 **b** £39.45 **c** £14.49 **d** £11.14 **e** £61.84 **f** £57
3 **a** 8150 **b** 8387 **c** 760.5
4 **a** 57 + 93 = 150 **b** 93 + 64 = 157 **c** 57 + 93 + 64 = 214
d 82 – 64 = 18
5 **a** Yes, £15 + £13 + £6.50 = £34.50 **b** 555.1 g, 444.9 g

Summary

The Year 6 key teaching objectives are:

- Order a set of measurements (29).
- Extend written methods of calculation to column addition and subtraction involving decimals (49–51).
- Identify and use appropriate number operations to solve problems (83–89).

Plenary activity

Give students five calculations:

- $^{-}43 - 23$
- $32.5 + 15.2$
- £1.86 + £2.70
- £5 − £1.25
- $93 - 27$

Discuss appropriate methods for solving them.

Check out commentary

1 Students read the 56 as fifty-six and so believe 3.56 is greater than 3.7.
Encourage the use of a number line to help overcome this. A place value table (as on **R4**) may help.

2 Students find negative numbers confusing and tend to ignore the signs. Encourage the use of a negative number scale as on **N1.2OHP** so students can see that minus moves in the opposite direction.

3 Encourage students to estimate when using partitioning or compensation.

4 Students make many mistakes when moving to written methods – failing to align units, not 'carrying' properly etc. Encourage students to build on successful mental methods (add units first then tens ...) and emphasise the use of an estimate as a check.

5 Students tend to use just one method or formula to solve all the problems. Emphasise that the best method would be successful, quick and easy to use and that students should always estimate before calculating. Encourage them to work through the list once, writing down any answers they can see then again making jottings and finally do any not yet answered using a written method or calculator.

6 Students need to understand the significance of the place values to answer the question.
Encourage the use of a number line and place value table.

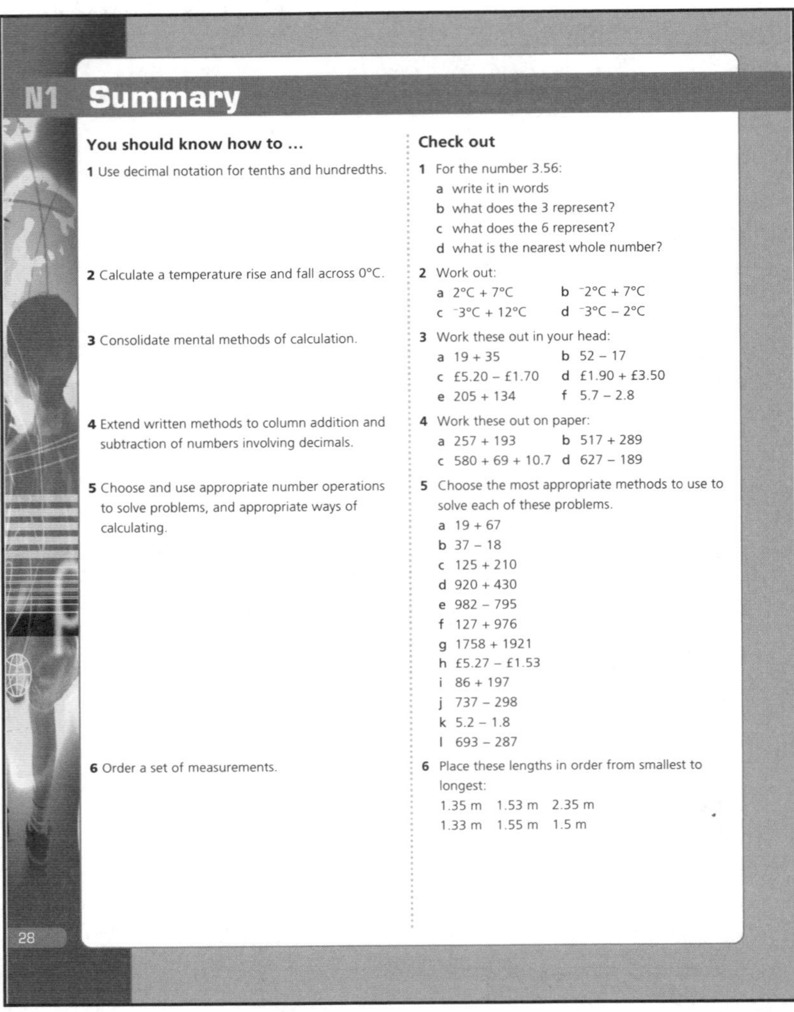

N1 Summary

You should know how to ...

1 Use decimal notation for tenths and hundredths.

2 Calculate a temperature rise and fall across 0°C.

3 Consolidate mental methods of calculation.

4 Extend written methods to column addition and subtraction of numbers involving decimals.

5 Choose and use appropriate number operations to solve problems, and appropriate ways of calculating.

6 Order a set of measurements.

Check out

1 For the number 3.56:
   a write it in words
   b what does the 3 represent?
   c what does the 6 represent?
   d what is the nearest whole number?

2 Work out:
   a 2°C + 7°C   b $^{-}$2°C + 7°C
   c $^{-}$3°C + 12°C   d $^{-}$3°C − 2°C

3 Work these out in your head:
   a 19 + 35   b 52 − 17
   c £5.20 − £1.70   d £1.90 + £3.50
   e 205 + 134   f 5.7 − 2.8

4 Work these out on paper:
   a 257 + 193   b 517 + 289
   c 580 + 69 + 10.7   d 627 − 189

5 Choose the most appropriate methods to use to solve each of these problems.
   a 19 + 67
   b 37 − 18
   c 125 + 210
   d 920 + 430
   e 982 − 795
   f 127 + 976
   g 1758 + 1921
   h £5.27 − £1.53
   i 86 + 197
   j 737 − 298
   k 5.2 − 1.8
   l 693 − 287

6 Place these lengths in order from smallest to longest:
   1.35 m   1.53 m   2.35 m
   1.33 m   1.55 m   1.5 m

28

Development

The themes of the unit are developed in N3 to include strategies for successful multiplication and division.

Links

Students should be encouraged to choose the most appropriate method whenever they are faced with number problems.

Mental starters

Objectives covered in this unit:

- Multiply and divide whole numbers by 10, 100, 1000.
- Know pairs of factors to 100.
- Recall multiplication facts to 10 × 10 and derive associated division facts.
- Use metric units of length.
- Use metric units for estimation.

Resources needed

* means class set needed

Essential:
S1.1OHP – Rectangles
S1.2OHP – A compound shape
S1.3OHP – Scales
S1.4OHP – Cuboid and net
Rulers*
Useful:
R1* – Digit cards
R2* – Decimal digit cards
R7 (OHP) – Function machines
R16 (OHP) – 3-D shapes
S1.1F* – Irregular shapes
S1.3F* – Reading scales
S1.2ICT* – Perimeter and area using Excel
Card, glue, scissors, Multilink cubes
Dice
Boxes to illustrate nets

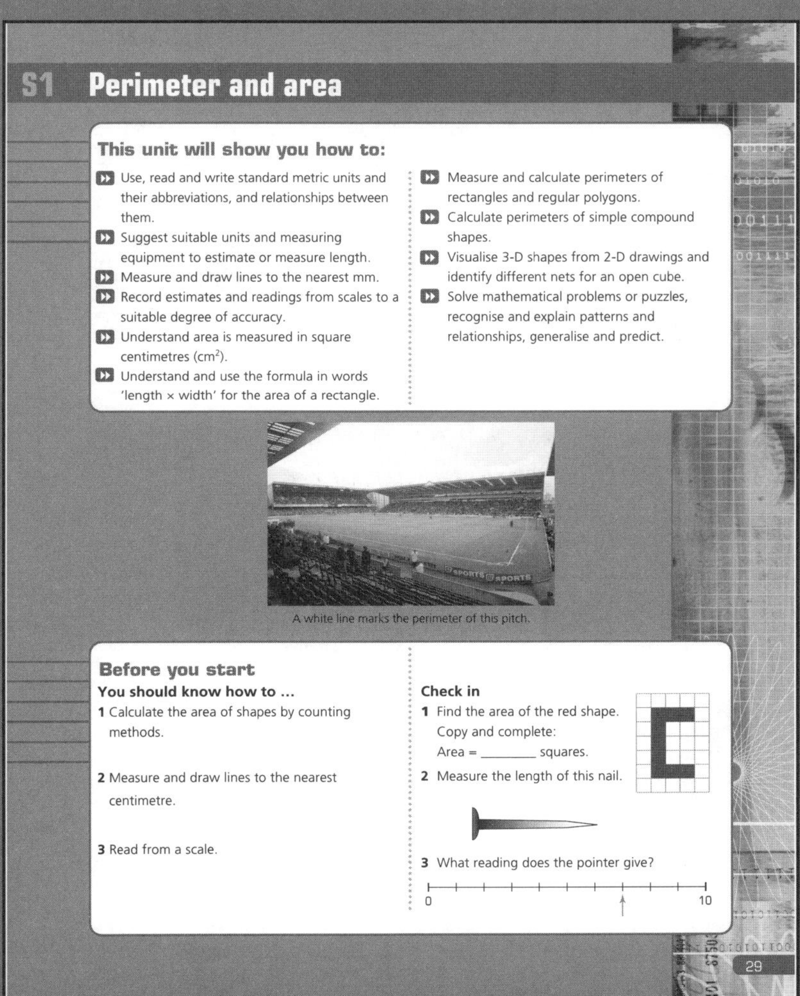

S1 Perimeter and area

This unit will show you how to:

- Use, read and write standard metric units and their abbreviations, and relationships between them.
- Suggest suitable units and measuring equipment to estimate or measure length.
- Measure and draw lines to the nearest mm.
- Record estimates and readings from scales to a suitable degree of accuracy.
- Understand area is measured in square centimetres (cm^2).
- Understand and use the formula in words 'length × width' for the area of a rectangle.
- Measure and calculate perimeters of rectangles and regular polygons.
- Calculate perimeters of simple compound shapes.
- Visualise 3-D shapes from 2-D drawings and identify different nets for an open cube.
- Solve mathematical problems or puzzles, recognise and explain patterns and relationships, generalise and predict.

A white line marks the perimeter of this pitch.

Before you start

You should know how to ...

1 Calculate the area of shapes by counting methods.

2 Measure and draw lines to the nearest centimetre.

3 Read from a scale.

Check in

1 Find the area of the red shape. Copy and complete: Area = ________ squares.

2 Measure the length of this nail.

3 What reading does the pointer give?

0 10

29

Check in activity

Discuss what students understand by the words 'perimeter' and 'area'.
Ask for everyday examples including ideas from in the classroom.
Discuss the difference between a perimeter and an area and lead on to solid shapes and their dimensions.

Unit commentary

Aim of the unit
This unit aims to consolidate students' ability to use measures and scales and develops strategies for finding the perimeter and area of a rectangle and introduces nets of open cubes.
Introduction
Are all football pitches the same size?
No – the rules are:

- 100 yards < length < 130 yards
- 50 yards < width < 100 yards
- It cannot be square.

Discuss how you would work out the largest and smallest possible pitches – would you measure area or perimeter?
Framework references
This unit focuses on:

- Year 6 teaching objectives pages: 91, 93, 95, 97, 105
- Problem solving objectives page: 79

The unit provides access to:

- Year 7 teaching objectives pages: 200, 228, 230, 234–240

Differentiation

Core tier focuses on the correct use of units and develops to include the area of a triangle.

Springboard 7

Pages 107–112, 114–122, 124–130, 132, 133, 375–378.

Mental starter

Factors

- Students are told they are one of a pair.
- Shout out a number, e.g. 12, 18, 20, 24, 15, 30 ...
- Ask one student to hold up a factor of the number.
- The other student must hold up the other factor.
- Students take it in turns to go first.

Useful resources

R1 digit cards for the mental starter.
S1.1OHP has the diagrams from the examples in the book and an irregular shape to discuss.

Introductory activity

Ask questions to find out how much students know about perimeter:

- What is perimeter?
- When/where is the word used?
- What units is it measured in?
- How would you measure the perimeter of a ... ?

Emphasise that perimeter is a length.

Repeat for area.
Emphasise that an area is measured using squares.
Squares have 2 dimensions: length and width, and so you use a little 2 to show it is an area.

S1.1OHP has the diagrams from the examples in the book. You can use it to discuss how to work out the perimeter and area of a rectangle.

Ask students how they would find the perimeter of the first rectangle.
Then ask about the area. If students are counting squares, ask them to show you where they start and how they count.
Emphasise that they count in rows or columns and that a quicker way is to multiply.

Discuss finding the area of an irregular shape using the last example. Encourage students to count the whole squares as 1 and the part squares as $\frac{1}{2}$.

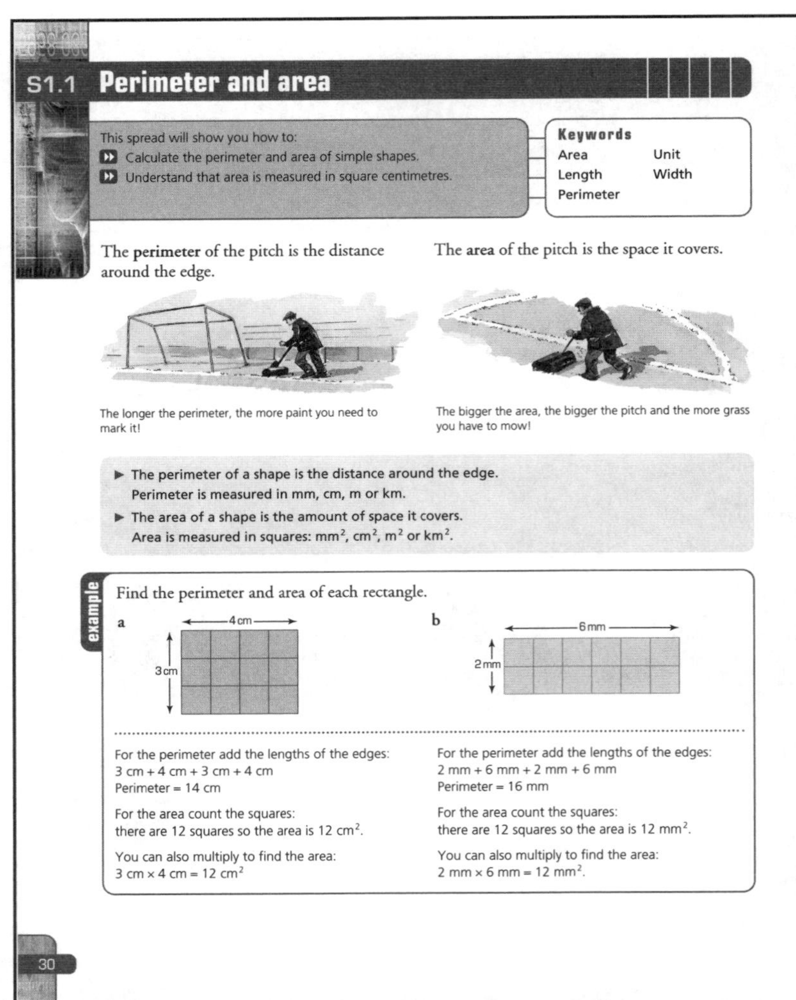

S1.1 Perimeter and area

This spread will show you how to:
- Calculate the perimeter and area of simple shapes.
- Understand that area is measured in square centimetres.

Keywords: Area, Length, Perimeter, Unit, Width

The **perimeter** of the pitch is the distance around the edge.

The **area** of the pitch is the space it covers.

The longer the perimeter, the more paint you need to mark it!

The bigger the area, the bigger the pitch and the more grass you have to mow!

- The perimeter of a shape is the distance around the edge. Perimeter is measured in mm, cm, m or km.
- The area of a shape is the amount of space it covers. Area is measured in squares: mm^2, cm^2, m^2 or km^2.

example

Find the perimeter and area of each rectangle.

a (4 cm by 3 cm)

b (6 mm by 2 mm)

a For the perimeter add the lengths of the edges:
3 cm + 4 cm + 3 cm + 4 cm
Perimeter = 14 cm
For the area count the squares:
there are 12 squares so the area is 12 cm^2.
You can also multiply to find the area:
3 cm × 4 cm = 12 cm^2

b For the perimeter add the lengths of the edges:
2 mm + 6 mm + 2 mm + 6 mm
Perimeter = 16 mm
For the area count the squares:
there are 12 squares so the area is 12 mm^2.
You can also multiply to find the area:
2 mm × 6 mm = 12 mm^2.

30

Plenary

Draw a rectangle on the board.

- Tell students that the area is 12 cm^2.
- Ask them what the dimensions are.
- Ask for other possibilities (you may need to redraw the rectangle to look longer/shorter).
- Discuss whether a 2 × 6 rectangle is the same as a 6 × 2 rectangle.
- Repeat for other areas.

Further activities

S1.1F contains some irregular shapes for students to estimate areas using the counting squares method.

Students can repeat question 4 using a different perimeter: 20 cm, and able students may find different perimeters while keeping the area fixed: 12 cm^2.

Differentiation

Support questions:

- Questions 1 and 2 involve counting squares. Weak students may go on to **S1.1F**. Springboard 7, page 107.
- Question 3 focuses on multiplying to find the area of a rectangle. Springboard 7, pages 108, 124, 125.
- Question 4 develops the idea that rectangles can have the same perimeter but different dimensions. Springboard 7, pages 109, 126.

Core tier: focuses on finding the area of compound shapes based on rectangles.

Exercise S1.1

1 a Copy these letters onto centimetre-squared paper.

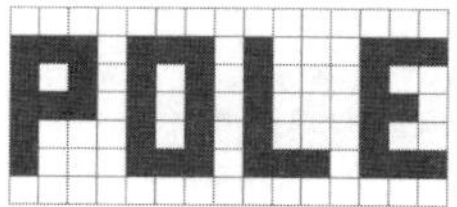

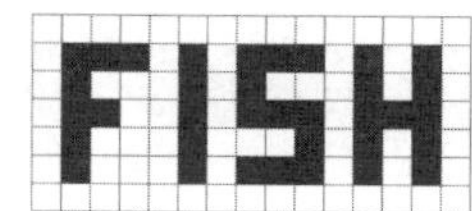

b The perimeter of the P is 16 cm. Find the perimeter of the other letters.
c The area of the P is 10 cm^2. Find the area of the other letters.

2 a Find the perimeter and area of these shapes.

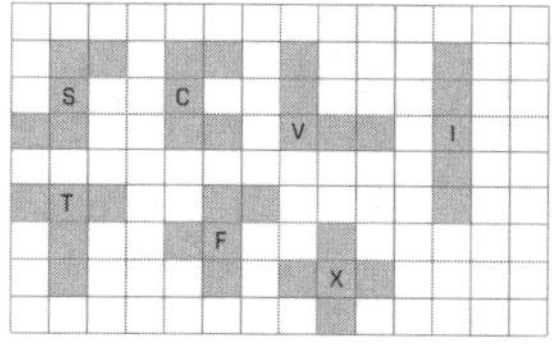

b Find the perimeter and area of these rectangles.

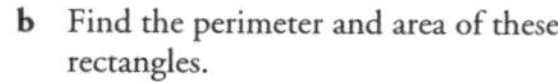

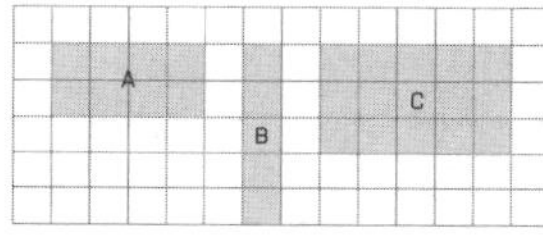

3 Find the perimeter and area of these shapes.

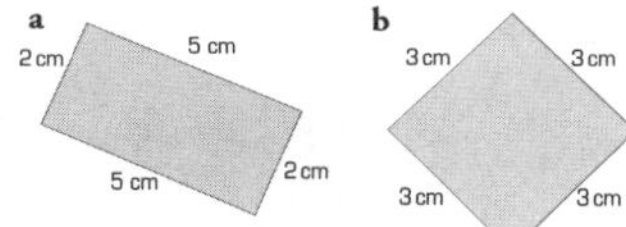

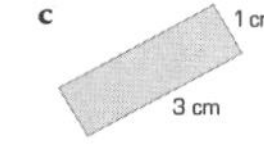

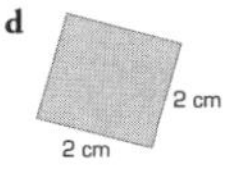

4 This rectangle has a perimeter of 10 cm:

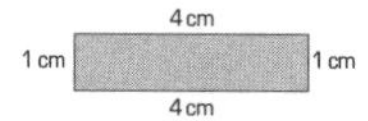

a Copy and complete this table of results for rectangles with a perimeter of 10 cm.
b Calculate the area of each of the rectangles.

length	width	perimeter
1 cm	4 cm	10 cm
2 cm		10 cm
3 cm		10 cm

length	width	perimeter
4 cm		10 cm
3.5 cm		10 cm
4.5 cm		10 cm

31

Exercise commentary

The questions assess the objectives on Primary Framework Page 97.

Problem solving

Question 3 assesses Primary Framework Page 81 as students need to generalise to find the area, and question 4 assesses Page 79.

Group work

Question 4 is suitable for pair work.

Misconceptions

Many students mix up perimeter and area. Emphasise that perimeter is a distance but area is the number of squares needed to cover a shape.

Discuss strategies for remembering as a class and perhaps find everyday examples of area for students to keep in mind as a reference.

Students often use all the numbers in the question rather than just those needed for the question.

Question 3 should highlight this problem. Encourage students to think about the problem from first principles, drawing squares on the shape.

Links

Measures: Primary Framework Page 91, and multiplication facts: Page 59.

Homework

S1.1HW provides practice at finding the area and perimeter of shapes based on rectangles by counting squares.

Answers

1 **b** O 16 cm, L 16 cm, E 22 cm, F 18 cm, I 12 cm, S 24 cm, H 24 cm
c O 12 cm^2, L 7 cm^2, E 10 cm^2, F 8 cm^2, I 5 cm^2, S 11 cm^2, H 11 cm^2

2 **a** All perimeters are 12 cm; all areas are 5 cm^2.
b A 12 cm, 8 cm^2; B 12 cm, 5 cm^2; C 16 cm, 15 cm^2

3 **a** 14 cm, 10 cm^2 **b** 12 cm, 9 cm^2 **c** 8 cm, 3 cm^2 **d** 8 cm, 4 cm^2

4 **a** Widths: 4 cm, 3 cm, 2 cm, 1 cm, 1.5 cm, 0.5 cm
b 4 cm^2, 6 cm^2, 6 cm^2, 4 cm^2, 5.25 cm^2, 2.25 cm^2

Mental starter

Number machines

Draw a number machine on the board or use R7.
Students take turns to suggest an input value.
You supply the operation – use a division wherever possible (unless they suggest a prime number).
The students hold up the output using digit cards.

Useful resources

R1 digit cards for the mental starter.
S1.2OHP has a compound shape for discussion.
Rulers for the exercise.
A **12-sided dice** for the plenary.
R7 shows blank function machines.

Introductory activity

Ask questions to find out how much students remember from last lesson:

- What is perimeter/area?
- What units is it measured in?
- How would you measure the perimeter/area of a ... ?

Remind students that perimeter is measured as a length and that area is measured using squares.

Draw a rectangle on the board with the length 5 cm and width 3 cm marked.

- Ask for the area/perimeter.
- Students to explain any methods.

Lead in to the formula for the area using words.

Encourage deeper understanding by asking questions such as: If the area is 18 cm^2 what are the dimensions?
Link to ×/ ÷ being inverse operations.

S1.2OHP shows a compound shape.

- Ask students for the perimeter.
- Emphasise that they need to know all the lengths to be able to find the perimeter.
- Ask them how to find the missing lengths.
- Now ask how to find the area.

You can split the shape up – ask students to show how they would do this. (There are 3 ways – vertically, horizontally or complete the rectangle and take the extra part away.)

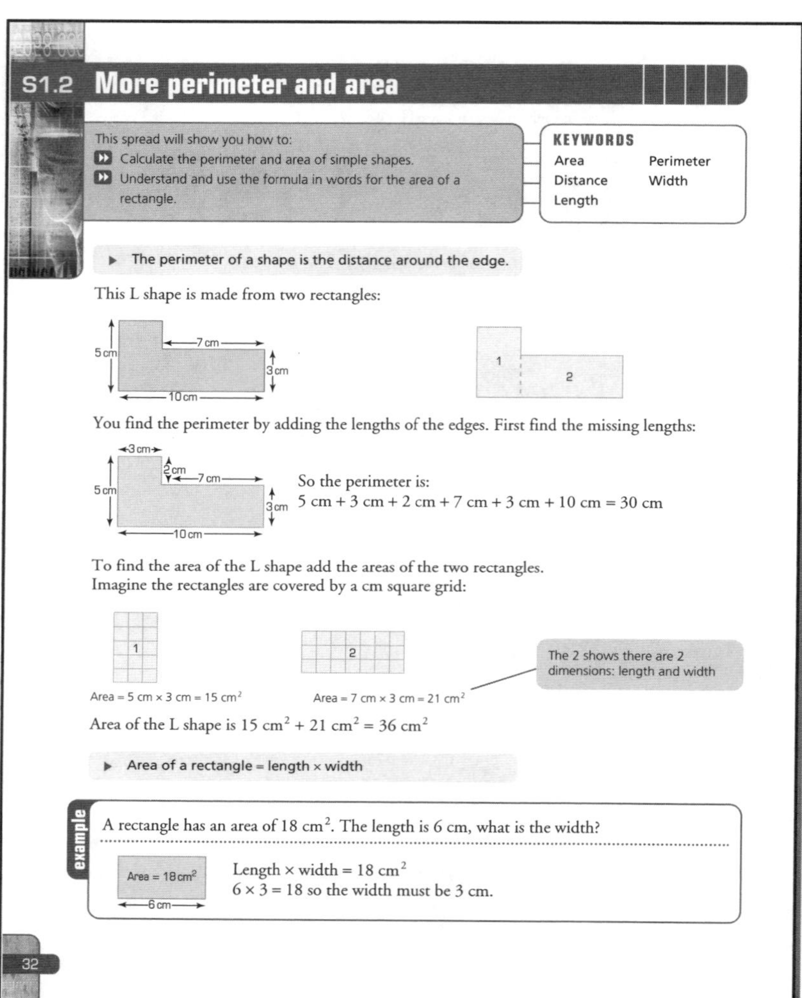

S1.2 More perimeter and area

This spread will show you how to:

- Calculate the perimeter and area of simple shapes.
- Understand and use the formula in words for the area of a rectangle.

KEYWORDS
Area, Perimeter, Distance, Width, Length

- The perimeter of a shape is the distance around the edge.

This L shape is made from two rectangles:

You find the perimeter by adding the lengths of the edges. First find the missing lengths:

So the perimeter is:
5 cm + 3 cm + 2 cm + 7 cm + 3 cm + 10 cm = 30 cm

To find the area of the L shape add the areas of the two rectangles.
Imagine the rectangles are covered by a cm square grid:

Area = 5 cm × 3 cm = 15 cm^2 Area = 7 cm × 3 cm = 21 cm^2

The 2 shows there are 2 dimensions: length and width

Area of the L shape is 15 cm^2 + 21 cm^2 = 36 cm^2

- Area of a rectangle = length × width

example

A rectangle has an area of 18 cm^2. The length is 6 cm, what is the width?

Length × width = 18 cm^2
6 × 3 = 18 so the width must be 3 cm.

32

Plenary

Bingo

Students choose any four numbers between 1 and 12 and put them into a 2 × 2 grid (draw one on the board).
Use a 12-sided dice to generate an answer (or two 6-sided dice) and then ask questions in the form:

- The area is 70 cm^2, the width is 7 cm – the length?
- The perimeter is 24 cm, the length is 6 cm – the width?

Students cross our their number if they get a correct answer.
The first student to cross out all four must explain the answers.

Further activities

In S1.2ICT, students use a spreadsheet to calculate the perimeter and area of a rectangle. It extends to cover surface area of cuboids (S1.4).

Encourage weaker students to make different rectangles with area 18 cm^2 using multilink cubes before trying question 7.

Some students may need to draw shapes on squared paper in question 8.

Differentiation

Support questions:

- Questions 1–3 involve straightforward multiplications.
- Questions 4–6 focus on understanding and using the formula for the area and perimeter of a rectangle. Springboard 7, pages 110, 111, 127, 128.
- Question 7 develops the idea that rectangles with the same area can have different dimensions and question 8 focuses on compound shapes. Springboard 7, pages 112, 129, 130.

Core tier: focuses on finding the area of compound shapes based on rectangles and triangles.

Exercise S1.2

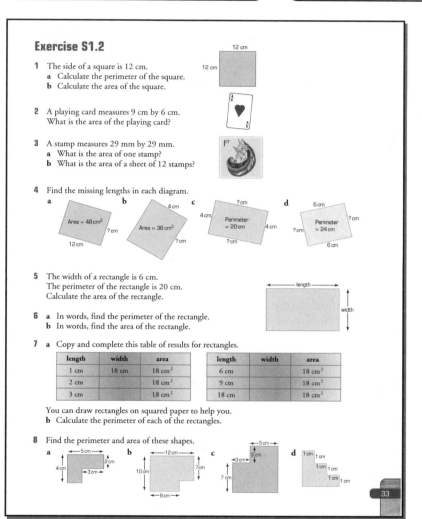

1 The side of a square is 12 cm.
  a Calculate the perimeter of the square.
  b Calculate the area of the square.

12 cm
12 cm

2 A playing card measures 9 cm by 6 cm.
What is the area of the playing card?

3 A stamp measures 29 mm by 29 mm.
  a What is the area of one stamp?
  b What is the area of a sheet of 12 stamps?

4 Find the missing lengths in each diagram.

a Area = 48 cm^2; 12 cm; ? cm
b Area = 36 cm^2; 4 cm; ? cm
c Perimeter = 20 cm; 4 cm; 4 cm; ? cm; ? cm
d Perimeter = 24 cm; 6 cm; 6 cm; ? cm; ? cm

5 The width of a rectangle is 6 cm.
The perimeter of the rectangle is 20 cm.
Calculate the area of the rectangle.

6 **a** In words, find the perimeter of the rectangle.
  b In words, find the area of the rectangle.

length
width

7 **a** Copy and complete this table of results for rectangles.

length	width	area
1 cm	18 cm	18 cm^2
2 cm		18 cm^2
3 cm		18 cm^2

length	width	area
6 cm		18 cm^2
9 cm		18 cm^2
18 cm		18 cm^2

You can draw rectangles on squared paper to help you.
  b Calculate the perimeter of each of the rectangles.

8 Find the perimeter and area of these shapes.

a 5 cm; 2 cm; 3 cm; 4 cm
b 12 cm; 7 cm; 10 cm; 8 cm
c 5 cm; 3 cm; 3 cm; 7 cm
d 1 cm; 1 cm; 1 cm; 1 cm; 1 cm; 1 cm

33

Exercise commentary

The questions assess the objectives on Primary Framework Page 97.

Problem solving

Question 5 assesses Primary Framework Page 81 as students generalise to find the formula, and question 7 assesses Page 79.

Group work

Question 1 is suitable for pair work.

Misconceptions

Students need a good grasp of multiplication facts and the associated division facts.

Weaker students would benefit from access to a multiplication grid.

In questions 4 and 5 students may find it hard to work out what information they need to use.

Encourage the use of a sketch showing the information given and emphasise the strategy of speaking the problem, supporting working using jottings:
4 + 4 + width + width is 20 so width + width must be 12 so the width is 6.

Links

Measures: Primary Framework Page 91, and multiplication facts: Page 59.

Homework

S1.2HW provides practice at finding the area of a rectangle by using a formula, and includes problems in context.

Answers

1 **a** 48 cm **b** 144 cm^2 **2** 54 cm^2 **3** **a** 841 mm^2 **b** 10 092 mm^2
4 **a** 6 cm **b** 6 cm **c** 4 cm **d** 9 cm **5** 24 cm^2
6 **a** 2 × length + 2 × width or 2(length + width)
  b length × width
7 **a** Widths: 18 cm, 9 cm, 6 cm, 3 cm, 2 cm, 1 cm
  b 38 cm, 22 cm, 18 cm, 18 cm, 22 cm, 38 cm
8 **a** 18 cm, 14 cm^2 **b** 44 cm, 108 cm^2
  c 36 cm, 71 cm^2 **d** 12 cm, 6 cm^2

S1.3 Measurement and scales

Mental starter

Students practise multiplying and dividing by 10.

- Ask students to hold up the answers to:
- 6 × 10, 12 × 10, 210 ÷ 10,
- Include decimals: 4.2 × 10, 68 ÷ 10 etc.

Students make up their own questions for the class to answer.

Useful resources

R2 digit cards for the mental starter.
S1.3OHP shows the scales from the student book.
Rulers and other measuring equipment.

Introductory activity

Draw a rectangle on the board.
Ask students what units they would use to measure the perimeter.
Ask what they would use to measure:

- the perimeter of the classroom
- the perimeter of a stamp
- the perimeter of a field.

Concentrate on the metric measures.

- Ask students to say how big they think a: mm, cm, m, km is.
- Ask for their ideas of benchmarks.
- Discuss the sort of equipment they would use for measuring short, medium and long lengths.

Ask students to estimate the length of their textbook (it is 246 mm × 189 mm) then measure using a ruler marked in cm and mm.
Remind them that they should measure from the zero mark on the ruler.

- Ask for the length.
- Ask for the width.
- Discuss the use of cm only, mm only or a mixture of cm and mm.

Emphasise the scale on the ruler and that there are 10 mm in 1 cm.

Ask students when they see scales.
Discuss at the scales on **S1.3OHP**.
Discuss the divisions and how to read the scales – ask students to explain their reasoning.
Encourage them to state what each division represents.

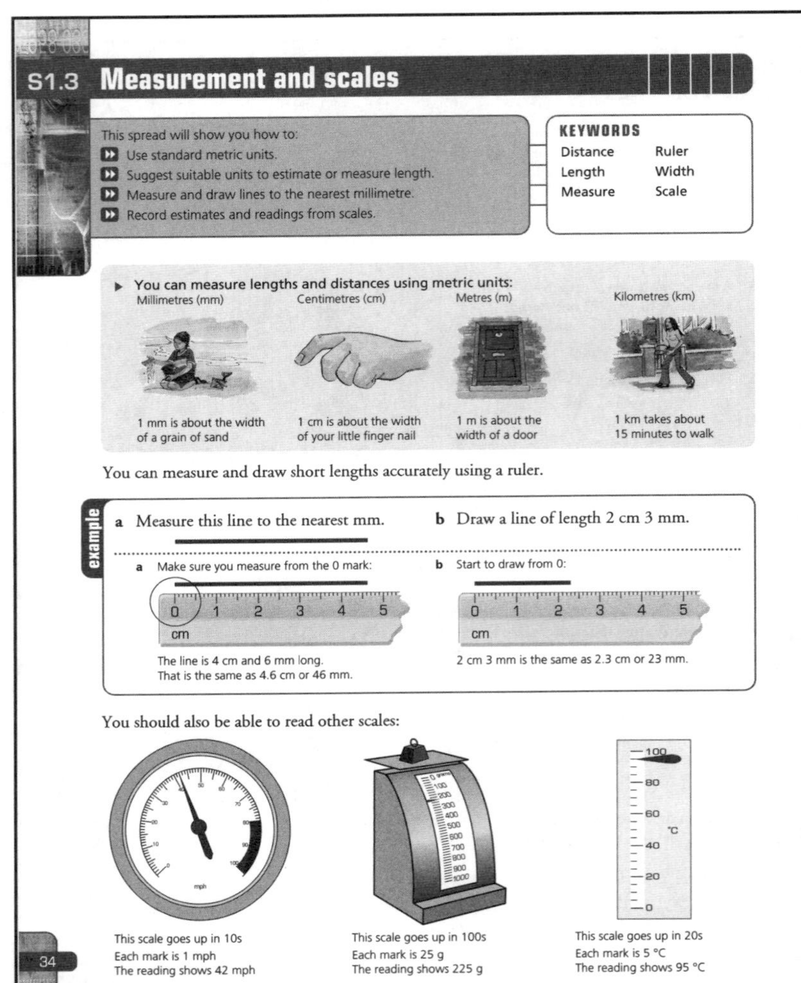

S1.3 Measurement and scales

This spread will show you how to:
- Use standard metric units.
- Suggest suitable units to estimate or measure length.
- Measure and draw lines to the nearest millimetre.
- Record estimates and readings from scales.

KEYWORDS
Distance, Ruler, Length, Width, Measure, Scale

- You can measure lengths and distances using metric units:

1 mm is about the width of a grain of sand
1 cm is about the width of your little finger nail
1 m is about the width of a door
1 km takes about 15 minutes to walk

You can measure and draw short lengths accurately using a ruler.

example

a Measure this line to the nearest mm.
b Draw a line of length 2 cm 3 mm.

a Make sure you measure from the 0 mark:

The line is 4 cm and 6 mm long.
That is the same as 4.6 cm or 46 mm.

b Start to draw from 0:

2 cm 3 mm is the same as 2.3 cm or 23 mm.

You should also be able to read other scales:

This scale goes up in 10s
Each mark is 1 mph
The reading shows 42 mph

This scale goes up in 100s
Each mark is 25 g
The reading shows 225 g

This scale goes up in 20s
Each mark is 5 °C
The reading shows 95 °C

34

Plenary

Ask students to estimate heights, widths and other distances around the classroom and local area for example.

- the length of the classroom
- the distance to the bus stop.

Ask them to explain their reasoning – what benchmarks they are using. Encourage them to compare with known distances.
Ask how they would measure the actual lengths to check their estimates.

Further activities

Students can challenge each other with problems as in questions 4 and 5.

Students can build on question 7 by measuring objects in the classroom using appropriate units and then calculating the area and perimeter.

S1.3F is a sheet of questions that involve reading scales.

Differentiation

Support questions:

- Questions 1 and 2 build on year 4 and 5 objectives. Springboard 7, pages 114–116.
- Questions 3–6 focus on estimating lengths and choosing appropriate units. Springboard 7, pages 117–120.
- Question 7 focuses on finding the area and perimeter of an object by measuring decimal lengths. Springboard 7, pages 121, 122, 375–378.

Core tier: focuses on estimating lengths and areas, and on converting between measures.

Exercise S1.3

1 Write down the values shown on each of these scales:

a 0 2 4 6 8 9 10 m **b** 15 20 25 30 35 mm

c 0 50 100 150 200 g **d** 0 50 kg

e 0 10 20 30 40 50 mm **f** 0 250 500 g

2 **a** Measure these lines to the nearest mm.

A B

b Draw lines of length 2.8 cm and 4 cm 3 mm.

3 Which line is longer: A or B?
Guess first, and then measure them to see if you guessed correctly.

A B

4 Which units would you use to measure each of these lengths?
Choose from mm, cm, m, km.

a The perimeter of this page **b** The perimeter of a field
c The perimeter of a sports arena **d** The perimeter of a stamp
e The perimeter of a room **f** The perimeter of England

5 Which units would you use to measure each of these areas?
Choose from mm^2, cm^2, m^2, km^2.

a The area of this page **b** The area of a field
c The area of a carpet **d** The area of a pinhead
e The area of a table top **f** The area of England

6 Copy and complete:
The length of my little finger is about ______ times the width of my fingernail so the length is approximately ______ cm.
The height of the classroom door is about ______ times the width of the door so the height is approximately ______ m.

7 Measure the length and width of:
a your text book **b** your calculator
In each case find the area and perimeter.

35

Exercise commentary

The questions assess the objectives on Primary Framework Pages 91–97.

Problem solving

Question 6 assesses Primary Framework Page 79 as students are encouraged to generalise and predict.

Group work

Questions 4 and 5 are suitable for pairs.

Misconceptions

Many students count each division on a scale as one unit.
Question 1 highlights this issue.
Emphasise that the marks on the scale divide up the range and so students need to divide to work out what each one is worth: 50 ÷ 5 = 10.
Poor use of a ruler is highlighted by questions 2 and 3.
Emphasise the need to place the ruler to measure from 0. You can use R19 on OHP to discuss this as a group.
When drawing a line students should make a mark to start from.

Links

Area and perimeter: Primary Framework Page 97, and interpreting graphs (using scales): Pages 115–117.

Homework

S1.3HW focuses on estimation and reading scales. Students are required to fill in gaps in a story.

Answers

1 **a** 3 m, 7 m **b** 19 mm, 26 mm
c 60 g, 120 g **d** 30 kg, 45 kg
e 17 mm, 34 mm **f** 100 g, 350 g
2 **a** A 4.1 mm, B 3.5 mm
3 A is 3.8 cm, B is 3.6 cm, so A is longer.
4 **a** cm **b** m **c** m **d** mm **e** m **f** km
5 **a** cm^2 **b** m^2 **c** m^2 **d** mm^2 **e** cm^2 **f** km^2

Mental starter

Discuss the homework from last lesson about estimating lengths and areas.

- Ask students the lengths and areas they estimated and draw up lists.
- Any 3-D shapes mentioned should be put in a separate list.
- Ask students to comment on this list and emphasise that they all have 3 dimensions – they found the area of a face of the object.

Useful resources

R16 shows 3-D shapes.
S1.4OHP shows a $2 \times 3 \times 4$ cuboid and its net.
Multilink cubes
Squared paper, card, scissors and **glue** for making nets.
Boxes for demonstration.

Introductory activity

Explore what students think is meant by the word 'dimension'.

- Emphasise that perimeters and lengths are 1-dimensional and that areas are 2-dimensional.
- Introduce terminology 3-D.
- Ask what objects have 3-D.

As students give you examples of 3-D shapes; try to categorise them in lists on the board.

- One list for cubes, one for cuboids, one for prisms, one for pyramids.
- Use prompts, e.g. chocolate boxes, **R6**.
- Ask students what the lists have in common and emphasise the properties of the faces.

Explain that a box is made from a flat net – demonstrate if possible (a photocopier paper box is useful).
Ignoring the flaps, count the number of faces and explain that the area is called the surface area. Ask how to find it – by adding all the areas together.

Give out multilink cubes and ask students to make these cuboids:
$2 \times 2 \times 2 \quad 1 \times 1 \times 4 \quad 1 \times 4 \times 2 \quad 2 \times 3 \times 4$
Each time ask students for the surface area.
Bring out the fact that it is quicker to work with pairs of faces.

The net of a $2 \times 3 \times 4$ cuboid is shown on S1.4OHP. Students can copy it onto squared paper and make up the cuboid.

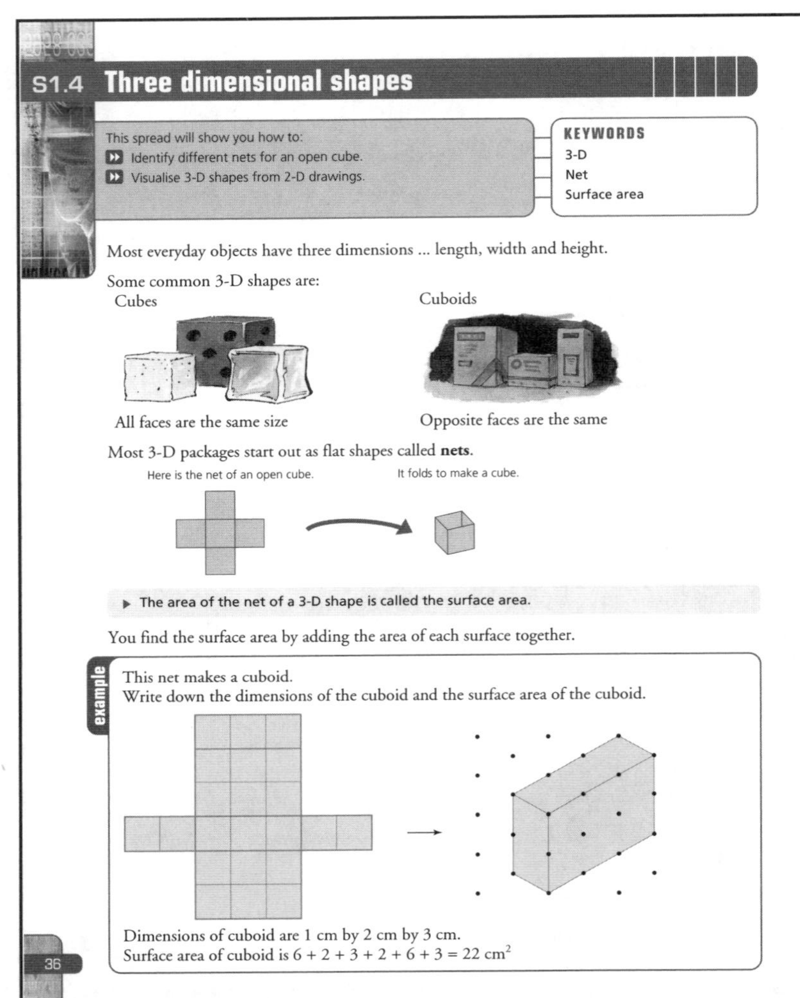

S1.4 Three dimensional shapes

This spread will show you how to:
- Identify different nets for an open cube.
- Visualise 3-D shapes from 2-D drawings.

KEYWORDS
3-D
Net
Surface area

Most everyday objects have three dimensions ... length, width and height.

Some common 3-D shapes are:

Cubes — All faces are the same size

Cuboids — Opposite faces are the same

Most 3-D packages start out as flat shapes called **nets**.

Here is the net of an open cube. It folds to make a cube.

- The area of the net of a 3-D shape is called the surface area.

You find the surface area by adding the area of each surface together.

example

This net makes a cuboid.
Write down the dimensions of the cuboid and the surface area of the cuboid.

Dimensions of cuboid are 1 cm by 2 cm by 3 cm.
Surface area of cuboid is $6 + 2 + 3 + 2 + 6 + 3 = 22\ \text{cm}^2$

36

Plenary

Discuss how to adapt the nets in questions 1 to become a net of a closed cube – the top of the cube will be opposite the base they have coloured.
For each example, sketch the net of the open cube on the board and ask a volunteer to add a square to make it the net of a closed cube. Ask another volunteer to suggest a 'pair of faces' that would be opposite each other on a dice.
This leads into the homework exercise.

Further activities

In question 1, weak students may want to draw the nets on squared paper and cut them out to see whether they can fold to a cube. More able students could investigate whether there are any further nets possible.

Students can develop question 4 by posing problems for partners to solve with different areas of faces, for example: 30 cm^2, 50 cm^2, 60 cm^2.

Differentiation

Support questions:

- Question 1 focuses on nets of open cubes which is Year 5 work. Springboard 7, page 132.
- Questions 2 and 3 focus on dimensions of nets of cuboids and finding the surface area by adding squares. Springboard 7, page 133.
- Question 4 extends to finding the dimensions from the areas of the surfaces then drawing the net of a closed cuboid.

Core tier: focuses on constructing nets of cuboids to find the surface area.

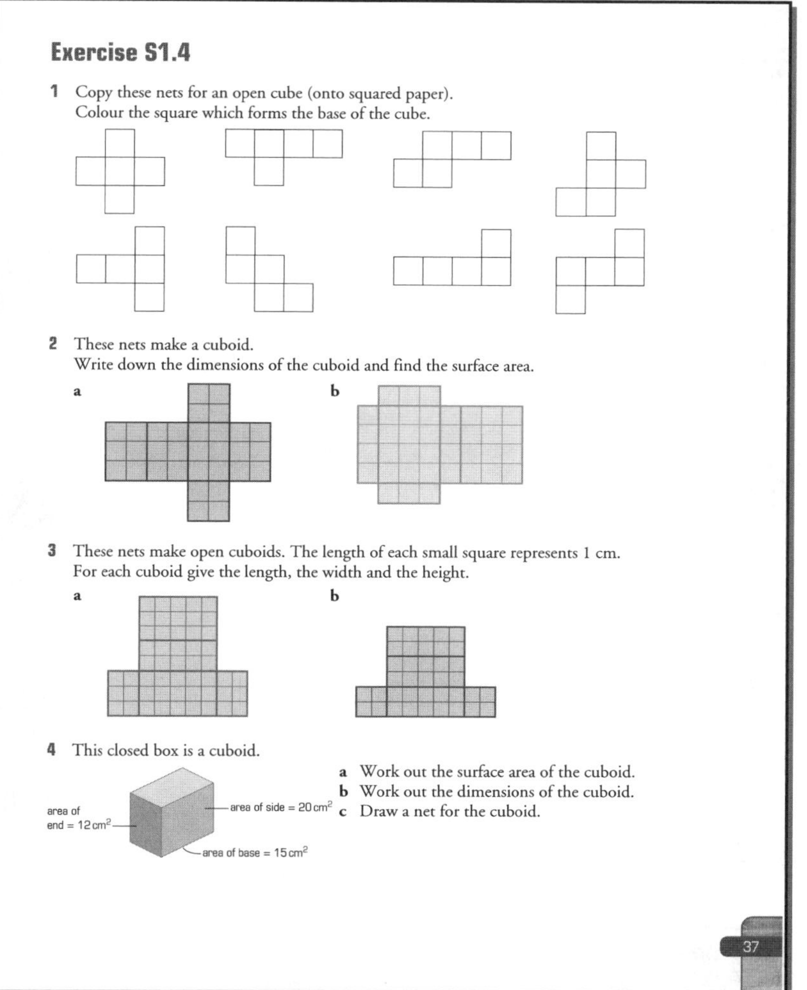

Exercise S1.4
1 Copy these nets for an open cube (onto squared paper).
Colour the square which forms the base of the cube.
2 These nets make a cuboid.
Write down the dimensions of the cuboid and find the surface area.
a
b
3 These nets make open cuboids. The length of each small square represents 1 cm.
For each cuboid give the length, the width and the height.
a
b
4 This closed box is a cuboid.
a Work out the surface area of the cuboid.
b Work out the dimensions of the cuboid.
c Draw a net for the cuboid.
area of end = 12 cm²
area of side = 20 cm²
area of base = 15 cm²
37

Exercise commentary

The questions assess the objectives on Primary Framework Pages 97 and 105.

Problem solving

Question 6 assesses Primary Framework Page 79 as students are encouraged to generalise and predict.

Group work

Questions 4 and 5 are suitable for pairs.

Misconceptions

Many students struggle to interpret 2-D drawings of 3-D shapes.

Using squared paper to draw the nets may help as students can fold the paper.

Having a variety of boxes can also help visualisation.

Surface area is approached very intuitively as a way of reinforcing area and may cause some difficulties as there are so many steps involved.

The use of multilink cubes may help students visualise the problem. Encourage students to think about the faces in pairs: top, side, front.

Links

Finding factors: Primary Framework Page 61

Homework

S1.4HW is based on nets of a cuboid, and requires students to calculate surface area.

Answers

2 **a** $2 \times 2 \times 3$, 32 square units
  b $3 \times 4 \times 1$, 38 square units

3 **a** 3 cm, 5 cm, 2 cm
  b 2 cm, 6 cm, 2 cm

4 **a** 94 cm^2 **b** 5 cm by 3 cm by 4 cm

Summary

The Year 6 key teaching objective in this unit is:

- Calculate the perimeter and area of simple compound shapes that can be split into rectangles (97).

Plenary activity

Discuss the nets in Exercise S1.4 question 1.
What is the area of each net? This depends on the length of the side of the cube! Change the dimensions and ask for the area of a face.
What is the perimeter of each net?
Which net gives the maximum perimeter?

Check out commentary

1 Students mix up perimeter and area and may add the lengths instead of multiplying, and if they do multiply they may not give squared units.
Emphasise that area is measured in squares and refer back to the squared grid. The ^{2} shows that there are two dimensions: length and width.
In part b students need to work backwards to find pairs of numbers that multiply to 48.
Simplify the problem – use 12 cm^2 and link the answers to the entries in the multiplication grid at the back of the book.
2 To find the perimeter of the shape students tend to add the lengths given instead of finding the distance around the shape.
Encourage them to write down the number of sides the shape has and then write down the length of each of those sides before adding them.
There are a few different ways of splitting the shape up to find the area.
Encourage students to use the most efficient method – in this case complete the whole rectangle and then subtract the small part.
3 In order to be successful students will need to take a structured approach to this question which links to factor pairs of numbers. It is important that they realise that 3 × 8 is the same as 8 × 3.
Refer to the multiplication grid at the end of the book so students can find pairs of factors easily.

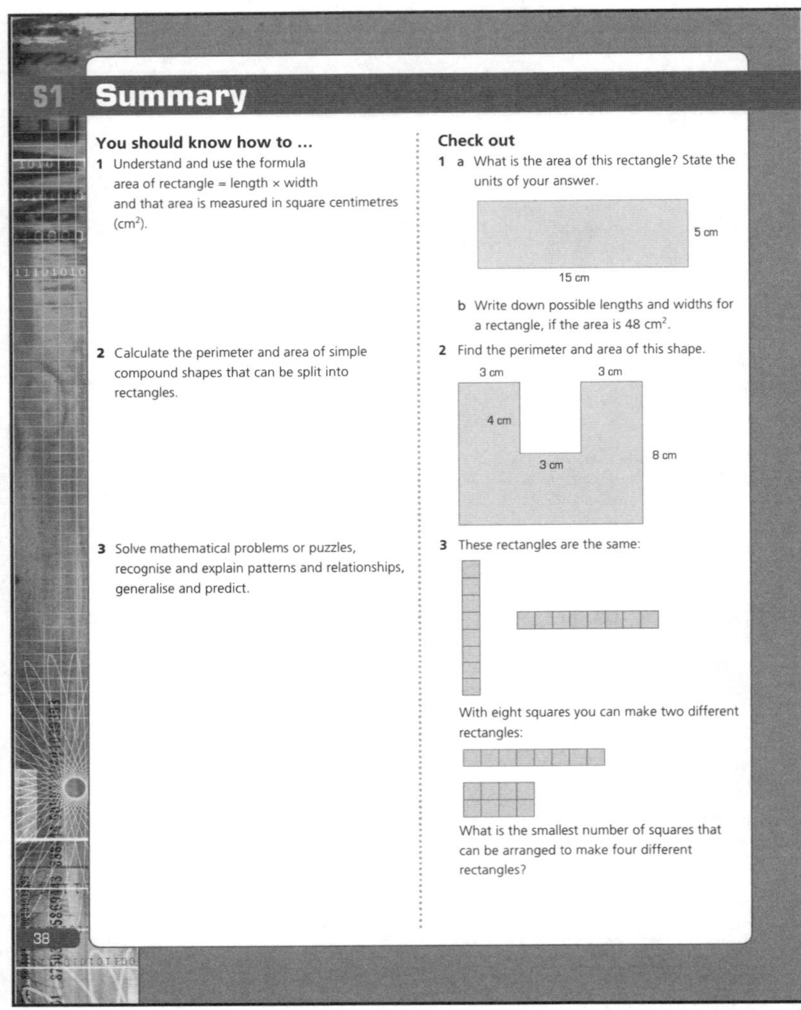

S1 Summary

You should know how to ...

1 Understand and use the formula area of rectangle = length × width and that area is measured in square centimetres (cm^2).

2 Calculate the perimeter and area of simple compound shapes that can be split into rectangles.

3 Solve mathematical problems or puzzles, recognise and explain patterns and relationships, generalise and predict.

Check out

1 a What is the area of this rectangle? State the units of your answer.

b Write down possible lengths and widths for a rectangle, if the area is 48 cm^2.

2 Find the perimeter and area of this shape.

3 These rectangles are the same:

With eight squares you can make two different rectangles:

What is the smallest number of squares that can be arranged to make four different rectangles?

38

Development

The use of measures is developed in N3.
Visualising and describing 3-D shapes is developed in S3.

Links

The area of a rectangle is used to illustrate real-life formulae in algebra (A2 and A5) and links to finding factors of numbers (N3 and A3).

Mental starters

Objectives covered in this unit:

- Multiply and divide whole numbers by 10 and 100.
- Convert between fractions, decimals and percentages.
- Find simple fractions of quantities.

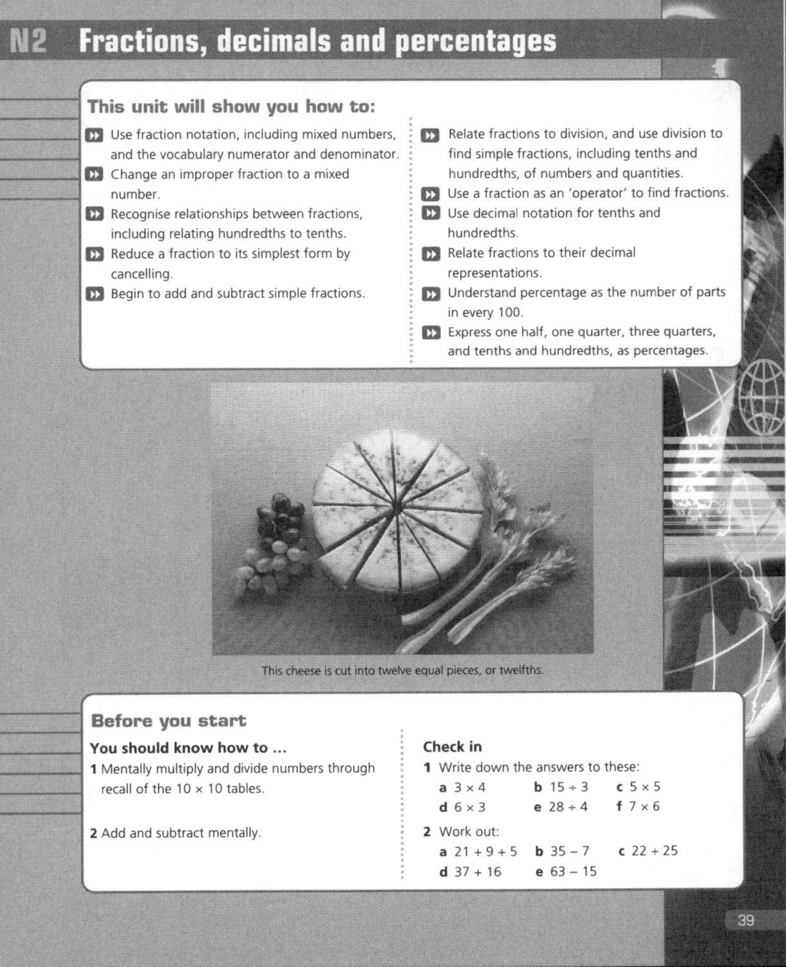

N2 Fractions, decimals and percentages

This unit will show you how to:

- Use fraction notation, including mixed numbers, and the vocabulary numerator and denominator.
- Change an improper fraction to a mixed number.
- Recognise relationships between fractions, including relating hundredths to tenths.
- Reduce a fraction to its simplest form by cancelling.
- Begin to add and subtract simple fractions.
- Relate fractions to division, and use division to find simple fractions, including tenths and hundredths, of numbers and quantities.
- Use a fraction as an 'operator' to find fractions.
- Use decimal notation for tenths and hundredths.
- Relate fractions to their decimal representations.
- Understand percentage as the number of parts in every 100.
- Express one half, one quarter, three quarters, and tenths and hundredths, as percentages.

This cheese is cut into twelve equal pieces, or twelfths.

Before you start

You should know how to ...

1 Mentally multiply and divide numbers through recall of the 10 × 10 tables.

2 Add and subtract mentally.

Check in

1 Write down the answers to these:

a 3 × 4 **b** 15 ÷ 3 **c** 5 × 5
d 6 × 3 **e** 28 ÷ 4 **f** 7 × 6

2 Work out:

a 21 + 9 + 5 **b** 35 − 7 **c** 22 + 25
d 37 + 16 **e** 63 − 15

39

Check in activity

Write these fractions on the board:

$\frac{2}{3}, \frac{1}{2}, \frac{1}{3}, \frac{3}{4}, \frac{1}{4}, \frac{1}{10}$

Discuss which fraction gives the largest piece of pizza!
Students justify choices using diagrams (a circle).

Resources needed

* means class set needed

Essential:

N2.1OHP – Shaded shapes
N2.2OHP – A fraction wall
N2.3OHP – Rectangles for equivalence
N2.4OHP – Conversions

Useful:

R1* – Digit cards
R2* – Decimal digit cards
R4 (OHP) – Place value table
R6 (OHP) – Number lines
R17* – 100 square
N2.1F* – Shading shapes
N2.6ICT* – Metric conversions in Excel

Unit commentary

Aim of the unit

This unit aims to consolidate students' understanding of simple fractions and introduces them to equivalent decimals and percentages.

Introduction

Refer to the picture in the student book and discuss the use of fractions to describe part of a whole.

Ask students when they share something equally – such as a cake or a bar of chocolate – and the fraction they may share into.

Introduce percentages: how much do you eat if you have 50%?

Framework references

This unit focuses on:

- Year 6 teaching objectives pages: 23, 25, 29, 31, 33
- Problem solving objectives page: 83

The unit provides access to:

- Year 7 teaching objectives pages: 60, 62, 64, 66, 70, 98

Differentiation

Core tier focuses on recognising the equivalence between fractions, decimals and percentages and using methods of calculation.

Springboard 7

Pages 175–179, 181–183, 185–191, 193–195.

Mental starter

What is a fraction?

- Ask 2 students to stand up – one boy, one girl. Ask the class what fraction are girls.
- Ask 4 students to put up their hand if they have a dog. Ask the class what fraction of the group have a dog.
- Ask similar questions involving $\frac{1}{2}$s and $\frac{1}{4}$s. Develop the idea into $\frac{1}{3}$s from groups of 3 and $\frac{1}{5}$s from groups of 5.

Useful resources

N2.1OHP has shapes with parts shaded for discussion.

Introductory activity

This is mainly revision from Primary school. **The mental starter will help you find out what students already know and you can start by asking questions:**

- What do you mean by a fraction?
- Give an example of when you use fractions.

Emphasise that equal shares can be described using fractions.
Show the first rectangle on **N2.1OHP**. Ask students whether $\frac{1}{4}$ is shaded or not. Continue with the other shapes on the OHP. Write down the fractions shaded and unshaded.
Emphasise the importance of dividing a shape into equal-sized pieces. The last two examples on the OHP illustrate this.

Introduce the terms 'numerator' and 'denominator'. Ask students what they mean in a fraction.

Use the example to introduce the idea that you can express one number as a fraction of another.
Reinforce the idea that the units must be the same – equal-sized pieces – before they can be compared.

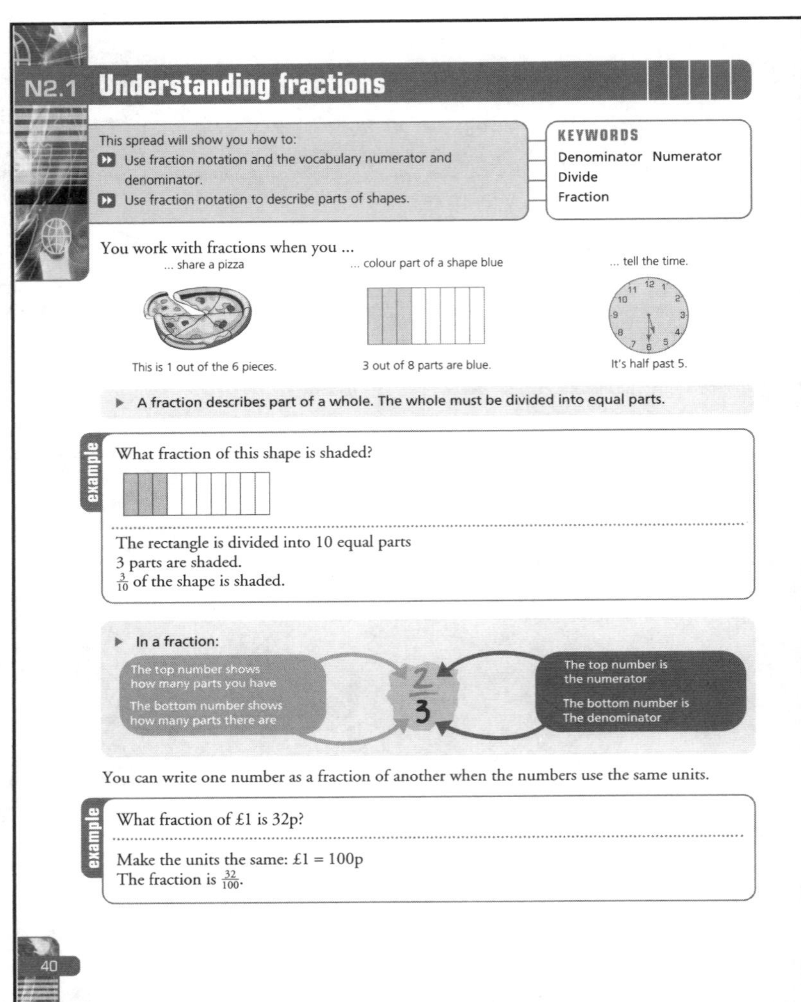

N2.1 **Understanding fractions**

This spread will show you how to:
- Use fraction notation and the vocabulary numerator and denominator.
- Use fraction notation to describe parts of shapes.

KEYWORDS
Denominator Numerator
Divide
Fraction

You work with fractions when you ...

... share a pizza — This is 1 out of the 6 pieces.

... colour part of a shape blue — 3 out of 8 parts are blue.

... tell the time. — It's half past 5.

- A fraction describes part of a whole. The whole must be divided into equal parts.

example

What fraction of this shape is shaded?

The rectangle is divided into 10 equal parts
3 parts are shaded.
$\frac{3}{10}$ of the shape is shaded.

- In a fraction:

The top number shows how many parts you have
The bottom number shows how many parts there are

$\frac{2}{3}$

The top number is the numerator
The bottom number is the denominator

You can write one number as a fraction of another when the numbers use the same units.

example

What fraction of £1 is 32p?

Make the units the same: £1 = 100p
The fraction is $\frac{32}{100}$.

40

Plenary

Go through question 6, asking students to explain their answers. Encourage the use of technical language: numerator and denominator by asking what the numbers mean.

Further activities

Students shade 3 × 4 grids into these fractions:

$\frac{1}{12}, \frac{5}{12}, \frac{1}{2}, \frac{1}{4}, \frac{1}{3}, \frac{2}{3}$

You can pose the same problem to able students by asking which is the biggest fraction and by how much.

N2.1F contains the shapes from questions 8 and 9.

Differentiation

Support questions:

- Questions 1–3 revise work from year 4 objectives. Springboard 7, page 175.
- Questions 4–7 focus on writing one number as a fraction of another. Springboard 7, page 176.
- Questions 8 and 9 focus on the need to have equal-sized parts.

Core tier: focuses on expressing one quantity as a fraction of another, using units of measure.

Exercise N2.1

1 Write down the fraction of each shape that is shaded.

a b c d e f

2 Copy these shapes and shade in the fraction given.

a $\frac{1}{4}$ b $\frac{1}{6}$ c $\frac{3}{6}$

3 Draw a 4 × 4 square grid 20 times.
Find as many ways as you can to shade:
a $\frac{1}{2}$ of the squares b $\frac{3}{4}$ of the squares
Compare your results with your classmates.

4 Write these amounts as fractions of 10p:
a 1p b 7p c 5p d 4p e 6p f 8p

5 Write these distances as fractions of 25 cm:
a 1 cm b 11 cm c 24 cm d 15 cm e 20 cm f 5 cm

6 Write these amounts as fractions of £1:
a 71p b 32p c 9p d 99p e 80p f 50p

7 Write these amounts as fractions of 1 hour:
a 30 mins b 15 mins c 45 mins d 20 mins e 50 mins f 80 mins

8 Copy this shape four times and shade in the fraction given.
a $\frac{1}{2}$ b $\frac{1}{4}$ c $\frac{1}{8}$ d $\frac{3}{8}$

9 For each of these shapes:

- Make sure the shape is split into **equal sized parts**.
- Write down how many equal sized parts there are.
- Write down how many equal sized parts are shaded.
- Write down the fraction of each shape that is shaded.

a b c d e f

41

Exercise commentary

The questions assess the objectives on Primary Framework Pages 22 and 23.

Problem solving

Question 4 assesses the objective from Primary Framework Page 79.

Group work

Question 3 is suitable for paired work.

Misconceptions

A common mistake with questions about shading is to write $\frac{1}{3}$ instead of $\frac{1}{4}$ for question 1b. Essentially students are writing the fraction as a ratio rather than a proportion.

Emphasise that the total number of parts is the denominator of the fraction and encourage students to write this number down first. Most students will answer question 1a correctly so you could discuss it as a group.

In questions 6 and 7 students tend to use the larger number as the denominator or forget to change units.

Emphasise that the word 'of' usually indicates the denominator and that units must be the same to be compared.

Links

Division: Primary Framework Pages 56–57.

Homework

N2.1HW is an investigation. Students are asked to find four different ways of dividing a 4 × 4 square into quarters.

Answers

1 a $\frac{1}{2}$ b $\frac{1}{4}$ c $\frac{3}{4}$ d $\frac{2}{5}$ e $\frac{3}{8}$ f $\frac{3}{8}$

2 a Any one rectangle shaded b Any one square shaded
c Any three squares shaded

4 a $\frac{1}{10}$ b $\frac{7}{10}$ c $\frac{1}{2}$ d $\frac{2}{5}$ e $\frac{3}{5}$ f $\frac{4}{5}$

5 a $\frac{1}{25}$ b $\frac{11}{25}$ c $\frac{24}{25}$ d $\frac{3}{5}$ e $\frac{4}{5}$ f $\frac{1}{5}$

6 a $\frac{71}{100}$ b $\frac{8}{25}$ c $\frac{9}{100}$ d $\frac{99}{100}$ e $\frac{4}{5}$ f $\frac{1}{2}$

7 a $\frac{1}{2}$ b $\frac{1}{4}$ c $\frac{3}{4}$ d $\frac{1}{3}$ e $\frac{5}{6}$ f $\frac{4}{3}$

9 a $\frac{1}{2}$ b $\frac{1}{4}$ c $\frac{1}{2}$ d $\frac{1}{8}$ e $\frac{3}{8}$ f $\frac{1}{2}$

Mental starter

How big?

- Give 6 students a fraction to hold: $\frac{1}{2}, \frac{1}{3}, \frac{1}{4}, \frac{1}{5}, \frac{1}{6}, \frac{1}{7}$
- Discuss which is the biggest and which is the smallest.
- Class to arrange the students in order of size.

Emphasise that $\frac{1}{2}$ is 1 of 2 shares and $\frac{1}{4}$ is 1 of 4 shares.

Useful resources

R1 digit cards are useful for the mental starter.

N2.2OHP has a fraction wall for discussion.

Introductory activity

Write the number 4 on the board and ask students for different ways of writing 4: 2 + 2, 2 × 2 etc.

Now ask if anyone knows different ways of writing $\frac{1}{2}$.

Use a rectangle to discuss the equivalences they suggest.

N2.2OHP has a fraction wall that will help produce some equivalences.

Ask students to fill in the sections. Ask for some simple equivalences:

- What is the same as $\frac{1}{2}$?
- What other equivalences can you see?
- Write the equivalences down on the board. $\frac{1}{2} = \frac{3}{6}$ etc.

Ask students what they notice about the equivalences.

Encourage students to explain that they have common factors and emphasise that they can be cancelled down.

Write $\frac{3}{12}$ on the board and ask how to simplify it.

Emphasise that each number can be written as a multiple of 3.

Show that it is the same as $\frac{1}{4}$ by drawing a rectangle.

Ask students for other equivalent fractions to $\frac{1}{4}$.

Ask them to explain their reasons.

Show that they can multiply – demonstrate using rectangles.

Refer to the mental starter activity and discuss how equivalences help you to order fractions.

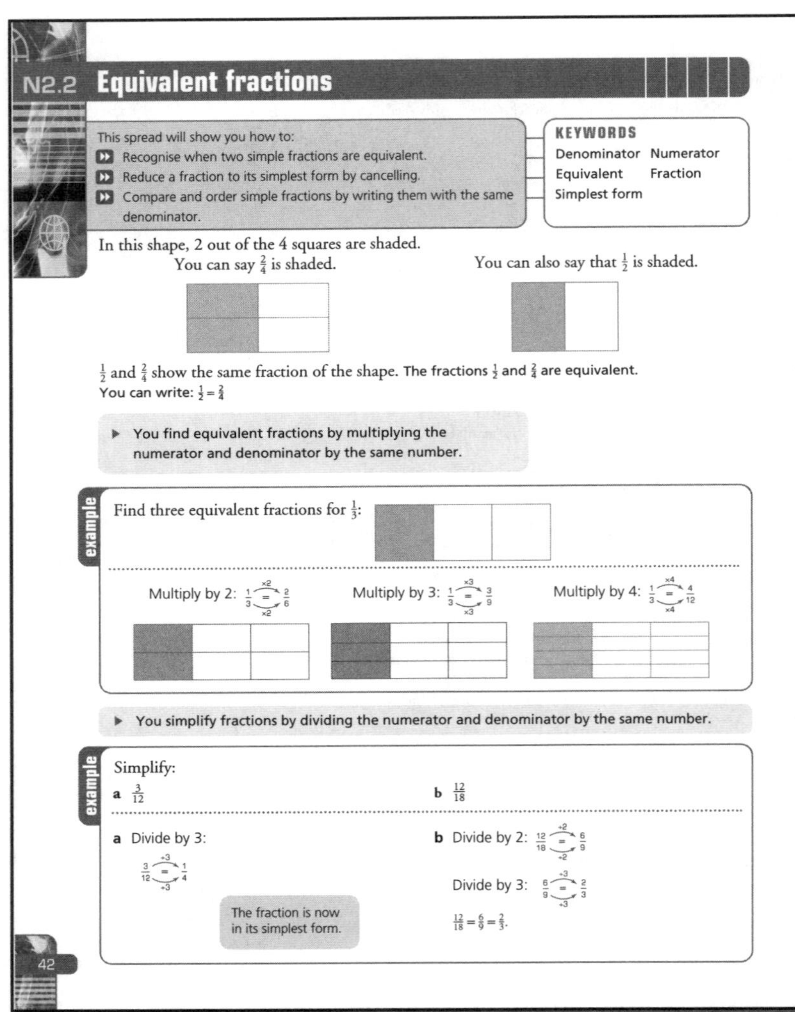

N2.2 Equivalent fractions

This spread will show you how to:
- Recognise when two simple fractions are equivalent.
- Reduce a fraction to its simplest form by cancelling.
- Compare and order simple fractions by writing them with the same denominator.

KEYWORDS: Denominator, Numerator, Equivalent, Fraction, Simplest form

In this shape, 2 out of the 4 squares are shaded. You can say $\frac{2}{4}$ is shaded. You can also say that $\frac{1}{2}$ is shaded.

$\frac{1}{2}$ and $\frac{2}{4}$ show the same fraction of the shape. The fractions $\frac{1}{2}$ and $\frac{2}{4}$ are equivalent. You can write: $\frac{1}{2} = \frac{2}{4}$

- You find equivalent fractions by multiplying the numerator and denominator by the same number.

example: Find three equivalent fractions for $\frac{1}{3}$:

Multiply by 2: $\frac{1}{3} = \frac{2}{6}$ Multiply by 3: $\frac{1}{3} = \frac{3}{9}$ Multiply by 4: $\frac{1}{3} = \frac{4}{12}$

- You simplify fractions by dividing the numerator and denominator by the same number.

example: Simplify: **a** $\frac{3}{12}$ **b** $\frac{12}{18}$

a Divide by 3: $\frac{3}{12} = \frac{1}{4}$

The fraction is now in its simplest form.

b Divide by 2: $\frac{12}{18} = \frac{6}{9}$ Divide by 3: $\frac{6}{9} = \frac{2}{3}$

$\frac{12}{18} = \frac{6}{9} = \frac{2}{3}$.

42

Plenary

Simplification bingo

Write a mix of 20 equivalent fractions on the board: 3 for $\frac{1}{2}$, 3 for $\frac{1}{3}$, 3 for $\frac{1}{4}$, 3 for $\frac{1}{5}$, 3 for $\frac{1}{6}$, 2 for $\frac{1}{8}$ and 2 for $\frac{1}{10}$ (don't use the unit fractions).

Students choose 9 fractions from the list and put them in a 3 × 3 grid.

Call out the simple fraction.

Students cross off any equivalent fractions in their grid.

The winner explains what they crossed off and why.

Further activities

Give students five fractions, three of which are equivalent and two others which aren't. They must find the odd ones out with reasons.

Differentiation

Support questions:

- Question 1 revises work from the previous lesson on shading.
- Questions 2–7 focus on finding equivalent fractions. Springboard 7, pages 179, 197–199.
- Questions 8 and 9 focus on using equivalent fractions to compare and order fractions with different denominators. Springboard 7, page 178.

Core tier: focuses on expressing a fraction in its lowest terms.

Exercise N2.2

1 For each of these shapes write down:
- the fraction that is shaded
- the fraction that is unshaded

a  **b** 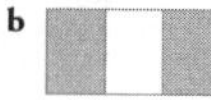 **c** 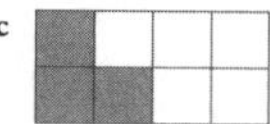 **d** 

2 Copy and complete the equivalent fractions for the shaded parts.

a 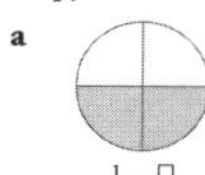 $\frac{1}{2} = \frac{\square}{4}$

b 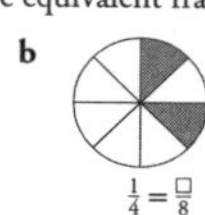 $\frac{1}{4} = \frac{\square}{8}$

c 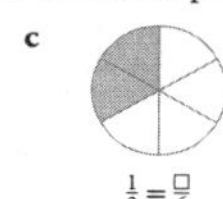 $\frac{1}{3} = \frac{\square}{6}$

d 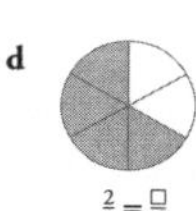 $\frac{2}{3} = \frac{\square}{6}$

3 Use two equivalent fractions to describe the shaded parts of these shapes.

a 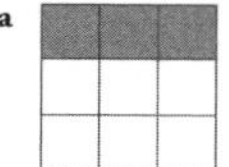 **b**  **c** 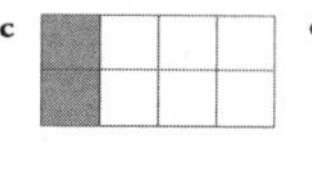 **d** 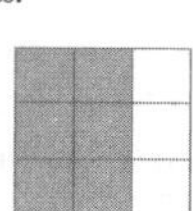

4 Use two equivalent fractions to describe the unshaded parts in question 3.

5 Write these fractions in order, starting with the smallest.
$\frac{7}{8}$ $\frac{5}{8}$ $\frac{1}{8}$ $\frac{2}{8}$ $\frac{6}{8}$

6 Copy and complete these equivalent fraction calculations:

a $\frac{1}{2} \xrightarrow{\times 3} \frac{\square}{6}$ (×3 top and bottom)
b $\frac{1}{3} \xrightarrow{\times 2} \frac{\square}{6}$ (×2 top and bottom)
c $\frac{1}{4} \xrightarrow{\times 2} \frac{2}{\square}$ (×2 top and bottom)
d $\frac{2}{3} \xrightarrow{\times 3} \frac{6}{\square}$ (×3 top and bottom)
e $\frac{3}{4} \xrightarrow{\times 2} \frac{\square}{\square}$ (×2 top and bottom)
f $\frac{2}{5} \xrightarrow{\times 3} \frac{\square}{\square}$ (×3 top and bottom)
g $\frac{3}{4} \xrightarrow{\times \square} \frac{9}{12}$ (×□ top and bottom)
h $\frac{2}{3} \xrightarrow{\times \square} \frac{\square}{12}$ (×□ top and bottom)

7 Find three fractions equivalent to each of these fractions:
a $\frac{1}{2}$ **b** $\frac{1}{4}$ **c** $\frac{1}{3}$ **d** $\frac{1}{10}$ **e** $\frac{2}{3}$ **f** $\frac{3}{4}$ **g** $\frac{3}{5}$ **h** $\frac{7}{10}$

8 Use your answers to question **7e** and **7f** to say which is larger: $\frac{2}{3}$ or $\frac{3}{4}$?

9 Write these fractions in order, starting with the smallest.
$\frac{1}{3}$ $\frac{1}{5}$ $\frac{1}{2}$ $\frac{1}{4}$ $\frac{1}{6}$

43

Exercise commentary

The questions assess the objectives on Primary Framework Pages 22 and 23.

Problem solving

Questions 8 and 9 assess the objective from Primary Framework Page 77 if students are encouraged to explain their reasoning.

Group work

Questions 8 and 9 could be usefully discussed in pairs or groups.

Misconceptions

Students find fractions confusing to work with and often add rather than multiply to find equivalent fractions.

Encourage students to use rectangles or circles to illustrate their answers until they build up confidence.

In question 9 some students think that $\frac{1}{2} < \frac{1}{6}$ as $2 < 6$.

Encourage them to think about shading a shape split into six. You can also use $\frac{1}{2}$s and $\frac{1}{4}$s to discuss which is bigger: $\frac{1}{2}$ or $\frac{1}{4}$.

There is a fraction wall on N2.2OHP you could use to illustrate the relative sizes of the fractions.

Links

Division: Primary Framework Page 57.

Homework

In N2.2HW, students are asked to identify equivalent fractions.

Answers

1 **a** $\frac{1}{2}, \frac{1}{2}$ **b** $\frac{2}{5}, \frac{3}{5}$ **c** $\frac{3}{8}, \frac{5}{8}$ **d** $\frac{5}{8}, \frac{3}{8}$

2 **a** 2 **b** 2 **c** 2 **d** 4

3 **a** $\frac{3}{9} = \frac{1}{3}$ **b** $\frac{6}{8} = \frac{3}{4}$ **c** $\frac{2}{8} = \frac{1}{4}$ **d** $\frac{6}{9} = \frac{2}{3}$

4 **a** $\frac{6}{9} = \frac{2}{3}$ **b** $\frac{2}{8} = \frac{1}{4}$ **c** $\frac{6}{8} = \frac{3}{4}$ **d** $\frac{3}{9} = \frac{1}{3}$

5 $\frac{1}{8}, \frac{2}{8}, \frac{5}{8}, \frac{6}{8}, \frac{7}{8}$

6 **a** $\frac{3}{6}$ **b** $\frac{2}{6}$ **c** $\frac{2}{8}$ **d** $\frac{6}{9}$ **e** $\frac{6}{8}$ **f** $\frac{6}{15}$ **g** $\times 3$ **h** $\times 4, \frac{8}{12}$

8 $\frac{3}{4}$ is larger

9 $\frac{1}{6}, \frac{1}{5}, \frac{1}{4}, \frac{1}{3}, \frac{1}{2}$

N2.3 Adding and subtracting fractions

Mental starter

Fraction cards

Give students two sets of **R1** digit cards.

Ask students to hold up cards to make up fractions, e.g. $\frac{5}{7}$.

Ask the questions in different ways such as:

- Show me two thirds.
- Show me a fraction with a numerator of 7.
- Show me a fraction greater than 1.

Useful resources

R1 digit cards for the mental starter.

N2.3OHP has rectangles split into $\frac{1}{6}$s and $\frac{1}{8}$s to help students add simple fractions and to illustrate mixed numbers.

Introductory activity

Discuss names of fractions using the mental starter.

Encourage students to think of fractions in families. This is more obvious when you describe them in words: eighths, quarters etc.

Discuss how to add simple fractions with the same denominator together.

$\frac{1}{8} + \frac{1}{8} = ?$

Often students give the answer $\frac{2}{16}$.

Use **N2.3OHP** to explain why this is not the case – ask students to complete the diagrams.

Use other examples.

Emphasise that the denominators must be the same to add or subtract. Ask students why this is the case. (Link to adding like terms in algebra.)

Check that students understand a fraction greater than 1:

- Ask for examples of fractions greater than 1.
- Ask what the fractions mean.

Ask how many halves: in a whole, in $1\frac{1}{2}$, in $2\frac{1}{2}$ etc.

Ask how to write as a single fraction.

Emphasise that fractions greater than 1 can be written in two different ways: mixed or improper.

Use **N2.3OHP** to illustrate:

$3\frac{1}{4} = \frac{13}{4}$.

Ask students how they would write $\frac{11}{4}$ as a mixed number.

Ask them to explain their methods.

Emphasise the grouping into 4s.

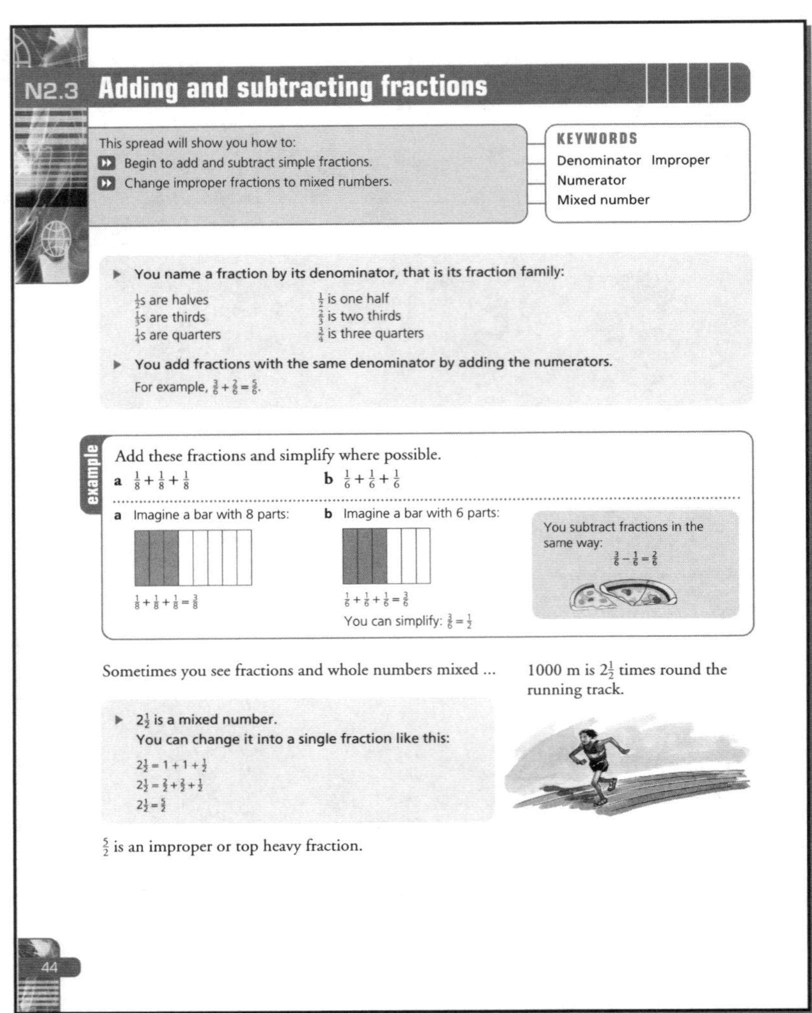

Plenary

Mixed number bingo

Write any 20 mixed numbers on the board.

Students choose 9 numbers from the list and put them in a 3 × 3 grid.

Call out the improper fraction.

Students cross off any equivalent mixed numbers in their grid.

The winner explains what they crossed off and why.

Alternatively play with improper fractions in the grid and call out mixed numbers, or use a mixture of the two.

Further activities

Give students three fractions with the same denominator:

$\frac{1}{4}$, $\frac{3}{4}$ and $\frac{7}{4}$.

Students investigate which other fractions (quarters) can be made using additions or subtractions of the fractions.

Differentiation

Support questions:

- Questions 1 and 2 revise Year 4 and 5 objectives. Springboard 7, page 177.
- Questions 3–7 focus on simple addition and subtraction and converting forms. Springboard 7, pages 181, 182.
- Questions 8 and 9 focus on adding and subtracting mixed numbers and fractions with different denominators. Springboard 7, page 183.

Core tier: focuses on mixed numbers and improper fractions.

Exercise N2.3

1 Write these fractions using words:

a $\frac{1}{2}$ **b** $\frac{1}{4}$ **c** $\frac{1}{3}$ **d** $\frac{1}{6}$ **e** $\frac{2}{3}$ **f** $\frac{3}{4}$
g $\frac{5}{8}$ **h** $\frac{11}{12}$ **i** $1\frac{1}{4}$ **j** $2\frac{2}{3}$ **k** $3\frac{5}{16}$ **l** $13\frac{2}{9}$

2 Write these fractions using numbers:

a three fifths **b** nine tenths **c** seven eighths
d two sevenths **e** one twelfth **f** seven twentieths

3 Work out the answer to each of these fraction problems.

a $\frac{1}{3}+\frac{1}{3}$ **b** $\frac{1}{5}+\frac{1}{5}+\frac{1}{5}$ **c** $\frac{1}{7}+\frac{1}{7}+\frac{1}{7}+\frac{1}{7}$
d $\frac{1}{8}+\frac{1}{8}+\frac{1}{8}$ **e** $\frac{1}{5}+\frac{1}{5}+\frac{1}{5}-\frac{1}{5}$ **f** $\frac{1}{4}+\frac{1}{4}+\frac{1}{4}-\frac{1}{4}-\frac{1}{4}$
g $\frac{1}{2}-\frac{1}{2}+\frac{1}{2}-\frac{1}{2}$ **h** $\frac{1}{3}-\frac{1}{3}+\frac{1}{3}+\frac{1}{3}$ **i** $\frac{3}{4}-\frac{1}{4}-\frac{1}{4}$

4 Work out the answer to each of these fraction problems.

a $\frac{3}{8}+\frac{2}{8}$ **b** $\frac{1}{9}+\frac{3}{9}$ **c** $\frac{2}{7}+\frac{2}{7}+\frac{1}{7}$
d $\frac{7}{9}-\frac{5}{9}$ **e** $\frac{4}{5}-\frac{1}{5}$ **f** $\frac{7}{8}-\frac{3}{8}+\frac{1}{8}$
g $\frac{3}{5}+\frac{2}{5}-\frac{4}{5}$ **h** $\frac{3}{6}+\frac{1}{6}-\frac{3}{6}$ **i** $\frac{2}{10}+\frac{5}{10}-\frac{3}{10}+\frac{5}{10}$

5 Work out the answer to each of these fraction problems.
Simplify your answers if possible.

a $\frac{1}{8}+\frac{1}{8}+\frac{1}{8}+\frac{1}{8}$ **b** $\frac{1}{6}+\frac{1}{6}+\frac{2}{6}$ **c** $\frac{7}{8}-\frac{5}{8}$
d $\frac{9}{10}-\frac{7}{10}$ **e** $\frac{7}{12}-\frac{3}{12}$ **f** $\frac{3}{12}+\frac{3}{12}+\frac{4}{12}$
g $\frac{6}{9}-\frac{3}{9}$ **h** $\frac{3}{16}+\frac{5}{16}-\frac{4}{16}$ **i** $\frac{11}{14}-\frac{4}{14}$

6 Change each of these mixed numbers into single fractions.

a $1\frac{1}{2}$ **b** $1\frac{1}{3}$ **c** $1\frac{3}{4}$ **d** $1\frac{5}{6}$ **e** $1\frac{1}{8}$ **f** $2\frac{1}{3}$
g $2\frac{1}{2}$ **h** $3\frac{1}{4}$ **i** $2\frac{7}{8}$ **j** $2\frac{5}{9}$ **k** $2\frac{1}{10}$ **l** $3\frac{5}{7}$

7 Change these fractions into mixed numbers.

a $\frac{6}{5}$ **b** $\frac{7}{4}$ **c** $\frac{9}{2}$ **d** $\frac{11}{3}$ **e** $\frac{16}{5}$ **f** $\frac{21}{5}$

8 Add these mixed numbers.
Simplify your answers if possible.

a $1\frac{1}{3}+1\frac{1}{3}$ **b** $2\frac{1}{5}+2\frac{1}{5}$ **c** $2\frac{3}{8}+1\frac{3}{8}$ **d** $4\frac{1}{4}+1\frac{3}{4}$ **e** $1\frac{1}{2}+2\frac{1}{2}$ **f** $4\frac{1}{6}+1\frac{5}{6}$

9 Copy and complete each of these sums. The first one is done for you.

a $\frac{1}{3}+\frac{1}{6}$ $=\frac{2}{6}+\frac{1}{6}$ $=\frac{3}{6}=\frac{1}{2}$
b $\frac{1}{2}+\frac{1}{4}$ $=\frac{\square}{4}+\frac{\square}{4}$ $=\frac{\square}{4}$
c $\frac{1}{4}+\frac{1}{8}$ $=\frac{\square}{8}+\frac{1}{8}$ $=\frac{\square}{8}$

45

Exercise commentary

The questions assess the objectives on Primary Framework Page 23 and Secondary Framework Pages 62 and 66.

Problem solving

Question 9 assesses the objective from Primary Framework Page 77 if students are encouraged to explain their reasoning.

Group work

The further activity could be discussed in pairs or small groups.

Misconceptions

The common error many students make is to add the denominators as well as the numerators: $\frac{1}{3}+\frac{1}{3}=\frac{2}{6}$.

Encourage students to read the fractions and link to adding like terms: one third and one third make two thirds.

Students can also shade in rectangles to help them see the relationships.

When students start to subtract they should see that the method does not work: $\frac{4}{5}-\frac{1}{5}=\frac{3}{0}$!

Links

Collecting like terms: Secondary Framework Page 116.

Homework

In **N2.3HW**, students are asked to identify fractions in their simplest form.

Answers

1 **a** One half **b** One quarter **c** One third **d** One sixth **e** Two thirds **f** Three quarters **g** Five eighths **h** Eleven twelfths **i** One and one quarter **j** Two and two thirds **k** Three and five sixteenths **l** Thirteen and two ninths

2 **a** $\frac{3}{5}$ **b** $\frac{9}{10}$ **c** $\frac{7}{8}$ **d** $\frac{2}{7}$ **e** $\frac{1}{12}$ **f** $\frac{7}{20}$ **3** **a** $\frac{2}{3}$ **b** $\frac{3}{5}$ **c** $\frac{4}{7}$ **d** $\frac{3}{8}$ **e** $\frac{2}{5}$ **f** $\frac{1}{4}$ **g** 0 **h** $\frac{2}{3}$ **i** $\frac{1}{4}$

4 **a** $\frac{5}{8}$ **b** $\frac{4}{9}$ **c** $\frac{5}{7}$ **d** $\frac{2}{9}$ **e** $\frac{3}{5}$ **f** $\frac{5}{8}$ **g** $\frac{1}{5}$ **h** $\frac{1}{6}$ **i** $\frac{9}{10}$

5 **a** $\frac{1}{2}$ **b** $\frac{2}{3}$ **c** $\frac{1}{4}$ **d** $\frac{1}{5}$ **e** $\frac{1}{3}$ **f** $\frac{5}{6}$ **g** $\frac{1}{3}$ **h** $\frac{1}{4}$ **i** $\frac{1}{2}$

6 **a** $\frac{3}{2}$ **b** $\frac{4}{3}$ **c** $\frac{7}{4}$ **d** $\frac{11}{6}$ **e** $\frac{9}{8}$ **f** $\frac{7}{3}$ **g** $\frac{5}{2}$ **h** $\frac{13}{4}$ **i** $\frac{23}{8}$ **j** $\frac{23}{9}$ **k** $\frac{21}{10}$ **l** $\frac{26}{7}$

7 **a** $1\frac{1}{5}$ **b** $1\frac{3}{4}$ **c** $4\frac{1}{2}$ **d** $3\frac{2}{3}$ **e** $3\frac{1}{5}$ **f** $4\frac{1}{5}$ **8** **a** $2\frac{2}{3}$ **b** $4\frac{2}{5}$ **c** $3\frac{3}{4}$ **d** 6 **e** 4 **f** 6

9 **b** $\frac{1}{2}+\frac{1}{4}=\frac{2}{4}+\frac{1}{4}=\frac{3}{4}$ **c** $\frac{1}{4}+\frac{1}{8}=\frac{2}{8}+\frac{1}{8}=\frac{3}{8}$

Mental starter

Ten times

- Give students a start number between 0 and 20: 6.
- Ask them to multiply by 10: 60.
- Repeat a few times.
- Include decimals (1 dp): 6.2 ⟶ 62.
- Multiply by 100.

Useful resources

N2.4OHP shows common fraction to decimal conversions on a number line.

R4 has a place value table.

Introductory activity

Revise what students know about decimals from N1.

- Ask what 0.3 and 0.05 mean.
- Encourage students to explain that a decimal describes part of a whole.
- Ask whether a decimal is the same as a fraction – it is!

Discuss how to convert a decimal to a fraction. Use R4.

- Start simply with 0.6.
- Revise the word 'tenths' and ask how to write the decimal using $\frac{1}{10}$s
- Move on to 0.05. Revise the word 'hundredths' and ask how to write the decimal using $\frac{1}{100}$s
- Now discuss decimals with 2 places: 0.25 and in particular that $\frac{2}{10}$ is $\frac{20}{100}$! Use the context of money to help if necessary, although students find it hard to link 0.2 with 20p!

Link to multiplication/division by 10, 100 etc.

N2.4OHP has a number line to show the fraction to decimal conversions students should already know.

Discuss how to work out and renumber the conversions.

Ask how to convert other fractions to decimals. Start with $\frac{2}{5}$.

- Encourage students to start with facts they already know: $\frac{1}{5}$ is 0.2

$\frac{2}{5} = 2 \times \frac{1}{5}$ may not be obvious!

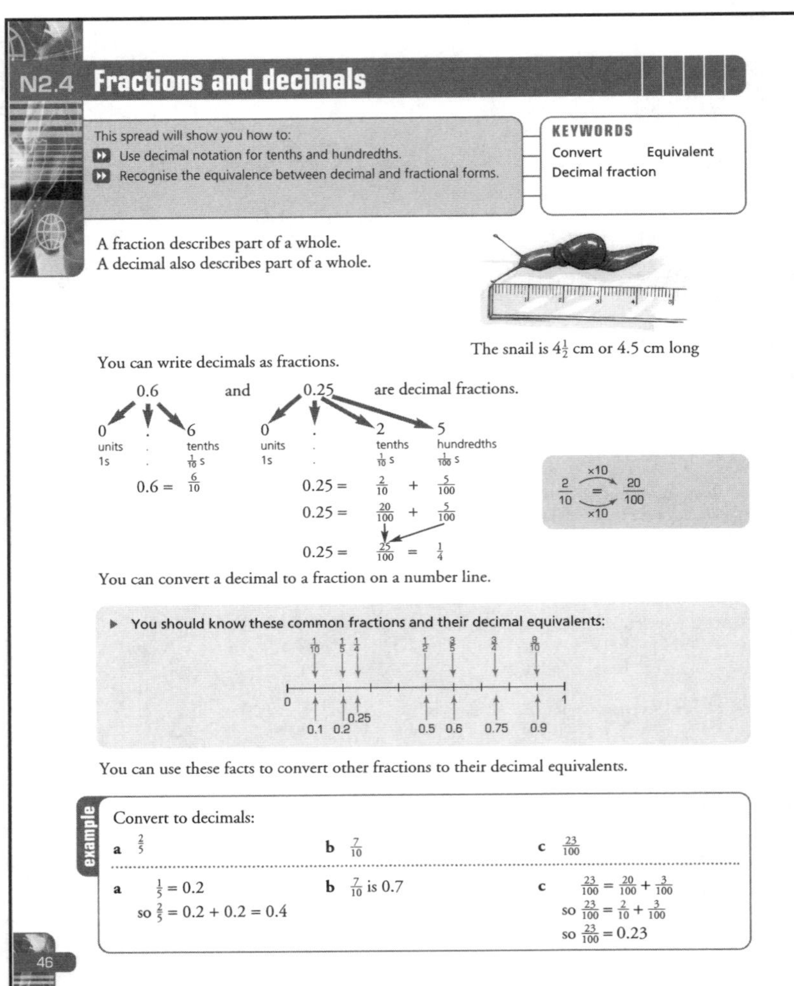

N2.4 Fractions and decimals

This spread will show you how to:
- Use decimal notation for tenths and hundredths.
- Recognise the equivalence between decimal and fractional forms.

KEYWORDS
Convert Equivalent
Decimal fraction

A fraction describes part of a whole.
A decimal also describes part of a whole.

The snail is $4\frac{1}{2}$ cm or 4.5 cm long

You can write decimals as fractions.

0.6 and 0.25 are decimal fractions.

0 units 1s . 6 tenths $\frac{1}{10}$s

$0.6 = \frac{6}{10}$

0 units 1s . 2 tenths $\frac{1}{10}$s 5 hundredths $\frac{1}{100}$s

$0.25 = \frac{2}{10} + \frac{5}{100}$

$0.25 = \frac{20}{100} + \frac{5}{100}$

$0.25 = \frac{25}{100} = \frac{1}{4}$

$\frac{2}{10} \xrightarrow{\times 10} \frac{20}{100}$

You can convert a decimal to a fraction on a number line.

- You should know these common fractions and their decimal equivalents:

$\frac{1}{10}$ $\frac{1}{5}$ $\frac{1}{4}$ $\frac{1}{2}$ $\frac{3}{5}$ $\frac{3}{4}$ $\frac{9}{10}$

0 0.1 0.2 0.25 0.5 0.6 0.75 0.9 1

You can use these facts to convert other fractions to their decimal equivalents.

example

Convert to decimals:

a $\frac{2}{5}$ b $\frac{7}{10}$ c $\frac{23}{100}$

a $\frac{1}{5} = 0.2$
so $\frac{2}{5} = 0.2 + 0.2 = 0.4$

b $\frac{7}{10}$ is 0.7

c $\frac{23}{100} = \frac{20}{100} + \frac{3}{100}$
so $\frac{23}{100} = \frac{2}{10} + \frac{3}{100}$
so $\frac{23}{100} = 0.23$

46

Plenary

Encourage students to explain how they convert between fractions and decimals.

Use questions 1 and 2 from the exercise to discuss methods.

Further activities

Students make up questions similar to those in question 6 for partners to solve.

Differentiation

Support questions:

- Question 1 and 2 revise Year 4 objectives. Springboard 7, page 185.
- Questions 3–5 focus on decimal and fraction equivalents, using them to order a mixture of fractions and decimals. Springboard 7, pages 186, 187, 189.
- Questions 6 and 7 require a good understanding of equivalent forms. Springboard 7, page 190.

Core tier: focuses on converting between decimals and fractions, including mixed numbers and improper fractions.

Exercise N2.4

1 Convert these decimals into fractions.
a 0.5 **b** 0.9 **c** 0.2 **d** 0.7 **e** 0.25 **f** 0.75

2 Convert these fractions into their decimal equivalents.
a $\frac{1}{10}$ **b** $\frac{2}{10}$ **c** $\frac{3}{10}$ **d** $\frac{6}{10}$ **e** $\frac{1}{5}$ **f** $\frac{2}{5}$ **g** $\frac{3}{5}$ **h** $\frac{3}{4}$

3 This number line is split into tenths.

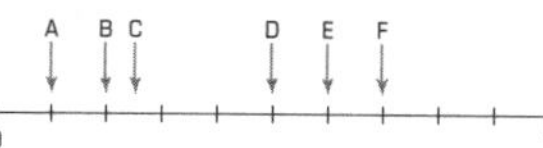

a Match each of these fractions and decimals to the points indicated on the number line:
0.5 $\frac{1}{10}$ 0.2 $\frac{7}{10}$ 0.6 $\frac{1}{4}$

b Write each fraction as its decimal equivalent, and each decimal as its fraction equivalent.

4 Put these fractions and decimals in order from lowest to highest.
$\frac{1}{2}$, $\frac{9}{10}$, 0.4, $\frac{3}{5}$, $\frac{7}{10}$, 0.25

5 Complete these sums. Here is an example:
$0.15 = \frac{1}{10} + \frac{5}{100}$

a $0.35 = \frac{3}{10} + \frac{\square}{100}$ **b** $0.24 = \frac{2}{10} + \frac{\square}{100}$ **c** $0.73 = \frac{\square}{10} + \frac{3}{100}$ **d** $0.81 = \frac{\square}{10} + \frac{\square}{100}$
e $0.9 = \frac{\square}{10}$ **f** $0.08 = \frac{\square}{100}$ **g** $0.07 = \frac{7}{\square}$ **h** $0.99 = \frac{9}{\square} + \frac{9}{\square}$

6 Use the numbers in the boxes to make up fractions and decimals that are equal to each other.

a $\frac{\square}{\square} = \square.\square$ [1 10 / 0 1] **b** $\frac{\square}{\square} = \square.\square$ [3 3 / 0 10] **c** $\frac{\square}{\square} = \square.\square$ [2 4 / 0 5]

d $\frac{\square}{\square} = \square.\square\square$ [1 0 5 / 2 4] **e** $\frac{\square}{\square} = \square.\square\square$ [0 4 / 3 5 7] **f** $\frac{\square}{\square\square\square} = \square.\square\square$ [7 0 0 7 / 1 0 0]

7 Put the correct sign between each pair of numbers. Choose from: > < =
The first one is done for you:

a $\frac{1}{2} > 0.25$ **b** 0.5 $\frac{3}{4}$ **c** 0.7 $\frac{3}{10}$ **d** $\frac{1}{5}$ 0.15
e $\frac{1}{4}$ 0.4 **f** 0.1 $\frac{1}{100}$ **g** 0.2 $\frac{1}{5}$ **h** 0.1 $\frac{1}{10}$

Exercise commentary

The questions assess the objectives on Primary Framework Pages 29 and 31.

Problem solving
Question 4 assesses the objective from Primary Framework Page 77 if students explain their reasoning, and question 6 assesses Page 79.

Group work
Question 6 and the further activity are ideal for work in pairs or small groups.

Misconceptions
Some students always use the denominator 10 to convert to a fraction: $0.25 = \frac{25}{10}$ etc.
Emphasise that the 0 means that the fraction is less than 1. Encourage students to place the decimal on a number line and estimate the equivalent fraction before trying to formulate the answer.
Students see $0.4 < 0.25$ as $4 < 25$.
Encourage the use of a number line and also a place value table.

Links
Division: Primary Framework Page 57.

Homework

Ask students to design a poster explaining how to convert between fractions and decimals. N2.4HW provides hints and suggestions.

Answers

1 **a** $\frac{1}{2}$ **b** $\frac{9}{10}$ **c** $\frac{1}{5}$ **d** $\frac{7}{10}$ **e** $\frac{1}{4}$ **f** $\frac{3}{4}$ **g** $\frac{3}{20}$ **h** $\frac{17}{50}$
2 **a** 0.1 **b** 0.2 **c** 0.3 **d** 0.6 **e** 0.2 **f** 0.4 **g** 0.6 **h** 0.75
3 **a** A: $\frac{1}{10}$, B: 0.2, C: $\frac{1}{4}$, D: 0.5, E: 0.6, F: $\frac{7}{10}$ **b** A: 0.1, B: $\frac{1}{5}$, C: 0.25, D: $\frac{1}{2}$, E: $\frac{3}{5}$, F: 0.7
4 0.25, 0.4, $\frac{1}{2}$, $\frac{3}{5}$, $\frac{7}{10}$, $\frac{9}{10}$
5 **a** 5 **b** 4 **c** 7 **d** 8, 1 **e** 9 **f** 8 **g** 100 **h** 10, 100
6 **a** $\frac{1}{10} = 0.1$ **b** $\frac{3}{10} = 0.3$ **c** $\frac{2}{5} = 0.4$ **d** $\frac{1}{4} = 0.25$ **e** $\frac{3}{4} = 0.75$ **f** $\frac{7}{100} = 0.07$
7 **b** $0.5 < \frac{3}{4}$ **c** $0.7 > \frac{3}{10}$ **d** $\frac{1}{5} > 0.15$ **e** $\frac{1}{4} < 0.4$ **f** $0.1 > \frac{1}{100}$ **g** $0.2 = \frac{1}{5}$
h $0.1 > \frac{1}{10}$

Mental starter

Put up 10 simple 'fractions of ...' questions ready for students:
$\frac{1}{2}$ of, $\frac{1}{3}$ of, $\frac{1}{4}$ of, $\frac{1}{5}$ of ... 10, 20, 30.
Ask students which ones they can do easily.
Put a tick by them (usually $\frac{1}{2}$s and often $\frac{1}{4}$s).
Ask which are the hardest to do (usually $\frac{1}{3}$s).

Useful resources

R2 digit cards are useful for the mental starter.

Introductory activity

Ask students for examples of when they find fractions of an amount:

- $\frac{1}{3}$ off all prices
- $\frac{3}{4}$ of an hour
- $2\frac{1}{2}$ times around the track ...

Using the mental starter, ask students their strategies for finding a half of something.

- Write 'to find a half you divide by 2'.
- Ask about finding a quarter.
- Write the strategy on the board.

Discuss the strategies and extend them to finding $\frac{1}{3}$ and then any unit fraction of an amount.

Ask students to explain how to do the examples in the student book.
Discuss what 'of' means when finding a fraction of something.
A quarter 'of' the class wear glasses.

Discuss how to find any fraction of an amount.

- Start with $\frac{3}{10}$ of £320.
- Encourage students to start with facts they know: $\frac{1}{10}$ of £320 is £32.
- Emphasise that $\frac{3}{10}$ means 3 lots of $\frac{1}{10}$.

Use the examples and ask students for their reasoning in working out the answers.
Encourage use of a number line to check answers.

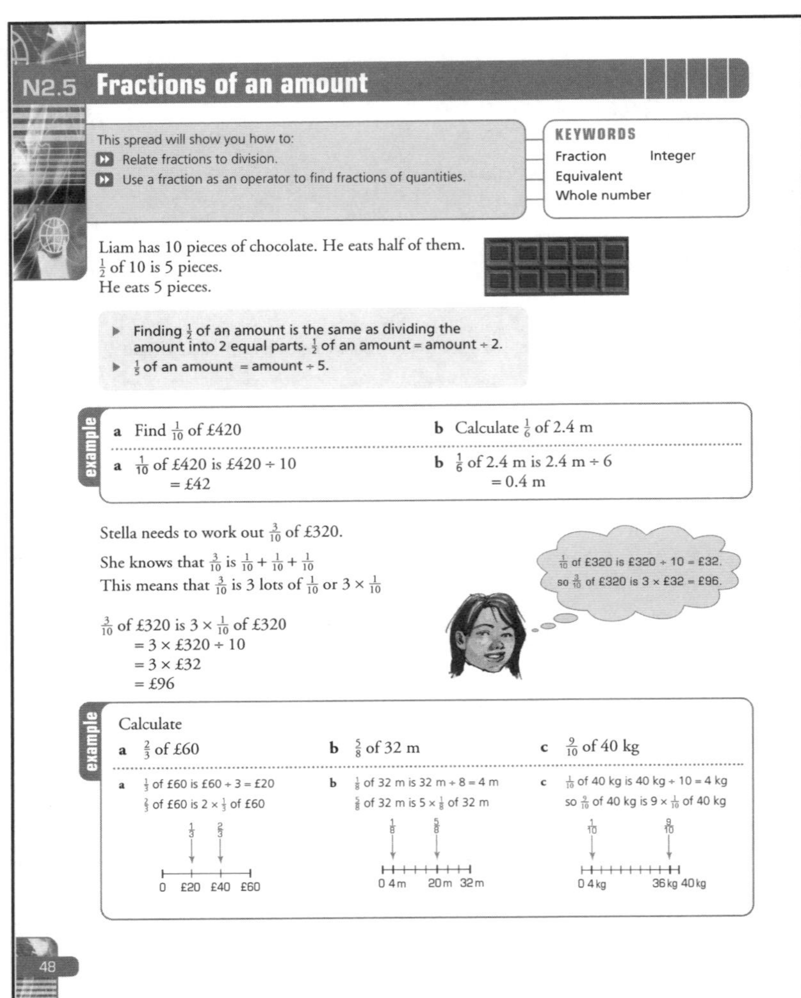

N2.5 **Fractions of an amount**

This spread will show you how to:

- Relate fractions to division.
- Use a fraction as an operator to find fractions of quantities.

KEYWORDS
Fraction, Integer, Equivalent, Whole number

Liam has 10 pieces of chocolate. He eats half of them.
$\frac{1}{2}$ of 10 is 5 pieces.
He eats 5 pieces.

- Finding $\frac{1}{2}$ of an amount is the same as dividing the amount into 2 equal parts. $\frac{1}{2}$ of an amount = amount ÷ 2.
- $\frac{1}{5}$ of an amount = amount ÷ 5.

example

a Find $\frac{1}{10}$ of £420 **b** Calculate $\frac{1}{6}$ of 2.4 m

a $\frac{1}{10}$ of £420 is £420 ÷ 10
= £42

b $\frac{1}{6}$ of 2.4 m is 2.4 m ÷ 6
= 0.4 m

Stella needs to work out $\frac{3}{10}$ of £320.

She knows that $\frac{3}{10}$ is $\frac{1}{10} + \frac{1}{10} + \frac{1}{10}$
This means that $\frac{3}{10}$ is 3 lots of $\frac{1}{10}$ or $3 \times \frac{1}{10}$

$\frac{1}{10}$ of £320 is £320 ÷ 10 = £32.
so $\frac{3}{10}$ of £320 is 3 × £32 = £96.

$\frac{3}{10}$ of £320 is $3 \times \frac{1}{10}$ of £320
= 3 × £320 ÷ 10
= 3 × £32
= £96

example

Calculate
a $\frac{2}{3}$ of £60 **b** $\frac{5}{8}$ of 32 m **c** $\frac{9}{10}$ of 40 kg

a $\frac{1}{3}$ of £60 is £60 ÷ 3 = £20
$\frac{2}{3}$ of £60 is $2 \times \frac{1}{3}$ of £60

b $\frac{1}{8}$ of 32 m is 32 m ÷ 8 = 4 m
$\frac{5}{8}$ of 32 m is $5 \times \frac{1}{8}$ of 32 m

c $\frac{1}{10}$ of 40 kg is 40 kg ÷ 10 = 4 kg
so $\frac{9}{10}$ of 40 kg is $9 \times \frac{1}{10}$ of 40 kg

48

Plenary

Write up 10 fractions on the board.
Use $\frac{1}{2}$s, $\frac{1}{4}$s, $\frac{1}{5}$s and $\frac{1}{10}$s.
Ask which of the fractions of £50 the students would want.
Discuss their reasoning.

Students can make up their own questions like this.

Further activities

Challenge students to find as many calculations as they can that have the answer 4, for example: $\frac{1}{2}$ of 8, $\frac{1}{4}$ of 16...

Differentiation

Support questions:

- Question 1–3 revise Year 4 objectives.
- Questions 4–10 focus on finding fractions of amounts. Springboard 7, page 188.
- Questions 11–13 are harder questions requiring a good grasp of fractions as operators. Springboard 7, page 191.

Core tier: focuses on finding harder fractions of an amount, including improper fractions.

Exercise N2.5

1 Write down the answers to these questions.
a $\frac{1}{2}$ of 20 **b** $\frac{1}{2}$ of 8 **c** $\frac{1}{2}$ of 16 **d** $\frac{1}{2}$ of 100 **e** $\frac{1}{2}$ of 7 **f** $\frac{1}{2}$ of 23

2 Write down the answers to these questions.
a $\frac{1}{3}$ of 9 **b** $\frac{1}{4}$ of 8 **c** $\frac{1}{3}$ of 15 **d** $\frac{1}{3}$ of 30 **e** $\frac{1}{4}$ of 12 **f** $\frac{1}{4}$ of 20

3 Work out the answers to these problems.
a $\frac{1}{2}$ of 30 **b** $\frac{1}{3}$ of 45 **c** $\frac{1}{6}$ of 18 **d** $\frac{1}{7}$ of 21 **e** $\frac{1}{8}$ of 24 **f** $\frac{1}{10}$ of 60

4 There are sixty minutes in an hour. Work out how many minutes there are in these fractions of one hour.
a $\frac{1}{2}$ **b** $\frac{1}{4}$ **c** $\frac{1}{3}$ **d** $\frac{1}{5}$ **e** $\frac{1}{10}$ **f** $\frac{1}{20}$

5 There are 100 cm in a metre. Work out how many centimetres there are in these fractions of one metre.
a $\frac{1}{2}$ **b** $\frac{1}{4}$ **c** $\frac{1}{10}$ **d** $\frac{1}{5}$ **e** $\frac{1}{100}$ **f** $\frac{1}{20}$

6 Work out the answers to these problems.
a $\frac{2}{3}$ of 9 **b** $\frac{3}{4}$ of 12 **c** $\frac{3}{4}$ of 20 **d** $\frac{2}{3}$ of 30 **e** $\frac{2}{5}$ of 30 **f** $\frac{3}{5}$ of 25

7 Work out how many minutes are in these fractions of one hour.
a $\frac{3}{4}$ **b** $\frac{2}{3}$ **c** $\frac{3}{10}$ **d** $\frac{5}{6}$ **e** $\frac{7}{20}$ **f** $\frac{5}{12}$

8 Work out how many centimetres are in these fractions of one metre.
a $\frac{3}{10}$ **b** $\frac{3}{4}$ **c** $\frac{4}{5}$ **d** $\frac{7}{20}$ **e** $\frac{21}{50}$ **f** $\frac{4}{25}$

9 Work out the following amounts of money.
a $\frac{2}{3}$ of £6 **b** $\frac{3}{4}$ of 80p **c** $\frac{5}{7}$ of 35p **d** $\frac{2}{3}$ of £90 **e** $\frac{4}{5}$ of £250 **f** $\frac{7}{10}$ of £2000

10 Jenny has £5. She spends two fifths of this on magazines.
How much money does she spend?

11 Jim has £2. He spends three fifths of it on sweets.
How much does he spend?

12 Sherry has £1.80. She spends $\frac{2}{9}$ of it on a comb.
a How much does she spend?
b How much does she have left?

13 Which is the bigger amount of money?
$\frac{3}{4}$ of £20 or $\frac{2}{5}$ of £30
Show how you worked it out.

49

Exercise commentary

The questions assess the objectives on Primary Framework Page 25.

Problem solving

Questions 10–12 assess the objective from Primary Framework Page 85, and question 13 assesses Page 77.

Group work

Weak students would benefit from discussing questions 4 and 5 in pairs.

Misconceptions

The most common difficulty is not knowing the division facts.

Students may benefit from having a multiplication grid to use until they are more confident of the facts.

Another common error is just to find one part of the amount, for example saying $\frac{3}{4}$ of 12 is 3.

Encourage students to work in logical steps: one quarter is 3 so three quarters is $3 \times 3 = 9$.

Questions 11 and 12 are easier if students change the £s to ps first.

Links

Division: Primary Framework Page 57.

Homework

N2.5HW provides practice at finding fractions of an amount.

Answers

1 **a** 10 **b** 4 **c** 8 **d** 50 **e** 3.5 **f** 11.5 **2** **a** 3 **b** 2 **c** 5 **d** 10 **e** 3 **f** 5
3 **a** 15 **b** 15 **c** 3 **d** 3 **e** 3 **f** 6 **6** **a** 6 **b** 9 **c** 15 **d** 20 **e** 12 **f** 15
4 **a** 30 minutes **b** 15 minutes **c** 20 minutes **d** 12 minutes **e** 6 minutes **f** 3 minutes
5 **a** 50 cm **b** 25 cm **c** 10 cm **d** 20 cm **e** 1 cm **f** 5 cm
7 **a** 45 minutes **b** 40 minutes **c** 18 minutes **d** 50 minutes **e** 21 minutes **f** 25 minutes
8 **a** 30 cm **b** 75 cm **c** 80 cm **d** 35 cm **e** 42 cm **f** 16 cm
9 **a** £4 **b** 60p **c** 25p **d** £60 **e** £200 **f** £1400 **10** £2 **11** £1.20 **12** **a** 40p **b** £1.40
13 $\frac{3}{4}$ of £20 = £15, $\frac{2}{5}$ of £30 = £12, so $\frac{3}{4}$ of £20 is bigger.

N2.6 Fractions, decimals and percentages

Mental starter

Call out a two-digit number and ask students to multiply it by 10.
Students write the answer on scrap paper and hold it up (or use **R2** digit cards).
Change the number and ask them to divide by 10.
Go on to multiplying and dividing by 100.
Discuss any difficulties.
Illustrate answers using a place value table (**R4**).

Useful resources

R6 has a 0–1 number line split into 10.
R4 has a place value table
R2 digit cards for the mental starter and plenary or lots of scrap paper.
R17 has a 100 square which may be useful.

Introductory activity

Find out what students know about the term 'percentage'.
Ask where they have come across the term and what they think it means.
Ask why students think percentages might be useful – to compare.
Ask for notation – encourage use of %.

Emphasise that a percentage is any amount split into parts per hundred.
Use **R17** to illustrate if necessary.
Ask what 50% means.
Ask about other common percentages such as 10%.
Encourage students to compare percentages – more than 50%, less than 75%.
Draw a number line on the board and mark the ends 0% and 100%, then students can show you where each percentage goes.

Discuss writing a percentage as a fraction (and vice versa).
Emphasise a % is a fraction out of 100.
Discuss percentages as decimals – $\frac{41}{100}$ means 41 ÷ 100 so you divide by 100.

Show R6, or draw a 0–1 number line on the board.
Ask students to give a fraction they know or a decimal or a percentage.
Encourage them to use common ones.
Ask for equivalents.
Use **R17** to illustrate if necessary.
Keep building up the line, discussing how to find equivalents.
Emphasise that they should use facts they already know.

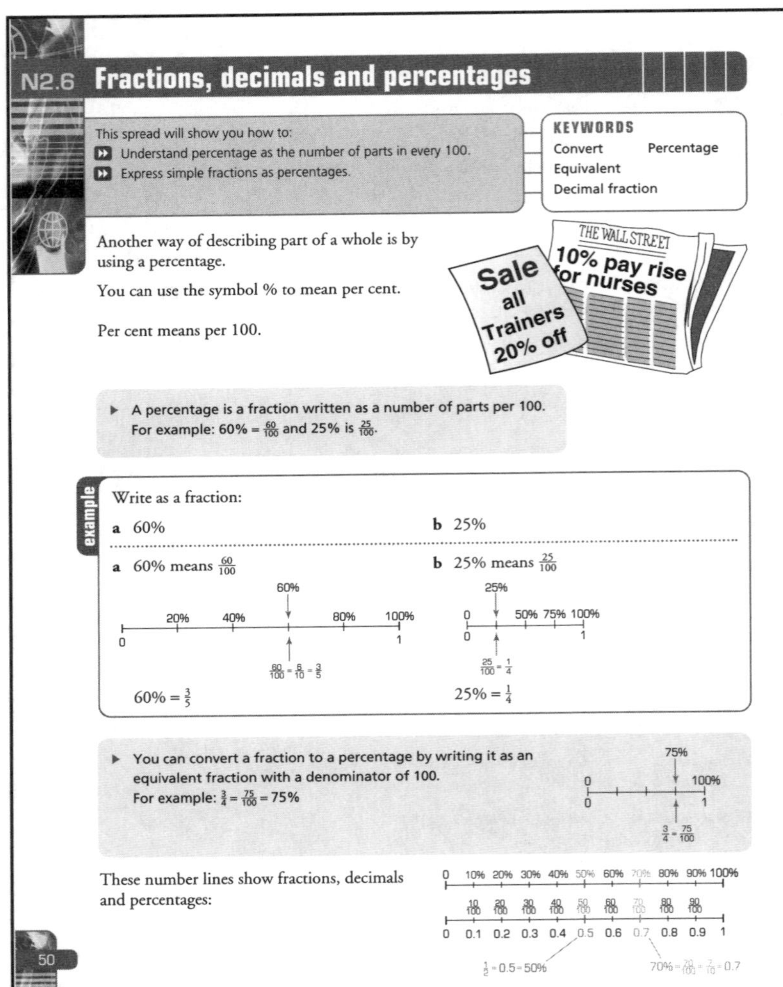
N2.6 **Fractions, decimals and percentages**

This spread will show you how to:
- Understand percentage as the number of parts in every 100.
- Express simple fractions as percentages.

KEYWORDS
Convert
Percentage
Equivalent
Decimal fraction

Another way of describing part of a whole is by using a percentage.

You can use the symbol % to mean per cent.

Per cent means per 100.

- A percentage is a fraction written as a number of parts per 100. For example: 60% = $\frac{60}{100}$ and 25% is $\frac{25}{100}$.

example

Write as a fraction:

a 60% **b** 25%

a 60% means $\frac{60}{100}$

60% = $\frac{3}{5}$

b 25% means $\frac{25}{100}$

25% = $\frac{1}{4}$

- You can convert a fraction to a percentage by writing it as an equivalent fraction with a denominator of 100. For example: $\frac{3}{4} = \frac{75}{100} = 75\%$

These number lines show fractions, decimals and percentages:

50

Plenary

Ask a series of quick-fire questions using fractions, decimals and percentages.
- What is 30% of 50?
- Write $\frac{2}{5}$ as a decimal.
- Calculate 3 tenths of 20.

Questions to be done mentally (make sure the numbers are straightforward – 1 dp and two-digit answers at most).
Students can take it in turns to ask the questions.
Students answer using digit cards or on scrap paper.

Further activities

In **N2.6ICT**, students construct a spreadsheet that converts fractions into decimals and percentages.

Students can place all the percentages in questions 1 and 2 on a number line.

Students can make up their own examples as in questions 8 for partners to solve.

Differentiation

Support questions:

- Question 1 focuses on % as a fraction out of 100. Springboard 7, page 193.
- Questions 2–6 focus on equivalent forms. Springboard 7, page 194.
- Questions 7 and 8 are harder questions requiring good recognition of the different forms of basic percentages. Springboard 7, page 195.

Core tier: focuses on finding percentages of an amount.

Exercise N2.6

1 Write the following percentages as fractions out of 100.
a 7% **b** 17% **c** 23% **d** 59% **e** 31% **f** 89% **g** 97% **h** 10%

2 Write these percentages as fractions, and cancel them down to their simplest form.
a 50% **b** 10% **c** 20% **d** 60% **e** 25% **f** 75% **g** 80% **h** 15%

3 Write the following fractions as percentages.
a $\frac{13}{100}$ **b** $\frac{20}{100}$ **c** $\frac{99}{100}$ **d** $\frac{50}{100}$ **e** $\frac{1}{2}$ **f** $\frac{1}{10}$ **g** $\frac{3}{10}$ **h** $\frac{1}{5}$

4 Convert these percentages into decimals.
a 20% **b** 25% **c** 50% **d** 80% **e** 10% **f** 75% **g** 17% **h** 37%

5 Convert these decimals into percentages.
a 0.25 **b** 0.75 **c** 0.32 **d** 0.81 **e** 0.4 **f** 0.9 **g** 0.01 **h** 0.07

6 This number line is split into 10 equal parts.

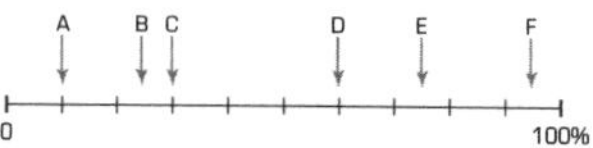

Match each of these fractions, decimals and percentages to the letters on the number line.
$\frac{3}{5}$ 10% $\frac{3}{4}$ 0.3 95% 0.25

7 This diagram shows the equivalences of 25%:

$25\% = \frac{25}{100} =$ 0.25, $\frac{1}{4}$

Complete these equivalences.

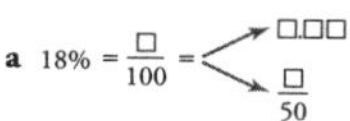

a $18\% = \frac{\square}{100} =$ □.□□, $\frac{\square}{50}$

b $20\% = \frac{20}{\square} =$ □.□, $\frac{\square}{5}$

c $75\% = \frac{75}{\square} =$ □.□□, $\frac{3}{\square}$

d $70\% = \frac{\square}{100} =$ □.□, $\frac{\square}{10}$

8 Use the numbers in the boxes to find equivalent fractions, decimals and percentages.

a □.□□ = □□% [7 7 3 / 0 3]

b □.□□ = □% 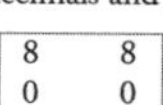 [8 8 / 0 0]

c □□% = $\frac{\square}{\square\square}$ [3 7 / 2 0 5]

d □.□ = $\frac{\square}{\square}$ [0 2 / 5 4]

51

Exercise commentary

The questions assess the objectives on Primary Framework Page 33.

Problem solving

Questions 7 and 8 assess the objective from Primary Framework Page 77.

Group work

Students would benefit from discussing questions 6–8 in pairs or groups.

Misconceptions

Many students will write 0.4 = 4% instead of 40%.

Encourage them to start from facts they already know and to use a number line to estimate before writing down the answer.

It is a good idea to have an equivalence line to hand or on the classroom wall and encourage them to refer to it until they have a firm grasp of the equivalences.

The decimal that seems to cause most difficult is $\frac{1}{5}$s – students may not recognise that $\frac{1}{5} = 0.2$ and 20%.

Use a rectangle shaded in 10s to emphasise that $\frac{1}{5}$ is double $\frac{1}{10}$.

Links

Division: Primary Framework Page 57.

Fractions and decimals: Page 31.

Homework

Ask students to design a set of loop cards to demonstrate the equivalence of fractions, decimals and percentages. **N2.6HW** provides hints and suggestions.

Answers

1 **a** $\frac{7}{100}$ **b** $\frac{17}{100}$ **c** $\frac{23}{100}$ **d** $\frac{59}{100}$ **e** $\frac{31}{100}$ **f** $\frac{89}{100}$ **g** $\frac{97}{100}$ **h** $\frac{10}{100}$

2 **a** $\frac{1}{2}$ **b** $\frac{1}{10}$ **c** $\frac{1}{5}$ **d** $\frac{3}{5}$ **e** $\frac{1}{4}$ **f** $\frac{3}{4}$ **g** $\frac{4}{5}$ **h** $\frac{3}{20}$

3 **a** 13% **b** 20% **c** 99% **d** 50% **e** 50% **f** 10% **g** 30% **h** 20%

4 **a** 0.2 **b** 0.25 **c** 0.5 **d** 0.8 **e** 0.1 **f** 0.75 **g** 0.17 **h** 0.37

5 **a** 25% **b** 75% **c** 32% **d** 81% **e** 40% **f** 90% **g** 1% **h** 7%

6 A: 10%, B: 0.25, C: 0.3, D: $\frac{3}{5}$, E: $\frac{3}{4}$, F: 95% **7** **a** $\frac{18}{100} = \frac{9}{50} = 0.18$ **b** $\frac{20}{100} = \frac{1}{5} = 0.2$ **c** $\frac{75}{100} = \frac{3}{4} = 0.75$ **d** $\frac{70}{100} = \frac{7}{10} = 0.7$ **8** **a** 0.37 = 37% or 0.73 = 73% **b** 0.08 = 8% **c** $35\% = \frac{7}{20}$ **d** $0.5 = \frac{2}{4}$ or $0.4 = \frac{2}{5}$

Summary

The Year 6 key teaching objectives in this unit are:

- Reduce a fraction to its simplest form by cancelling common factors (23).
- Use a fraction as an operator to find fractions of numbers or quantities (25).
- Understand percentage as the number of parts in every 100 (33).

Plenary activity

Write these three statements:

- I get $\frac{1}{5}$ of the pizza.
- I get 15% of the pizza.
- I get 0.5 of the pizza.

Discuss who gets the most pizza.
Students justify answers using a circle for the pizza.

Check out commentary

1a Students fail to use the total number of squares as the denominator, writing part **i** as $\frac{1}{2}$.
Emphasise that the fraction is the number shaded/total number.
1c students may not convert metres to cm, writing part **ii** as $\frac{2}{50}$.
Emphasise that the word 'of' usually indicates the quantity that is the denominator.

2 Students may add to find equivalent fractions or treat the numerator and denominator differently.
Encourage students to use rectangles so they can see the equivalences.

3a Students add the denominators as well as the numerators or just give the numerator as the answer.
Encourage them to read the fractions aloud: three eighths and two eighths make five eighths etc.
3b Students tend to divide by the smaller number, working out 4 ÷ 3 instead of 3 ÷ 4.
Emphasise the similarity with a ÷ sign and that the top number naturally comes first.

4 There are many errors students may make, mostly due to a poor recognition of place value: 0.4 = 4%, $\frac{2}{5}$ = 2.5 etc.
This question will show any misconceptions and students should be encouraged to use a place value table and number line to help them visualise and recognise what each entry means.

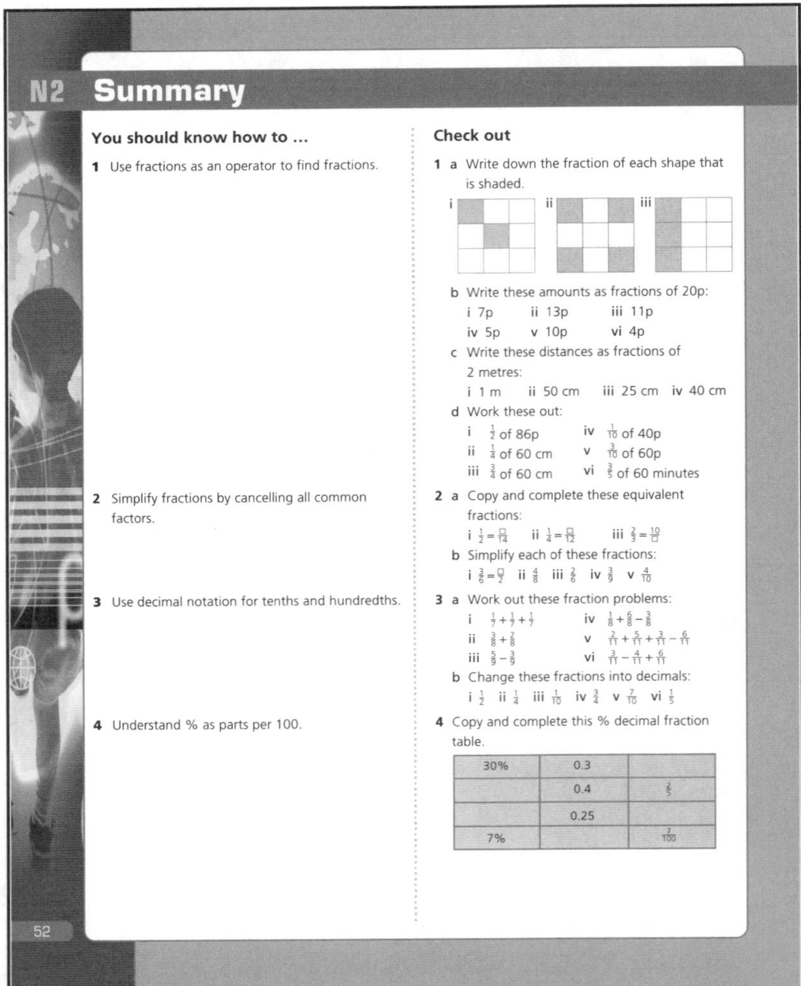

N2 Summary

You should know how to ...

1 Use fractions as an operator to find fractions.

2 Simplify fractions by cancelling all common factors.

3 Use decimal notation for tenths and hundredths.

4 Understand % as parts per 100.

Check out

1 a Write down the fraction of each shape that is shaded.
i ii iii

b Write these amounts as fractions of 20p:
i 7p ii 13p iii 11p
iv 5p v 10p vi 4p

c Write these distances as fractions of 2 metres:
i 1 m ii 50 cm iii 25 cm iv 40 cm

d Work these out:
i $\frac{1}{2}$ of 86p iv $\frac{1}{10}$ of 40p
ii $\frac{1}{4}$ of 60 cm v $\frac{3}{10}$ of 60p
iii $\frac{3}{4}$ of 60 cm vi $\frac{3}{5}$ of 60 minutes

2 a Copy and complete these equivalent fractions:
i $\frac{1}{2} = \frac{\square}{14}$ ii $\frac{1}{4} = \frac{\square}{12}$ iii $\frac{2}{3} = \frac{10}{\square}$

b Simplify each of these fractions:
i $\frac{3}{6} = \frac{\square}{2}$ ii $\frac{4}{8}$ iii $\frac{2}{6}$ iv $\frac{3}{9}$ v $\frac{4}{10}$

3 a Work out these fraction problems:
i $\frac{1}{7}+\frac{1}{7}+\frac{1}{7}$ iv $\frac{1}{8}+\frac{6}{8}-\frac{3}{8}$
ii $\frac{3}{8}+\frac{2}{8}$ v $\frac{2}{11}+\frac{5}{11}+\frac{3}{11}-\frac{6}{11}$
iii $\frac{5}{9}-\frac{3}{9}$ vi $\frac{3}{11}-\frac{4}{11}+\frac{6}{11}$

b Change these fractions into decimals:
i $\frac{1}{2}$ ii $\frac{1}{4}$ iii $\frac{1}{10}$ iv $\frac{3}{4}$ v $\frac{7}{10}$ vi $\frac{1}{5}$

4 Copy and complete this % decimal fraction table.

30%	0.3	
	0.4	$\frac{2}{5}$
	0.25	
7%		$\frac{7}{100}$

52

Development

The relationship between fractions, decimals and percentages is developed in N4.

Links

Students will use fractions in probability work (D1) and percentages when using pie charts (D1 and D2).

Mental starters

Objectives covered in this unit:

- Order, add and subtract numbers in context.
- Convert between fractions, decimals and percentages.
- Find simple fractions of quantities.
- Add and subtract several small numbers.

Resources needed

* means class set needed

Essential:

D1.2OHP – Levelling blocks
D1.3OHP – Statistical diagrams
R11 (OHP) – Tally chart
Dice, coins, multilink cubes
Calculators*

Useful:

R1* – Digit cards
R2* – Decimal digit cards
R6 (OHP) – Number lines
D1.2ICT* – Averages in Excel

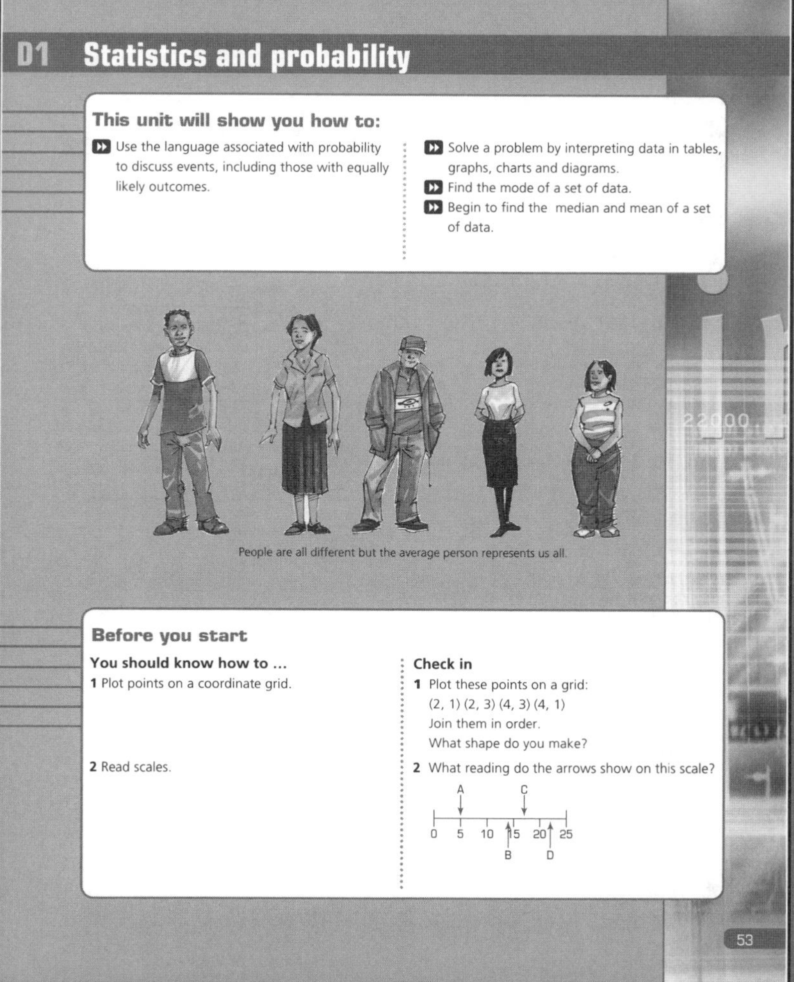

D1 Statistics and probability

This unit will show you how to:

- Use the language associated with probability to discuss events, including those with equally likely outcomes.
- Solve a problem by interpreting data in tables, graphs, charts and diagrams.
- Find the mode of a set of data.
- Begin to find the median and mean of a set of data.

People are all different but the average person represents us all.

Before you start

You should know how to ...	Check in
1 Plot points on a coordinate grid.	1 Plot these points on a grid: (2, 1) (2, 3) (4, 3) (4, 1) Join them in order. What shape do you make?
2 Read scales.	2 What reading do the arrows show on this scale?

53

Unit commentary

Aim of the unit

This unit aims to consolidate students' understanding of the mode and introduces the median and mean.
Basic statistical diagrams are reviewed and quantitative ideas of probability are introduced. It lays the foundation for the project work in D2 and D3.

Introduction

Discuss what students understand by the term average. Use the picture to discuss the likelihood of choosing a person at random, who might be described as typical of the group – depends on what's being measured.

Framework references

This unit focuses on:

- Year 6 teaching objectives pages: 113, 115, 117
- Problem solving objectives page: 76, 79, 85, 87

The unit provides access to:

- Year 7 teaching objectives pages: 256, 258, 260, 268, 270, 276–282.

Check in activity

Ask 10 students how many brothers or sisters they have. Write the data on the board.
Discuss which is the modal answer – the one that occurs the most often.
Move on to discuss the modal colour of car in the car park.
Discuss how students would find this information – record the number of cars and see which is the most popular one.
Discuss why this information may be useful to a car manufacturer.

Differentiation

Core tier focuses on the same concepts but uses more complex numbers and includes the use of decimals and percentages in probability.

Springboard 7

Pages 145–150, 152–155, 252–261.

D1.1 Finding the average

Mental starter

What's halfway?

- Students need a set of **R2** digit cards.
- Call out two numbers, for example 13 and 17.
- Ask them to hold up the number halfway between the two: 15.
- Ask students to justify answers on a number line on the board.
- Include $\frac{1}{2}$s – for example halfway between 12 and 15 is 13.5

Useful resources

R2 decimal digit cards for the mental starter.

Introductory activity

Ask questions to find out what students understand by 'average':

- When do you hear people use the word average?
- What does average mean?

Emphasise use of technical terms and find out what they mean to students, explaining that they will be learning more about them.

Introduce the mode.

- Ask 9 students to arrange themselves in order of shoe size.
- Ask which is the most common size and why this information would be important – shopkeepers need to know.
- Ask what would happen if other people joined the group.
- Discuss whether there can be more than one mode or no mode.

Emphasise that the *mo*de is the *mo*st common and discuss any other ways students remember the term.

Introduce the median.

Scene: a class photographer organises a shoot around the average person.

Ask which person in a group might be considered the average – 'the middle person'.

Emphasise the need to define the quantity that you are measuring.

Emphasise the need for order.

Explain the middle person is called the median.

Discuss how students might remember this term – **medi**um = **medi**an.

Ask 9 students to come to the front of the class. Ask how to find the median person – stand in order.

Ask/demonstrate what would happen if another person joined the group.

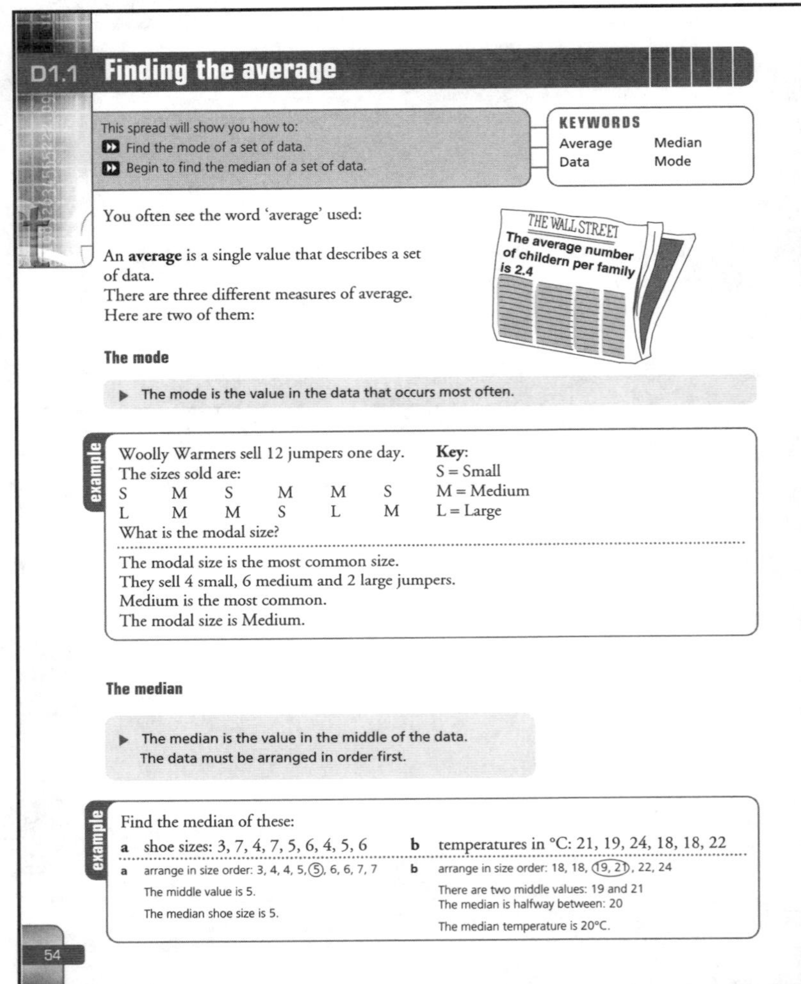

D1.1 **Finding the average**

This spread will show you how to:
- Find the mode of a set of data.
- Begin to find the median of a set of data.

KEYWORDS
Average Median
Data Mode

You often see the word 'average' used:

An **average** is a single value that describes a set of data.
There are three different measures of average.
Here are two of them:

THE WALL STREET
The average number of childern per family is 2.4

The mode

- The mode is the value in the data that occurs most often.

example

Woolly Warmers sell 12 jumpers one day.
The sizes sold are:

S	M	S	M	M	S
L	M	M	S	L	M

What is the modal size?

Key:
S = Small
M = Medium
L = Large

The modal size is the most common size.
They sell 4 small, 6 medium and 2 large jumpers.
Medium is the most common.
The modal size is Medium.

The median

- The median is the value in the middle of the data.
  The data must be arranged in order first.

example

Find the median of these:

a shoe sizes: 3, 7, 4, 7, 5, 6, 4, 5, 6 **b** temperatures in °C: 21, 19, 24, 18, 18, 22

a arrange in size order: 3, 4, 4, 5, (5), 6, 6, 7, 7
The middle value is 5.
The median shoe size is 5.

b arrange in size order: 18, 18, (19, 21), 22, 24
There are two middle values: 19 and 21
The median is halfway between: 20
The median temperature is 20°C.

54

Plenary

Discuss students' solutions to questions 3, 5 and 8.

- For questions 3 and 5 discuss which is better to use in each of the question parts – the median or the mode.
- For question 5 focus on strategies for finding the median of an even number of data.
- For question 8 ask students to explain their strategies for solving the problem. Emphasise the need to organise the data first.

Further activities

Students can find the median in question 2 and discuss which is the more useful average.

Extend question 8 by giving students a set of four data: 4, 9, 3, 13 and asking them to find a fifth piece of data that makes the median of the five items 8.
Ask for data that give different medians: 4, 9.

Differentiation

Support questions:

- Questions 1 and 2 involve finding the mode of a data set. Springboard 7, page 152.
- Questions 3–6 focus on ordering data and finding the median. Springboard 7, page 153.
- Question 7 involves harder numbers and question 8 uses a problem solving approach. Springboard 7, pages 154, 155.

Core tier: extends to finding the range and mode from a discrete frequency table.

Exercise commentary

The questions assess the objectives on Primary Framework Page 117.

Problem solving

Question 8 assesses Primary Framework Page 79. The further activity assesses Page 75 as students choose the most appropriate average.

Group work

The further activity is suitable for pairs.

Misconceptions

Many students mix up the mode with the frequency, for example giving the mode in question 1 as 3 not V.
Emphasise that the mode is always part of the data set and encourage students to refer back.
Students give just one mode when there are two (question 2c).
One strategy is to rank the categories though students can find it confusing.
Students often forget to order the data to find the median.
Encourage them to always order the data first, whichever average they want to find.
Emphasise that this makes it easier to group and calculate.

Links

Ordering numbers: Primary Framework Page 15. Mental addition: Page 43.

Exercise D1.1

1 The registration letters of cars for sale in a garage were:

T R V P W Y Y X V W V

What was the modal letter?

2 Find the mode for each of these sets of data:

- **a** Shoe sizes: 5, 4, 10, 3, 3, 4, 7, 4, 6, 5
- **b** Dress sizes: 10, 12, 10, 18, 12, 14, 12
- **c** Hours of sunshine one week: 4, 5, 3, 4, 5, 0, 1
- **d** Daily temperatures one week in °C: 17, 25, 22, 18, 22, 16, 19

3 Nine students wrote their shoe size on the board:

- **a** Arrange the shoe sizes in order.
- **b** What is the median shoe size?

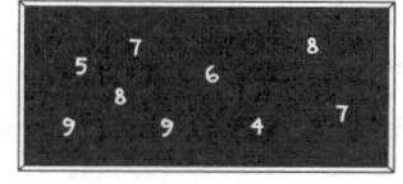

4 Arrange each of these sets of data in order and find the median:

- **a** Shoe sizes: 3, 6, 9, 1, 2, 5, 8, 4, 7
- **b** Dress sizes: 12, 10, 8, 14, 20, 16, 14, 16, 18
- **c** Daily temperatures one week in °C: 18, 20, 16, 17, 22, 25, 24

5 Six students wrote their shoe size on the board:

- **a** Arrange the shoe sizes in order.
- **b** Find the halfway value.
- **c** What is the median shoe size?

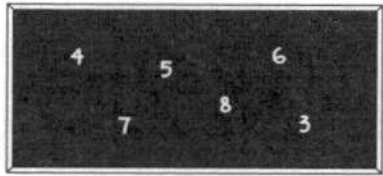

6 Find the median of each of these sets of data:

- **a** Shoe sizes: 3, 6, 9, 1, 2, 5, 8, 4, 7, 3
- **b** Temperatures one fortnight in °C: 18, 20, 16, 17, 22, 25, 24, 19, 22, 21, 23, 17, 20, 21

7 This table shows the length of five rivers:

- **a** Write the rivers in order of size starting with the smallest.
- **b** Write down the median length of the five rivers.

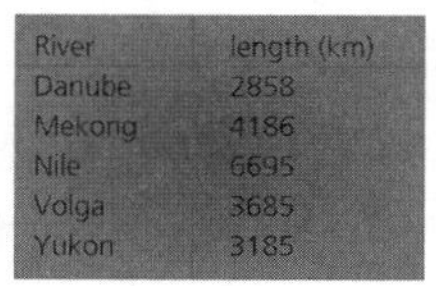

River	length (km)
Danube	2858
Mekong	4186
Nile	6695
Volga	3685
Yukon	3185

8 The median of this set of six lengths is 4.3 m.

4 m 4.7 m  4.1 m 4.2 m 4.5 m

What is the missing length?

Homework

D1.1HW provides practice at finding the mode and median of a set of data.

Answers

1 V **2** **a** 4 **b** 12 **c** 4 and 5 **d** 22 **3** **a** 4, 5, 6, 7, 7, 8, 8, 9, 9 **b** 7

4 **a** 1, 2, 3, 4, 5, 6, 7, 8, 9; median is 5 **b** 8, 10, 12, 14, 14, 16, 16, 18, 20; median is 14 **c** 16, 17, 18, 20, 22, 24, 25; median is 20

5 **a** 3, 4, 5, 6, 7, 8 **b** 5.5 **c** 5.5

6 **a** Size 4.5 **b** 20.5 °C

7 **a** Danube 2858, Yukon 3185, Volga 3685, Mekong 4186, Nile 6695 **b** 3685 km

8 4.4 m

D1.2 The mean

Mental starter

Call out sets of 3 numbers at a time – all under 20.
Ask students to add them mentally.
They show the answers on digit cards.
Increase the size and range of the numbers.
Go on to 4 numbers at a time.
Increase to 5 if they can cope.

Useful resources

R1 digit cards for the mental starter.
A **calculator** for the exercise.
D1.2OHP shows blocks before and after levelling.
Multilink cubes for the exercise.

Introductory activity

Remind students that last lesson they were looking at averages.
Revise the terms 'median' and 'mode'.

Discuss what most people mean by the term 'average' – number of matches in a box, number of runs/goals scored per game etc.

Introduce the term 'mean' as what most people mean!

Emphasise that for the mean you level all the data out so it is evenly spread – all the heights are the same.

Use D1.2OHP to illustrate the mean as a levelling process.

- Ask how to level out the blocks.
- Emphasise this is the mean.
- The second set of blocks can be used to illustrate that the mean is not always part of the data set.

Discuss how to find the mean of a set of numbers using the examples.

- Encourage students to work in stages – find the total and then divide by the number of pieces of data.
- Illustrate using the towers examples – it's like building one large tower and then cutting into the required number of blocks.

Explain that the mean is the only average to use all the values.

Discuss how to remember the term mean – mean means average, or it's mean because you work it out.

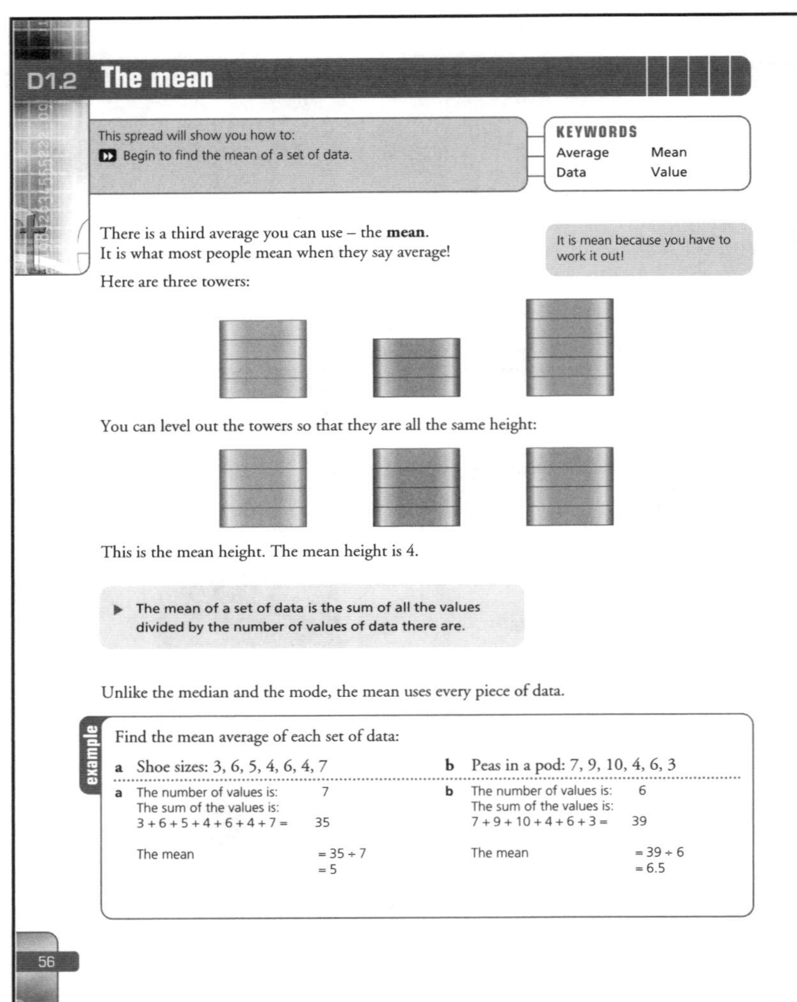

D1.2 The mean

This spread will show you how to:
» Begin to find the mean of a set of data.

KEYWORDS
Average Mean
Data Value

There is a third average you can use – the **mean**.
It is what most people mean when they say average!

It is mean because you have to work it out!

Here are three towers:

You can level out the towers so that they are all the same height:

This is the mean height. The mean height is 4.

► The mean of a set of data is the sum of all the values divided by the number of values of data there are.

Unlike the median and the mode, the mean uses every piece of data.

example

Find the mean average of each set of data:

a Shoe sizes: 3, 6, 5, 4, 6, 4, 7
b Peas in a pod: 7, 9, 10, 4, 6, 3

a The number of values is: 7
The sum of the values is:
3 + 6 + 5 + 4 + 6 + 4 + 7 = 35
The mean = 35 ÷ 7
= 5

b The number of values is: 6
The sum of the values is:
7 + 9 + 10 + 4 + 6 + 3 = 39
The mean = 39 ÷ 6
= 6.5

56

Plenary

Ask students for the averages of:

- Temperatures: 12 °C, 13 °C, 15 °C and 22 °C
- Shoe sizes: 6, 6, 5, 4, 7, 8, 9
- Prices: £3, £5, £9, £2, £11, £17

They should do the calculations mentally.

Discuss how useful each average is for each example.
Decide which is the most typical value and hence the best average to use.

Further activities

In **D1.2ICT**, students input discrete data onto a spreadsheet and find the average and range.

Challenge students to find the mean using mixed measures: 1.2 m, 80 cm, 96 cm, 2 m.

Able students could find the missing value from a set of data (4, 8, 2, 5, ?) given a mean (5).

Differentiation

Support questions:

- Question 1 involves finding the mean by levelling.
- Questions 2, 3a and 3b focus on finding the mean from the total of the data.
- Question 3c includes mixed measures and question 4 involves harder numbers.

Core tier: focuses on finding the mean in a range of contexts.

Exercise D1.2

1 **a** Find the mean number of blocks for this set of towers:

b Find the mean number of pencils in a group:

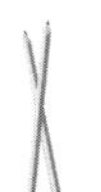

c Find the mean number of matches per box:

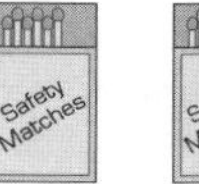

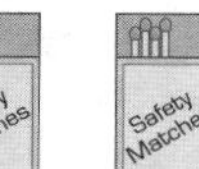

d Find the mean number of blocks:

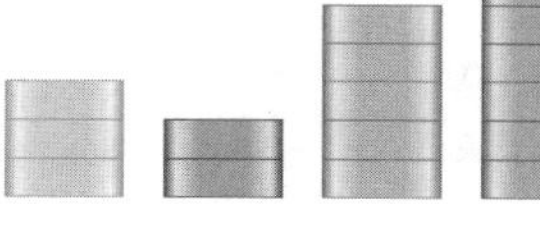

2 Here are four shapes made of cubes:
a What is the total number of cubes used?
b What is the mean number of cubes used?

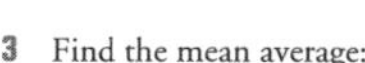

3 Find the mean average:
a number of chocolates in boxes containing: 10, 14, 9, 15
b length of fabric on rolls containing: 4 m, 5 m, 4 m, 2 m, 5 m
c price per kilogram of apples bought from shops charging: 98p, £1.02, 96p, £1.05, 95p, £1.04

4 Find the mean of each set of data. Use a calculator to help you.
a number of sweets in a packet: 29, 34, 24, 26, 27
b number of matches in a box: 49, 56, 39, 52, 47, 42, 29, 44, 54, 28
c money spent on food in a week: £78, £84, £86, £93, £49

Exercise commentary

The questions assess the objectives on Primary Framework Page 117.

Problem solving

Questions 3 and 4 assess Primary Framework Pages 85 and 87.

Group work

Students could work in pairs in questions 1 and 2, modelling the questions with multilink cubes.

Misconceptions

There are many possible causes of difficulty when finding the mean as there are many steps to each question.

Commonly students will find the total but then fail to divide, or divide by the highest value not the number of values.

Emphasise the method of levelling and encourage students to always start from first principles, visualising the towers.

Encourage students to check that the mean is within the range of the data.

Problems with division can cause problems so ensure there is a multiplication grid handy.

Links

Division: Primary Framework Page 57.

Mental addition: Page 43.

Using measures: Page 91.

Homework

D1.2HW provides practice in finding the mean of a small set of data in context.

Answers

1 **a** 3 **b** 4.4 **c** 6 **d** 4
2 **a** 16 **b** 4
3 **a** 12 **b** 4 m **c** £1
4 **a** 28 sweets **b** 44 matches **c** £78

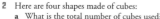

Mental starter

Fractions as percentages
Give students fractions in context – 3 out of 4 people, 15 out of 20 pets, 40 out of 80 marks etc. and ask for what simple fraction it is.
Keep the fractions simple: $\frac{1}{4}$, $\frac{1}{2}$, $\frac{3}{4}$, $\frac{1}{5}$, $\frac{2}{5}$, $\frac{3}{5}$, $\frac{4}{5}$
Students use number cards to show their answers.
Discuss any misconceptions.
Challenge: Ask what percentage each fraction is.

Useful resources

R1 digit cards for the mental starter.
D1.3OHP has diagrams for discussion.
Calculator for the exercise.
R11 has a blank tally chart.

Introductory activity

Ask students how they would collect data.
Expect answers such as using questionnaires and surveys.
Tell them you are going to carry out a simple survey about hair colour. Ask how you should keep the data.
Encourage the answer 'tally chart' and ask if they know another name for it – frequency table.
Collect the data on R11.

Find out what students know about displaying data in diagrams. Ask questions such as:

- How can you communicate results to other people?
- Why use diagrams?
- What diagrams can you use?

Ask students to explain terms they use.

- What is a bar chart?
- What is a pie chart?
- Why/when are they useful?

D1.3OHP shows the pie chart and bar chart from the student book as well as comparative charts and a line graph.
Use D1.3OHP to discuss how to read a chart or diagram.

- Emphasise that a pie chart uses a circle to show proportions when there are only a few categories.
- Emphasise that a bar chart uses bars and is good for comparisons.

Illustrate how to work out the totals from each chart and what the modal group is.

Ask students how to go about drawing a bar and pie chart for the data in your survey. Discuss which is best to use and why.

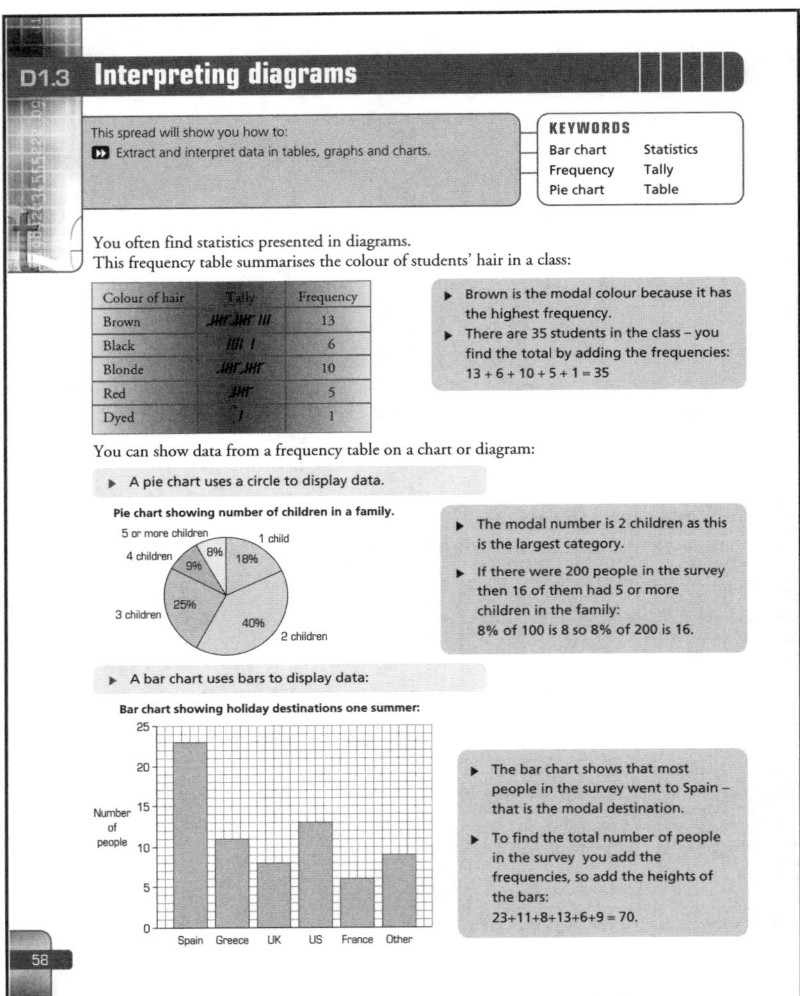

D1.3 **Interpreting diagrams**

This spread will show you how to:
- Extract and interpret data in tables, graphs and charts.

KEYWORDS
Bar chart, Frequency, Pie chart, Statistics, Tally, Table

You often find statistics presented in diagrams.
This frequency table summarises the colour of students' hair in a class:

Colour of hair	Tally	Frequency
Brown	卌 卌 |||	13
Black	卌		6
Blonde	卌 卌	10
Red	卌	5
Dyed			1

- Brown is the modal colour because it has the highest frequency.
- There are 35 students in the class – you find the total by adding the frequencies: 13 + 6 + 10 + 5 + 1 = 35

You can show data from a frequency table on a chart or diagram:

- A pie chart uses a circle to display data.

- The modal number is 2 children as this is the largest category.
- If there were 200 people in the survey then 16 of them had 5 or more children in the family:
8% of 100 is 8 so 8% of 200 is 16.

- A bar chart uses bars to display data:

- The bar chart shows that most people in the survey went to Spain – that is the modal destination.
- To find the total number of people in the survey you add the frequencies, so add the heights of the bars:
23+11+8+13+6+9 = 70.

58

Plenary

Discuss the use of diagrams – makes statistics/data easier to digest.
Discuss why you need to interpret diagrams – so you can draw conclusions about the data.

Go through questions 1 and 2, highlighting in particular:

1 Reading information from a pie chart given the % and the totals.
2 Reading information from a bar chart that uses a scale.

Further activities

Students can plot the information in question 1 on a bar chart. Some students will need guidance on choosing the vertical scale.

Differentiation

Support questions:

- Question 1 involves reading a simple pie chart. Springboard 7, page 145.
- Questions 2 focuses on reading a simple dual bar chart. Springboard 7, pages 146–148.
- Question 3 extends to interpreting dual pie charts. Springboard 7, pages 149, 150.

Core tier: focuses on interpreting and critically analysing a variety of diagrams.

Exercise D1.3

1 The pie chart shows the percentages of different film ratings in the *Movie and Video Guide*.

- **a** What is the modal rating in the Guide?
- **b** The Guide rated 100 films. How many 2* films are there?
- **c** How many of each rating are there if 1000 films are reviewed in the Guide?
- **d** As a fraction, 20% is $\frac{1}{5}$.

20% of the films in the Guide were given no stars.

- **e** What fraction of the films were given a rating of 3 stars or more?

2 This bar chart shows the number of mobile phone users in four secondary schools.

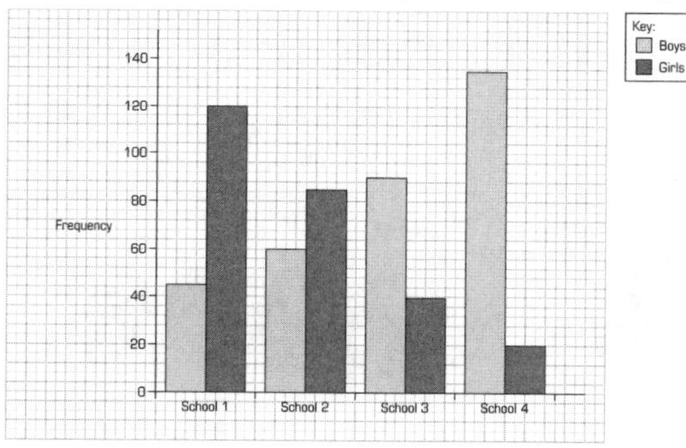

- **a** Which school has the largest number of girls with mobile phones?
- **b** Which school has the smallest total number of mobile phone users?
- **c** In which school is there the biggest difference between the numbers of boys and girls who own mobile phones?

3 The pie chart shows the proportion of different types of room in two hotels.

- **a** Roughly what percentage of the rooms at the Majestic Hotel are *Basic*?
- **b** Hanif says 'You can see that there must be more *Superior* rooms at the Majestic Hotel than at the Broadway.' Explain why Hanif is wrong.

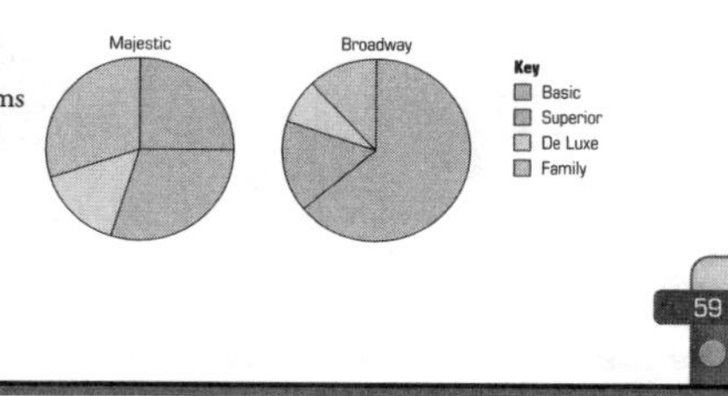

59

Exercise commentary

The questions assess the objectives on Primary Framework Page 115.

Problem solving
Question 3 assesses the objective on Primary Framework Page 76.

Group work
Students could work in pairs or groups to discuss question 3b.

Misconceptions
Students find pie charts confusing as, for example, in question 1 the answers depend on the total whereas in question 3 they depend on the proportion and the total is irrelevant. Emphasise that pie charts show fractions, not totals.
The use of a scale in question 2 can cause problems.
Encourage students to work out what each division means before answering the questions.

Links
Percentages: Primary Framework Page 33.

Homework

D1.3HW requires students to interpret two bar charts depicting real data.

Answers

1 **a** 2 stars **b** 30
c No stars: 200, 1 star: 250, 2 stars: 300, 3 stars: 200, 4 stars: 50
d $\frac{(20 + 5)}{100} = \frac{1}{4}$

2 **a** School 1 **b** School 3 **c** School 4

3 **a** 25%
b The pie chart doesn't show the total number of rooms in either hotel.

D1.4 Introducing probability

Mental starter

Put some multilink cubes in a box: 5 green ones, 2 blue ones and 3 red ones. Show students how many of each are in the box.
Ask students which colour they think you'll pull out of the box.
Ask them to explain their reasons.
Pull out a cube – ask how many were right.
Repeat.

Useful resources

R6 contains 0–1 probability lines.
Dice
Multilink cubes

Introductory activity

Discuss vocabulary from Key words.
Ask which word describes the following situations:

- A pig will fly past the window.
- Next month will be June.
- You will go swimming this summer.
- It will rain every day during the summer holidays.

Encourage the use of comparatives: more likely and less likely, by giving two events such as:

- John will come to school with blonde hair tomorrow.
- John will remember his homework tomorrow.

Discuss what is meant by 'even chance' – as likely as not, 50–50...
Ask students for examples of events that have an even chance of happening and not happening.

Introduce the probability line – impossible to certain. Use R6.
Discuss where to place the events you've discussed so far on a probability line.
Ask students to give a reason for their answers.

Emphasise that probability is a measure of the chance of something happening.
Encourage students to start to put numbers on these chances – use the example from the student book.

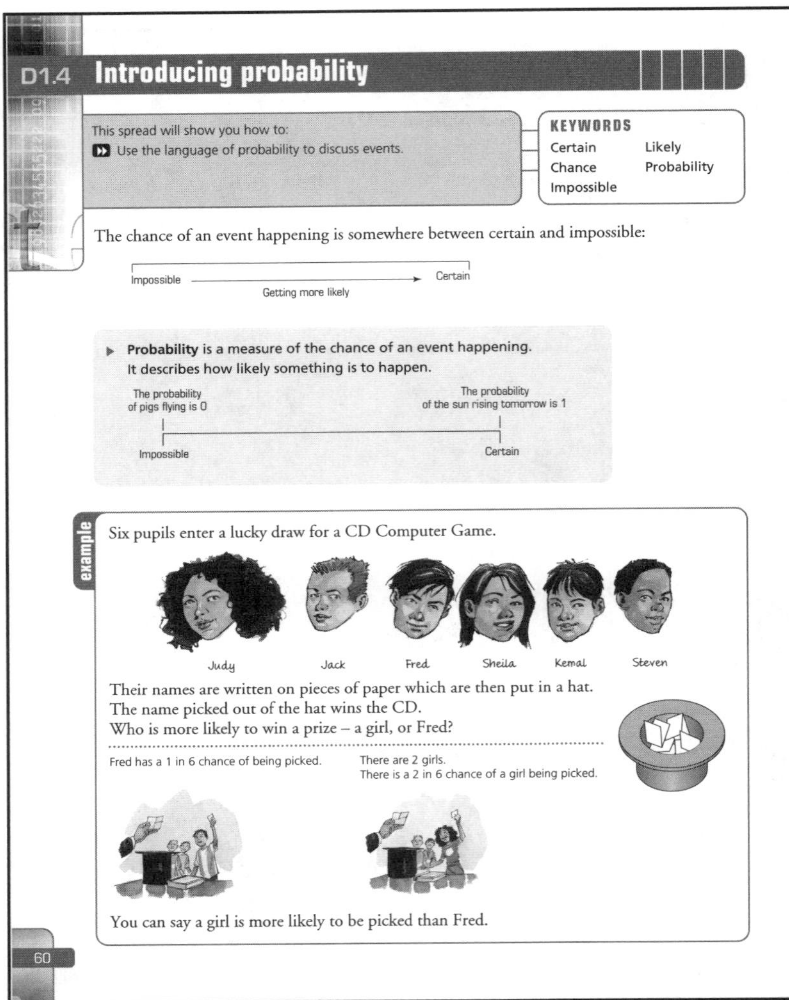

D1.4 Introducing probability

This spread will show you how to:
- Use the language of probability to discuss events.

KEYWORDS
Certain
Chance
Impossible
Likely
Probability

The chance of an event happening is somewhere between certain and impossible:

Impossible — Getting more likely → Certain

- **Probability** is a measure of the chance of an event happening.
It describes how likely something is to happen.

The probability of pigs flying is 0 — Impossible
The probability of the sun rising tomorrow is 1 — Certain

example

Six pupils enter a lucky draw for a CD Computer Game.

Judy Jack Fred Sheila Kemal Steven

Their names are written on pieces of paper which are then put in a hat.
The name picked out of the hat wins the CD.
Who is more likely to win a prize – a girl, or Fred?

Fred has a 1 in 6 chance of being picked.

There are 2 girls.
There is a 2 in 6 chance of a girl being picked.

You can say a girl is more likely to be picked than Fred.

60

Plenary

The plenary should ensure that students understand the terms: certain, likely, unlikely, impossible, equal chance, even chance.

- Ask students to give their own examples.
- Discuss the probability of things happening at different times of the day or week, for example doing maths homework!
- Discuss where to place different weather conditions for tomorrow on a probability line.

Further activities

Students can work in groups of five to carry out their own survey as in question 5.

Encourage them to discuss how to make the survey fair so that each choice has an equal chance of being picked.

Differentiation

Support questions:

- Questions 1–3 focus on a qualitative approach to probability using increasingly precise language. Springboard 7, page 252.
- Question 4 starts to quantify the probability of an event in terms of the chance of an event. Springboard 7, pages 253, 254.
- Question 5 introduces the idea of writing probabilities as fractions.

Core tier: focuses on evaluating probabilities as fractions.

Exercise D1.4

1 Copy this probability line: Impossible ——— Certain

Show these events on your line:

a You will have a birthday next year. **b** A dog will have kittens.
c There will be snow next Christmas. **d** It will be sunny next week.

2 a Write down the names of four animals.
Label them A, B, C and D.
Which do you think are more likely to hurt you?
b Put the animals in the order you think are the most likely to hurt you.

Least likely ———→ Most

3 You may get hurt playing these sports:
A: Soccer B: Rugby C: Cricket D: Tennis
a Are you more likely to get hurt playing A or B?
b Compare the other events in pairs. Write:
Getting hurt playing A is more likely than...
c Put the events in order, least likely to most likely.

4 Use the information in the example to answer these questions:
a What is the probability of Kemal being picked?
Copy and complete:
Kemal has a __ in __ chance of being picked.
b Order these events on a probability line:
A: Kemal gets picked. B: A boy gets picked.
C: Either Jack or Sheila gets picked. D: No-one wins the CD.

5 Five friends are trying to decide where to go on Friday.
They each write down their preferred choice on a card:

Cinema | Bowling | Skating | Cinema | Club

a Copy and complete this sentence:
There is a __ in __ chance they will go to the cinema.
b Write the probability they will go to the cinema as a fraction: $\frac{\square}{\square}$
c Order these events on a probability line:
A They go to the Club B They to to the Cinema
C They go to the Theatre D They do not go Bowling

61

Exercise commentary

The questions assess the objectives on Primary Framework Page 113.

Problem solving

The exercise assesses the objective on Primary Framework Page 76 if students are encouraged to explain reasoning.

Group work

Students could work in pairs in questions 1–3, discussing the order of likelihood in each case.

The further activity is group work.

Misconceptions

The 1 in 5 chance notation is a useful introduction but it is important to stress that probabilities are written as fractions (and decimals or percentages).

Discuss as a group the sensible way of recording numbers between 0 and 1 and refer back to N2.6 where students placed equivalent forms on a number line.

Some students will write $\frac{2}{3}$ instead of $\frac{2}{5}$ for question 2d.

Encourage students to write down the total number of parts as the denominator, linking back to N2.1.

Links

Fractions: Primary Framework Page 23, decimals: Page 29, percentages: Page 33.

Homework

D1.4HW requires students to evaluate the likelihood of outcomes in a game.

Answers

4 a Kemal has a one in six chance of being picked.

5 a There is a two in five chance they will go to the cinema.

b $\frac{2}{5}$

Mental starter

Fractions, decimals, percentages

- Give students a fraction or decimal or percentage and ask them to give equivalents.
- They can hold up digit cards (**R2** includes a decimal point).
- Keep the fractions simple: $\frac{1}{2}$, 0.1, 25% ...
- Discuss any difficulties using a number line.

Useful resources

R6 number lines
R2 digit cards for the mental starter.
Dice

Introductory activity

Discuss what students learnt last lesson. Ask what they understand by the term probability.

Discuss how to find probabilities.

- Place the cards 1, 2, 3, 4 and 5 in a box. Show students what you are doing.
- Ask them to write down which card they think you will pull out.
- Show the card. Ask who got the answer right and what was the chance of guessing right.
- Repeat with the 4 cards left.
- Discuss how to find the probability in each case.

Emphasise that probability depends on the number of possible outcomes.
The fewer the cards the more people guess correctly as the higher the probability of guessing correctly.

- Now put the cards into the box and ask for the probability of choosing an even number, a card greater than 1 etc.

Encourage use of the formula.

Emphasise the need for equally likely outcomes.

Explain that a probability can be placed on a number line between 0 and 1. Discuss the fact that a certain event has a probability of 1 and an impossible event has a probability of 0.

Ask students to mark the probabilities of the events you've discussed so far on a 0–1 number line (R6).
Discuss.

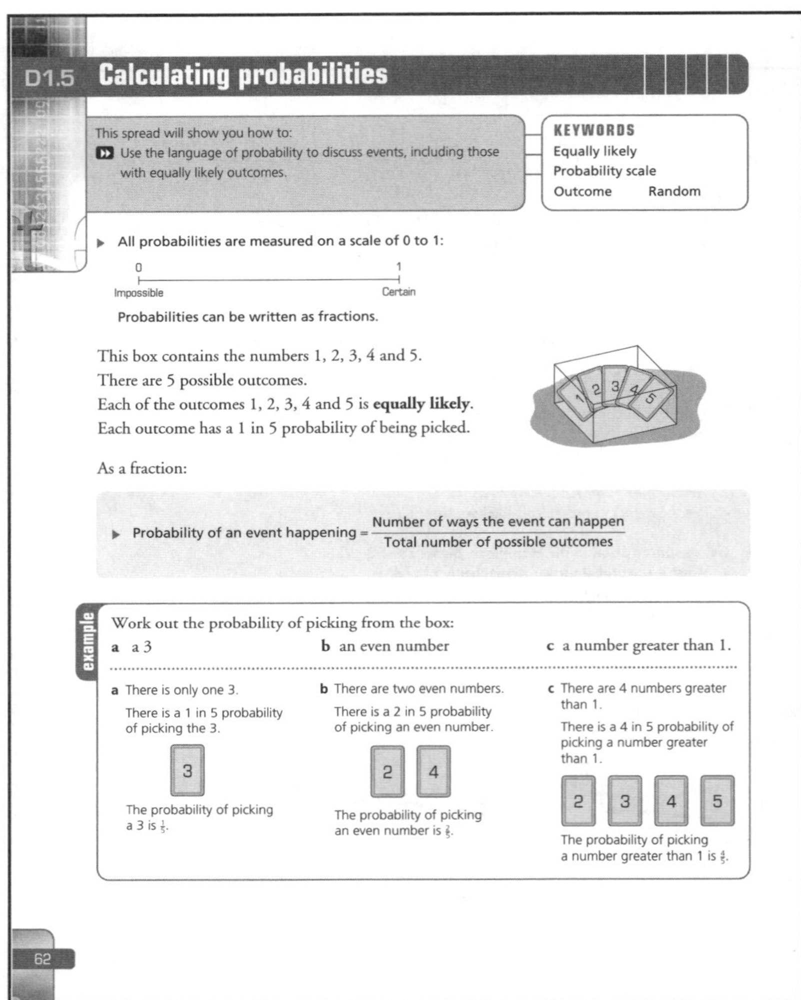

Plenary

Introduce a question for discussion (there is a similar question for homework).
A box of chocolates has 10 soft and 4 hard centres.
Ask for the probability of a soft/hard centre.
How many of each would you have to eat so that the probability of picking a hard centre becomes 0.5?
Discuss all the ways this could happen: when there are equal numbers of soft and hard centres.
Ask how many you'd eat to make the probability $\frac{1}{4}$.
Discuss all the possible ways this could happen:
9–3, 6–2, 3–1.

Further activities

Students can investigate the answers to question 2 using different spinners.
R10 has a 10-sided spinner students could make.
Able students could link the probability of an even number with the number of sides.

Students can devise a problem similar to question 4 based on their own favourite CDs.

Differentiation

Support questions:

- Question 1 builds on the chance approach to probability. Springboard 7, pages 255–257.
- Questions 2 and 3 focus on writing probabilities involving equally likely outcomes as fractions. Springboard 7, pages 258–260.
- Question 4 introduces the idea of an event not happening. Springboard 7, page 261.

Core tier: focuses on extracting relevant information from context, including a two-way table.

Exercise D1.5

1 The letters in the word APRIL are placed in a bag and one letter is picked out.
Copy and complete:
There are ____ possible outcomes.
Each outcome has a 1 in ____ chance of being picked.

What is the probability of picking out:
a an A? **b** an R? **c** a vowel? **d** a consonant?
Show your answers on a probability line.

2 An 8-sided spinner is used to play a game.

a How many possible outcomes are there from one spin?
b How many ways are there of getting an even number?
c What is the probability of getting an even number.

3 Joe shuts his eyes and presses one of the options on this drinks machine:

What is the probability of him getting:
a coffee **b** milk **c** hot chocolate **d** tea?

4 There are 10 tracks on a CD:
5 tracks have female singers,
3 have male singers,
the rest are dance tracks with no singing.
Martine presses the 'Random' button, which plays the tracks in a random order.
What is the probability that:
a The first track to play features a male singer?
b The first track does *not* have a female singer?
c The first track has no singing at all?

63

Exercise commentary

The questions assess the objectives on Primary Framework Page 113.

Problem solving

The exercise assesses the objective on Primary Framework Page 76 if students are encouraged to explain reasoning.

Group work

Students could work in pairs in questions 1–3, discussing the order of likelihood in each case.
The further activity is group work.

Misconceptions

Students fail to make the leap to using fractions to describe probabilities.
Emphasise that using fractions is quicker and simpler than the cumbersome sentence about chance.
Encourage use of a 0 to 1 number line as this will also reinforce the earlier number work and help emphasise that probabilities are always between 0 and 1.
As in D1.4, some students will write $\frac{1}{4}$ instead of $\frac{1}{5}$ for question 1a.
The question tries to emphasise that the denominator is the total number of parts.

Links

Fractions: Primary Framework Page 23, decimals: Page 29, percentages: Page 33.

Homework

D1.5HW is based on calculating probabilities associated with selecting from a box of chocolates.

Answers

1 There are 5 possible outcomes. Each outcome has a 1 in 5 chance of being picked.
a $\frac{1}{5}$ **b** $\frac{1}{5}$ **c** $\frac{2}{5}$ **d** $\frac{3}{5}$

2 **a** 8 **b** 4 **c** $\frac{4}{8} = \frac{1}{2}$

3 **a** $\frac{3}{6} = \frac{1}{2}$ **b** $\frac{3}{6} = \frac{1}{2}$ **c** $\frac{1}{6}$ **d** $\frac{2}{6} = \frac{1}{3}$

4 **a** $\frac{3}{10}$ **b** $\frac{5}{10} = \frac{1}{2}$ **c** $\frac{2}{10} = \frac{1}{5}$

D1.6 Experimental probability

Mental starter

Fractions of multiples

- Give a total: 50.
- Write down simple fractions:
  $\frac{1}{2}$ of, $\frac{1}{3}$ of, $\frac{1}{4}$ of, $\frac{1}{5}$ of, $\frac{1}{6}$ of, $\frac{1}{8}$ of, $\frac{1}{10}$ of
- Ask students if they can tell you any of the answers.
- Discuss why some are easy, others are hard.
- Emphasise 50 is a multiple of 2, 5 and 10.

Useful resources

R11 has a tally chart you can fill in.
Dice
Coins

Introductory activity

Remind students of how to find probabilities.
Emphasise that probability depends on the number of possible outcomes.
Refer to the formula.

Ask students to say whether a coin will land on heads or tails.
Emphasise that you can write down the probability but that it is only a measure of chance and so not guaranteed.

Ask for instances of when the list of possible outcomes is not known – for example what someone will name a baby – or when the likelihood is not known exactly – for example the final score in a football match.
Introduce the idea that you can estimate the chance of an event occurring by doing an experiment.
Refer back to the starter activity and say that for unknown data you can use a similar technique.

Carry out a class experiment to test whether a dice is biased.

- Before you start, ask students how they would expect the scores to spread out – roughly equally if not biased.
- Each student rolls the dice twice and you record the outcome – use **R11**.
- They keep passing the dice until there are 60 outcomes.
- Discuss the experimental probability of each outcome.

Emphasise there is no reason why the dice should be biased but the experiment shows useful techniques.

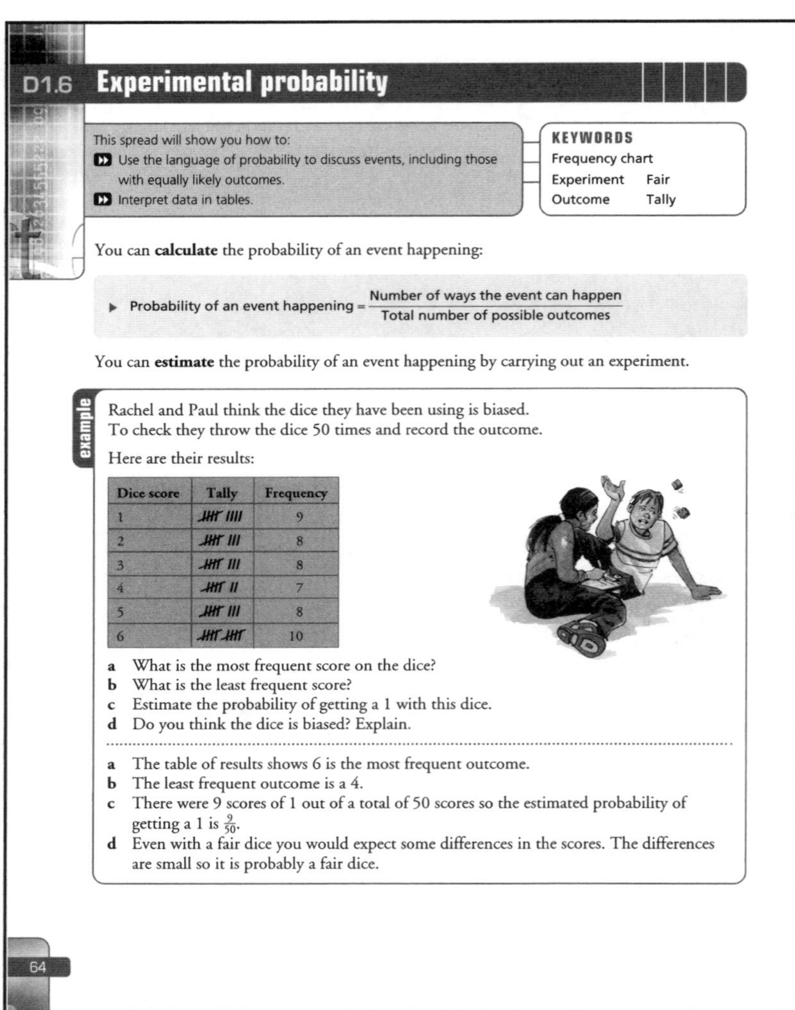

D1.6 **Experimental probability**

This spread will show you how to:
- Use the language of probability to discuss events, including those with equally likely outcomes.
- Interpret data in tables.

KEYWORDS
Frequency chart
Experiment
Fair
Outcome
Tally

You can **calculate** the probability of an event happening:

- Probability of an event happening = $\frac{\text{Number of ways the event can happen}}{\text{Total number of possible outcomes}}$

You can **estimate** the probability of an event happening by carrying out an experiment.

example

Rachel and Paul think the dice they have been using is biased.
To check they throw the dice 50 times and record the outcome.

Here are their results:

Dice score	Tally	Frequency
1	~~IIII~~ IIII	9
2	~~IIII~~ III	8
3	~~IIII~~ III	8
4	~~IIII~~ II	7
5	~~IIII~~ III	8
6	~~IIII~~ ~~IIII~~	10

a What is the most frequent score on the dice?
b What is the least frequent score?
c Estimate the probability of getting a 1 with this dice.
d Do you think the dice is biased? Explain.

a The table of results shows 6 is the most frequent outcome.
b The least frequent outcome is a 4.
c There were 9 scores of 1 out of a total of 50 scores so the estimated probability of getting a 1 is $\frac{9}{50}$.
d Even with a fair dice you would expect some differences in the scores. The differences are small so it is probably a fair dice.

64

Plenary

Ask students to explain when they might need to use experimental probability. It is useful for predicting outcomes of future events.
Go over the results from the first experiment.
Ask which is the most likely result: heads or tails.
Compare with theoretical probability where the outcomes are equally likely.
Emphasise that each group got different results and that putting them all together would give the best estimates.

Further activities

Students can investigate experiment 2 using different spinners or more trials.

You could challenge students to weight the spinner to produce twice as many 4s as any other number.

Differentiation

Support questions:

- Experiment 1 uses ready-made equipment in a straightforward practical activity.
- In experiment 2 students need to make the spinner before undertaking the activity.
- Able students should be encouraged to consider how to weight the pin or spinner to produce given outcomes.

Core tier: extends to sampling without replacement.

Exercise D1.6

1 **Experiment 1: Test a drawing pin**

- Take a drawing pin
- Drop it on your table 50 times
- Record whether it lands 'point up' or 'point down'
- Record your results in a copy of this table:

Outcome	Tally	Frequency
Point up		
Point down		

Use your table to answer these questions:

a Which outcome seems to be the most likely?

b Estimate the probability of the pin landing point down

How could you get a more reliable estimate for the probability that the pin lands point down?

Experiment 2: Test a spinner

Make a rectangular spinner with the design shown:

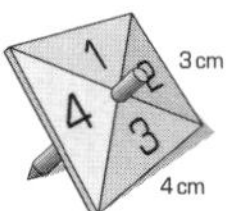

Now test your spinner:

- Spin it 100 times
- Record the results in a copy of this table:

Spinner score	Tally	Frequency
1		
2		
3		
4		

a Which score seems to be most likely?

b Which score seems to be least likely?

c Use your table to estimate the probability of each score.

d Do you think your spinner is fair? Explain.

Exercise commentary

The questions assess the objectives on Primary Framework Page 113.

Problem solving

Question 2 assesses the objective on Primary Framework Page 76 as students are encouraged to explain reasoning.

Group work

Both experiments are suitable for pairs.

Misconceptions

Students get confused as to what data gives the probability and forget to use the total number of trials as the denominator, commonly writing the probability of heads as number of heads ÷ number of tails. Emphasise that the total number of outcomes gives the denominator and encourage students to write this down before finding probabilities. It is useful to discuss findings in these experiments as a group, considering how the probability changes as the number of trials increase. Encourage students to work mentally as the trials are performed in batches of 50. In experiment 2 some students will need help constructing the spinner.

Links

Fractions: Primary Framework Page 23, decimals: Page 29, percentages: Page 33. Students usually need to perform experiments in Science lessons.

Homework

D1.6HW requires students to estimate probabilities and expected frequencies based on experimental data.

Answers

The answers will depend on the results of the students' own experiments.

Summary

The Year 6 key teaching objective is:

- Solve a problem by extracting and interpreting data in tables, graphs and charts (115, 117).

Plenary activity

Ask ten students how many brothers and sisters they have.
Discuss:

- How to record the answers.
- How to find the average which is the most appropriate.
- How to display the data on an appropriate chart.
- The probability that a person chosen at random from the group has 1, 0, >10 siblings.

Check out commentary

a Students often fail to order the data before finding the median.
Emphasise that when handling data it is important to put it into size order to be able to properly analyse it and encourage students to always do so as a matter of course.

b Some students will write the highest frequency as the mode.
Emphasise that the mode is always one of the values and encourage students to consider whether their answer is sensible.

c There are many steps involved in finding the mean and some students lose track of what to divide by.
Encourage them to start by writing down the number of data values.

d Most students will be able to draw a bar chart but may find labelling the axes difficult. Some students will draw ten bars with the heights shown.
Emphasise that the x-axis displays the variable age (the y-axis is usually used for the frequency) and emphasise the need to group the data in order.

e and **f** Students find probability using numerical data a difficult area, mainly because there are so many different numbers involved, causing confusion. Students will benefit from supportive questioning:

- How many people in total?
- How many are over 15?
- What's the probability?

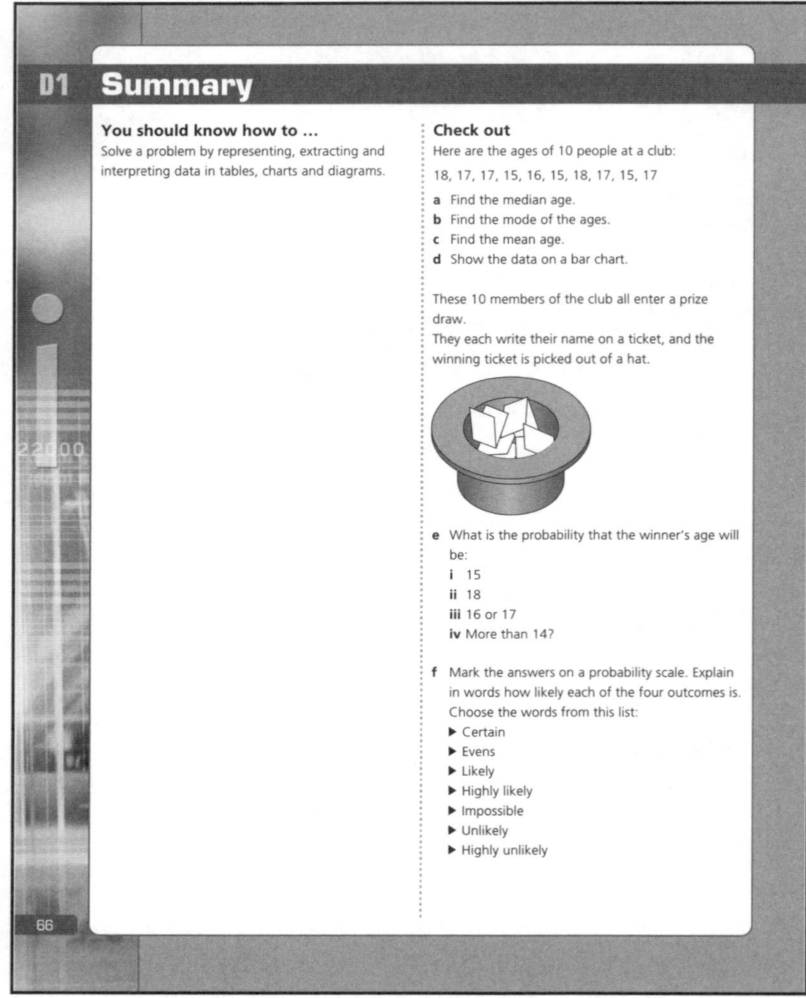

D1 Summary

You should know how to ...
Solve a problem by representing, extracting and interpreting data in tables, charts and diagrams.

Check out
Here are the ages of 10 people at a club:

18, 17, 17, 15, 16, 15, 18, 17, 15, 17

a Find the median age.
b Find the mode of the ages.
c Find the mean age.
d Show the data on a bar chart.

These 10 members of the club all enter a prize draw.
They each write their name on a ticket, and the winning ticket is picked out of a hat.

e What is the probability that the winner's age will be:
i 15
ii 18
iii 16 or 17
iv More than 14?

f Mark the answers on a probability scale. Explain in words how likely each of the four outcomes is.
Choose the words from this list:

- Certain
- Evens
- Likely
- Highly likely
- Impossible
- Unlikely
- Highly unlikely

66

Development

Interpretation of data is developed in D2 and D3.
Use of averages is developed in D3.
Probability is developed in D4.

Links

Probability uses fractions (N4) and use of pie charts links to percentages (N4) and area (S1). The use of scales when drawing graphs links to measures (S1) and the use of tables links to algebra (A3).

Mental starters

Objectives covered in this unit:

- Recognise multiples and use simple tests of divisibility.
- Add and subtract pairs of numbers.
- Find doubles and halves of numbers.
- Use units of time for calculations.

Resources needed

* means class set needed

Essential:

A2.3OHP – Section of a 100 square

A2.4OHP – The Dice Run

Useful:

R1* – Digit cards

R2* – Decimal digit cards

R20 (OHP) – Analogue clock

A2.2ICT* – Expressions in Excel

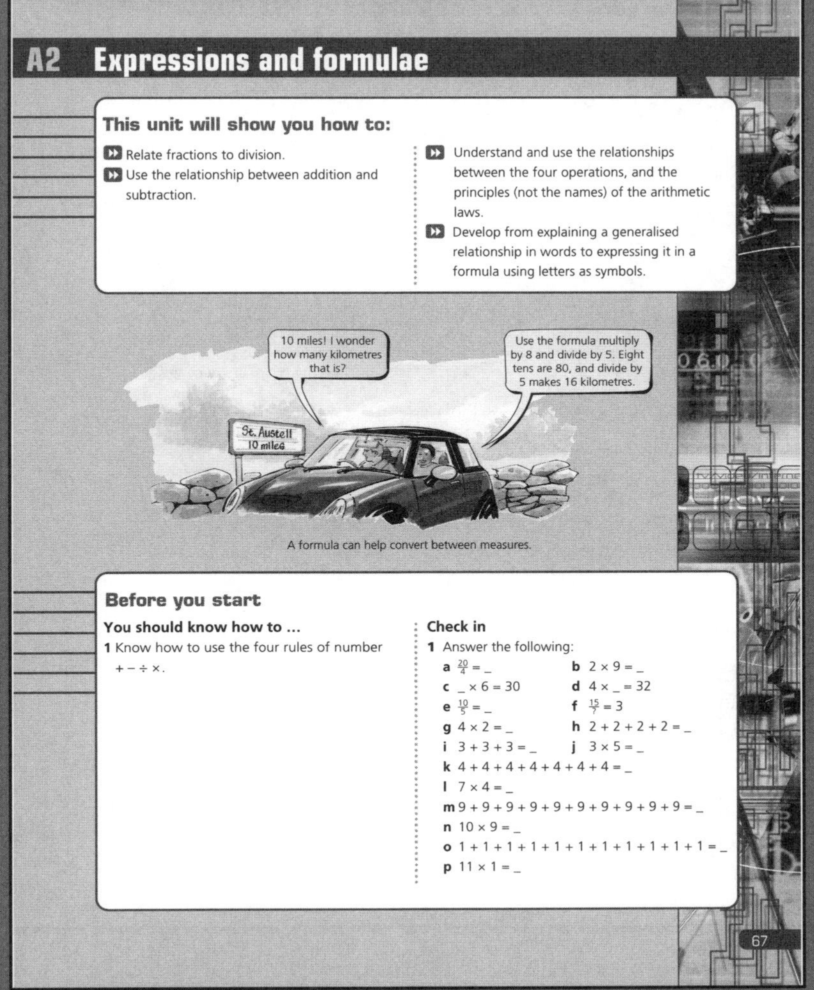

A2 Expressions and formulae

This unit will show you how to:

- Relate fractions to division.
- Use the relationship between addition and subtraction.
- Understand and use the relationships between the four operations, and the principles (not the names) of the arithmetic laws.
- Develop from explaining a generalised relationship in words to expressing it in a formula using letters as symbols.

10 miles! I wonder how many kilometres that is?
Use the formula multiply by 8 and divide by 5. Eight tens are 80, and divide by 5 makes 16 kilometres.
St. Austell 10 miles

A formula can help convert between measures.

Before you start

You should know how to …

1 Know how to use the four rules of number + − ÷ ×.

Check in

1 Answer the following:

a $\frac{20}{4}$ = _ b 2 × 9 = _
c _ × 6 = 30 d 4 × _ = 32
e $\frac{10}{5}$ = _ f $\frac{15}{?}$ = 3
g 4 × 2 = _ h 2 + 2 + 2 + 2 = _
i 3 + 3 + 3 = _ j 3 × 5 = _
k 4 + 4 + 4 + 4 + 4 + 4 + 4 = _
l 7 × 4 = _
m 9 + 9 + 9 + 9 + 9 + 9 + 9 + 9 + 9 + 9 = _
n 10 × 9 = _
o 1 + 1 + 1 + 1 + 1 + 1 + 1 + 1 + 1 + 1 + 1 = _
p 11 × 1 = _

67

Unit commentary

Aim of the unit

This unit aims to consolidate students' ability to use letters as symbols to stand for numbers. Students consider the use of letters for unknown values and also for variables. They will express simple relationships using letters and evaluate simple expressions.

Introduction

Discuss what students understand by the term 'formula': two or more variables linked by a rule. Discuss any formulae they know and use already – refer to S1 and the formula for the area of a rectangle. Use the picture to emphasise that you use a formula to convert between units of measure.

Framework references

This unit focuses on:

- Year 6 teaching objectives pages: 25, 43, 53, 55
- Problem solving objectives page: 81

The unit provides access to:

- Year 7 teaching objectives pages: 112, 114, 138, 140

Check in activity

Calculation chain

- Start with a number: 20.
- Ask students to divide by 5 and hold up the answer using **R1** digit cards.
- Ask them to perform one calculation after another: add 6, divide by 5, multiply by 9, subtract 17 etc.

Differentiation

Core tier focuses on recognising and using algebraic expressions, including x^2, and formulating formulae.

Mental starter

Divisibility test

Write down a number, say 355, and ask if it can be divided by 2, 3 or 5. Quickly explain the tests of divisibility for these numbers (2 – even; 3 – sum of digits is a multiple of 3; 5 – ends in 5 or 0), and write down 10 numbers, varying in size between 1 and 1000. Take each one in turn, asking the class which it is divisible by: 2, 3, 5 or none of them. Try to include numbers that have common multiples.

Useful resources

R1 digit cards are useful for the mental starter.

Introductory activity

Discuss the word 'algebra'.

Ask what it means, and encourage responses related to the use of letters to represent numbers.

Discuss the words 'variable' and 'unknown'.

Discuss variable quantities in real life, for example the speed of a bike or the amount of money that you have.

The examples in the student book will help distinguish between variables and unknowns.

Emphasise that algebra is concerned with:

- describing real-life situations
- finding the value of unknowns: values that are fixed but you don't know them.

Look at the example in the student book.

Johnny eats d donuts a day for 5 days.

He eats $5d$ donuts altogether.

Discuss the conventions of algebra.

Link multiplication to repeated addition:

$2 + 2 + 2 + 2 + 2 = 5 \times 2$

$d + d + d + d + d = 5 \times d$

- Don't use multiplication signs because they get mixed up with the letter x.
- Numbers come before letters, for example $2x$ not $x2$.
- You can choose which letter you want to use when describing a particular situation. For example, Johnny eats d donuts a day.
- f means a single lot of f, or $1 \times f$, or $f \times 1$.

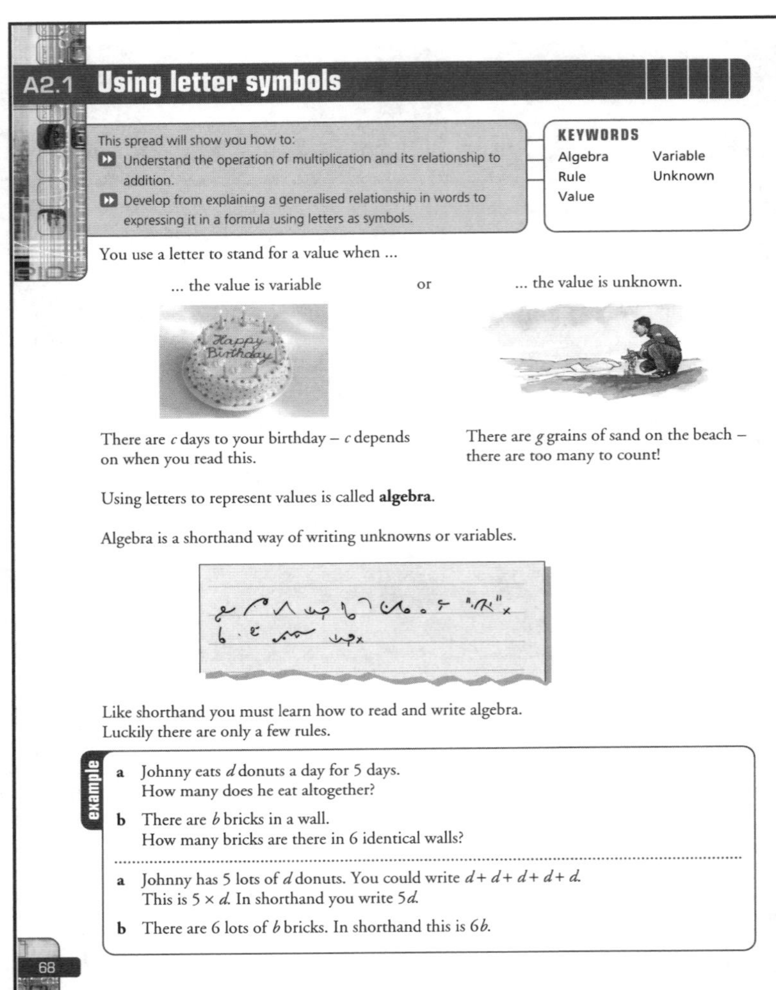

A2.1 Using letter symbols

This spread will show you how to:
- Understand the operation of multiplication and its relationship to addition.
- Develop from explaining a generalised relationship in words to expressing it in a formula using letters as symbols.

KEYWORDS
Algebra
Variable
Rule
Unknown
Value

You use a letter to stand for a value when ...

... the value is variable or ... the value is unknown.

There are c days to your birthday – c depends on when you read this.

There are g grains of sand on the beach – there are too many to count!

Using letters to represent values is called **algebra**.

Algebra is a shorthand way of writing unknowns or variables.

Like shorthand you must learn how to read and write algebra. Luckily there are only a few rules.

example

a Johnny eats d donuts a day for 5 days. How many does he eat altogether?

b There are b bricks in a wall. How many bricks are there in 6 identical walls?

a Johnny has 5 lots of d donuts. You could write $d + d + d + d + d$. This is $5 \times d$. In shorthand you write $5d$.

b There are 6 lots of b bricks. In shorthand this is $6b$.

68

Plenary

Discuss suitable letters to use in question 1.

Discuss answers to question 3, and explain that you write xy not yx by convention because letters follow in alphabetical order.

Further activities

Students can make up sentences for each other to solve as in question 1.

An extension is to ask students to develop expressions for sentences and then ask partners to guess the sentence. They will need to provide clues as to the subject matter!

Differentiation

Support questions:

- Question 1 focuses on generalising number with letters.
- Question 2 focuses on multiplying with algebra.
- Question 3 should only be attempted by students with a good grasp of the work.

Core tier: focuses on using algebra to express positions on a grid.

Exercise A2.1

1 Use algebra shorthand to represent these sentences.
The first one is done for you.

- **a** The number of cars in the world.
  There are n cars in the world.
- **b** The number of hairs on your head.
  There are __ hairs on your head.
- **c** The number of words in a newspaper.
- **d** The number of burgers in America.
- **e** The number of fish in the sea.
- **f** The number of stars in the sky.
- **g** The number of blades of grass in a field.
- **h** The number of plants in a garden.
- **i** The number of books in the library.
- **j** The number of internet users in the UK.

2 Use algebra shorthand to represent these sentences.
The first one is done for you.

- **a** The number of hairs on 10 heads.
  There are t hairs on 1 head, so there are $10t$ hairs on 10 heads
- **b** The number of words in 5 newspapers.
  There are __ words in 1 newspaper, so there are __ in 5 newspapers.
- **c** The number of blades of grass in 5 fields.
- **d** The number of plants in 6 gardens.
- **e** The number of books in 20 libraries.
- **f** The number of sweets in 20 tubes.
- **g** The number of coins in 12 moneyboxes.
- **h** The number of bricks in 8 houses.
- **i** The number of houses in 35 streets.
- **j** The number of leaves on 100 trees.
- **k** The number of pairs of trainers in 5 sports shops.

3 If there are x leaves on a tree, and y trees in a forest, how many leaves are in the forest?

69

Exercise commentary

The questions assess the objectives on Primary Framework Pages 53 and 81.

Problem solving

The exercise assesses Primary Framework Page 81.

Group work

The further activity is suitable for pairs.

Misconceptions

Students tend to choose letters to stand for the object rather than the number of objects, leading to later misunderstandings.
Question 1a encourages students to use n for number rather than c for car.
In question 2 emphasise that $10t$ means 10 lots of t to help students to make the link between multiplication and addition.
Encourage them to use a multiplication sign as an interim step if that helps emphasise the method.

Links

Estimation: Primary Framework Page 11.
The use of letter symbols to generalise is widely applied in maths and other subjects providing plenty of opportunities for reinforcement.

Homework

A2.1HW provides practice in using algebra to represent statements.

Answers

1 **b** There are h hairs on your head. **c** There are w words in a newspaper.
d There are s burgers in America. **e** There are f fish in the sea.
f There are s stars in the sky. **g** There are b blades of grass in a field.
h There are t plants in a garden. **i** There are b books in a library.
j There are m internet users in the UK.

2 **b** w, $5w$ **c** b, $5b$ **d** t, $6t$ **e** b, $20b$ **f** s, $20s$ **g** c, $12c$ **h** b, $8b$ **i** h, $35h$
j l, $100l$ **k** p, $5p$

3 xy

Mental starter

Sum and difference

Ask students to add and subtract a pair of numbers, for example 74 and 48: $74 + 48 = 122$ $74 - 48 = 26$

Then write down some related numbers:

740 and 480, 7400 and 4800

Ask students for the sum and difference of these pairs – what strategy do they use?

Try with decimals: $7.4 + 4.8$

Useful resources

R2 decimal digit cards are useful for the mental starter.

Introductory activity

Recap the previous lesson and ask what students understand by the words: *algebra, variable, unknown.*

Build an expression from a real context. You could use the example in the student book on Johnny's donuts, or you could use one that relates more directly to the students in your class, such as hours of homework per week.

Emphasise that n is an unknown amount, so $n + 1$ means the unknown amount plus 1.

Explain that $n + 1$ and $d - 2$ are **expressions.**

Describe a simple expression in words and write it using algebra.

For example, say: 'I start with s and then I subtract 7.'

Then write: $s - 7$.

Give the students a few to do. You could vary the subtraction ones to make them harder.

For example: 'I start with 6 and I subtract y.'

Discuss why $6 - y$ is different to $y - 6$.

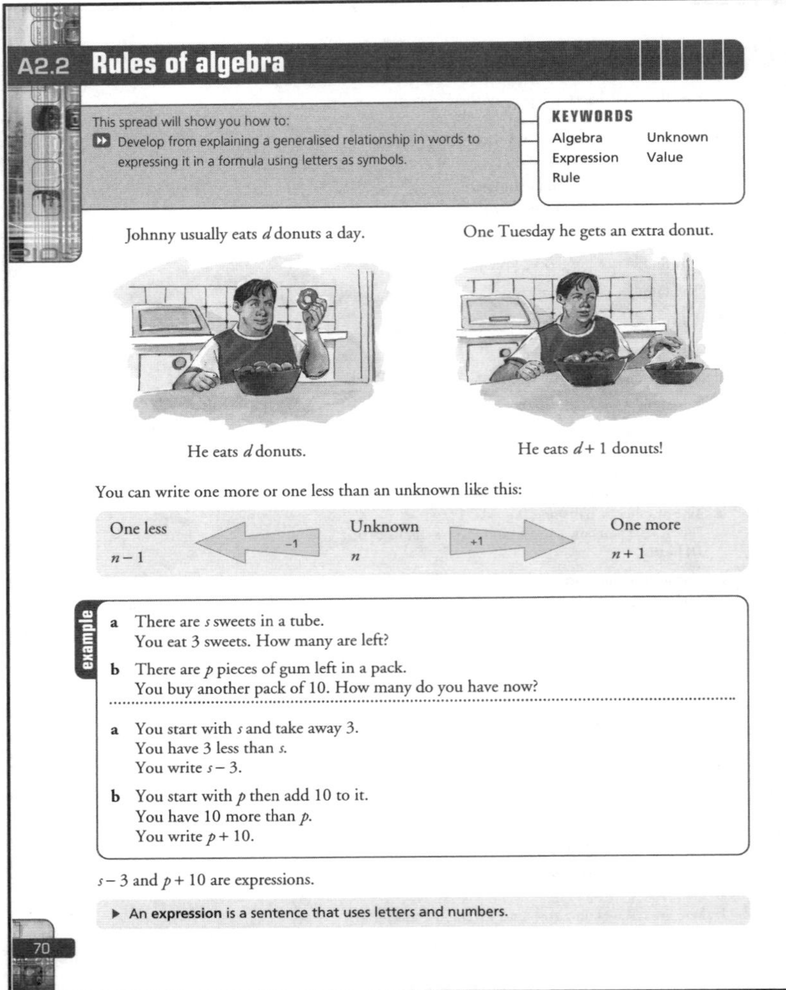

A2.2 **Rules of algebra**

This spread will show you how to:
- Develop from explaining a generalised relationship in words to expressing it in a formula using letters as symbols.

KEYWORDS
Algebra, Unknown, Expression, Value, Rule

Johnny usually eats d donuts a day. One Tuesday he gets an extra donut.

He eats d donuts. He eats $d + 1$ donuts!

You can write one more or one less than an unknown like this:

One less $n - 1$ ← −1 Unknown n +1 → One more $n + 1$

example

a There are s sweets in a tube. You eat 3 sweets. How many are left?

b There are p pieces of gum left in a pack. You buy another pack of 10. How many do you have now?

a You start with s and take away 3. You have 3 less than s. You write $s - 3$.

b You start with p then add 10 to it. You have 10 more than p. You write $p + 10$.

$s - 3$ and $p + 10$ are expressions.

- An **expression** is a sentence that uses letters and numbers.

70

Plenary

Discuss question 3 in the exercise.

Provide a variation of this question:

- a is the weight of an apple, b is the weight of a banana and c is the weight of a carrot.
- What is an expression for... e.g. the combined weight of 4 apples, 3 bananas and 2 carrots?
- ... the difference in weight between 6 carrots and 2 apples? etc.

Further activities

In **A2.2ICT**, students learn how expressions are written in Excel.

Pose some counter problems as in question 1 but include more information:

- drop 2, then pick up 5,
- double the number, then drop 6. etc.

Differentiation

Support questions:

- Question 1 focuses on generalising number with letters.
- Question 2 focuses on describing unknown numbers with letters.
- Question 3 features a complex problem using expressions.

Core tier: focuses on adding and multiplying terms.

Exercise A2.2

1 Write an expression for each of these sentences.
Use n to stand for the number of counters.

a I have some counters.
I drop 4 on the floor.
I now have __ counters.

b I have some counters.
I find 6 counters on the floor.
I now have __ counters.

c I have some counters.
I give 20 counters to a teacher.
I now have __ counters.

d I have some counters.
I find 3 more in the cupboard.
I now have __ counters.

e I have some counters.
I drop five counters.
I now have __ counters.

f I have some counters.
I find 10 counters on the floor.
I now have __ counters.

g I had some counters.
I buy 3 more.
I now have __ counters.

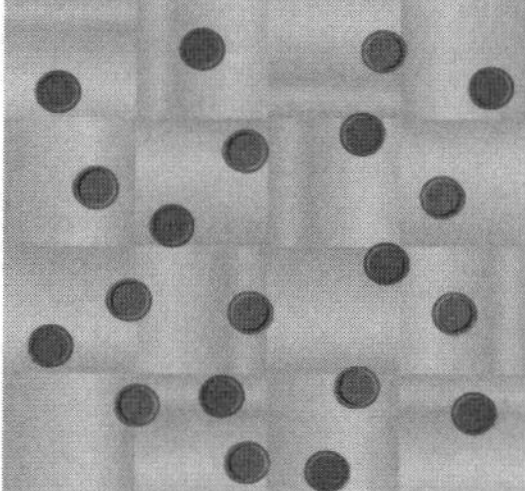

2 Write expressions for these sentences.

a Add 5 to an unknown number.
b Take 5 away from an unknown number.
c Take an unknown number away from 10.
d 5 minus an unknown number.
e Subtract an unknown number from 20.
f Add an unknown number to 10.
g Add an unknown number to 3.
h Add 7 to an unknown number.

3 The cost of a chocolate bar is c pence.
The cost of a can of pop is d pence.

a Which of these expressions give the total cost of 4 chocolate bars and 3 cans of pop?

b Write an expression for the cost of 6 cans of pop and 1 bar of chocolate.

c Write a sentence to describe the expression $2c + d$.

71

Exercise commentary

The questions assess the objectives on Primary Framework Page 81.

Problem solving

The exercise assesses Primary Framework Page 81.

Group work

Question 3 and the further activity are suitable for pairs.

Misconceptions

Students tend to choose letters to stand for the object rather than the number of objects, leading to later misunderstandings.
Students tend to oversimplify, writing $n + 5$ as $n5$.
Question 1 will help set the ideas in context, providing a concrete example to refer back to.
In question 2 the subtraction questions cause lots of difficulties as students tend to write the expression in the order it is given: 2b gives $5 - n$ and 2c gives $n - 10$.
Emphasise that the word 'from' often indicates what the original amount is and encourage students to refer to a numeric example if necessary.

Links

Estimation: Primary Framework Page 11.

Homework

A2.2HW provides practice at writing simple algebraic expressions.

Answers

1 **a** $n - 4$ **b** $n + 6$ **c** $n - 20$ **d** $n + 3$
e $n - 5$ **f** $n + 10$ **g** $n + 3$

2 **a** $n + 5$ **b** $n - 5$ **c** $10 - n$ **d** $5 - n$
e $20 - n$ **f** $n + 10$ **g** $n + 3$ **h** $n + 7$

3 **a** $4c + 3d$ **b** $c + 6d$
c $2c + d$ is the cost of 2 chocolate bars and 1 can of pop.

Mental starter

Explain the word 'complement' with an example: the complement to 100 of 35 is 65.

- Ask students for the complement to 100 of 23.
- Give various numbers and ask for the complement to 100.
- You could extend this slightly by including simple decimals (1 dp), or fractions.

Useful resources

A2.3OHP contains a 100 square for discussion.

Introductory activity

Look at a 100 square.

There is one in the student book, and there is an identical one on **A2.3OHP**.

Select a random square around the centre of the grid and look at what happens when you:

- move one square to the right
- move one square to the left
- move one square up
- move one square down.

Try to make generalisations and encourage answers like 'you always add 10'.

Move on to exploring diagonals, and then moving more than one square.

Draw a part of a 100 square that is 3 down and 4 across (like the one in the student book). You can use the one on **A2.3OHP**.

Place the letter x centrally.

Ask students how you would label the square immediately to its right.

Start to fill the grid in, writing expressions clearly such as $x - 11$.

Introduce some of the words associated with algebra.

$x + x + 1$ is an **expression**.

An expression is composed of **terms** separated by plus or minus signs.

Introduce like terms.

Terms are **like** when they contain the same letters.

When terms are like they can be collected together, or **simplified**.

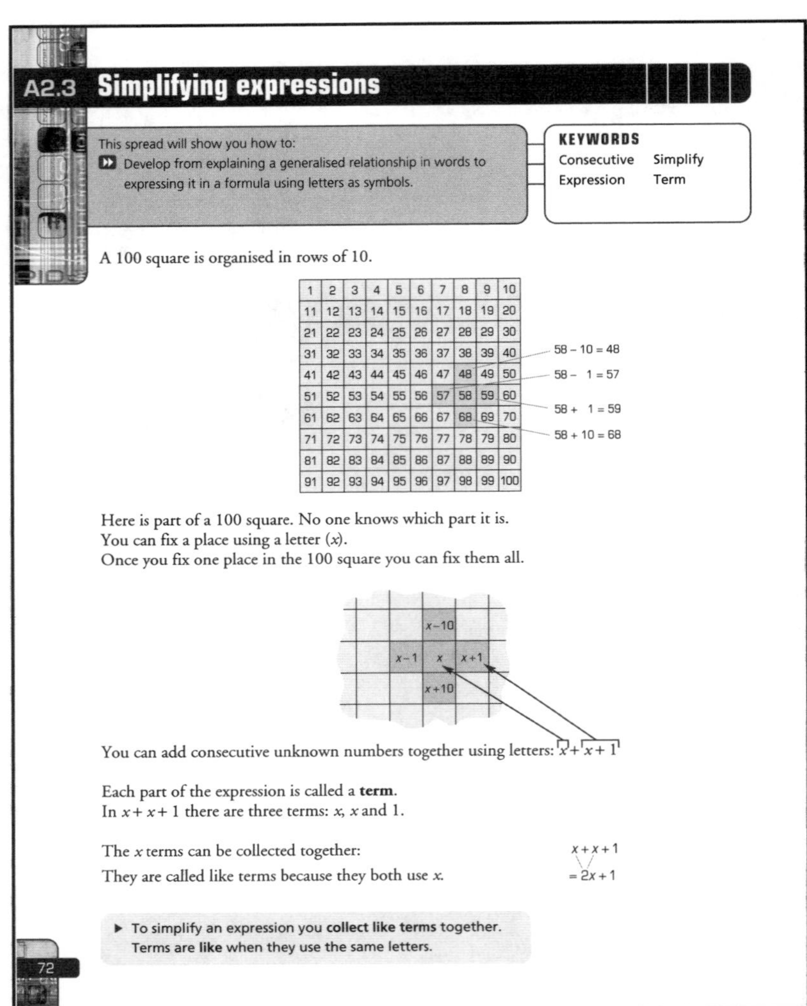

A2.3 **Simplifying expressions**

This spread will show you how to:

- Develop from explaining a generalised relationship in words to expressing it in a formula using letters as symbols.

KEYWORDS
Consecutive Simplify
Expression Term

A 100 square is organised in rows of 10.

1	2	3	4	5	6	7	8	9	10
11	12	13	14	15	16	17	18	19	20
21	22	23	24	25	26	27	28	29	30
31	32	33	34	35	36	37	38	39	40
41	42	43	44	45	46	47	48	49	50
51	52	53	54	55	56	57	58	59	60
61	62	63	64	65	66	67	68	69	70
71	72	73	74	75	76	77	78	79	80
81	82	83	84	85	86	87	88	89	90
91	92	93	94	95	96	97	98	99	100

58 − 10 = 48
58 − 1 = 57
58 + 1 = 59
58 + 10 = 68

Here is part of a 100 square. No one knows which part it is.
You can fix a place using a letter (x).
Once you fix one place in the 100 square you can fix them all.

You can add consecutive unknown numbers together using letters: $x + x + 1$

Each part of the expression is called a **term**.
In $x + x + 1$ there are three terms: x, x and 1.

The x terms can be collected together:
They are called like terms because they both use x.

$x + x + 1$
$= 2x + 1$

- To simplify an expression you **collect like terms** together. Terms are **like** when they use the same letters.

72

Plenary

Discuss strategies for simplifying expressions in questions 2 and 3.

In particular, address these questions:

- Can you work from left to right?
- Can you do all the additions first, then the subtractions?
- Can you do the letters first and then the numbers?

Stress that there is more than one way to get equivalent answers.

Further activities

On a blank 3 × 3 grid, students fix the middle square as x and fill in all the surrounding squares using letters.
As a challenge, students can find the total of each row and describe the pattern made by each total.

Differentiation

Support questions:

- Question 1 focuses on simplifying number expressions.
- Questions 2 and 3 focus on simplifying expressions involving letter terms.
- Question 4 focuses on using letters in context.

Core tier: focuses on forming and simplifying expressions containing both letters and numbers.

Exercise A2.3

1 Simplify these expressions:

a	$5 + 4 + 2 - 3$	**b**	$12 - 3 + 4 - 2 + 10$
c	$10 - 2 + 1 + 7$	**d**	$10 - 1 + 6 + 5 - 3$
e	$3 - 1 + 5$	**f**	$2 + 3 + 4 - 9$

2 Simplify these expressions

a	$x + x + x$	**b**	$b + b + b + b$
c	$y + y + 2y$	**d**	$d + 2d + d + 2d$
e	$t + t + t - t$	**f**	$2f + 3f - f$
g	$x + 4x + 3x + 6x$	**h**	$2x + 5x + 2x - 4x + 6x$
i	$7y - 3y + 5y + 3y$	**j**	$12r - 3r - 2r - r$
k	$10n - 4n + 2n$	**l**	$5x + 5x + 5x + 5x + 5x + 5x$
m	$5y + 3y - 10y$	**n**	$2y + 2y + 5y - 2y$

3 Simplify these expressions by collecting like terms.

a $x + x + 3 + 2$
b $w + 2w + 1 + 2$
c $10y + 3y + 4 + 2$
d $17 + 3 + 13x - 2x$
e $3t + 5t - 2t + 10 + 3 - 2 - 1$
f $5x + 2x + 6 - 1$
g $5y - 2y + 3y + 10 - 3 + 6$
h $y + 2y + 3y + 1 + 3$
i $3x + 4x - 2 + 5$
j $w + 3 + 3w + 4 + 2w$
k $3t + 3 + 2t + 2$
l $3 + 2 + 4t + 10 + 6t - 2t$

4 Write an expression for the perimeter of the shape below.
All sides are cm.

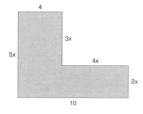

4
3x
5x
4x
2x
10

Exercise commentary

The questions assess the objectives on Primary Framework Page 81.

Problem solving

The exercise assesses Primary Framework Page 81.

Group work

The further activity is suitable for pairs.

Misconceptions

Students tend to add all the terms together regardless of whether they are like, for example in question 3a they write $12x$.
Similarly students leave out the letters and just write the numbers: in question 3d they write 31.
Emphasise that the letter terms and number terms are different – encourage students to read $3x$ as 3 lots of x.
Subtraction may cause problems in questions like 1d, 2c and 3e as students find it hard to see which sign goes with which number, especially when there are a string of calculations.
Encourage students to work logically from left to right and to collect like terms at the very end.

Links

Collecting like terms can link to fractions with different denominators: Primary Framework Page 23.

Homework

A2.3HW provides practice in simplifying expressions by collecting like terms.

Answers

1 **a** 8 **b** 21 **c** 16 **d** 17 **e** 7 **f** 0
2 **a** $8x$ **b** $21w$ **c** $16y$ **d** $17k$ **e** $7t$ **f** 0 **g** $14x$ **h** $11x$
i $12y$ **j** $6r$ **k** $8n$ **l** $30x$ **m** $^{-}2y$ **n** $7y$
3 **a** $7x + 5$ **b** $9w + 3$ **c** $13y + 6$ **d** $11x + 20$
e $6t + 10$ **f** $7x + 5$ **g** $6y + 13$ **h** $6y + 4$
i $7x + 3$ **j** $6w + 7$ **k** $5t + 5$ **l** $8t + 15$
4 $14x + 14$ cm

Mental starter

Double and halve

Write down an even 2-digit number, for example 48.
Ask for double the number (96), and half the number (24).
Write down some more even 2-digit numbers, and ask students to double them and halve them. Discuss strategies.

Extend to odd 2-digit numbers and 3-digit numbers.

Useful resources

A2.4OHP is the Dice Run game board, which is also shown in the student book exercise.

R2 digit cards may be useful for the mental starter.

Introductory activity

Refer to the mental starter.
Let d be a number.
Ask how you would write:

- 'double the number' ($2d$)
- 'half the number' ($\frac{d}{2}$)

using algebra.
Emphasise that these are **terms**.

Discuss how you would write 'double the number and add 1' using algebra.
Encourage the response '$2d + 1$'.
Emphasise that this is an **expression.**

Explain that you can evaluate an expression by substituting a value for the variable.
Ask what value $2d + 1$ would have if you started with 6. Emphasise that the answer is 13. If students add 1 first they will get 14, which is incorrect.
Stress the importance of the correct order of operations.

Explain the example in the student book, which shows how to substitute values into simple expressions.

Explain the rules of the Dice Run game, which forms the basis of Exercise A2.4 and is shown on **A2.4OHP**.
Roll a dice and move a counter along the OHP, encouraging students to tell you how many spaces to move.
Complete a circuit of the board as a whole class activity. This will help with the exercise and homework.

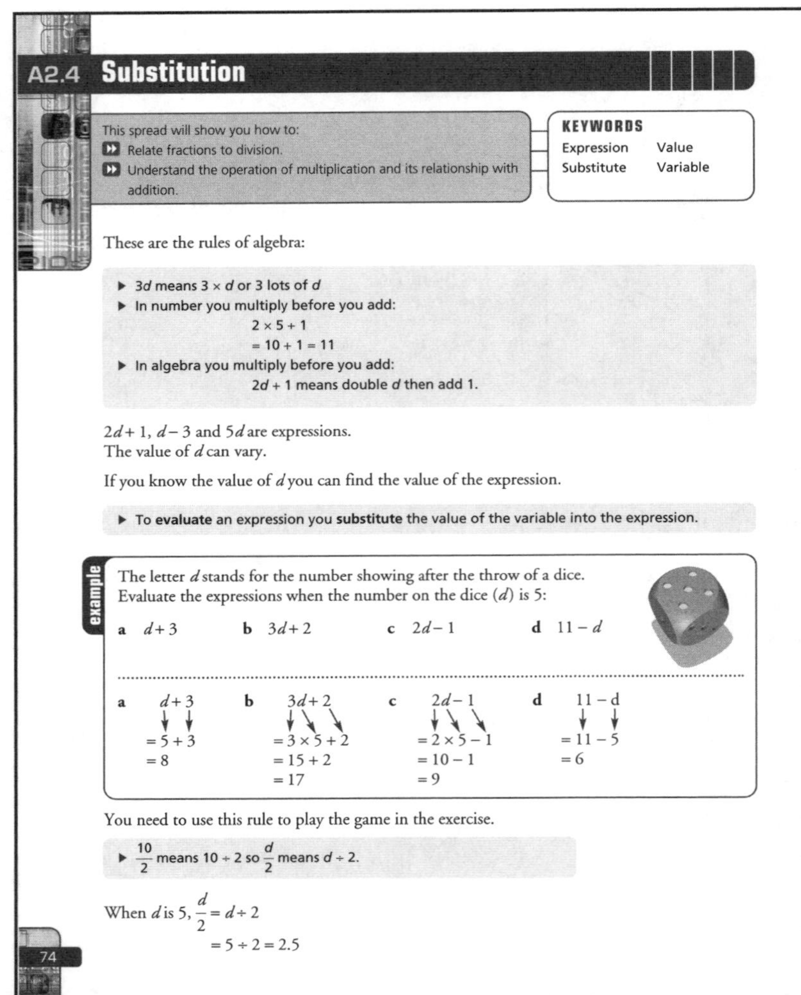

A2.4 Substitution

This spread will show you how to:

- Relate fractions to division.
- Understand the operation of multiplication and its relationship with addition.

KEYWORDS
Expression Value
Substitute Variable

These are the rules of algebra:

- $3d$ means $3 \times d$ or 3 lots of d
- In number you multiply before you add:
  $2 \times 5 + 1$
  $= 10 + 1 = 11$
- In algebra you multiply before you add:
  $2d + 1$ means double d then add 1.

$2d + 1$, $d - 3$ and $5d$ are expressions.
The value of d can vary.

If you know the value of d you can find the value of the expression.

- To **evaluate** an expression you **substitute** the value of the variable into the expression.

example

The letter d stands for the number showing after the throw of a dice.
Evaluate the expressions when the number on the dice (d) is 5:

a $d + 3$ **b** $3d + 2$ **c** $2d - 1$ **d** $11 - d$

a $d + 3 = 5 + 3 = 8$

b $3d + 2 = 3 \times 5 + 2 = 15 + 2 = 17$

c $2d - 1 = 2 \times 5 - 1 = 10 - 1 = 9$

d $11 - d = 11 - 5 = 6$

You need to use this rule to play the game in the exercise.

- $\frac{10}{2}$ means $10 \div 2$ so $\frac{d}{2}$ means $d \div 2$.

When d is 5, $\frac{d}{2} = d \div 2$
$= 5 \div 2 = 2.5$

74

Plenary

Discuss the Dice Run game, in particular:

- Which expressions combined with which values of d give the largest values?
- Which give negative values?
- Which expressions are most difficult to evaluate?

Focus on the correct order of operations.

Further activities

Students play the game again in the opposite direction.

Students can work out all the possible outcomes if a 3 is thrown and use the answers to decide which is the best '3' square to land on.

Able students can investigate for all six outcomes.

Differentiation

Support questions:
This exercise is designed to be accessible to all.

- Weak students will benefit from help in working out the substitutions.
- Most students will manage to play the game at least once.
- Able students should be encouraged to consider strategies – what throw would you most like when on a particular square?

Core tier: extends to substitutions involving squared terms.

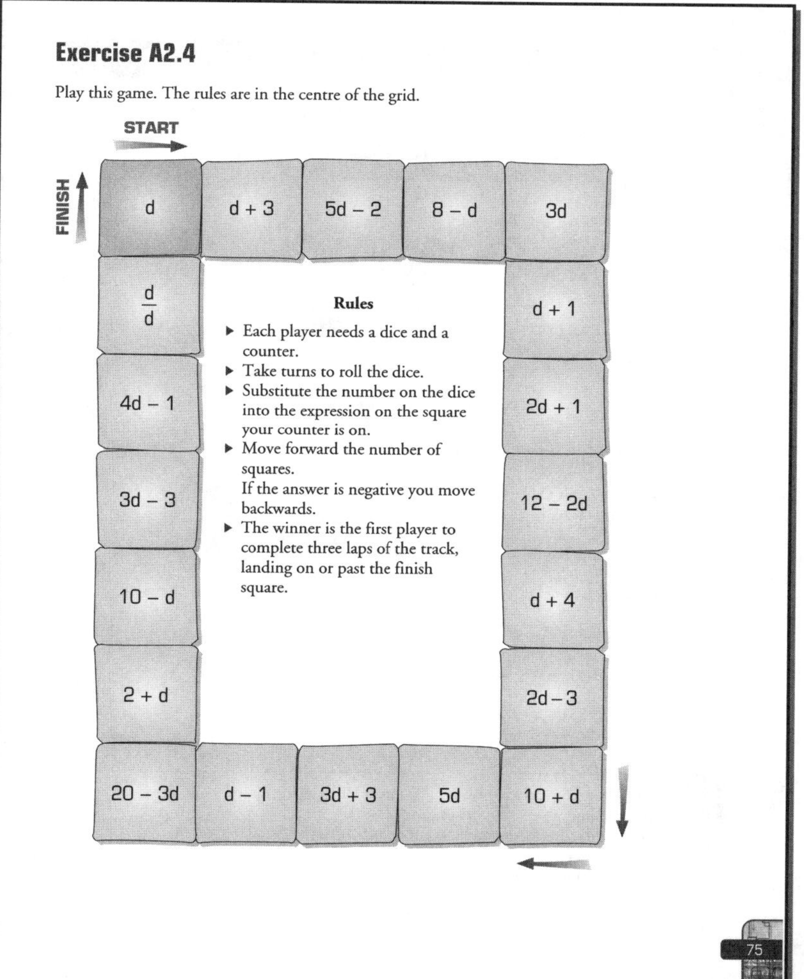

Exercise A2.4
Play this game. The rules are in the centre of the grid.
START
FINISH
d
d + 3
5d – 2
8 – d
3d
d/d
d + 1
4d – 1
2d + 1
3d – 3
12 – 2d
10 – d
d + 4
2 + d
2d – 3
20 – 3d
d – 1
3d + 3
5d
10 + d
Rules
Each player needs a dice and a counter.
Take turns to roll the dice.
Substitute the number on the dice into the expression on the square your counter is on.
Move forward the number of squares.
If the answer is negative you move backwards.
The winner is the first player to complete three laps of the track, landing on or past the finish square.
75

Exercise commentary

The questions assess the objectives on Primary Framework Pages 25, 53 and 81.

Problem solving
The exercise assesses Primary Framework Page 81.

Group work
The exercise is suitable for pairs.

Misconceptions
The game provides a chance to practice substitution in a fun way and most of the expressions will cause little difficulty, serving mostly to reinforce learning from earlier in the unit that letters and numbers are distinctive terms that cannot be collected.
Most difficulties centre around the multiplication problems with many students thinking that if $d = 2$ then $3d$ will be 32.
Encourage students to think of $3d$ as 3 lots of d.
The expressions that include subtraction may also cause problems.
Emphasise that you work from right to left and that you multiply first then subtract.

Links
Negative numbers: Primary Framework Page 15. Order of operations: Page 53.

Homework

A2.4HW provides practice in simple linear substitution.

Answers

Exercise A2.4 is a game, so there are no unique answers.

Mental starter

Days in a week

Ask how many days there are in a week. Then 2, 5, 12, 15, 20 weeks etc.
Ask how many weeks are in 21 days, 35 days etc. Vary the question to leave a remainder e.g. 40 days is the same as 5 weeks and 5 days.
Ask how many weeks are in a year, and encourage the answer 52.
Ask how students would work out 7×52 mentally (perhaps $7 \times 50 + 7 \times 2$).
Discuss the significance of the leap year.

Useful resources

R1 digit cards may be useful for the mental starter.

Introductory activity

Refer to the mental starter.
Write the statement:
Number of days = number of weeks ×7
Check that this statement is true by substituting a few values.
Explain that this statement is a **formula.**

Explain that a formula is a statement that links variables.
Explain that formulae (plural of formula) are often used for converting one quantity into another.

Discuss the formula for converting pounds into 10 pence, as described in the student book. Substitute a few values for pounds, such as £6.30, £9.40 etc.

You may need to recap multiplying and dividing decimals by 10.

Discuss the example in the student book. Write the formula for converting hours to minutes, and substitute a few values for hours. Vary the form of the substitution e.g. 4.5 hours, $1\frac{1}{2}$ hours.

Discuss the importance of using the correct units, as for example in converting 2 hours 15 minutes into minutes.

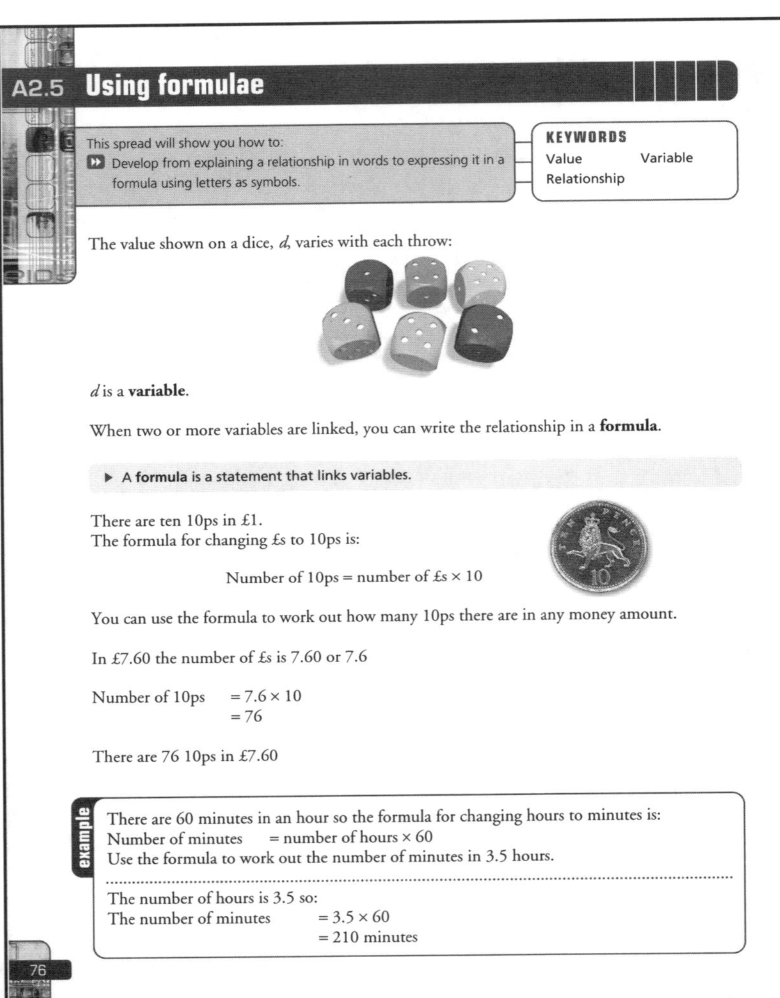

A2.5 **Using formulae**

This spread will show you how to:
- Develop from explaining a relationship in words to expressing it in a formula using letters as symbols.

KEYWORDS
Value Variable
Relationship

The value shown on a dice, *d*, varies with each throw:

d is a **variable.**

When two or more variables are linked, you can write the relationship in a **formula.**

▶ A **formula** is a statement that links variables.

There are ten 10ps in £1.
The formula for changing £s to 10ps is:

Number of 10ps = number of £s × 10

You can use the formula to work out how many 10ps there are in any money amount.

In £7.60 the number of £s is 7.60 or 7.6

Number of 10ps = 7.6 × 10
= 76

There are 76 10ps in £7.60

example

There are 60 minutes in an hour so the formula for changing hours to minutes is:
Number of minutes = number of hours × 60
Use the formula to work out the number of minutes in 3.5 hours.

The number of hours is 3.5 so:
The number of minutes = 3.5 × 60
= 210 minutes

76

Plenary

Discuss question 6. You may need to recap the perimeter and area of a rectangle from S1.

Extend question 6 parts a and b to find the perimeter.
Discuss how to write a formula for the perimeter of a rectangle in words.

Further activities

Students can devise their own questions for partners to solve, based on the formulae given.

Challenge students to devise a formula for a mobile phone that uses a 'pay as you talk' tariff, or for the cost of using the internet at a rate of £2 per hour.

Differentiation

Support questions:

- Questions 1 and 2 focus on substituting into a formula.
- Questions 3 and 4 focus on using a formula backwards.
- Questions 5 and 6 mix up the methods in context.

Core tier: focuses on constructing a formula.

Exercise A2.5

1 Use the formula

Number of 10ps = number of £s × 10

to work out the number of:
a 10ps in £5 **b** 10ps in £2.30 **c** 10ps in £21.20

2 Use the formula

Number of minutes = number of hours × 60

to work out the number of minutes in:
a 3 hours **b** 6 hours **c** 2.5 hours
d $1\frac{1}{2}$ hours **e** $2\frac{1}{4}$ hours **f** a day

3 Use the formula in question 1 to work out the number of:
a 10ps in 90p **b** £s in 120p **c** £s in 2700p

4 Use the formula in question 2 to work out the number of hours in:
a 120 minutes **b** 240 minutes **c** 90 minutes
d 135 minutes **e** 100 minutes **f** 2 hours 20 minutes

5 Use the formula

Total Cost = number of items × price of one item

to solve these problems:
a Joe buys five pencils. The price of each pencil is 20p.
b Daniel buys three cans of pop. Each can cost 40p.
c Arif pays in total 55p. He bought five erasers. What is the price of one?
d Luke paid 99p for some collector cards. Each card was 33p. How many did he buy?

6 Use the formula

Area = length × width

to find the missing values for these rectangles.
a length = 3 and width = 5 **b** area = 15 and length = 15
c width = 4 and length = 8 **d** area = 25 and width = 5
e length = 14 and width = 2 **f** width = 6 and length = 6
All lengths are measured in cm and areas in cm^2.

77

Exercise commentary

The questions assess the objectives on Primary Framework Page 81.

Problem solving

The exercise assesses Primary Framework Page 81. Questions 2 and 4 assess Page 89 and questions 1, 3 and 5 assess Page 85.

Group work

The further activity is suitable for pairs.

Misconceptions

Students tend to use the information given in the most direct way and take no account of whether the working makes sense, for example in question 3a writing 90 × 10 = 900 ten pences.

Encourage students to estimate before they calculate using a formula to try to stop them using it blindly. They should also check their answers back with the original question to see whether it is reasonable.

The use of units can also confuse students and they find it difficult to change between units.

Discuss the links before the exercise, asking students to devise the formulae if possible.

Links

Measures, including money and time: Primary Framework Pages 91–101.

Homework

A2.5HW provides practice in using a formula.

Answers

1 **a** 50 **b** 23 **c** 212
2 **a** 180 minutes **b** 360 minutes **c** 150 minutes **d** 90 minutes **e** 135 minutes **f** 1440 minutes
3 **a** 9 **b** 1.2 **c** 27
4 **a** 2 hours **b** 4 hours **c** $1\frac{1}{2}$ hours **d** $2\frac{1}{4}$ hours **e** $1\frac{2}{3}$ hours **f** $2\frac{1}{3}$ hours
5 **a** 100p or £1 **b** 120p or £1.20 **c** 11p **d** 3
6 **a** Area = 15 cm^2 **b** Width = 1 cm **c** Area = 32 cm^2 **d** Length = 5 cm **e** Area = 28 cm^2 **f** Area = 36 cm^2

Summary

The unit provides access to the Year 7 key teaching objectives:

- Know and use the order of operations (Secondary Framework Page 86).
- Use letter symbols to represent unknown numbers or variables (Secondary Framework Page 112).

Plenary activity

Write an expression on the board: $x + 7$

Discuss what the expression means:

- There are some people at the cinema, after the film starts seven more come in.

Repeat for other simple expressions:

$y - 5$, $3f$, $\frac{w}{2}$

Check out commentary

1 Students need to work out whether to add, subtract, multiply or divide and then use the correct algebra.
Encourage them to write down the operation they need to use first: more means add, left means subtract, each means divide etc.
When adding or subtracting using algebra students often leave out the operation, writing $d5$ or simply 5 instead of $d - 5$.
Encourage students to use numbers to stand for the letters and to write down the steps in their working so they can see where the use of the operation comes from.

2 The same comment applies as for question **1** and in addition students may confuse the order of the calculation, writing $6 - x$ in part **a**.
Emphasise that the word 'than' tends to indicate the first part or start of an expression and 'by' indicates the second part.

3 Students may need to use examples to understand why to multiply.
Encourage students to write the multiplication without the sign, giving the formulae $29n$ and $35m$. In part **c** students may not know where to start.
Emphasise the link with parts **a** and **b** – encourage students to write the letters in alphabetical order: my rather than ym.

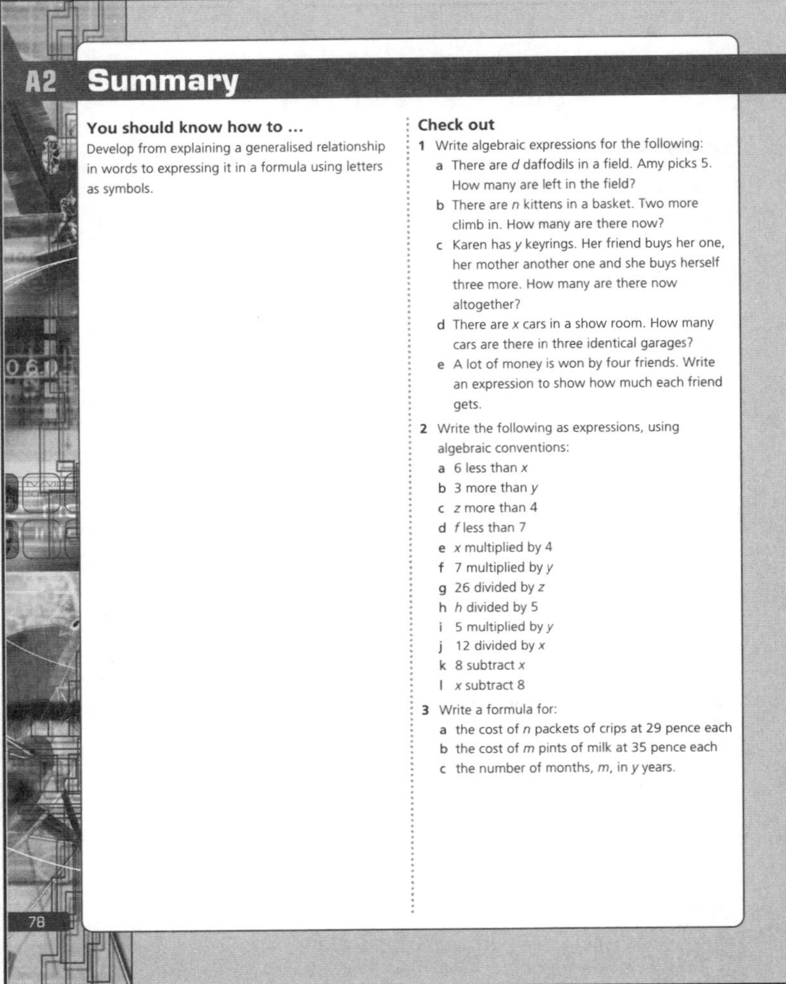

A2 Summary

You should know how to ...

Develop from explaining a generalised relationship in words to expressing it in a formula using letters as symbols.

Check out

1 Write algebraic expressions for the following:
  a There are d daffodils in a field. Amy picks 5. How many are left in the field?
  b There are n kittens in a basket. Two more climb in. How many are there now?
  c Karen has y keyrings. Her friend buys her one, her mother another one and she buys herself three more. How many are there now altogether?
  d There are x cars in a show room. How many cars are there in three identical garages?
  e A lot of money is won by four friends. Write an expression to show how much each friend gets.

2 Write the following as expressions, using algebraic conventions:
  a 6 less than x
  b 3 more than y
  c z more than 4
  d f less than 7
  e x multiplied by 4
  f 7 multiplied by y
  g 26 divided by z
  h h divided by 5
  i 5 multiplied by y
  j 12 divided by x
  k 8 subtract x
  l x subtract 8

3 Write a formula for:
  a the cost of n packets of crips at 29 pence each
  b the cost of m pints of milk at 35 pence each
  c the number of months, m, in y years.

78

Development

The themes of this unit are developed in A4.

Links

The work on formulae links to measures (S3 and N3) and proportion (N4). Students should be encouraged to use the correct algebraic conventions at every opportunity throughout the course.

Mental starters

Objectives covered in this unit:

- Visualise, describe and sketch 2-D shapes in different orientations.
- Estimate and order acute and obtuse angles.
- Use metric units and units of time for calculations.

Resources needed

* means class set needed

Essential:

R14 (OHP) – Special triangles
R15 (OHP) – Special quadrilaterals
R20 (OHP) – Analogue clockface
Graph or squared paper

Useful:

R9* (OHP) – Axes in one quadrant
S2.2ICT* – Basic constructions
TV timetable

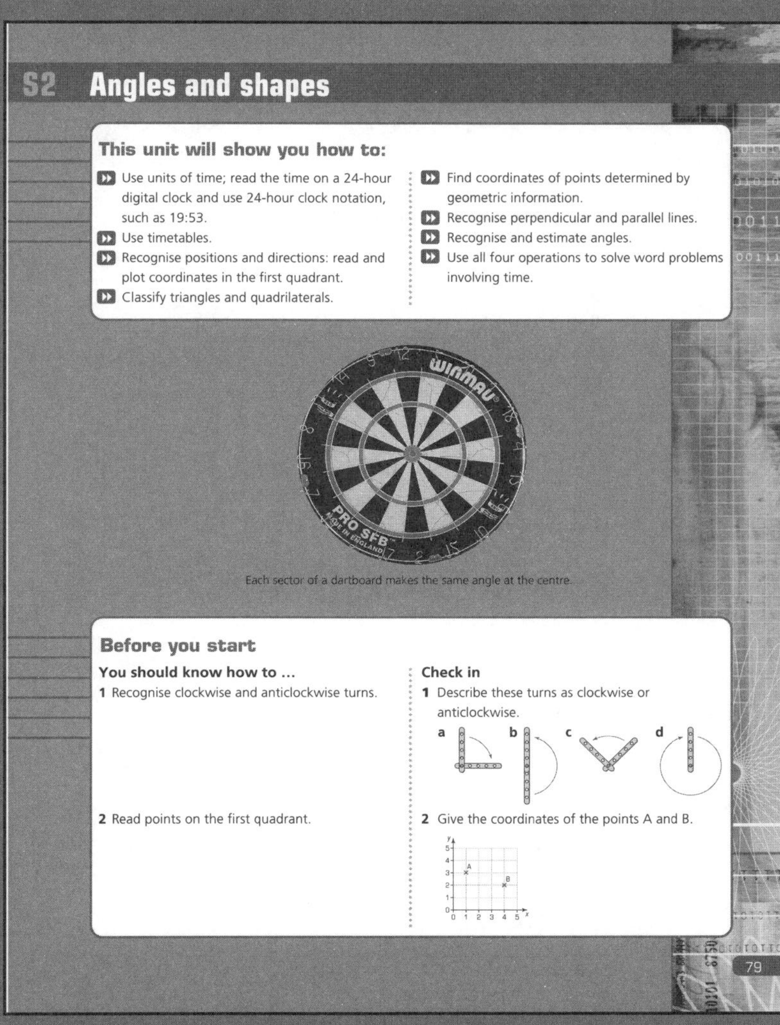

S2 Angles and shapes

This unit will show you how to:

- Use units of time; read the time on a 24-hour digital clock and use 24-hour clock notation, such as 19:53.
- Use timetables.
- Recognise positions and directions: read and plot coordinates in the first quadrant.
- Classify triangles and quadrilaterals.
- Find coordinates of points determined by geometric information.
- Recognise perpendicular and parallel lines.
- Recognise and estimate angles.
- Use all four operations to solve word problems involving time.

Each sector of a dartboard makes the same angle at the centre.

Before you start

You should know how to …	Check in
1 Recognise clockwise and anticlockwise turns.	1 Describe these turns as clockwise or anticlockwise. a b c d
2 Read points on the first quadrant.	2 Give the coordinates of the points A and B.

79

Unit commentary

Aim of the unit

This unit aims to consolidate students' understanding of time, angles and shapes. Students solve time problems then consider the angle made between the hands of a clock, developing to the angle between two lines. Finally, students use geometric properties of shapes to find missing vertices.

Introduction

Discuss what students understand by the term 'angle': amount of turn.

Discuss when angles are used: playing darts and snooker, reading clocks.

Framework references

This unit focuses on:

- Year 6 teaching objectives pages: 99, 101, 109, 111
- Problem solving objectives pages: 87, 89

The unit provides access to:

- Year 7 teaching objectives pages: 180, 182, 218

Check in activity

Give out copies of **R9** and ask students to plot sets of points. For each set, students join the points in order and name the shape.

1. (1, 1) (3, 2) (1, 2) (1, 1) – right-angled triangle
2. (3, 0) (4, 3) (5, 0) (3, 0) – isosceles triangle
3. (1, 3) (2, 5) (4, 3) (1, 3) – scalene triangle

Differentiation

Core tier focuses on measuring angles accurately, finding missing angles and plotting points determined by geometric information using all four quadrants.

Springboard 7

Pages 269–271, 273–277, 380–383.

Mental starter

How long…?

- Give students a time which is the beginning of an event: say 0830
- Give them the end time: 0900
- Ask how long the event took: 30 mins.
- Start simply, build up to longer times including hours.

Useful resources

R20 shows an analogue clock.

A **TV timetable** is useful for the starter.

Introductory activity

Refer to the mental starter.
Discuss what students are doing at 8.30 during the week.
Emphasise that it depends whether it is morning or evening.

Discuss how to distinguish between morning and evening times: am and pm.

Encourage 24-hour clock as an alternative – refer to microwaves, videos and other digital displays.
Discuss how to convert between 12- and 24-hour clock times.

Use an analogue clockface to introduce angle as a measure of turn.
Emphasise you measure 'straight' lines with a ruler in cm or mm, but an angle is a 'circular' turn and is measured in degrees.

Discuss the number of degrees in a full turn: 360° and deduce 180° is a half turn and 90° is a $\frac{1}{4}$ turn.
Emphasise $\frac{1}{4}$ turn, 90°, is a right angle.

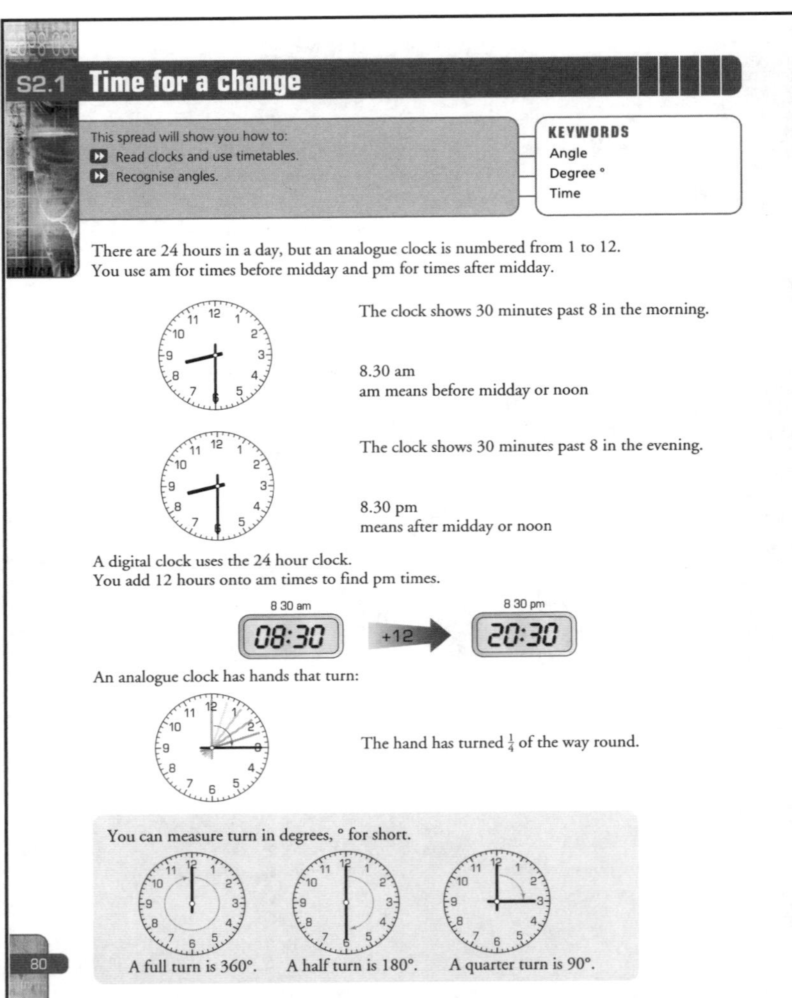

S2.1 Time for a change

This spread will show you how to:
- Read clocks and use timetables.
- Recognise angles.

KEYWORDS
Angle
Degree °
Time

There are 24 hours in a day, but an analogue clock is numbered from 1 to 12.
You use am for times before midday and pm for times after midday.

The clock shows 30 minutes past 8 in the morning.

8.30 am
am means before midday or noon

The clock shows 30 minutes past 8 in the evening.

8.30 pm
means after midday or noon

A digital clock uses the 24 hour clock.
You add 12 hours onto am times to find pm times.

8 30 am 08:30 +12 8 30 pm 20:30

An analogue clock has hands that turn:

The hand has turned $\frac{1}{4}$ of the way round.

You can measure turn in degrees, ° for short.

A full turn is 360°. A half turn is 180°. A quarter turn is 90°.

80

Plenary

Discuss question 7.
Students explain reasoning behind their answers.
Emphasise that a full turn is 360°.
Discuss how to work out the turn from 12 ⟶ 1. (360 ÷ 12)
For each angle discuss whether it is less than, greater than or equal to 90°.

Further activities

Students can develop their own timetables as in question 2 using 12- and 24-hour clocks.

Develop question 5 by asking students to add different times onto the clock times in question 7. Vary the times to include irregular ones such as 37 minutes.

Differentiation

Support questions:

- Question 1 is a simple question about reading clocks. Springboard 7, page 380.
- Questions 2–4 involve converting between 12- and 24-hour clock times. Springboard 7, pages 381, 382.
- Questions 5 and 6 introduce addition of time and question 7 focuses on angles made by the arms of a clock. Springboard 7, page 383.

Core tier: focuses on estimating and measuring angles.

Exercise S2.1

1 These clocks all show pm times. Write the times using the 24 hour clock.

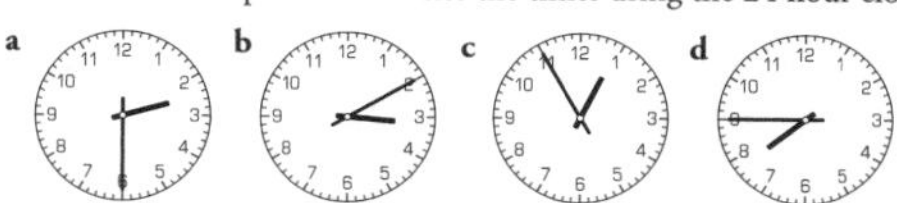

Describe what you were doing at each of these times yesterday.

2 Copy and complete this table.

Event	12 hour clock	24 hour clock
Breakfast	8.00 am	08.00
Morning Break	11.00 am	
Lunch	12.30 pm	
Afternoon Break	3.00 pm	
Tea	5.30 pm	
Supper	9.30 pm	

3 Write these times using am or pm:
a 14.30 **b** 10.25 **c** 08.45 **d** 22.25

4 Write these times using the 24 hour clock:
a 8.30 pm **b** 9.45 am **c** 10.20 pm **d** midday

5 Add 30 minutes to each of these times:
a 8.15 am **b** 6.45 pm **c** 7.05 am **d** 7.55 pm
e 08.30 **f** 16.10 **g** 17.45 **h** 10.50

6 Here is part of a tram timetable:

High Street	19.40
Arena	19.50
Meadowhall	19.55

How long is the journey from:

a High Street to Meadowhall **b** High Street to Arena?

7 What angle is shown on each clockface?

a 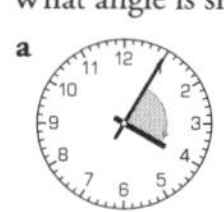 **b** 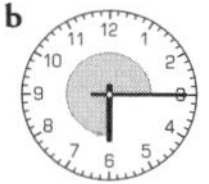 **c** 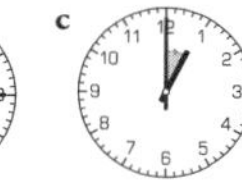 **d** 

81

Exercise commentary

The questions assess the objectives on Primary Framework Page 101 and 110.

Problem solving

Question 6 assesses Primary Framework Page 89.

Group work

Question 2 and the further activity are suitable for pair work.

Misconceptions

Many students mix up 12- and 24-hour clock times, perhaps writing 1800pm. Emphasise that you use one or the other and that the 24-hour clock means there is no need for pm.

Students add 10 onto the am time rather than 12, writing 6pm as 1600. Emphasise that 12 midday is the changeover time and reinforce a particular time such as 6pm as 1800 so students have a benchmark to refer to.

Many students struggle to calculate with times especially when they go over the hour, trying to use decimals. Encourage students to count in sensible steps to get to the hour mark, using a number line or a clock face.

Links

Estimating time: Primary Framework Page 99.

Homework

S2.1HW provides practice at reading clock times.

Answers

1 **a** 14.30 **b** 15.10 **c** 12.55 **d** 19.45
2 24-hour clock times: 08.00, 11.00, 12.30, 15.00, 17.30, 21.30
3 **a** 2.30 pm **b** 10.25 am **c** 8.45 am **d** 10.25 pm
4 **a** 20.30 **b** 09.45 **c** 22.20 **d** 12.00
5 **a** 8.45 am **b** 7.15 pm **c** 7.35 am **d** 8.25 pm
e 09.00 **f** 16.40 **g** 18.15 **h** 11.20
6 **a** 15 minutes **b** 10 minutes
7 **a** 90° **b** 270° **c** 30° **d** 150°

S2.2 Angles and lines

Mental starter

Acute or obtuse

- Define a right angle as 90°.
- Define an acute angle as less than 90°.
- Define an obtuse angle as between 90° and 180°.

Students need two pieces of scrap paper each and should write A and O on them.
Give students an angle in degrees up to 180°.
They must decide whether it is A or O, holding up a piece of paper to say so.
Include reflex angles with a good group.

Useful resources

R15 shows common quadrilaterals.

Introductory activity

Build on the mental starter activity.

- Ask students which kind of angle 90° is – it's not acute or obtuse, it's a right angle.

Ask students to show you an object with two lines meeting at right angles.
Discuss what to call these lines.
Discuss the notation used.

Discuss what happens when 2 lines meet at an angle – vertically opposite angles.
Introduce the term 'intersect'.

Discuss what you call 2 lines/edges that never intersect and ask for examples.
Discuss the definition of parallel lines and the notation used.

R15 has common quadrilaterals that you can use to discuss parallel and perpendicular lines.
Students should mark pairs on the sheet using the correct notation.

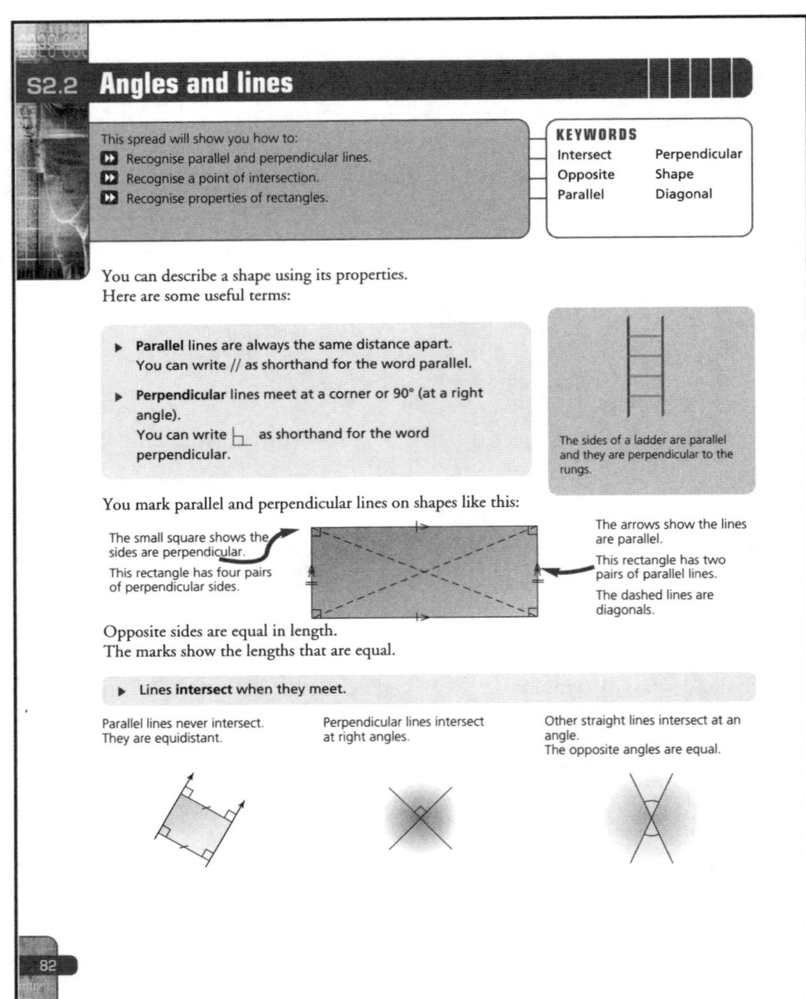

S2.2 **Angles and lines**

This spread will show you how to:
- Recognise parallel and perpendicular lines.
- Recognise a point of intersection.
- Recognise properties of rectangles.

KEYWORDS
Intersect, Perpendicular, Opposite, Shape, Parallel, Diagonal

You can describe a shape using its properties.
Here are some useful terms:

- **Parallel** lines are always the same distance apart. You can write // as shorthand for the word parallel.
- **Perpendicular** lines meet at a corner or 90° (at a right angle). You can write ∟ as shorthand for the word perpendicular.

The sides of a ladder are parallel and they are perpendicular to the rungs.

You mark parallel and perpendicular lines on shapes like this:

The small square shows the sides are perpendicular.
This rectangle has four pairs of perpendicular sides.
The arrows show the lines are parallel.
This rectangle has two pairs of parallel lines.
The dashed lines are diagonals.

Opposite sides are equal in length.
The marks show the lengths that are equal.

- Lines **intersect** when they meet.

Parallel lines never intersect. They are equidistant.
Perpendicular lines intersect at right angles.
Other straight lines intersect at an angle. The opposite angles are equal.

82

Plenary

Either

Use other shapes from **R15** and ask students to mark in parallel and perpendicular lines.

Or

Ask students to write down on scrap paper and hold up the name of a quadrilateral with given features:

- 1 pair/2 pairs parallel sides
- 0 sets/1 set of perpendicular sides etc.

Discuss answers.

Further activities

In S2.2ICT, students are introduced to the basic elements of construction and start to investigate geometrical relationships using Geometer's Sketch Pad.

Students can trace the shapes in question 2 and colour code the equal angles and equal sides.
Able students can estimate the size of each of the interior angles in degrees.

Differentiation

Support questions:

- Question 1 focuses on recognising parallel and perpendicular lines. Springboard 7, page 269.
- Questions 2 and 3 focus on properties of rectangles. Springboard 7, page 270.
- Question 4 focuses on using geometrical language precisely. Springboard 7, page 271.

Core tier: focuses on finding missing angles by calculation.

Exercise S2.2

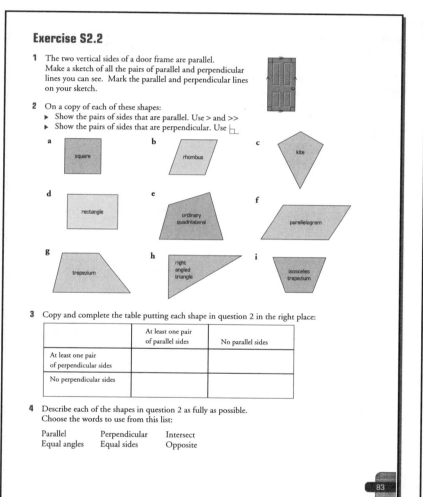

1 The two vertical sides of a door frame are parallel.
Make a sketch of all the pairs of parallel and perpendicular lines you can see. Mark the parallel and perpendicular lines on your sketch.

2 On a copy of each of these shapes:

- Show the pairs of sides that are parallel. Use > and >>
- Show the pairs of sides that are perpendicular. Use ⌞

a square b rhombus c kite

d rectangle e ordinary quadrilateral f parallelogram

g trapezium h right angled triangle i isosceles trapezium

3 Copy and complete the table putting each shape in question 2 in the right place:

	At least one pair of parallel sides	No parallel sides
At least one pair of perpendicular sides		
No perpendicular sides		

4 Describe each of the shapes in question 2 as fully as possible.
Choose the words to use from this list:

Parallel	Perpendicular	Intersect
Equal angles	Equal sides	Opposite

83

Exercise commentary

The questions assess the objectives on Primary Framework Page 103 and 109.

Problem solving

Question 4 assesses Primary Framework Page 81.

Group work

Questions 1 and 3 are suitable for pair work.

Misconceptions

Students often confuse equal sides and parallel sides, especially in kites.
Emphasise that parallel lines never meet and refer to specific examples in the classroom. At the same time find examples of objects with equal-length sides that meet and discuss the similarities and differences.
Students struggle with the language of geometry, finding the terms difficult to read, write and remember.
Discuss strategies for remembering the words as a group so good ideas are shared.
Ensure the terms are displayed prominently on the walls along with illustrations to reinforce the language.

Links

Angle measure: Primary Framework Page 111.

Homework

S2.2HW is based on a clock face. Students are required to identify lines that test their understanding of the words 'parallel', 'perpendicular', 'bisect' etc.

Answers

3 top left a, d; top right h; bottom left b, f, g, i; bottom right c, e

4 **a** Opposite sides parallel. Adjacent sides perpendicular. Equal angles, equal sides. **b** Opposite sides parallel. Opposite angles equal. Equal sides. **c** Adjacent sides equal. One pair of opposite angles equal.
d Opposite sides equal and parallel. Adjacent sides perpendicular. Equal angles. **e** No parallel sides. **f** Opposite sides equal and parallel. Opposite angles equal. **g** One pair of opposite sides parallel.
h One pair of sides perpendicular. No parallel sides. **i** One pair of opposite sides parallel. The other pair equal. Two pairs of equal angles.

S2.3 Coordinates and shapes

Mental starter

Naming quadrilaterals

Ask students to sketch special quadrilaterals (such as a trapezium) and hold up their shapes.

Ask students to explain the angle and side properties of the shapes and discuss any misconceptions.

Encourage use of technical terms: parallel, perpendicular, equal acute, obtuse.

R15 has a copy of all the quadrilaterals.

Useful resources

R9 has a blank coordinate grid.

Graph paper – or copies of **R9**.

R14 shows common triangles.

R15 shows common quadrilaterals.

Introductory activity

Put a cross on a blank OHP.

Ask students how they would describe to another person exactly where the cross is.

- Encourage the use of technical language.
- Draw out the need for axes.
- You can superimpose **R9** which has coordinate axes on.

Emphasise that coordinate axes are a way of fixing the position of a point on a grid.

Emphasise a coordinate is a pair and discuss how to plot them.

Play a game of 'hot spot'.

Students draw a coordinate grid from 0 to 6 in their books (use **R9** but only from 0 to 6).

They mark any six points on their grid.

Encourage the use of a cross rather than a dot.

Students take turns to call out a coordinate (not marked on their grid!).

The class marks off the coordinates as they are said – you can demonstrate on the OHP.

The student with the last cross wins.

Explain that you are going to draw different triangles – three angles means three vertices – on a grid.

Ask the name of a triangle with all sides, 2 sides and 0 sides equal.

Plot the points (4, 4) and (3, 2).

Discuss how to place a third point so that the triangle would be scalene, isosceles and equilateral.

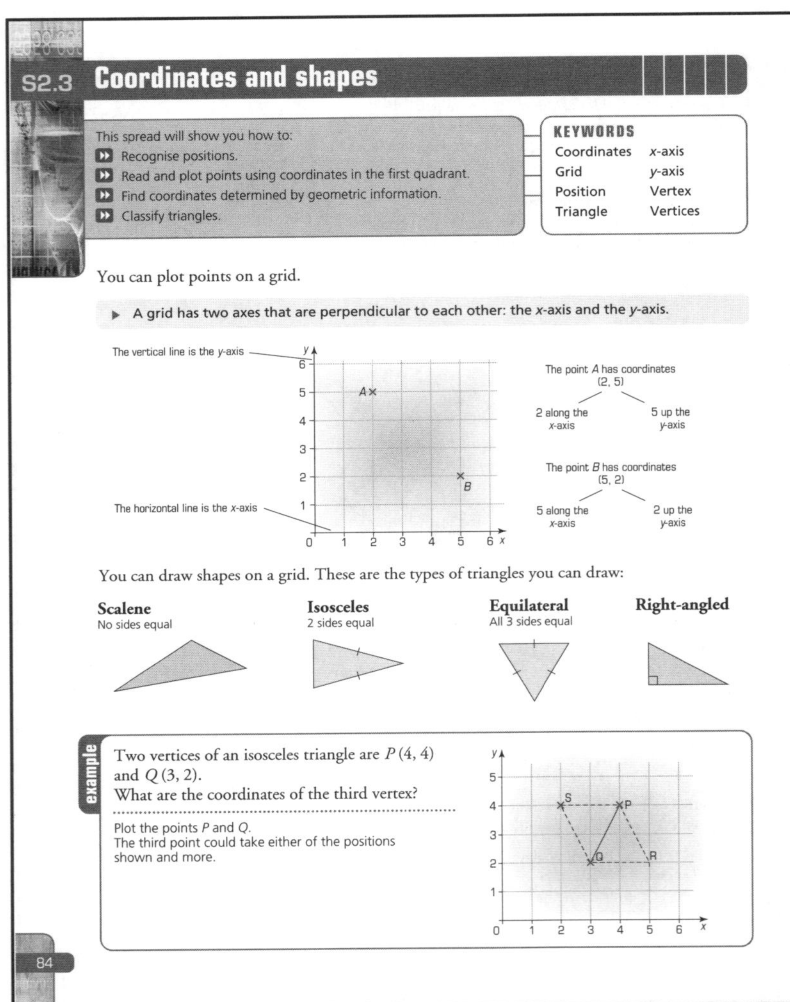

S2.3 Coordinates and shapes

This spread will show you how to:
- Recognise positions.
- Read and plot points using coordinates in the first quadrant.
- Find coordinates determined by geometric information.
- Classify triangles.

KEYWORDS
Coordinates, Grid, Position, Triangle, x-axis, y-axis, Vertex, Vertices

You can plot points on a grid.

▶ A grid has two axes that are perpendicular to each other: the x-axis and the y-axis.

You can draw shapes on a grid. These are the types of triangles you can draw:

example

Two vertices of an isosceles triangle are $P(4, 4)$ and $Q(3, 2)$. What are the coordinates of the third vertex?

Plot the points P and Q.
The third point could take either of the positions shown and more.

84

Plenary

Ask students to give you 3 points that will make an isosceles or an equilateral triangle.

Ask for 4 points that will make a given quadrilateral.

Plot sets of three vertices and ask students to complete a given quadrilateral – use this to review the properties of quadrilaterals, and parallel and perpendicular lines in particular.

Further activities

Students work in pairs to develop the work in question 2, one student plotting two points and asking their partner for a third point that will make a particular shape. This can be extended to include quadrilaterals.

Differentiation

Support questions:

- Question 1 focuses on reading coordinates from a grid. Springboard 7, page 273.
- Questions 2–5 focus on plotting points and finding vertices of shapes. Springboard 7, pages 274–276.
- Question 6 focuses on reasoning using the geometrical properties of triangles. Springboard 7, page 277.

Core tier: focuses on identifying parallel and perpendicular lines in a coordinate grid.

Exercise S2.3

1 Write down the coordinates of the points A → J on the grid.

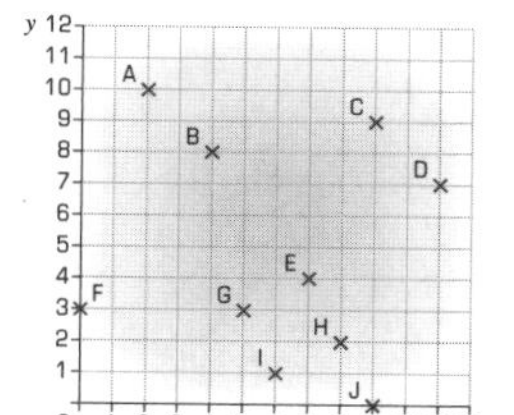

2 Plot the following points and complete the shapes. Each shape has one vertex missing. Write down the missing coordinate for each shape.

a Right-angled triangle (2, 3) (2, 9) (,)
b Isosceles right-angled △ (2, 3) (2, 9) (,)
c Isosceles triangle (2, 3) (2, 9) (,)
d Scalene triangle (2, 3) (2, 9) (,)
e Scalene right-angled triangle (2, 3) (2, 9) (,)

3 The points (1, 4) (5, 4) (5, 2) are three vertices of a rectangle. Write down the coordinates of the fourth vertex. Find the perimeter and area of the rectangle.

4 Plot these three points: (3, 3) (8, 8) and (8, 3) What fourth point will make a square? Find the perimeter and area of the square.

5 Find two other possible positions of the third vertex in the Example on page 84.

6 On squared paper draw axes as shown and plot the points A (5, 6) and B (7, 8). A (5, 6) and B (7, 8) are two vertices of a triangle. Plot point C to make different size triangles. Record your results in a table. Which type of triangle couldn't you get?

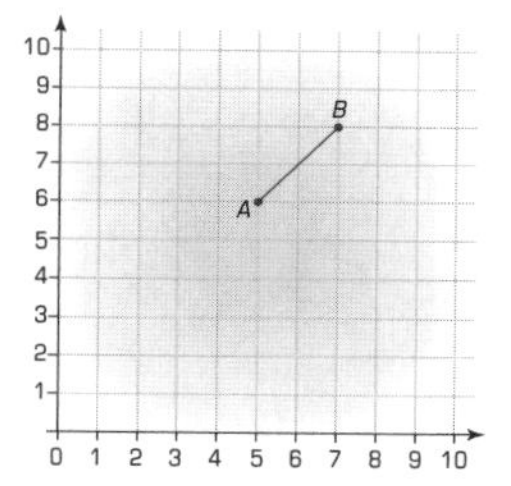

Co-ordinates of point C	Type of triangle
(4, 2)	Scalene right-angled triangle

Try to explain why.

85

Exercise commentary

The questions assess the objectives on Primary Framework Pages 103 and 109.

Problem solving

Question 6 assesses Primary Framework Page 77.

Group work

Questions 2 and 6 are suitable for paired work.

Misconceptions

Many students will plot (y, x) rather than (x, y).

Emphasise that x comes before y in the alphabet (and a for across comes before u for up) and x also comes first in a coordinate pair. So the first coordinate is x.

Students need to know the properties well in order to find missing vertices. Even if they do, they may not be able to visualise shapes in different orientations (seeing a square as a diamond) and so can't find vertices.

Encourage students to rotate the page until they have looked from all angles.

Links

Perimeter and area: Primary Framework Page 97.

Drawing graphs: Pages 114–117.

Homework

In **S2.3HW**, students are required to plot coordinates from geometrical information.

Answers

1 a A (2, 10), B (4, 8), C (9, 9), D (11, 7), E (7, 4), F (0, 3), G (5, 3), H (8, 2), I (6, 1), J (9, 0)
3 (1, 2), Perimeter 12, Area 8
4 (3, 8), Perimeter 20, Area 25
5 (4, 0), (3, 6)

Summary

The Year 5 key teaching objectives are:

- Recognise properties of rectangles (103).
- Recognise perpendicular and parallel lines (109).

The Year 6 key teaching objective is:

- Identify and use appropriate operations to solve word problems (87, 89).

Plenary activity

Give out copies of **R9** and ask students to plot sets of points. For each set, students join the points in order and name the shape.

1. (5, 0) (6, 1) (5, 2) (4, 1) (5, 0) – square
2. (3, 4) (3, 6) (0, 6) (0, 4) (3, 4) – rectangle
3. (0, 0) (1, 1) (1, 4) (0, 3) (0, 0) – parallelogram
4. (6, 5) (5, 6) (3, 5) (5, 4) (6, 5) – kite
5. (2, 0) (3, 2) (2, 4) (1, 2) (2, 0) – rhombus

Check out commentary

1 This question checks students' knowledge of the properties of special quadrilaterals. The language involved can cause problems and put off less confident students.
Discuss ways of remembering each of the quadrilaterals as a group so good strategies can be shared.
Ensure there is a display of special quadrilaterals in the classroom so there is constant visual reinforcement of their properties and general shape.

2 Students mark intersecting lines as parallel, especially the pair pointing to the middle of the top side as they may look parallel in perspective. This may lead to an interesting discussion!
Emphasise that parallel lines never meet and ensure students have a reference in the classroom such as the side of the desk.

3 Students find working with time difficult as it is not in the decimal system and so you can't use a calculator!
Encourage the use of timelines (link to adding and subtracting in Number) and counting up to the hour and then after it, adding the times together.

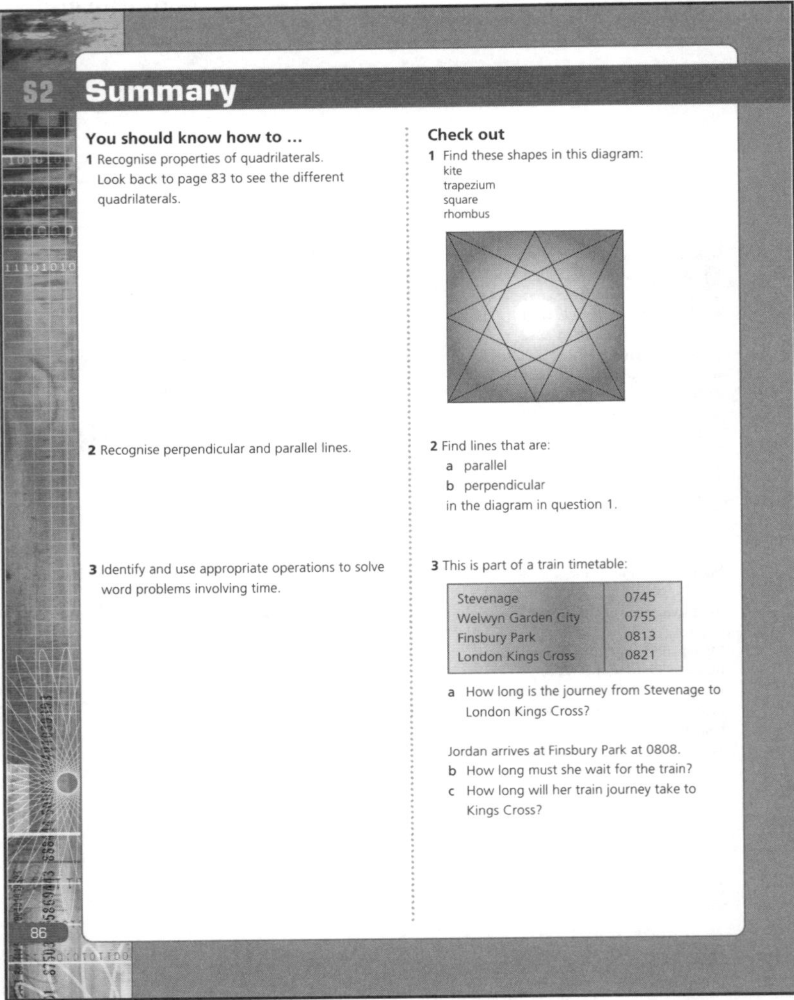

S2 **Summary**

You should know how to …

1 Recognise properties of quadrilaterals.
Look back to page 83 to see the different quadrilaterals.

2 Recognise perpendicular and parallel lines.

3 Identify and use appropriate operations to solve word problems involving time.

Check out

1 Find these shapes in this diagram:
kite
trapezium
square
rhombus

2 Find lines that are:
a parallel
b perpendicular
in the diagram in question 1.

3 This is part of a train timetable:

Stevenage	0745
Welwyn Garden City	0755
Finsbury Park	0813
London Kings Cross	0821

a How long is the journey from Stevenage to London Kings Cross?

Jordan arrives at Finsbury Park at 0808.
b How long must she wait for the train?
c How long will her train journey take to Kings Cross?

86

Development

The angle work is developed further in S3.

Links

The angle work lays the foundations for further shape work in constructions (S5) and rotations (S4). It also links to drawing pie charts using angles (D2).

Mental starters

Objectives covered in this unit:

- Order, add and subtract integers.
- Add several small numbers and find their mean.
- Use metric units and units of time for calculations.
- Convert between m, cm and mm.
- Discuss and interpret graphs.

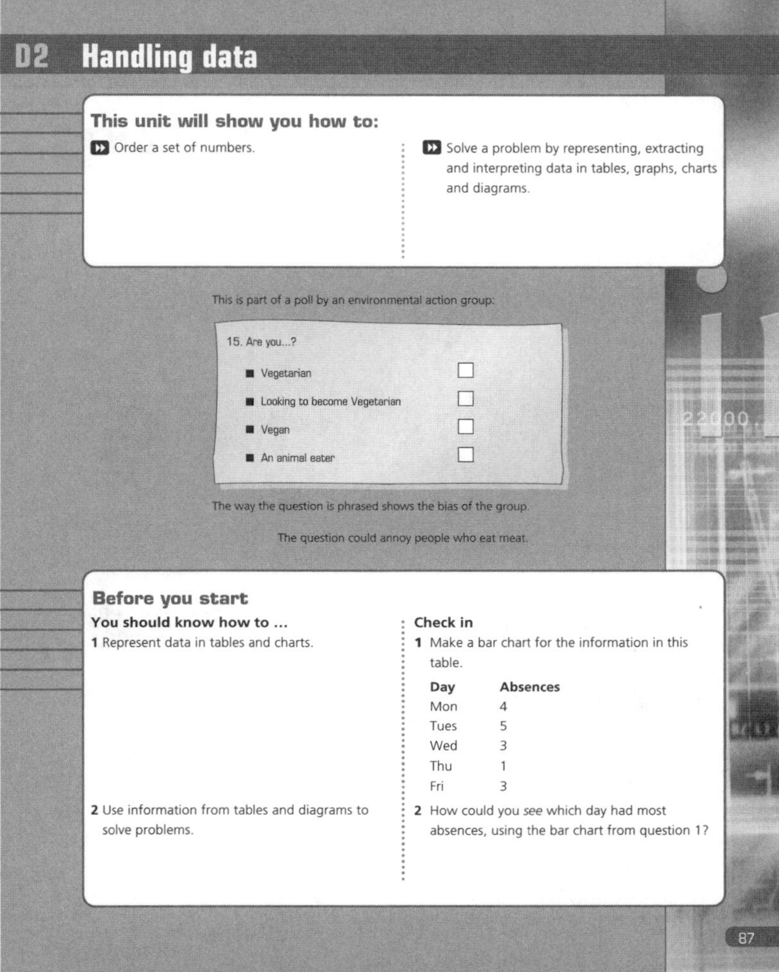

D2 Handling data

This unit will show you how to:

- Order a set of numbers.
- Solve a problem by representing, extracting and interpreting data in tables, graphs, charts and diagrams.

This is part of a poll by an environmental action group:

15. Are you...?

- Vegetarian ☐
- Looking to become Vegetarian ☐
- Vegan ☐
- An animal eater ☐

The way the question is phrased shows the bias of the group.

The question could annoy people who eat meat.

Before you start

You should know how to ...

1 Represent data in tables and charts.

2 Use information from tables and diagrams to solve problems.

Check in

1 Make a bar chart for the information in this table.

Day	Absences
Mon	4
Tues	5
Wed	3
Thu	1
Fri	3

2 How could you *see* which day had most absences, using the bar chart from question 1?

87

Check in activity

Discuss the difference between data that you collect yourself (primary data: colours of cars in the car park) and data you find in books or the internet (secondary data which has already been collected).

Discuss who might want to find data on the internet: a private individual looking for weather information for a holiday resort or a researcher looking into the cost of implementing a new computer network in a business. Discuss other possibilities.

Resources needed

* means class set needed

Essential:

D2.2OHP – Questionnaire
D2.3OHP – A frequency table
D2.4OHP – Statistical diagrams
D2.5OHP – Handling data cycle

Useful:

R1* – Digit cards
R6 (OHP) – Number lines
R11* (OHP) – Tally chart
D2.4ICT* – Diagrams in Excel

Unit commentary

Aim of the unit

This unit aims to support students in carrying out their own statistical enquiry as suggested on Page 18 of the Secondary Framework.

Introduction

Discuss why you might want to collect data: to improve a product, to decide where to go on holiday, to decide which mobile phone to buy!

Emphasise that research is more effective if you ask good questions at the outset.

Discuss why the example in the student book is not a good one and why it may lead to biased results.

Framework references

This unit focuses on:

- Year 6 teaching objectives pages: 9, 115, 117
- Problem solving objectives page: 77

The unit provides access to:

- Year 7 teaching objectives pages: 248–254, 262, 264, 268, 270

Differentiation

Core tier focuses on categorising types of data and choosing the most appropriate diagram to use to display data.

Springboard 7

Pages 393, 398–402.

D2.1 Discussing statistical methods

Mental starter

Averages recap

Revise the term 'mean'.

Give students a set of five numbers and ask them to work out the mean.

Repeat with a set of six numbers (ensure that they add up to a multiple of 3 or 6).

Students use number cards to show their answers.

Useful resources

R1 digit cards for the mental starter.

Introductory activity

Start with a general discussion.

- What is a survey?
- Why do people conduct surveys?

Ask students if they have ever carried out a survey, maybe at primary school. Ask them to describe all aspects of it, such as questionnaires or diagrams they may have drawn.

Introduce the problem:

> 'The road outside Maypole High School is blocked by parked cars at the beginning and end of the school day and this poses a threat to safety.'

Start with general questions:

- Why should there be lots of parked cars at these times?
- Why is it dangerous?

Brainstorm to identify the issues that need to be explored before action can be taken.

Ask students to consider the traffic issues around their own school.

For each of the issues they raise, emphasise the need to phrase the question as a statement so that it can be quantified.

Explain, with an example, that a survey can be used to test whether a statement is true or false.

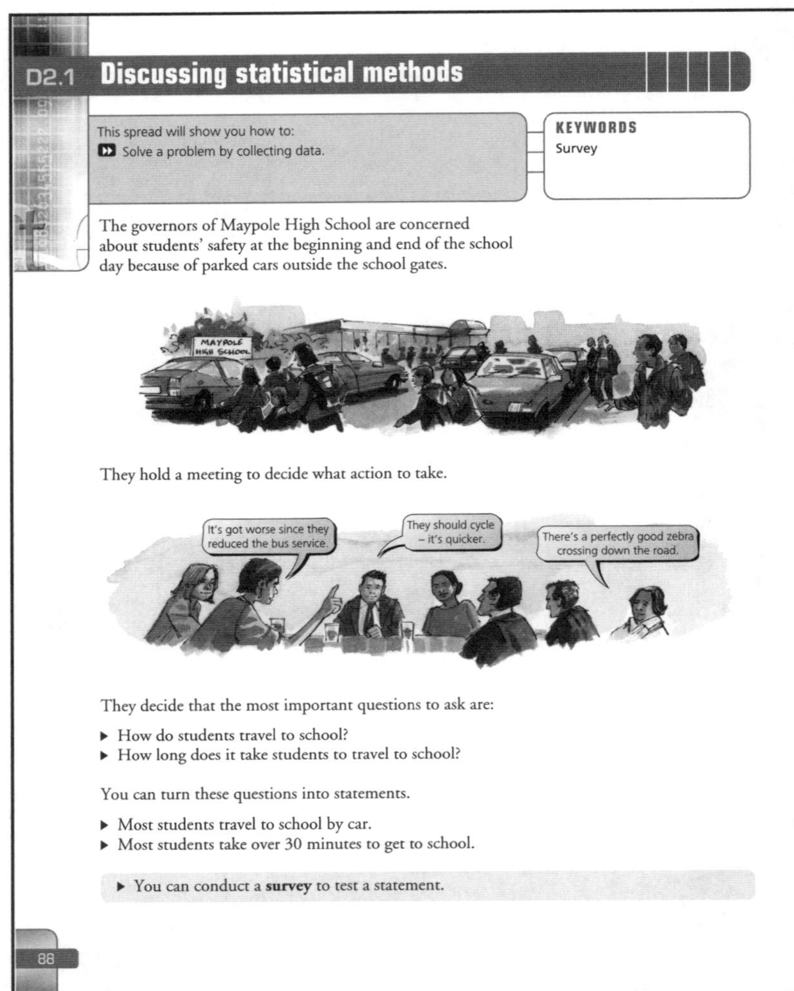

D2.1 Discussing statistical methods

This spread will show you how to:
- Solve a problem by collecting data.

KEYWORDS
Survey

The governors of Maypole High School are concerned about students' safety at the beginning and end of the school day because of parked cars outside the school gates.

They hold a meeting to decide what action to take.

They decide that the most important questions to ask are:

- How do students travel to school?
- How long does it take students to travel to school?

You can turn these questions into statements.

- Most students travel to school by car.
- Most students take over 30 minutes to get to school.

- You can conduct a **survey** to test a statement.

88

Plenary

Discuss the questions students identify for question 2.

For each question students should suggest how to turn the question into a statement to test.

You can go onto discuss how to collect the data for each statement identified.

Further activities

Students should be encouraged to develop their own projects to carry through in this unit. There are some examples on Pages 248 and 250 of the Secondary Framework which can provoke useful discussion, alternatively there are examples in the questions in exercise D2.2.
The Census at School website provides real student data:
www.censusatschool.ntu.ac.uk

Differentiation

Support questions:

- Question 1 focuses on formulating statements from questions.
- Question 2 gives students the opportunity to formulate statements and could be replaced by their own project work.
- In question 3 students consider the relevance of questions and statements.

Core tier: focuses on identifying and discussing relevant issues.

Exercise D2.1

1 The Governors of Maypole High School ask Year 7 to identify the issues affecting the traffic at the beginning and the end of the day.

Here are their suggestions:

a The Governors need to turn each of these suggestions into a statement. Match each of these statements to one of the Year 7 suggestions.

A: The school car park is usually full.
B: Most students live more than a mile from school.
C: The buses to school are usually full.
D: More than half of the parked cars do not belong to a parent or a teacher.

b Which two suggestions are not matched by one of the statements in **a**? Try to write a statement for each of these.

2 Imagine you need to identify the issues affecting the traffic outside school. Make a list of all the questions you would ask.

3 At Maypole High School, class 7W decide to find out if:

- the number of people that travel in each car is only two
- most students travel to school by bus
- students who walk to school have less distance to travel
- most cars bring only one student to school
- students living furthest away take the longest time to travel to school

Compare these questions with your own.
Comment on which questions are the most relevant and why.

Exercise commentary

The questions assess the objective on Primary Framework Page 115.

Problem solving
Question 3 assesses the objective on Primary Framework Page 77 as students are encouraged to explain reasoning.

Group work
The exercise is suitable for pair or group work.

Misconceptions
The distinction between a suggestion and a statement is a subtle one and one which some students may find difficult.
Emphasise that a suggestion is personal but a statement is specific and measurable and so it is possible to use it to collect data with. It may help to discuss with students exactly what a suggestion means until they get to the point of it.

Links
Students will need to collect data in other areas of the school curriculum such as geography and sociology.

Homework

D2.1HW requires students to formulate statements for their own projects.

Answers

1 a A: There aren't enough proper parking spaces.
B: A lot of us live too far away to walk.
C: There should be more buses.
D: Some of the parked cars may not be to do with the school.

Mental starter

Give students times measured in hours, and ask them to convert them to minutes. For example, 1 hour, 3 hours, $2\frac{1}{4}$ hours, $1\frac{3}{4}$ hours etc.
You could try a few in reverse.

Give students distances measured in centimetres, and ask them to convert them to millimetres.

Useful resources

D2.2OHP contains a questionnaire and a data collection sheet for discussion.

Introductory activity

Recap the situation at Maypole High.
Review the statements to be investigated from D2.1 and discuss how to go about this.
Emphasise that you are collecting data to answer specific questions and so you must be careful to phrase your survey properly.

Explain the use of a questionnaire in conducting a survey.
Discuss with students when they might have used a questionnaire before, or filled one in for somebody else.

Explain that the Maypole High questionnaire is being targeted at drivers, and refer to the questions identified in the student book.
These are also on **D2.2OHP**.
Discuss which questions are:
- ones which require a tick in a box
- ones which require a sentence as an answer
- ones which require circling an answer on a scale.

Emphasise the differences between open and closed questions.
Closed questions invite limited choice and can be easier to collate.
Open questions can invite responses that the questioner had not thought of.

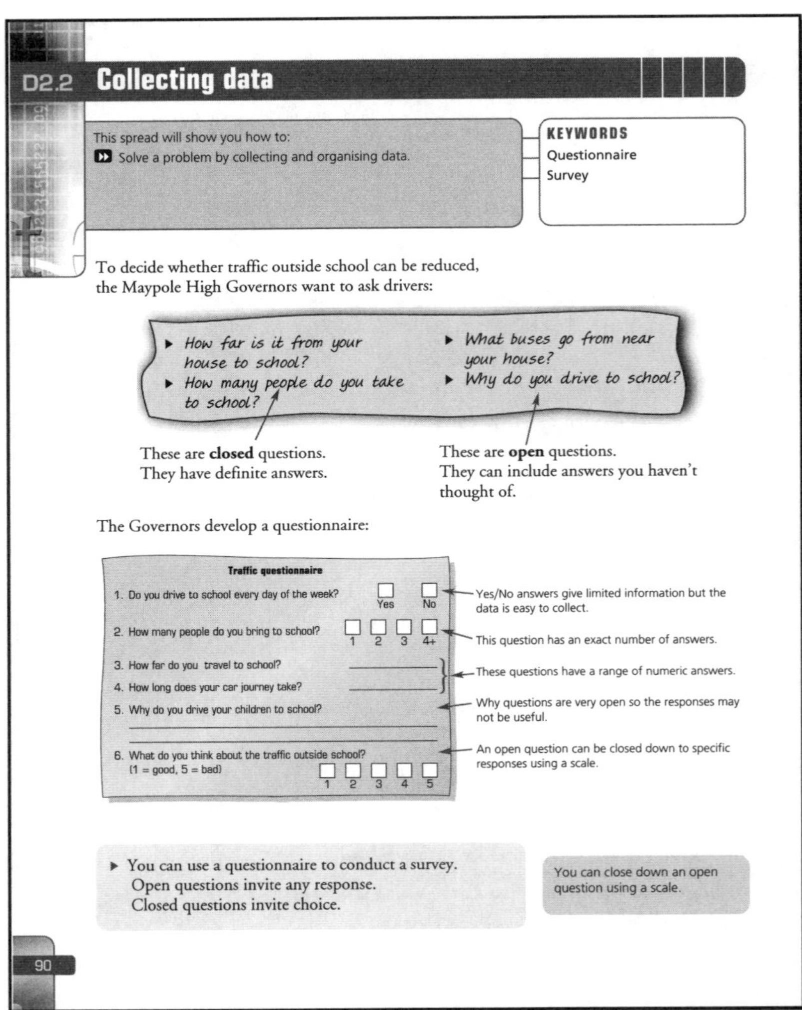

D2.2 Collecting data

This spread will show you how to:
- Solve a problem by collecting and organising data.

KEYWORDS
Questionnaire
Survey

To decide whether traffic outside school can be reduced, the Maypole High Governors want to ask drivers:

- *How far is it from your house to school?*
- *How many people do you take to school?*
- *What buses go from near your house?*
- *Why do you drive to school?*

These are **closed** questions. They have definite answers.

These are **open** questions. They can include answers you haven't thought of.

The Governors develop a questionnaire:

Traffic questionnaire

1. Do you drive to school every day of the week? ☐ Yes ☐ No
2. How many people do you bring to school? ☐ 1 ☐ 2 ☐ 3 ☐ 4+
3. How far do you travel to school? ______
4. How long does your car journey take? ______
5. Why do you drive your children to school? ______
6. What do you think about the traffic outside school? (1 = good, 5 = bad) ☐ 1 ☐ 2 ☐ 3 ☐ 4 ☐ 5

Yes/No answers give limited information but the data is easy to collect.
This question has an exact number of answers.
These questions have a range of numeric answers.
Why questions are very open so the responses may not be useful.
An open question can be closed down to specific responses using a scale.

- You can use a questionnaire to conduct a survey.
  Open questions invite any response.
  Closed questions invite choice.

You can close down an open question using a scale.

90

Plenary

Discuss the use of a data collection sheet for collecting numerical data.
D2.2OHP contains the traffic questionnaire from the student book, and also a possible data collection sheet for the numerical questions.
Use it to discuss the different ways you can monitor responses.

Further activities

Students should be encouraged to use these techniques in devising a survey to collect data for their own projects.

Differentiation

Support questions:

- Question 1 focuses on analysing survey questions.
- Questions 2–4 focus on writing and improving survey questions.
- In question 5 students devise questions for a survey or alternatively they can devise a survey for their own projects.

Core tier: focuses on evaluating the effectiveness of different types of question in a questionnaire.

Exercise D2.2

1 Rakhi and Jem are investigating people's journeys to school. They are designing a questionnaire. Here are the first three questions.

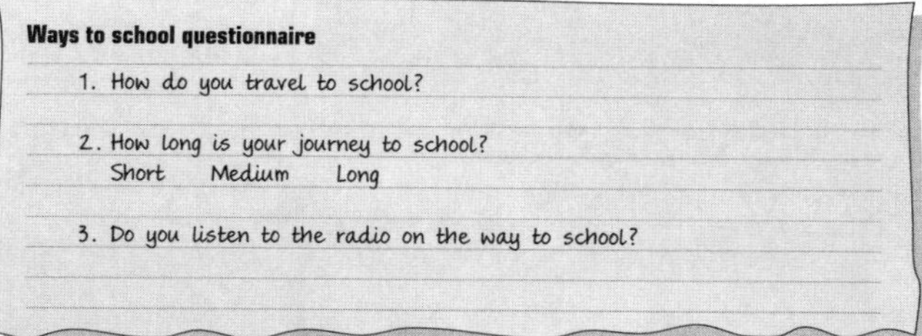

Ways to school questionnaire
1. How do you travel to school?
2. How long is your journey to school?
Short Medium Long
3. Do you listen to the radio on the way to school?

a For each question, decide:

- Does it ask for important information?
- Is it easy to answer?
- Will the answers be easy for Rakhi and Jem to use?

b Suggest improvements to each question.

2 Write down one more question for a school journey survey.
Try to make sure that it will be easy to answer, and will give clear information.

3 Improve each of these questions by giving some options for people to choose from.
a What is your favourite sort of television programme?
b How good is your local bus service?
c How many hours a week do you spend playing computer games?
d What time do you go to bed on a school day?

4 Rewrite each of these questions to make them fairer.
a How much time do you waste each week sending pointless text messages?
b Why don't people like sprouts?
c Do you agree that there are far too many sports programmes on television, and sometimes you can't even find a good film or drama?
d Which shampoo would you rather use – one of the boring old ones, or the new super enriched GlamLite shampoo, which is rich in vitamins and came top in a recent survey?

5 Sheila works in a school library. She wants to find out what young people want to read.
Design a short questionnaire to help her decide.
Your questionnaire should have about 5 good questions.

Exercise commentary

The questions assess the objective on Primary Framework Page 115.

Problem solving
The exercise assesses the objective on Primary Framework Page 77 as students are encouraged to explain reasoning.

Group work
The exercise is suitable for pair or group work.

Misconceptions
Most students are good at spotting questions that are obviously biased but find it more difficult to be critical of questions they devise themselves.
They may also find it hard to design an appropriate range of response choices as their own experience is limited.
Encourage the use of a pilot survey to overcome any difficulties – at this stage, simple discussion in pairs or groups should suffice.

Links
Students should be encouraged to take a critical approach to surveys whenever they come across them.

Homework

D2.2HW requires students to design a questionnaire.

Answers

1 Question 3 is not particularly relevant.
Question 2 should give distance ranges so the data can be analysed.
Question 1 would be better if there were some options to choose from.

4 For example:
a How much time per week do you spend sending text messages?
b Do you like sprouts? Yes or No.
c What is your favourite type of TV programme? Give categories.
d Which shampoo do you prefer? Give categories.

Mental starter

Draw up a tally chart and leave the frequency column blank; there is one on **R11**.
Students use number cards to show what the frequencies are.
Write the correct frequencies on the tally chart.
Discuss why tally marks are grouped in fives.
- Give a different example to include the frequencies and ask students to fill in the tally column.

Useful resources

R11 contains a blank tally chart for the mental starter.
R1 digit cards for student responses.
D2.3OHP shows the tally chart and frequency table from the student book.

Introductory activity

Recap that you can use a questionnaire or data collection sheet to collect data.

Discuss the meaning of the term 'discrete data'.
You may need to recap or define numerical data first.
Emphasise that discrete data can take a limited number of exact values (often but not necessarily whole numbers).
Offer a few examples, and ask students for some more.

Draw a frequency table on the board, using discrete data. You can use D2.3OHP.
Ask students to explain the table, and tease out misconceptions – for example, there are 6 cars with 1 passenger, not 1 car with 6 passengers.

Draw a grouped frequency table on the board or use D2.3OHP.
- Discuss the meaning of **continuous data**, using journey time as an example.
- Keep the explanation as simple as possible.
- Discuss what the frequency table shows, and why it is split up into intervals.

With a good group you can start to discuss the class boundaries – where would 10.5 minutes go?

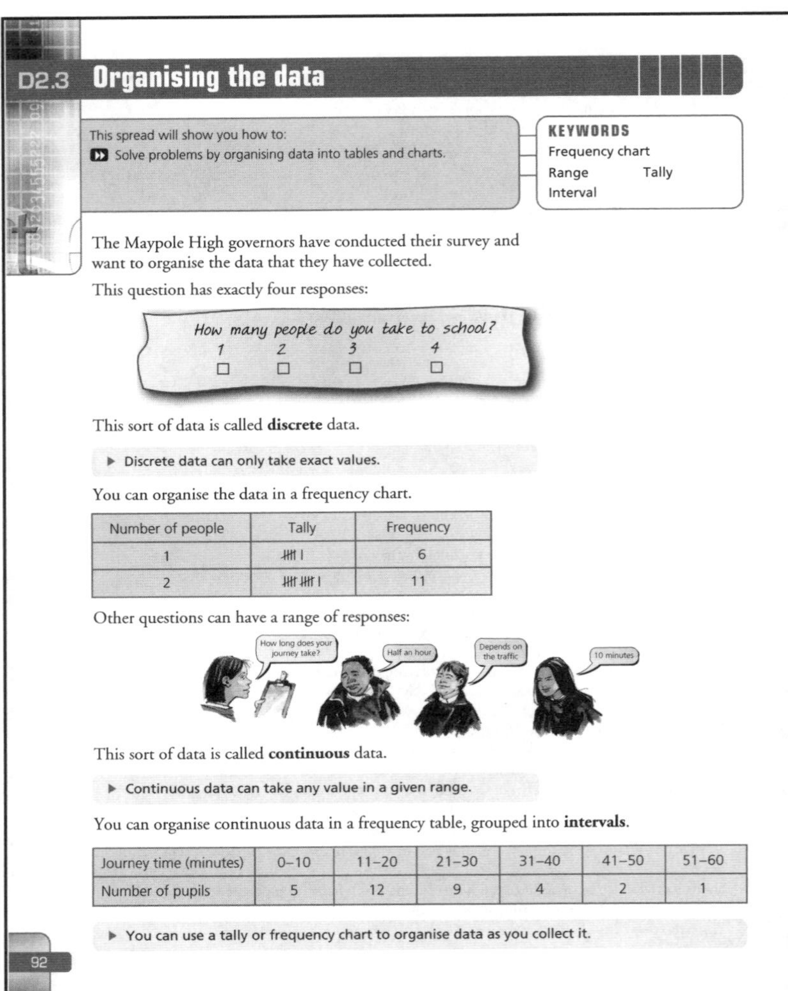

D2.3 **Organising the data**

This spread will show you how to:
- Solve problems by organising data into tables and charts.

KEYWORDS
Frequency chart
Range
Tally
Interval

The Maypole High governors have conducted their survey and want to organise the data that they have collected.
This question has exactly four responses:

How many people do you take to school?
1 ☐ 2 ☐ 3 ☐ 4 ☐

This sort of data is called **discrete** data.

- Discrete data can only take exact values.

You can organise the data in a frequency chart.

Number of people	Tally	Frequency
1	𝍸 I	6
2	𝍸 𝍸 I	11

Other questions can have a range of responses:

How long does your journey take?
Half an hour
Depends on the traffic
10 minutes

This sort of data is called **continuous** data.

- Continuous data can take any value in a given range.

You can organise continuous data in a frequency table, grouped into **intervals**.

Journey time (minutes)	0–10	11–20	21–30	31–40	41–50	51–60
Number of pupils	5	12	9	4	2	1

- You can use a tally or frequency chart to organise data as you collect it.

92

Plenary

- Discuss why you want to organise data – so you can make it easier to process.
- Discuss question 2 of the exercise, focusing on the distinction between discrete and continuous data.
- Discuss question 3b. Students should have used categories: 0, 1, 2, 3 and 4, not groups.

Further activities

Students should be encouraged to use these techniques in organising data collected for their own projects.

Students can draw bar charts for questions 1 and 2. Able students may draw a frequency diagram for question 3.

Students could find more examples of discrete or continuous data in question 4.

Differentiation

Support questions:

- Question 1 involves sorting discrete data into given categories.
- Questions 2 and 3 focus on categorising data with larger values, including continuous data.
- In question 4 students identify discrete and continuous data.

Core tier: focuses on choosing appropriate class intervals.

Exercise D2.3

1 Mandy collected data about how many pets people have.
Here are her results:
0, 3, 1, 2, 1, 0, 2, 2, 5, 6, 4, 7, 3, 2, 4, 2, 1, 0, 2, 2.

Copy and complete this frequency table for the data.

Number of pets	0–1	2–3	4–5	6–7
Tally				
Number of people				

2 Alison counted the number of matches in 20 boxes.
Here are her results:
48, 50, 49, 53, 61, 45, 48, 51, 52, 49, 44, 48, 54, 43, 51, 60, 50, 49, 47, 39.

Copy and complete this frequency table:

Number of matches	30–39	40–49	50–59	60–69
Tally				
Number of people				

3 Complete a frequency table for each of these sets of data.

a Heights of members of class 7Y (to the nearest cm):
152, 161, 148, 139, 158, 163, 160, 155, 153, 147, 141, 162, 154, 160, 153, 151, 159, 152, 155, 150

Height (cm)	135–139	140–144	145–149	150–154	155–159	160–164
Tally						
Frequency						

b Number of brothers or sisters of class 7Y:
2, 0, 1, 1, 2, 0, 0, 3, 0, 1, 2, 1, 1, 1, 0, 2, 4, 1, 0, 2

4 Say whether each of these sets of data is discrete or continuous.

a The age of teachers in your school.
b The time taken to run 100 metres.
c The number of rooms in each house in a street.
d The height of the trees in a forest.

Exercise commentary

The questions assess the objectives on Primary Framework Pages 115 and 117.

Problem solving
The exercise can assess the objective on Primary Framework Page 77 if students are encouraged to explain reasoning.

Group work
Question 4 is suitable for pair work.

Misconceptions
Some students find it difficult to distinguish between discrete and continuous data, especially as most of the data they have met so far has already been rounded and so appears to be discrete. Emphasise that measured data naturally can take a range of values and that when measuring, for example, height or weight, the measurement is rounded.

Links
Rounding: Primary Framework Page 11.

Homework

In D2.3HW students are asked to organise data into tables.

Answers

1 Number of people: 6, 9, 3, 2
2 Number of people: 1, 10, 7, 2
3 **a** Frequency: 1, 1, 2, 7, 4, 5
b Frequency: 1, 7, 7, 2, 2, 1
c Frequency: 6, 7, 5, 1, 1
4 **a** Discrete **b** Continuous **c** Discrete **d** Continuous

D2.4 Displaying your results

Mental starter

Nearer and nearer

Give students a number with 1 dp: 19.6

Ask whether it is nearer 0 or 100? 0 or 50? 0 or 20? 10 or 20? 15 or 20? 19 or 20?

Repeat for other decimals, asking questions to help students find the nearest whole number.

Useful resources

D2.4OHP contains the statistical diagrams in the student book.

R6 number lines may be useful for the mental starter.

Introductory activity

Find out what different types of graphs and diagrams students know, and highlight the ones that deal with data.

Ask questions such as:

- When are pie charts useful?
- When are bar charts useful?

Emphasise that pie charts and bar charts are used mainly for non-numerical (categorical) and discrete data.

D2.4OHP shows the diagrams in the student book.

Discuss the main features of a pie chart and a bar chart, using the diagrams supplied.

Note that there is also a frequency diagram on D2.4OHP – mention briefly that this can be used to display continuous data, and is similar to a bar chart.

Emphasise that you should always draw the most appropriate diagram for the data that you are trying to present, and that you can create statistical diagrams either by drawing them or by using ICT.

Discuss the pros and cons of pie charts and bar charts, emphasising that bar charts make the actual numbers easy to read but pie charts make the relative proportions very clear.

Emphasise that graphs should always have a title and should be clearly labelled, particularly with regard to units.

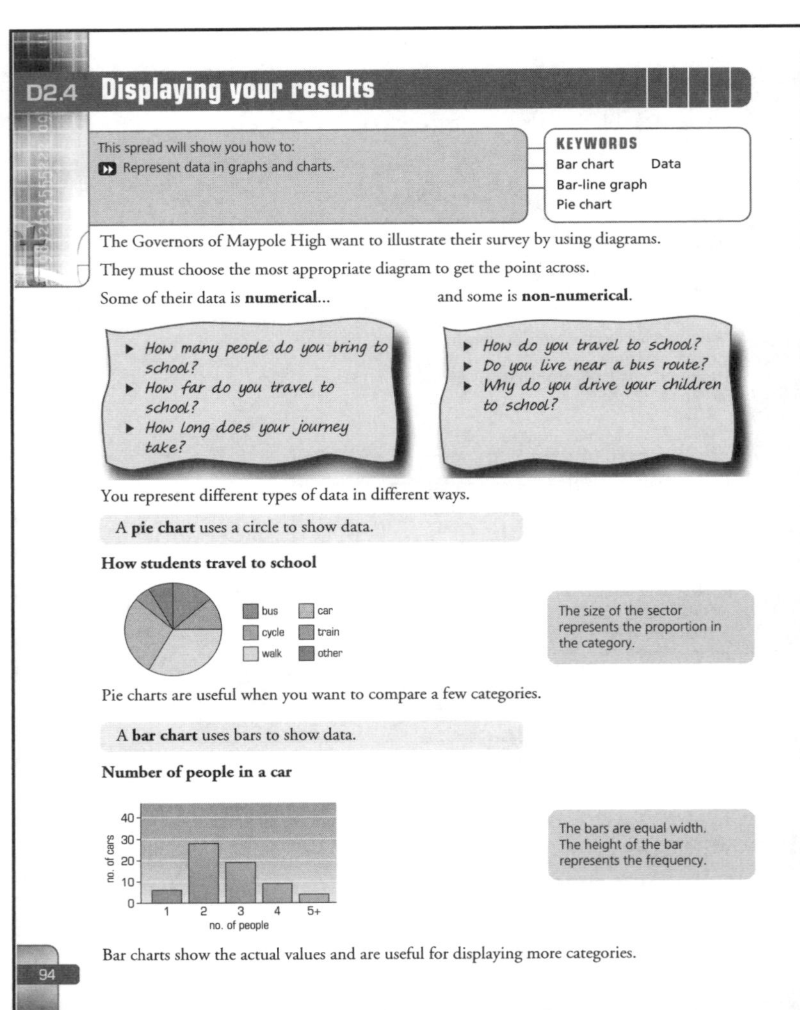

D2.4 Displaying your results

This spread will show you how to:

- Represent data in graphs and charts.

KEYWORDS
Bar chart
Data
Bar-line graph
Pie chart

The Governors of Maypole High want to illustrate their survey by using diagrams.
They must choose the most appropriate diagram to get the point across.

Some of their data is **numerical**...

- *How many people do you bring to school?*
- *How far do you travel to school?*
- *How long does your journey take?*

and some is **non-numerical**.

- *How do you travel to school?*
- *Do you live near a bus route?*
- *Why do you drive your children to school?*

You represent different types of data in different ways.

A **pie chart** uses a circle to show data.

How students travel to school

The size of the sector represents the proportion in the category.

Pie charts are useful when you want to compare a few categories.

A **bar chart** uses bars to show data.

Number of people in a car

The bars are equal width. The height of the bar represents the frequency.

Bar charts show the actual values and are useful for displaying more categories.

94

Plenary

Go through question 1 of the exercise.

Highlight any common mistakes or omissions in the students' bar charts.

Discuss the use of a scale in question 3.

Further activities

In **D2.4ICT**, students use a spreadsheet to generate simple bar charts.

Students should be encouraged to use these techniques to draw charts to display the data they collect for their own projects.

Able students may draw pie charts to represent their own data and that in question 4.

Differentiation

Support questions:

- Question 1 involves drawing bar charts.
- Question 2 is a reminder about finding the mode from a bar chart and question 3 involves interpreting a line graph.
- In question 4 students need to organise data in a table and use it to draw a line graph.

Core tier: extends to bar-line graphs and frequency diagrams.

Exercise D2.4

1 For each set of data:

- Organise the data in a frequency table.
- Draw a bar chart on squared paper.

a Number of goals scored by a football team:
2, 3, 0, 0, 1, 5, 2, 0, 1, 1, 6, 2, 1

b Number of hours of sunshine one fortnight:
7, 2, 0, 1, 8, 9, 5, 4, 6, 0, 0, 0, 1, 4

c Favourite colour of a group of students:
green, purple, pink, green, pink, red, green, blue, orange, red, blue, red, green, blue, purple, orange, purple

2 Use your bar charts to write down the mode of each set of data in question 1.

3 The bar-line chart shows the results of a survey about the number of cats people own.

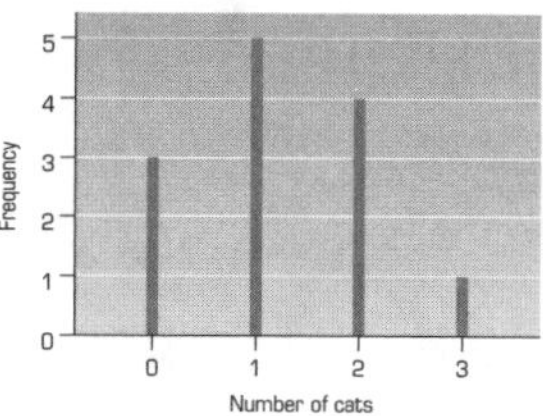

Use the chart to answer these questions:

a What was the most number of cats anyone owned?
b How many people owned no cats?
c How many people took part in the survey?
d What was the most common number of cats owned?

4 a Use this data to make a frequency table:

Number of goals scored in 20 football matches
1, 2, 0, 0, 1, 2, 5, 3, 0, 0, 1, 3, 3, 3, 2, 4, 3, 2, 1, 2.

b Now use the frequency table to produce a bar-line chart.

95

Exercise commentary

The questions assess the objectives on Primary Framework Pages 115 and 117.

Problem solving
The exercise can assess the objective on Primary Framework Page 77 if students are encouraged to explain reasoning.

Group work
D2.4ICT is suitable for pair work.

Misconceptions
Some students find it difficult to interpret data given on graphs and in particular how to find the total in a survey.
Emphasise the link between the frequency table and the chart and encourage them to write the information from the chart in a table and then to find the total number.
In reading the mode some students will give the highest value rather than the highest frequency, so the mode in 1a would be 6.
Emphasise that it is the category with the highest bar and that the height represents the frequency.

Links
Rounding: Primary Framework 11.

Homework

In **D2.4HW**, students are asked to display their own data in a bar chart.

Answers

1 a Number of goals scored: 0, 1, 2, 3, 4, 5, 6
Frequency: 3, 4, 3, 1, 0, 1, 1
b Number of hours of sun: 0, 1, 2, 3, 4, 5, 6, 7, 8, 9
Frequency: 4, 2, 1, 0, 2, 1, 1, 1, 1, 1
c Favourite colour: pink, green, red, blue, orange, purple
Frequency: 2, 4, 3, 3, 2, 3

2 a 1 **b** 0 **c** Green

3 a 3 **b** 3 **c** 13 **d** 1

Mental starter

What's the chart?

Use **D2.4OHP**. Ask students questions:

- What fraction of students walk to school?
- If 20 students walk, how many use the car?
- How many cars were in the (bar chart) survey?
- What was the modal number of cars?

Useful resources

D2.5OHP shows the handling data cycle for discussion.

D2.4OHP has diagrams for discussion in the mental starter.

Introductory activity

Recap the use of statistical diagrams – it is easier to interpret data when you have a picture.

Suggest that people can interpret statistics in different ways – use the illustration in the student book as an example.
Emphasise that neither interpretation is any more correct than the other.

Discuss the graphs produced by the traffic survey.
Ask students how they would interpret them.
Discuss whether the governors' conclusions are reasonable.

Discuss briefly what questions have not been addressed by Maypole High.
For instance, seeing if there are differences in the modes of transport between year groups, or between girls and boys.
Emphasise that these are limitations of your survey.

Explain that a survey can often lead to new areas of research.
Use **D2.5OHP** to discuss the stages involved in each new area of research.
Discuss the possible statements you could start with in order to investigate further.

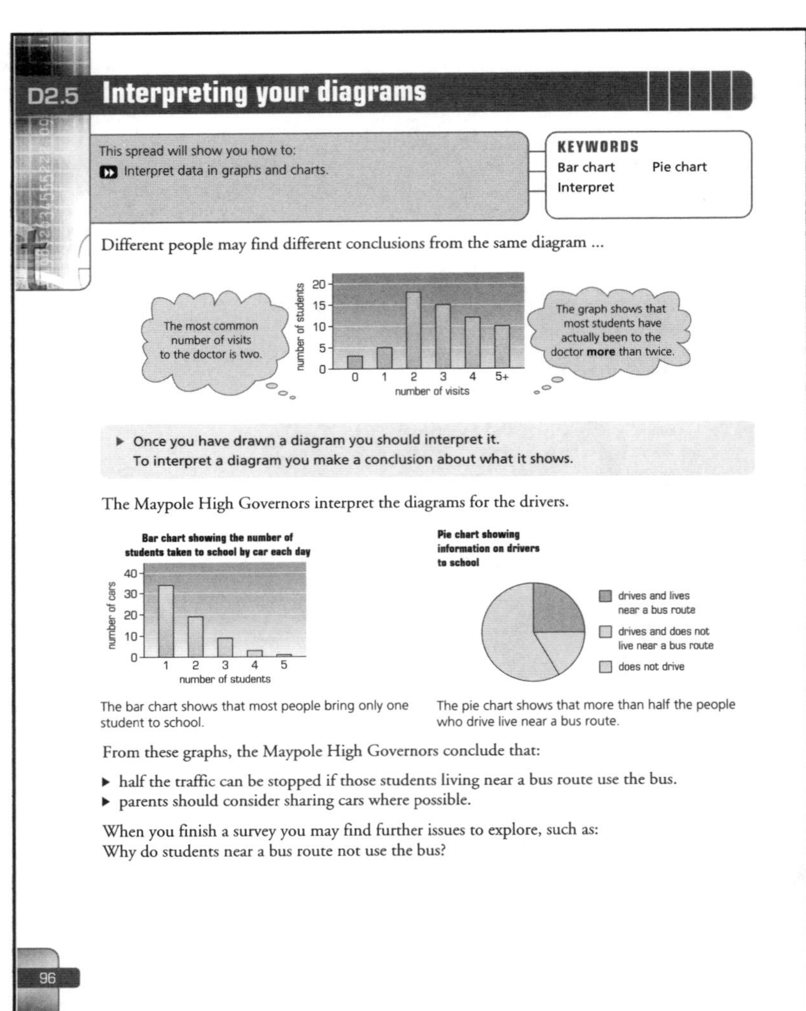

D2.5 **Interpreting your diagrams**

This spread will show you how to:
- Interpret data in graphs and charts.

KEYWORDS
Bar chart
Pie chart
Interpret

Different people may find different conclusions from the same diagram ...

- Once you have drawn a diagram you should interpret it.
  To interpret a diagram you make a conclusion about what it shows.

The Maypole High Governors interpret the diagrams for the drivers.

The bar chart shows that most people bring only one student to school.

The pie chart shows that more than half the people who drive live near a bus route.

From these graphs, the Maypole High Governors conclude that:

- half the traffic can be stopped if those students living near a bus route use the bus.
- parents should consider sharing cars where possible.

When you finish a survey you may find further issues to explore, such as:
Why do students near a bus route not use the bus?

96

Plenary

Discuss the use of statistics in everyday life.
You could ask for examples from:

- the pop charts
- adverts
- the media
- the health service.

Refer to the census at school website.

Further activities

Students should look critically at the graphs they draw for their projects and write a paragraph explaining what each graph shows in the light of the initial statements they investigated.

Students can discuss why the graph used is the best one to illustrate their findings and derive a list of pros and cons of each type of chart.

Differentiation

Support questions:

- Question 1 involves interpreting a simple bar charts. Springboard 7, pages 398, 402.
- Question 2 involves a dual bar chart and question 3 focuses on interpreting a pie chart. Springboard 7, pages 393, 399.
- Question 4 focuses on a time series line graph. Springboard 7, pages 400, 401.

Core tier: focuses on interpreting a wider range of graphs, including frequency diagrams.

Exercise D2.5

1 Kim is a photographer. She records the number of sucessful photographs that she gets from each film she develops. The chart shows her results.

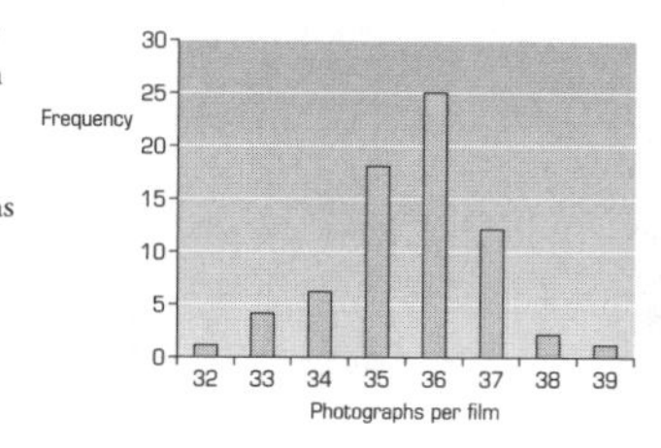

Use the chart to answer these questions:

a What was the highest number of photographs that Kim got from a film?
b What was the mode of the number of photographs?
c How many films does the chart show data for?

2 The chart shows how many boys and girls attended some some school clubs one week.

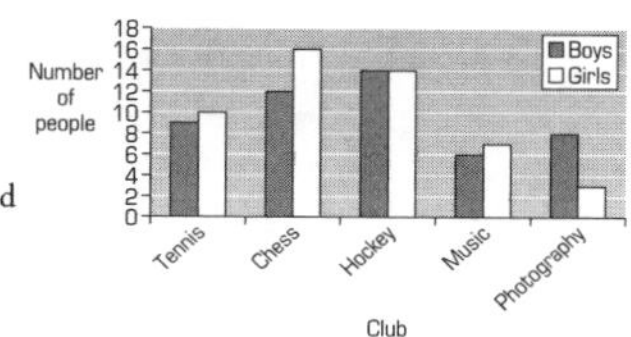

Use the chart to answer these questions:

a How many people went to chess club?
b Which club had equal numbers of boys and girls?
c Which club had more boys than girls?
d What was the total attendance at all of the clubs?

3 A shop sells five flavours of crisps. The pie chart shows information about how many of each flavour were sold.

a Which of these statements are true:
A: The most popular flavour was cheese.
B: The shop sold twice as many packets of tomato flavour as bacon flavour.
C: More than a quarter of the packets sold were tomato flavour.

b Which two flavours of crisps made up more than 50% of the total amount sold?

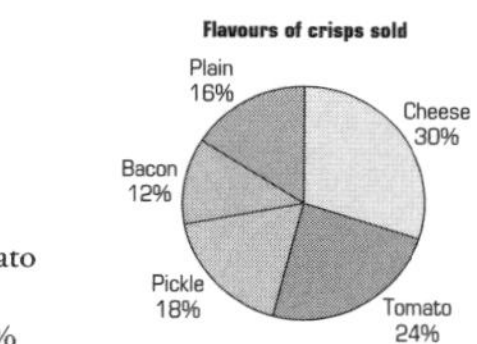

4 Jo is a school technician. She keeps a record of how many times she has to fix the photocopier.

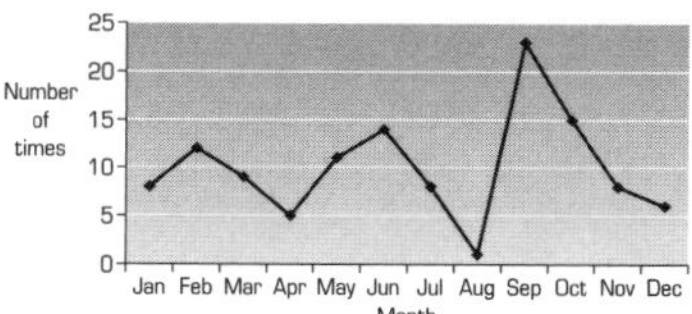

Use the chart to answer these questions.

a Which month had the biggest number of breakdowns?
b Which three months had the smallest number of breakdowns?
c Explain why you think the number of breakdowns has the pattern shown in the chart.

97

Exercise commentary

The questions assess the objectives on Primary Framework Pages 115 and 117.

Problem solving

Question 3b assesses the objective on Primary Framework Page 79 and question 4c assesses Page 77.

Group work

Question 4c can be discussed in pairs.

Misconceptions

Use of a scale can cause problems.
Encourage students to ensure they understand the scale used before they start to answer the question.
Some students find it difficult to find the total in a survey.
Emphasise the link between the frequency table and the chart.
Many students find pie charts hard to interpret. Question 3 is based on using simple fractions and percentages which may cause some problems.
Emphasise how simple it can be to interpret a pie chart by asking questions: which is the biggest/smallest category?

Links

Fractions: Primary Framework 23.
Percentages: Page 33. Scales: Pages 94–95.

Homework

In D2.5HW, students are asked to interpret their own statistical diagrams.

Answers

1 **a** 39 **b** 36 **c** 69
2 **a** 28 **b** Hockey **c** Photography **d** 99
3 **a** A True, B True, C False **b** Cheese and Tomato
4 **a** September **b** August, April, December

Summary

The Year 6 key teaching objective is:

- Solve a problem by extracting and interpreting data in tables and charts (115, 117).

Plenary activity

Reuse **D2.5OHP** to summarise and discuss the data handling cycle.

Emphasise that each stage is essential in any enquiry and that it is the quality of the question that affects the quality of the enquiry.

Check out commentary

1 Students find compound bar charts confusing and find it difficult to answer part **a** in particular.

The use of supportive questioning will help: How many girls found the meals 'Very Good'? How many boys? How many altogether?

In part **c** students tend to think the highest bar represents the best result and so give the answer 'boys'.

Encourage them to consider the results as a whole and to give a simple explanation for their answer.

2 This questions focuses on interpreting a pie chart and will highlight whether students have the basic understanding of each sector representing a proportion of the total.

The questions are answerable by analysing the percentage figures alone but it is important to emphasise the use of the pie chart itself in any reasoning as this will help overcome later misconceptions about interpreting pie charts. However students will need to look at the figures to ensure the accuracy of their answers particularly in statement A.

The use of percentages may cause difficulties especially if students don't realise that 25% is a quarter.

This question will highlight any students who can't recall this fact.

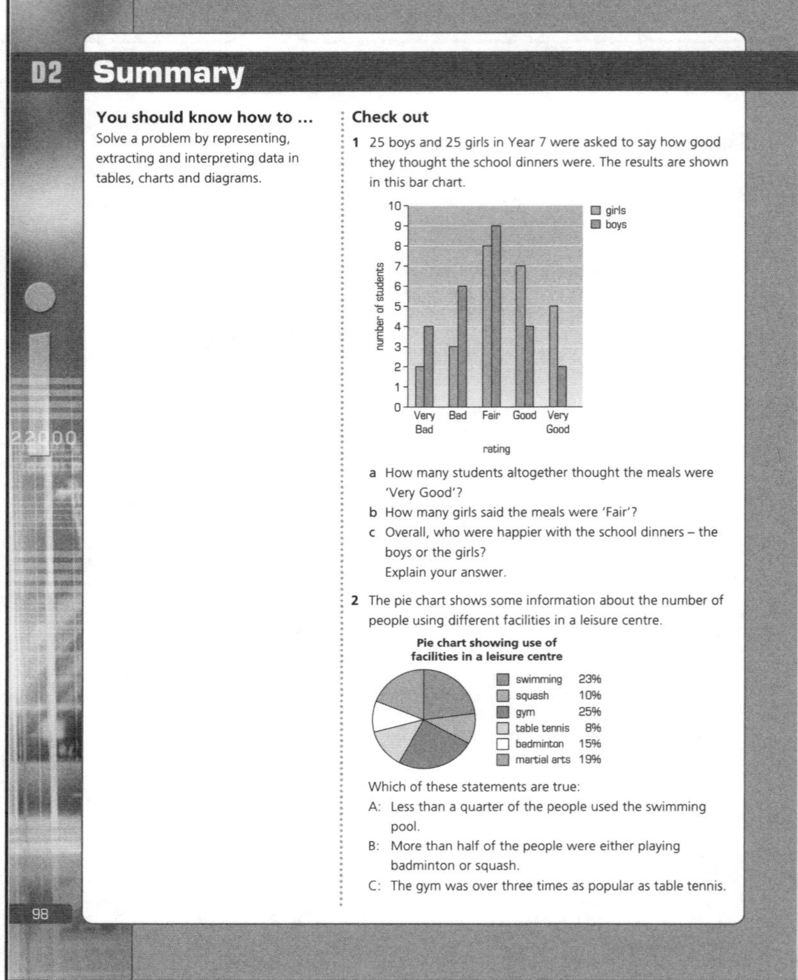

D2 Summary

You should know how to ...

Solve a problem by representing, extracting and interpreting data in tables, charts and diagrams.

Check out

1 25 boys and 25 girls in Year 7 were asked to say how good they thought the school dinners were. The results are shown in this bar chart.

a How many students altogether thought the meals were 'Very Good'?

b How many girls said the meals were 'Fair'?

c Overall, who were happier with the school dinners – the boys or the girls?
Explain your answer.

2 The pie chart shows some information about the number of people using different facilities in a leisure centre.

Pie chart showing use of facilities in a leisure centre

Which of these statements are true:

A: Less than a quarter of the people used the swimming pool.

B: More than half of the people were either playing badminton or squash.

C: The gym was over three times as popular as table tennis.

Development

This work is further developed in D3 where students undertake a second project or build on this one.

Links

Students should apply the data handling cycle when they undertake statistical enquiries in other areas of the school curriculum and the principles may form part of a whole-school numeracy policy.

Mental starters

Objectives covered in this unit:

- Multiply and divide decimals by 10, 100, 1000.
- Know pairs of factors to 100.
- Add and subtract pairs of numbers.
- Find halves and doubles of numbers.
- Recall multiplication and division facts.
- Derive answers to calculations.
- Multiply and divide a two-digit by a one-digit number.
- Convert between m, cm and mm.

Resources needed

* means class set needed

Essential:

R1* – Digit cards
N3.3OHP – Partitioning grids
N3.4OHP – More partitioning
N3.5OHP – Grid method
N3.6OHP – Repeated subtraction
N3.7OHP – More repeated subtraction
Calculators*

Useful:

R4 (OHP) – Place value table
R19 (OHP) – Ruler
N3.2OHP – Order of operations
N3.8OHP – Calculator
N3.1F* – Scales and measures
N3.7F* – Division game
N3.1ICT* – Place value in Excel
Playing cards, 0–9 dice, metre rule

N3 Multiplication and division

This unit will show you how to:

- Multiply and divide any positive integer by 10 or 100 and understand the effect.
- Understand the effect of and relationships between the four operations, and the principles (not the names) of the arithmetic laws as they apply to multiplication. Begin to use brackets.
- Know all multiplication facts up to 10 × 10 and corresponding division facts.
- Use doubling or halving, starting from known facts; partition.
- Recognise multiples up to 10 × 10.
- Factorise number up to 100.
- Extend written methods to:
  - short multiplication of HTU or U.t by U;
  - long multiplication of TU by TU;
  - short division of HTU by U.
- Use a calculator effectively.
- Estimate by approximating then check result.
- Use, read and write standard metric units (km, m, cm, mm), including their abbreviations, and relationships between them.
- Convert larger to smaller units.
- Identify and use appropriate operations to solve word problems.

Eight CDs at £8.95, that'll be £96 then please.
Eight nines are 72
That's too much – can you check that please?

Sometimes you need to be able to estimate quickly.

Before you start

You should know how to ...	Check in
1 Add and subtract integers.	1 a Work out these mentally: i 34 + 22 ii 63 – 21 iii 31 + 23 + 18 iv 61 – 19 + 2 b Work out these additions and subtractions using the column written method: i 325 + 134 ii 768 – 253 iii 327 + 158 iv 625 – 371
2 Recall multiplication and division facts up to 10 × 10.	2 Work these out: a 3 × 7 b 24 ÷ 3 c 9 × 4 d 8 × 5 e 45 ÷ 9
3 Use a calculator for basic calculations.	3 Use a calculator to work out each of these: a 1026 + 953 b 527 – 369 c 21 × 36 d 562 × 45 e 4707 ÷ 9 f 7981 ÷ 23

99

Unit commentary

Aim of the unit

This unit aims to develop students' ability to multiply and divide with numbers. Starting with powers of 10 and order of operations, leading into multiplication and division, the unit develops successful mental strategies into informal written methods.

Introduction

Discuss when students need to be able to multiply in their heads – you can refer to buying CDs in a shop: how do you find the cost of 6 CDs at £11.99? Emphasise the use of an estimate.

Framework references

This unit focuses on:

- Year 6 teaching objectives pages: 7, 19, 21, 53, 55, 59, 67, 69, 71, 73, 91
- Problem solving objectives pages: 83, 85, 87, 89

The unit provides access to:

- Year 7 teaching objectives pages: 86, 104, 106, 110

Check in activity

Play a game of Number countdown.
Give students the numbers: 1, 3, 5, 6, 25, 9.
Ask them to make the totals: 162, 250, 379 and 749.
They can use each number at most once (they do not have to use them all) and can use any of the operations +, −, ×, ÷ as often as they like.
Students work in pairs and justify their answers.

Differentiation

Core tier focuses on choosing the most appropriate method to use for any calculation, including dividing by a two-digit number and multiplying by a three-digit number.

Springboard 7

Pages 72–74, 215–221, 231–233, 235–237, 332, 336, 338–342, 350–352, 365–373, 489.

N3.1 Number and measures

Mental starter

Practice multiplying and dividing whole numbers by 10.
Read out some multiplications: 3 × 10, 5 × 10, 12 × 10 etc.
Students respond using digit cards.
Try some divisions: 50 ÷ 10, 450 ÷ 10, 3000 ÷ 10 etc.
Extend to cases giving a decimal answer.
Ask students to describe what is happening when you multiply or divide by 10.

Useful resources

R1 digit cards for the mental starter.
R4 contains a place value table.
R19 contains a ruler.
A **metre rule** for the plenary.

Introductory activity

Refer to the mental starter.
Extend to multiplying by 100, and ask students to describe what is happening.

Encourage the response that the number gets larger, but use a place value table to demonstrate that the digits move one place to the left for ×10, and two places to the left for ×100.
There is a blank place value table on **R4**.
Use this to demonstrate a few examples of ×10 and ×100.

Extend to decimals e.g. 35.65 × 10
Emphasise that the digits still move to the left, and the decimal point stays fixed.
Discuss the role of zero.

Discuss what happens when you divide by 10 and 100.
Encourage the response that the digits move to the right:
- One place for ÷10
- Two places for ÷100

Emphasise that × and ÷ are opposite.

Discuss metric measures of length.
Explain that metric measures are based on the decimal system. You can use a ruler to demonstrate the relationship between cm and mm. There is a ruler on **R19**.
Explain how to convert between mm, cm, m and km, and refer to the example in the student book.

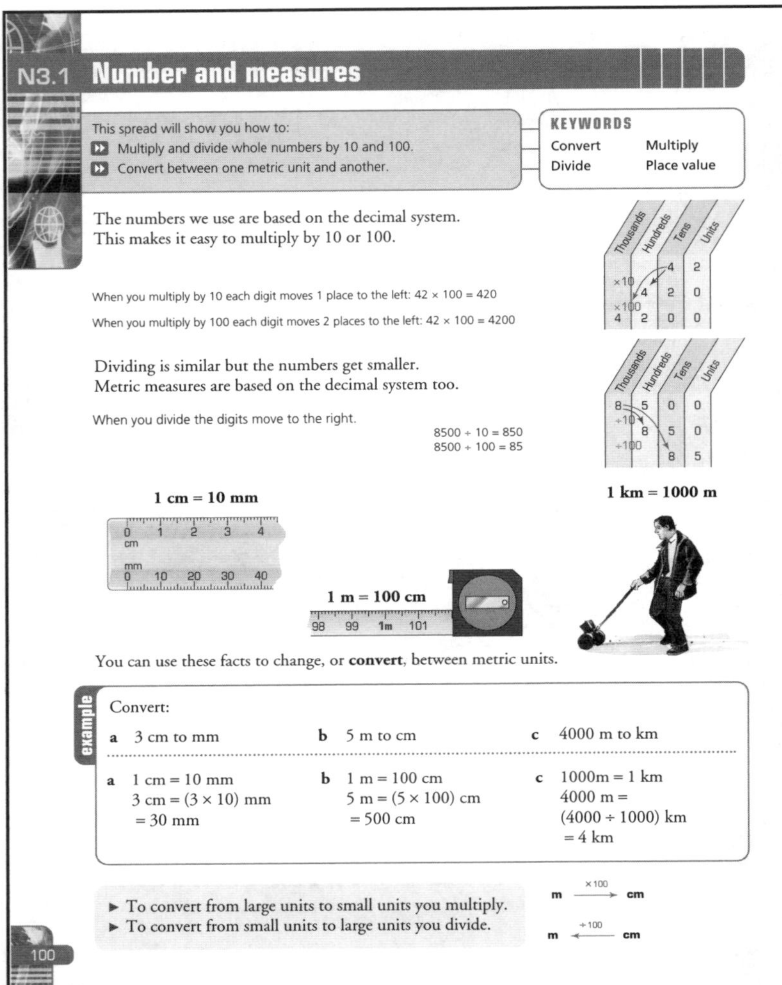

N3.1 **Number and measures**

This spread will show you how to:
- Multiply and divide whole numbers by 10 and 100.
- Convert between one metric unit and another.

KEYWORDS
Convert Multiply
Divide Place value

The numbers we use are based on the decimal system.
This makes it easy to multiply by 10 or 100.

When you multiply by 10 each digit moves 1 place to the left: 42 × 100 = 420
When you multiply by 100 each digit moves 2 places to the left: 42 × 100 = 4200

Dividing is similar but the numbers get smaller.
Metric measures are based on the decimal system too.

When you divide the digits move to the right.
8500 ÷ 10 = 850
8500 ÷ 100 = 85

You can use these facts to change, or **convert**, between metric units.

example

Convert:
a 3 cm to mm b 5 m to cm c 4000 m to km

a 1 cm = 10 mm
3 cm = (3 × 10) mm
= 30 mm

b 1 m = 100 cm
5 m = (5 × 100) cm
= 500 cm

c 1000m = 1 km
4000 m =
(4000 ÷ 1000) km
= 4 km

- To convert from large units to small units you multiply.
- To convert from small units to large units you divide.

100

Plenary

Discuss how many millimetres are in 1 kilometre.
You can start by discussing the number of millimetres in a cm then in a m. It would help to have a metre rule available.

Further activities

In **N3.1ICT**, students use a spreadsheet to build a metric converter as shown on Framework Page 288.

Students can challenge each other to convert between units of measure.

N3.1F provides extra practice at reading scales and solving problems involving measures.

Differentiation

Support questions:

- Questions 1–2 revise work from Year 4 objectives. Springboard 7, page 72.
- Questions 3–11 focus on multiplying and dividing by 10 and 100 involving whole numbers. Springboard 7, pages 73, 365–368.
- Questions 12–14 include decimals and km conversions. Springboard 7, pages 74, 369–373.

Core tier: extends to multiplying and dividing by 1000.

Exercise N3.1

1 Multiply these numbers by 10.
a 8 **b** 9 **c** 10 **d** 12 **e** 15 **f** 18 **g** 100 **h** 220

2 Divided these numbers by 10.
a 70 **b** 60 **c** 200 **d** 500 **e** 300 **f** 180 **g** 230 **h** 3700

3 Multiply these numbers by 100.
a 3 **b** 8 **c** 20 **d** 70 **e** 68 **f** 130 **g** 155 **h** 178

4 Divide these numbers by 100.
a 500 **b** 400 **c** 900 **d** 2000 **e** 5000 **f** 2500 **g** 18 000

5 Jade buys 100 ice lollies at 20p each for a youth club picnic.
Work out how much she spends in total.
a Write your answer in pence.
b Write your answer in pounds.

6 100 plastic toy soldiers cost £4 in total.
a What is £4 in pence?
b Work out in pence how much each soldier costs.

7 Josie has 60 sweets. She and her nine friends share the sweets equally.
a Write down how many people share the sweets.
b Work out how many sweets each person gets.

8 Here are four metric units for measuring distance.
km mm m cm
Write them in order of size, starting with the smallest.

9 Change each of these measurements into millimetres (mm).
a 5 cm **b** 3 cm **c** 8 cm **d** 10 cm **e** 50 cm **f** 72 cm

10 Change each of these measurements into centimetres (cm).
a 3 m **b** 7 m **c** 11 m **d** 40 m **e** 23 m **f** 100 m

11 Joel buys 13 m of ribbon. How much is this in cm?

12 Change each of these measurements into metres (m).
a 2 km **b** 5 km **c** 8 km **d** 12 km **e** 28 km **f** 87 km

13 Nandini runs 5 km. How far has she run in metres?

14 Convert each of these measurements.
The first one is done for you.
a 3.7 cm into mm **b** 6.2 cm into mm **c** 12.5 cm into mm
d 3.85 m into cm **e** 8.15 m into cm **f** 12.7 km into m

Exercise commentary

The questions assess the objectives on Primary Framework Pages 7 and 91.

Problem solving

Questions 5–7, 11 and 13 assess the objective from Primary Framework Pages 82–89.

Group work

The further activity is suitable for paired work.

Misconceptions

Commonly students will not know whether to multiply or divide in conversion questions.

Emphasise that a smaller unit means there are more of them, so multiply.

Encourage students to have a feel for the size before attempting the question – it is a good idea to refer to a ruler for cm to mm conversions and to have a benchmark for m to cm such as the height of a door or a person.

When dealing with decimals it is common to just add a zero when multiplying:
3.7 cm = 3.70 mm.

Again, estimation can help.

Links

Division: Primary Framework Page 57.
Estimation: Page 93.

Homework

N3.1HW provides practice at multiplying and dividing by 10 and 100.

Answers

1 a 80 **b** 90 **c** 100 **d** 120 **e** 150 **f** 180 **g** 1000 **h** 2200
2 a 7 **b** 6 **c** 20 **d** 50 **e** 30 **f** 18 **g** 23 **h** 370
3 a 300 **b** 800 **c** 2000 **d** 7000 **e** 6800 **f** 13 000 **g** 15 500 **h** 17 800
4 a 5 **b** 4 **c** 9 **d** 20 **e** 50 **f** 25 **g** 180
5 a 2000p **b** £20 **6 a** 400p **b** 4p **7 a** 10 **b** 6 **8** mm, cm, m, km
9 a 50 mm **b** 30 mm **c** 80 mm **d** 100 mm **e** 500 mm **f** 720 mm
10 a 300 cm **b** 700 cm **c** 1100 cm **d** 4000 cm **e** 2300 cm **f** 10 000 cm **11** 1300 cm
12 a 2000 m **b** 5000 m **c** 8000 m **d** 12 000 m **e** 28 000 m **f** 87 000 m **13** 5000 m
14 a 37 mm **b** 62 mm **c** 125 mm **d** 385 cm **e** 815 cm **f** 12 700 m

Mental starter

Order!

Write: $4 + 8 \div 2 + 2$

Ask for all the possible answers **if** the order of operations did not matter.

Try a few more, for example: $3 \times 7 - 5 + 4$

Useful resources

R1 digit cards for the mental starter.

N3.2OHP contains examples from the student book for discussion.

Introductory activity

Refer to the mental starter.

Discuss briefly how confusing arithmetic would be if there were more than one answer.

Use $4 + 6 \div 2$ as a simple case, and ask for the correct answer.

Many will say 5, though some might say the correct answer of 7.

Ask students to justify their answers.

State that the correct answer is 7, and say that in arithmetic you must use the **correct order of operations:**

- Brackets
- Division or multiplication
- Addition or subtraction

Show that this leads to a correct answer of 7.

Explain the role of brackets in arithmetic.

Refer to the first example in the student book, which is also on **N3.2OHP**.

Emphasise that brackets come first in any calculation.

Revisit the calculation in the starter:

$4 + 8 \div 2 + 2$

$= 4 + 4 + 2 = 10$

Explain that if more than one + or –, or more than one × or ÷, appear in a calculation then you should work from left to right.

Illustrate with the last example in the student book, which is also on N3.2OHP.

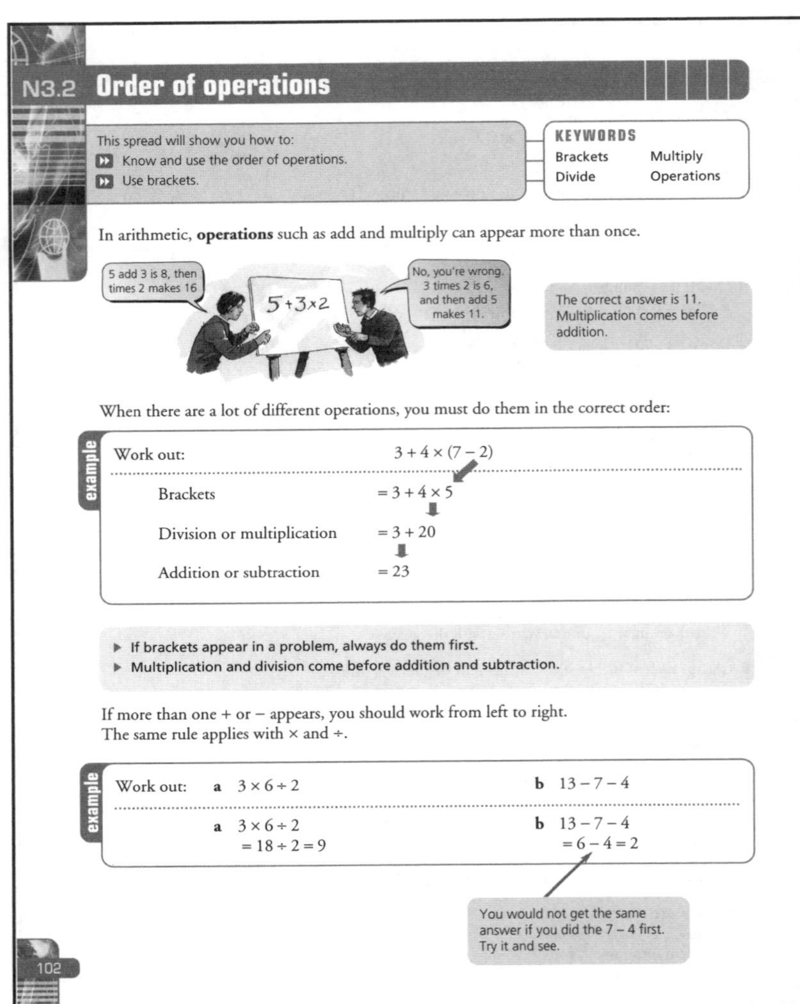

N3.2 **Order of operations**

This spread will show you how to:
- Know and use the order of operations.
- Use brackets.

KEYWORDS: Brackets, Divide, Multiply, Operations

In arithmetic, **operations** such as add and multiply can appear more than once.

5 add 3 is 8, then times 2 makes 16
5+3×2
No, you're wrong. 3 times 2 is 6, and then add 5 makes 11.

The correct answer is 11. Multiplication comes before addition.

When there are a lot of different operations, you must do them in the correct order:

example

Work out: $3 + 4 \times (7 - 2)$

Brackets	$= 3 + 4 \times 5$
Division or multiplication	$= 3 + 20$
Addition or subtraction	$= 23$

- If brackets appear in a problem, always do them first.
- Multiplication and division come before addition and subtraction.

If more than one + or – appears, you should work from left to right.
The same rule applies with × and ÷.

example

Work out: **a** $3 \times 6 \div 2$ **b** $13 - 7 - 4$

a $3 \times 6 \div 2$
$= 18 \div 2 = 9$

b $13 - 7 - 4$
$= 6 - 4 = 2$

You would not get the same answer if you did the 7 – 4 first. Try it and see.

102

Plenary

Investigate what happens when two of the same sign appear in a calculation, using the numbers 8, 4 and 2.

$8 + 4 + 2 = 14$ whichever one you do first.

Similarly, $8 \times 4 \times 2 = 64$

However, with $8 - 4 - 2$, and $8 \div 4 \div 2$, it matters that you apply the rule: 'work from left to right'.

Further activities

Students can challenge each other to find the missing brackets as in question 6.

Give able students examples like question 6 but involving four operations, for example:
$4 \times 2 + 3 - 11 = 9$

Differentiation

Support questions:

- Questions 1–2 revise work from Year 4 objectives.
- Questions 3–4 focus on applying the order of operations in problems using brackets.
- Questions 5–6 develop order of operations problems with all operations.

Core tier: focuses on arithmetic operations including powers.

Exercise N3.2

Do all these questions in your head.

1 Work out the answers to each of these.

a $8 + 2 + 3$ b $7 + 5 - 3$
c $3 - 2 + 5$ d $10 - 6 - 3$
e $8 - 3 + 7$ f $6 + 5 - 8$
g $8 - 3 + 10$ h $12 - 7 + 3$
i $14 + 6 - 10$ j $3 + 9 - 7$

2 Work out the answers to each of these.

a $2 \times 4 \div 2$ b $8 \div 4 \times 2$
c $6 \div 3 \times 3$ d $3 \times 3 \times 2$
e $4 \times 4 \div 2$ f $8 \div 4 \div 2$
g $10 \div 2 \times 3$ h $12 \div 2 \div 2$
i $5 \times 4 \div 2$ j $10 \times 2 \div 5$

3 Work out the answers to these problems.
Remember to do the brackets first.

a $(8 + 4) - 6$ b $6 + (8 - 2)$
c $12 - (5 - 2)$ d $15 - (8 + 3)$
e $6 - (8 - 6)$ f $(12 + 5) - 3$

4 These are a little harder but you still do the brackets first.

a $6 + (5 - 3) - 2$ b $8 - (8 - 6) + 5$
c $7 + (8 - 3) + 2$ d $7 + 8 - (3 + 5)$
e $12 - 5 - (8 - 6)$ f $16 - (3 + 9) + 6$

5 Work out the answers to these problems.
Remember to think which operation to do first.

a $2 \times 4 + 3$ b $4 + 3 \times 2$
c $3 + 6 \div 2$ d $6 \div 2 + 3$
e $10 \div 2 + 3$ f $12 - 3 \times 2$
g $12 - 8 \div 2$ h $8 + 3 \times 4$
i $3 + 10 \div 2$ j $7 - 12 \div 4$

6 Put brackets into these problems if they are needed.

a $8 + 4 - 3 = 9$ b $6 - 3 \times 2 = 6$
c $8 + 4 \times 2 = 24$ d $8 \div 3 + 1 = 2$
e $9 \div 3 + 5 = 8$ f $6 + 3 \times 2 = 18$
g $6 \div 3 + 5 = 7$ h $7 - 5 \div 2 = 1$
i $14 \div 6 + 1 = 2$ j $20 - 10 \div 2 = 5$

Exercise commentary

The questions assess the objectives on Primary Framework Page 53.

Problem solving

Question 6 and the further activity assess the objective from Primary Framework Page 75.

Group work

The further activity is suitable for paired work.

Misconceptions

When questions get hard some students will ignore the brackets and just work from left to right.

Use the acromyn Bidmas to emphasise that the brackets come first and when there are no brackets, multiplying before adding.

Students may get confused by minus signs in front of brackets and ignore them.

Encourage a structured approach as shown on page 102.

Links

Multiplication and division facts: Primary Framework Page 59.

Add several numbers: Page 43.

Arithmetic laws: Page 53.

Homework

N3.2HW is an investigation based on the order of operations.

Answers

1 **a** 13 **b** 9 **c** 6 **d** 1 **e** 12 **f** 3 **g** 15 **h** 8 **i** 10 **j** 5
2 **a** 4 **b** 4 **c** 6 **d** 18 **e** 8 **f** 1 **g** 15 **h** 3 **i** 10 **j** 4
3 **a** 6 **b** 12 **c** 9 **d** 4 **e** 4 **f** 14
4 **a** 6 **b** 11 **c** 14 **d** 7 **e** 5 **f** 10
5 **a** 11 **b** 10 **c** 6 **d** 6 **e** 8 **f** 6 **g** 8 **h** 20 **i** 8 **j** 4
6 **b** $(6 - 3) \times 2 = 6$ **c** $(8 + 4) \times 2 = 24$ **d** $8 \div (3 + 1) = 2$
f $(6 + 3) \times 2 = 18$ **h** $(7 - 5) \div 2 = 1$ **i** $14 \div (6 + 1) = 2$
j $(20 - 10) \div 2 = 5$

N3.3 Mental methods

Mental starter

Doubling and halving

Start with 2 and ask students to double the number (4, 8, 16, ...)
Go around the class, choosing each student in turn.
Change the start number at regular intervals to keep it both straightforward and lively.

Choose a large number and keep halving – 800 is a good start number.

Useful resources

N3.3OHP contains partitioning diagrams to help illustrate the examples in the student book.

Introductory activity

Discuss strategies for multiplying by 2, 3, 4 and 5.

Ask students to describe their own strategies.

- ×2 is just double the number
- ×3 is double and add the number again
- ×4 is double the number twice
- ×5 is ×10 then halve the answer.

Discuss how knowing these strategies can help with multiplying by 6, 7, 8 and 9 as well.

Write down 21 × 8 and ask how to solve it mentally.
21 × 8 = 21 × 2 × 2 × 2, so just double three times (42, 84, 168).
Ask a volunteer to explain how to work out 21 × 6 (= 21 × 3 × 2 = 63 × 2 = 126).

Explain that you can use partitioning to multiply by 7 or 9.

Work through the first example in the student book. **N3.3OHP** contains diagrams that help visualise the partitioning in this example.

Explain that knowing multiplication facts up to 10 × 10 can help with division.

Use 12 ÷ 3 as an example, and write it as 3 × = 12. The missing number is 4, so 12 ÷ 3 = 4
Emphasise that division is the opposite of multiplication.

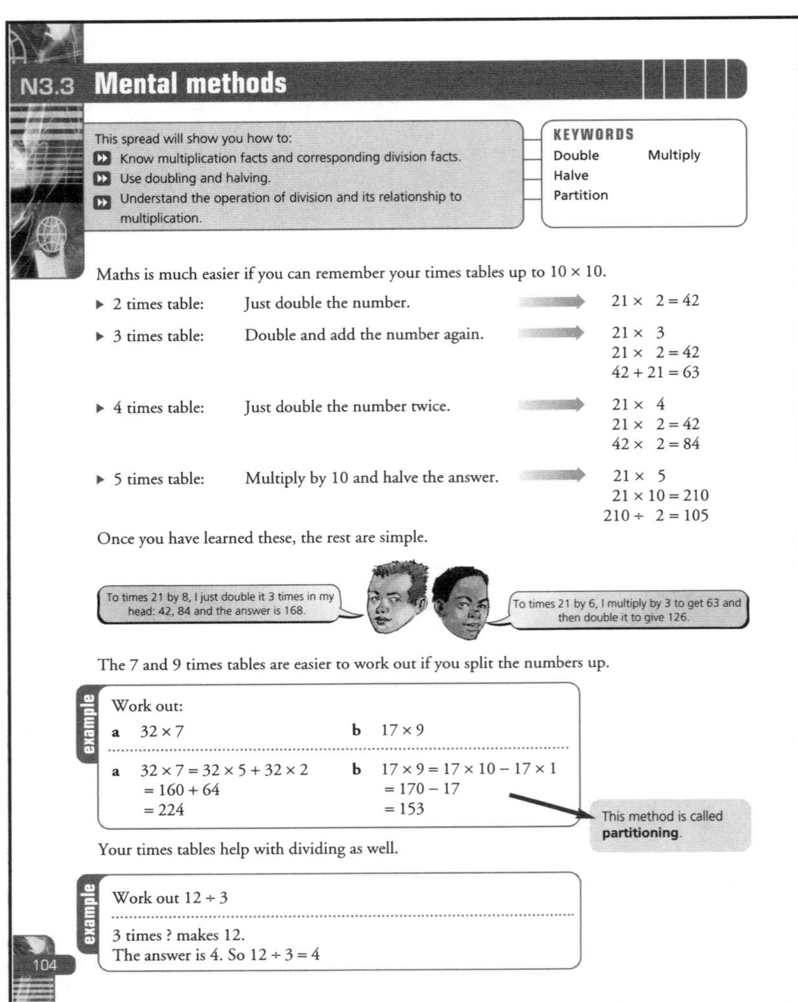

N3.3 **Mental methods**

This spread will show you how to:

- Know multiplication facts and corresponding division facts.
- Use doubling and halving.
- Understand the operation of division and its relationship to multiplication.

KEYWORDS
Double
Halve
Partition
Multiply

Maths is much easier if you can remember your times tables up to 10 × 10.

- 2 times table: Just double the number. → 21 × 2 = 42
- 3 times table: Double and add the number again. → 21 × 3; 21 × 2 = 42; 42 + 21 = 63
- 4 times table: Just double the number twice. → 21 × 4; 21 × 2 = 42; 42 × 2 = 84
- 5 times table: Multiply by 10 and halve the answer. → 21 × 5; 21 × 10 = 210; 210 ÷ 2 = 105

Once you have learned these, the rest are simple.

The 7 and 9 times tables are easier to work out if you split the numbers up.

example

Work out:
a 32 × 7 **b** 17 × 9

a 32 × 7 = 32 × 5 + 32 × 2
= 160 + 64
= 224

b 17 × 9 = 17 × 10 − 17 × 1
= 170 − 17
= 153

This method is called **partitioning**.

Your times tables help with dividing as well.

example

Work out 12 ÷ 3

3 times ? makes 12.
The answer is 4. So 12 ÷ 3 = 4

104

Plenary

Recap the methods for multiplying by numbers up to 10.

Discuss question 9b, which links to solving equations.

Further activities

Students can devise grids like those in question 9 for partners to solve.

Students can discuss simple tests of divisibility based on questions 3–8.

Differentiation

Support questions:

- Questions 1 and 2 revise work from Year 4 objectives. Springboard 7, pages 215, 216.
- Questions 3–8 focus on mental strategies. Springboard 7, pages 217–219, 332.
- Question 9 involves using mental strategies in a problem solving context. Springboard 7, page 333.

Core tier: focuses on mental strategies for multiplying with decimals.

Exercise N3.3

Do all these questions in your head.

1 Work out these times table questions.
a 3 × 3 **b** 4 × 5 **c** 2 × 6 **d** 3 × 4 **e** 6 × 3 **f** 5 × 5
g 2 × 8 **h** 3 × 9 **i** 9 × 2 **j** 4 × 3 **k** 3 × 6 **l** 8 × 2

2 Work out these division questions.
a 16 ÷ 2 **b** 16 ÷ 4 **c** 15 ÷ 3 **d** 15 ÷ 5 **e** 12 ÷ 4 **f** 20 ÷ 4
g 25 ÷ 5 **h** 18 ÷ 3 **i** 30 ÷ 5 **j** 28 ÷ 7 **k** 24 ÷ 6 **l** 27 ÷ 3

3 Work out the answers to these 2 times table questions by doubling.
a 15 × 2 **b** 21 × 2 **c** 42 × 2 **d** 16 × 2 **e** 26 × 2 **f** 38 × 2

4 Work out the answers to these 4 times table questions by doubling twice.
a 15 × 4 **b** 21 × 4 **c** 31 × 4 **d** 13 × 4 **e** 17 × 4 **f** 28 × 4

5 Work out the answers to these 8 times table questions by doubling 3 times.
a 13 × 8 **b** 21 × 8 **c** 31 × 8 **d** 40 × 8 **e** 16 × 8 **f** 102 × 8

6 Work out the answers to these 5 times table questions by multiplying by 10 and then halving.
a 15 × 5 **b** 18 × 5 **c** 21 × 5 **d** 43 × 5 **e** 70 × 5 **f** 102 × 5

7 Work out the answers to these 3 times table questions.
a 11 × 3 **b** 21 × 3 **c** 25 × 3 **d** 17 × 3 **e** 31 × 3 **f** 43 × 3

8 Work out the answers to these 6 times table questions by multiplying by 3 and then doubling.
a 15 × 6 **b** 21 × 6 **c** 25 × 6 **d** 31 × 6 **e** 43 × 6 **f** 102 × 6

9 Try to use the methods you have learned.
Copy and complete these multiplication grids.

a

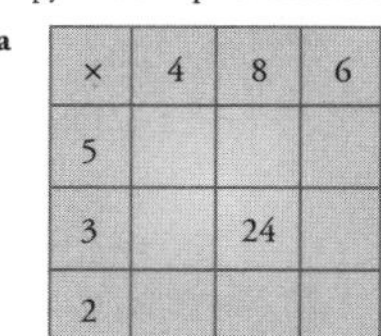

×	4	8	6
5			
3		24	
2			

b

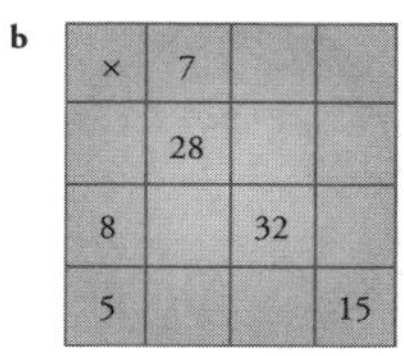

×	7		
	28		
8		32	
5			15

105

Exercise commentary

The questions assess the objectives on Primary Framework Pages 53, 55 and 59.

Problem solving

Question 9 assesses the objective from Primary Framework Page 79.

Group work

It is useful if students can discuss mental strategies together – in pairs, groups or as a class.

Misconceptions

Students tend to lose track of where they are in a calculation and what they need to do next, especially when there are lots of steps as in question 5.

Encourage the use of jottings.

Many students find division harder than multiplication and may struggle to see some of the answers in question 2.

Ensure there is a multiplication grid to hand so that they have a hint. Emphasise the link between multiplication and division. It may help to consider addition and subtraction first.

Links

Addition as the inverse of subtraction: Primary Framework Page 37.

Homework

N3.3HW is a multiplication grid to complete.

Answers

1 **a** 9 **b** 20 **c** 12 **d** 12 **e** 18 **f** 25 **g** 16 **h** 27 **i** 18 **j** 12 **k** 18 **l** 16
2 **a** 8 **b** 4 **c** 5 **d** 3 **e** 3 **f** 5 **g** 5 **h** 6 **i** 6 **j** 4 **k** 4 **l** 9
3 **a** 30 **b** 42 **c** 84 **d** 32 **e** 52 **f** 76 **4** **a** 60 **b** 84 **c** 124 **d** 52 **e** 68 **f** 112 **5** **a** 104 **b** 168 **c** 248 **d** 320 **e** 128 **f** 816
6 **a** 75 **b** 90 **c** 105 **d** 215 **e** 350 **f** 510
7 **a** 33 **b** 63 **c** 75 **d** 51 **e** 93 **f** 129
8 **a** 90 **b** 126 **c** 150 **d** 186 **e** 258 **f** 612
9 **a** Rows are: ×, 4, 6, 8; 5, 20, 40, 30; 3, 12, 24, 18; 2, 8, 16, 12
b Rows are: ×, 7, 4, 3; 4, 28, 16, 12; 8, 56, 32, 24; 5, 35, 20, 15

Mental starter

Times tables

Give students a start number between 1 and 10.
Students take turns to roll two dice and add the scores.
They all then multiply the start number by the score.
Focus on 6, 7, 8 and 9 so students can practise these times tables.

Useful resources

N3.3OHP contains partitioning diagrams.

N3.4OHP illustrates the technique of partitioning.

Introductory activity

Refer to the multiplication strategies in the previous lesson.
In particular, recap how to multiply by 7 or 9.
N3.3OHP shows the technique of splitting numbers up, or partitioning, to make multiplication easier.
N3.4OHP illustrates the technique further by showing 21×7.

Discuss how to extend the technique to include multiplying by 11.
Emphasise that you just:

- multiply the number by 10
- add the number.

Students should note that this is very similar to multiplying by 9.

Illustrate the technique with 17×11.

Extend the technique to include more difficult products.
Discuss the example: 23×24
Ask if students can think of another way of partitioning this:

23 lots of 24 = 10 lots of 24
+ 10 lots of 24
+ 3 lots of 24

Check that students get the same answer.

Emphasise that there is often more than one way to multiply two numbers mentally. The best strategies are the successful ones!

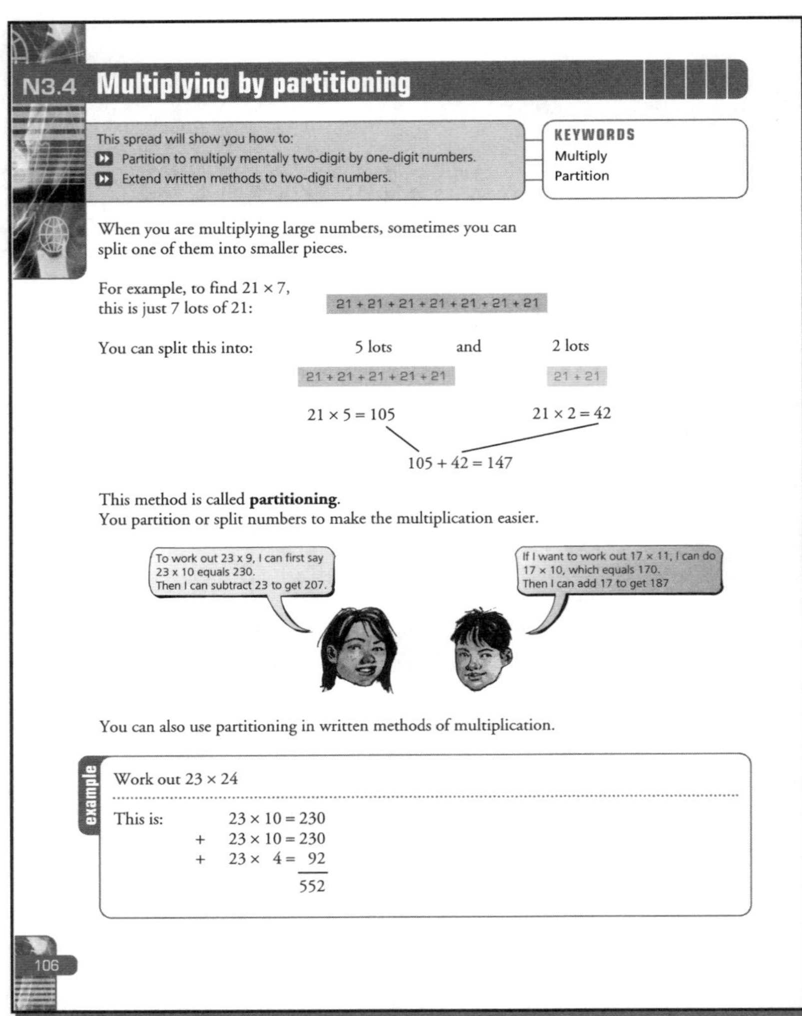

N3.4 **Multiplying by partitioning**

This spread will show you how to:

- Partition to multiply mentally two-digit by one-digit numbers.
- Extend written methods to two-digit numbers.

KEYWORDS
Multiply
Partition

When you are multiplying large numbers, sometimes you can split one of them into smaller pieces.

For example, to find 21×7, this is just 7 lots of 21: 21 + 21 + 21 + 21 + 21 + 21 + 21

You can split this into: 5 lots (21 + 21 + 21 + 21 + 21) and 2 lots (21 + 21)

$21 \times 5 = 105$ $\quad$ $21 \times 2 = 42$

$105 + 42 = 147$

This method is called **partitioning**.
You partition or split numbers to make the multiplication easier.

You can also use partitioning in written methods of multiplication.

example

Work out 23×24

This is:
$23 \times 10 = 230$
$+ \; 23 \times 10 = 230$
$+ \; 23 \times 4 = 92$
552

106

Plenary

Write the product: 21×102
Discuss how to work this out mentally.

Further activities

Students can devise word problems for questions 1 and 5.

Students can make up multiplication problems in context like those in questions 2–4 or in questions 6–8, depending on ability.

Differentiation

Support questions:

- Question 1 provides a structured introduction to partitioning. Springboard 7, page 220.
- Questions 2–5 focus on applying mental strategies. Springboard 7, page 221.
- Questions 6–8 are more complex multiplication problems including money amounts and therefore up to 2 dp. Springboard 7, pages 334–336.

Core tier: focuses on the standard method of multiplication.

Exercise N3.4

Use the partitioning method to answer questions 1–4 in your head.

1 Work out:

a 7 × 9	**b** 7 × 11	**c** 8 × 9	**d** 8 × 11
e 12 × 9	**f** 13 × 11	**g** 18 × 9	**h** 18 × 11
i 23 × 9	**j** 31 × 11	**k** 26 × 9	**l** 35 × 11

2 A music cassette costs £3.
- **a** How much would 10 cassettes cost?
- **b** How much would 11 cassettes cost?
- **c** How much would 9 cassettes cost?

3 A magazine costs 80p.
- **a** How much would 10 magazines cost?
- **b** How much would 11 magazines cost?
- **c** How much would 9 magazines cost?

4 A bag of porridge weighs 3.5 kg.
- **a** How much would 10 bags weigh?
- **b** How much would 9 bags weigh?
- **c** How much would 11 bags weigh?

Do questions 5 – 8 using a written method.

5 Work out:

a 22 × 11	**b** 21 × 21	**c** 31 × 21	**d** 50 × 19
e 32 × 31	**f** 32 × 19	**g** 35 × 29	**h** 42 × 41

6 John is holding a big barbeque.
A bag of sausages costs £4.50. The shop only has 21 bags.
How much will it cost John to buy all 21 bags?

7 Sally and 18 other friends are going to a nightclub.
Tickets cost £7.50 each.
How much do Sally and her friends pay in total?

8 Josh weighs a packet of crisps. It weighs 55 g.
How much will 29 identical bags weigh?

Exercise commentary

The questions assess the objectives on Primary Framework Pages 61 and 63.

Problem solving

Questions 2–4 and 6–8 assess the objectives from Primary Framework Pages 85 and 87.

Questions 5–8 assess Page 75 and also Page 77 if students are encouraged to explain methods.

The further activity assesses Page 75.

Group work

It is useful if students can discuss mental strategies together – in pairs, groups or as a class.

Misconceptions

The move from mental to written methods may cause some problems.

Encourage written methods that build on successful mental methods, using jottings to support mental calculations.

Emphasise the strategy of starting from facts they can recall, e.g. multiples of 10.

Students may lose track of where they are in questions 5–8.

This emphasises the need for jottings.

Links

Multiplication and division facts: Primary Framework Page 59.

Homework

Ask students to design a poster to illustrate the method of partitioning.

N3.4HW offers hints and suggestions.

Answers

1 **a** 63 **b** 77 **c** 72 **d** 88 **e** 108 **f** 143
g 162 **h** 198 **i** 207 **j** 341 **k** 234 **l** 385

2 **a** £30 **b** £33 **c** £27

3 **a** £8 **b** £8.80 **c** £7.20

4 **a** 35 kg **b** 31.5 kg **c** 38.5 kg

5 **a** 242 **b** 441 **c** 651 **d** 950 **e** 992 **f** 608 **g** 1015 **h** 1722

6 £94.50 **7** £142.50 **8** 1595 g

Mental starter

Write these products: 2×4, 2×40, 40×2, 20×4, 400×2, 400×200 etc.
Students should attempt to work out as many as they can mentally.

Useful resources

N3.5OHP illustrates the grid method for class discussion.

Introductory activity

Refer to the mental starter.
Demonstrate that if you know 3×2, then you can also do 30×2, 2×30, 20×3 etc. including 200×300.
Students should describe the patterns of zeros.

Discuss why you may need to use a written method when you multiply large numbers, particularly when the numbers are not multiples of 10.
Emphasise that you should first **estimate** in your head. You can estimate by:

- rounding the numbers to the nearest 10 (or 100)
- multiplying them together.

Discuss the product 32×18.
Ask for an estimate, and encourage answers based on $30 \times 20 = 600$.
Introduce the **grid method**:

- Split the numbers into 10s and units and put them into a grid.
- Multiply the numbers together and write the answers in the grid.
- Add the numbers inside the grid.
- Compare your answer with the estimate.

You can use N3.5OHP, which provides grids to complete for this example and for the ones in the student book.

The last example uses a real context.
Emphasise the importance of including appropriate units in answers.

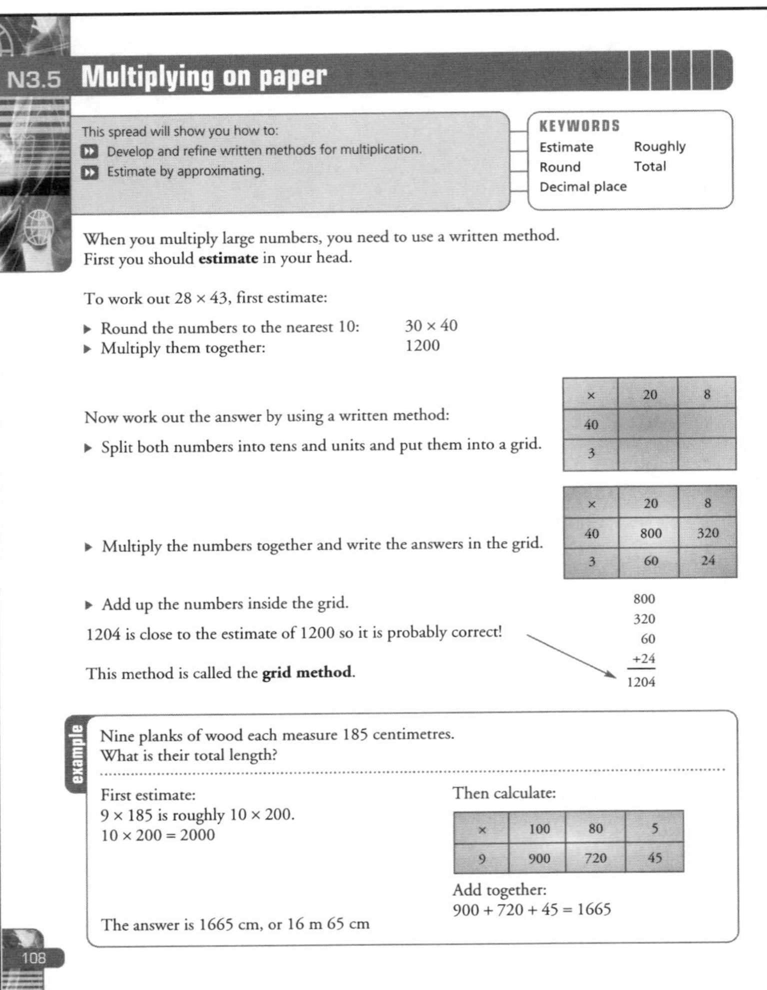

N3.5 **Multiplying on paper**

This spread will show you how to:
- Develop and refine written methods for multiplication.
- Estimate by approximating.

KEYWORDS: Estimate, Round, Decimal place, Roughly, Total

When you multiply large numbers, you need to use a written method.
First you should **estimate** in your head.

To work out 28×43, first estimate:

- Round the numbers to the nearest 10: 30×40
- Multiply them together: 1200

Now work out the answer by using a written method:

- Split both numbers into tens and units and put them into a grid.

×	20	8
40		
3		

- Multiply the numbers together and write the answers in the grid.

×	20	8
40	800	320
3	60	24

- Add up the numbers inside the grid.

800
320
60
+24
1204

1204 is close to the estimate of 1200 so it is probably correct!

This method is called the **grid method**.

example

Nine planks of wood each measure 185 centimetres.
What is their total length?

First estimate:
9×185 is roughly 10×200.
$10 \times 200 = 2000$

Then calculate:

×	100	80	5
9	900	720	45

Add together:
$900 + 720 + 45 = 1665$

The answer is 1665 cm, or 16 m 65 cm

108

Plenary

Write the product: 125×15.

Discuss how the grid method could be used for a 3-digit number × a 2-digit number.

Further activities

Students can devise word problems for questions 2 and 3.

Students work in pairs and roll a dice four times, writing down the outcomes. Challenge them to multiply numbers to find the closest answer to 1000 and then 2000, for example, with 2, 4, 5, 6: 46 × 25 = 1150 and 46 × 52 = 2392.

Differentiation

Support questions:

- Questions 1 and 2 focus on multiplying using multiples of 10. Springboard 7, page 231.
- Questions 3–8 focus on applying the grid method to multiply two numbers. Springboard 7, page 232.
- Question 9 involves doing lots of calculations in a problem solving context. Springboard 7, page 233.

Core tier: focuses on written multiplication involving decimals.

Exercise commentary

The questions assess the objectives on Primary Framework Page 67.

Problem solving

Questions 4–8 assess the objectives from Primary Framework Pages 83 and 85. Question 9 assesses Page 79.

Group work

Students should work in pairs on question 9 and the further activity.

Misconceptions

When multiplying by more than one digit, partitioning the numbers into their place value parts can cause problems. Even if the students manage to label the grid successfully, the number of calculations to do can lead to mistakes.

Encourage students to take a logical and structured approach to labelling and then filling in the grid. Always start with the number to be multiplied across and do the first row first.

Emphasise the need to estimate the answers first to ensure mistakes are clear. This usually involves looking at the first digit and hence should help students label the table.

Links

Multiplication: Primary Framework Pages 59 and 65. Multiplying by multiples of 10: Page 7. Estimation: Page 73.

Exercise N3.5

1 Copy and complete these number patterns.

	a		b
	4 × 2 = 8		5 × 3 = 15
	40 × 2 = 80		50 × 3 = 150
	4 × 20 = ___		5 × 30 = ___
	40 × 20 = ___		50 × 30 = ___
	400 × 20 = ___		500 × 30 = ___
	40 × 200 = ___		50 × 300 = ___

2 Work out the answers to each of these in your head.

a 30 × 3 **b** 3 × 20 **c** 50 × 5 **d** 80 × 4 **e** 30 × 30 **f** 30 × 20
g 50 × 50 **h** 80 × 40 **i** 300 × 30 **j** 30 × 200 **k** 500 × 50 **l** 800 × 400

3 For each of the following questions:

- Work out a rough estimate first.
- Use the grid method to work out the actual answer.

a 53 × 8 **b** 6 × 48 **c** 251 × 3 **d** 325 × 4 **e** 6 × 234 **f** 565 × 8
g 828 × 6 **h** 639 × 9 **i** 25 × 28 **j** 24 × 33 **k** 35 × 52 **l** 46 × 51

4 Four people each have £64.

a Work out a rough estimate for how much they have in total.
b Use the grid method to work out exactly how much they have.

For questions 5 to 8:

- Do a rough estimate first.
- Use the grid method of multiplication to work out the exact answer.

5 Janice runs 6 caravan parks. Each park has exactly 285 caravans. How many caravans are there in total in the 6 parks?

6 Westdene High School puts on a play for 8 nights. There are 175 tickets each night and each night is sold out. How many tickets are sold altogether?

7 Stan buys some bricks. They are sold in packs of 75. He buys 25 packs. How many bricks does he buy in total?

8 Plastic cups are sold in packs of 32. How many cups are there in 36 packs?

9 Using the digits 2, 3, 4 and 5:

- Make a two-digit number. For example: 23.
- Make another number with the remaining digits. For example: 45.
- Multiply them together. 23 × 45
- What is the biggest answer you can make?
- Repeat with different two-digit numbers.
- What is the smallest answer you can make?

Homework

N3.5HW provides practice at the grid method of multiplication.

Answers

1 a 4 × 2 = 8, 40 × 2 = 80, 4 × 20 = 80, 40 × 20 = 800, 400 × 20 = 8000, 40 × 200 = 8000 **b** 5 × 3 = 15, 50 × 3 = 150, 5 × 30 = 150, 50 × 30 = 1500, 500 × 30 = 15 000, 50 × 300 = 15 000

2 a 90 **b** 60 **c** 250 **d** 320 **e** 900 **f** 600 **g** 2500 **h** 3200 **i** 9000 **j** 6000 **k** 25 000 **l** 320 000

3 a 424 **b** 288 **c** 753 **d** 1300 **e** 1404 **f** 4520 **g** 4968 **h** 5751 **i** 700 **j** 792 **k** 1820 **l** 2346 **4 a** 4 × £60 = £240 **b** £256

5 1710 **6** 1400 **7** 1875 **8** 1152

9 52 × 43 = 2236 is the biggest answer; 24 × 35 = 840 is the smallest answer.

N3.6 Dividing on paper

Mental starter

Tables game

Select three students to come to the front and sit down.
Each student is allocated a times table, for example 3, 7 and 8.
The remaining students suggest numbers. If a particular number is in any of the three students' times tables, they stand up.
For example, if 24 is called out the 3 times table and 8 times table would stand up.

The object of the game is for the class to identify each of the times tables.

Useful resources

N3.6OHP illustrates the repeated subtraction method.
A pack of **playing cards** is useful for the introductory activity.

Introductory activity

Recap the relationship between multiplication and division.
Write 6 × 7 = 42.
Ask what other facts can be derived.
Encourage responses like 42 ÷ 7 = 6.
Use a 6 by 7 rectangular array of dots to demonstrate the relationship.

6 × 7 = 42
7 × 6 = 42
42 ÷ 7 = 6
42 ÷ 6 = 7

Now discuss divisions such as 56 ÷ 7.
If students don't know the multiplication 7 × 8 = 56, they need to use a different method.
As + and × link (× is repeated +), − and ÷ link (÷ is repeated −).

Demonstrate the method of repeated subtraction.

- Choose four students.
- Deal out 20 cards between them, one card at a time.
- Record how many cards are left each time you have gone round all four i.e. 20, 16, 12, 8, 4, 0.
- At the end, each student should have received 5 cards.

Show **N3.6OHP**, which illustrates the card dealing, and shows each step as a repeated subtraction.
Emphasise the important link between 4 × 5 = 20 and 20 ÷ 4 = 5.

Demonstrate repeated subtraction again, with 48 ÷ 4, using the written method.
Emphasise the importance of:

- working methodically
- laying out each step on the correct line.

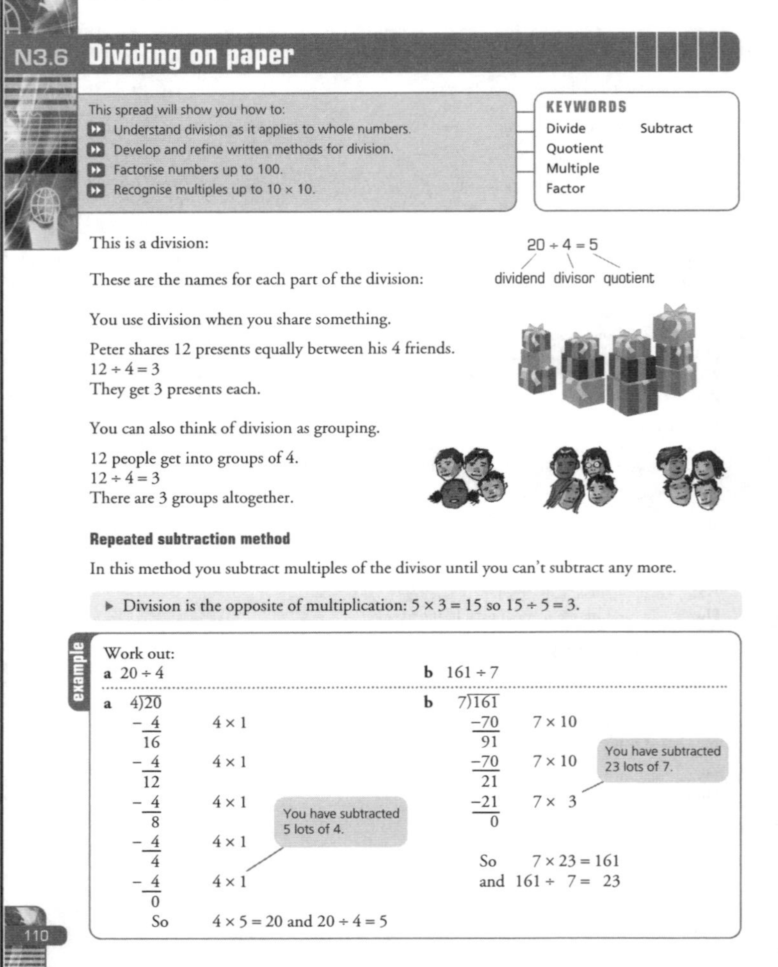

N3.6 **Dividing on paper**

This spread will show you how to:
- Understand division as it applies to whole numbers.
- Develop and refine written methods for division.
- Factorise numbers up to 100.
- Recognise multiples up to 10 × 10.

KEYWORDS
Divide, Subtract, Quotient, Multiple, Factor

This is a division: 20 ÷ 4 = 5

These are the names for each part of the division: dividend divisor quotient

You use division when you share something.

Peter shares 12 presents equally between his 4 friends.
12 ÷ 4 = 3
They get 3 presents each.

You can also think of division as grouping.

12 people get into groups of 4.
12 ÷ 4 = 3
There are 3 groups altogether.

Repeated subtraction method

In this method you subtract multiples of the divisor until you can't subtract any more.

- Division is the opposite of multiplication: 5 × 3 = 15 so 15 ÷ 5 = 3.

example

Work out:
a 20 ÷ 4 **b** 161 ÷ 7

a 4)20
− 4 (4 × 1) → 16
− 4 (4 × 1) → 12
− 4 (4 × 1) → 8
− 4 (4 × 1) → 4
− 4 (4 × 1) → 0
You have subtracted 5 lots of 4.
So 4 × 5 = 20 and 20 ÷ 4 = 5

b 7)161
−70 (7 × 10) → 91
−70 (7 × 10) → 21
−21 (7 × 3) → 0
You have subtracted 23 lots of 7.
So 7 × 23 = 161 and 161 ÷ 7 = 23

110

Plenary

Discuss question 6, which is an investigation.

- Encourage the response that numbers dividing exactly by 5 always end in a 5 or 0 digit.
- Are there rules for any other divisors e.g. 4?

Link to rules for finding multiples (N3.3).

Further activities

Students can devise word problems for questions 2 and 4.

Give students improper fractions to change into mixed numbers after completing question 8.

Differentiation

Support questions:

- Question 1 revises recall of division facts. Springboard 7, page 235.
- Questions 2–7 focus on dividing by a single digit. Springboard 7, pages 236, 237.
- Question 8 involves dividing by two-digit numbers.

Core tier: extends to four-digit by two-digit divisions.

Exercise N3.6

1 Work out these divisions in your head.

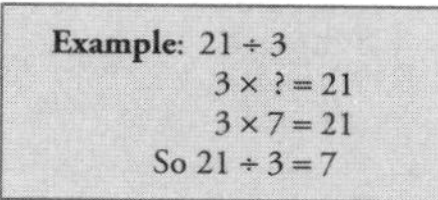
Example: 21 ÷ 3
3 × ? = 21
3 × 7 = 21
So 21 ÷ 3 = 7

a 15 ÷ 5 **b** 12 ÷ 3 **c** 14 ÷ 7 **d** 16 ÷ 4 **e** 32 ÷ 4 **f** 35 ÷ 5

2 Work out these divisions on paper. Do a rough estimate first.
a 123 ÷ 3 **b** 115 ÷ 5 **c** 148 ÷ 4 **d** 215 ÷ 5 **e** 216 ÷ 3 **f** 248 ÷ 8

3 Work out which of the numbers in the grid are **multiples** of:
a 7 **b** 6 **c** 9

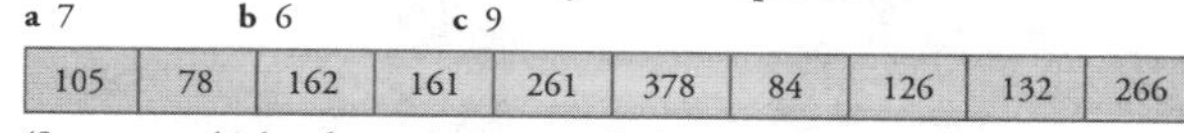

105	78	162	161	261	378	84	126	132	266

(Some are multiples of more than one number.)

4 Calculate:
a 184 ÷ 8 **b** 468 ÷ 9 **c** 217 ÷ 7 **d** 210 ÷ 6 **e** 360 ÷ 8 **f** 648 ÷ 9

5 **Investigation**
The number 12 has exactly six **factors** (1, 2, 3, 4, 6 and 12):
1 × 12 = 12
2 × 6 = 12
3 × 4 = 12
a Find all the factors of 20, 60 and 180
b Find a number less than 100 with exactly seven factors.

6 **Investigation**
'All numbers that divide by 2 always end in a 0, 2, 4, 6 or 8 digit.'
For example, 124 ÷ 2 = 62.
a Investigate numbers that divide by 5
What do you notice?
b Investigate other divisors.

7 Convert these fractions to mixed numbers.
(Turn to page 44 to remind yourself about improper fractions.)
a $\frac{24}{6}$ **b** $\frac{35}{7}$ **c** $\frac{112}{8}$ **d** $\frac{153}{9}$
Explain how you worked out your answers.

8 Calculate the following.
a 154 ÷ 11 **b** 204 ÷ 12 **c** 225 ÷ 15 **d** 247 ÷ 13
e 252 ÷ 21 **f** 506 ÷ 22 **g** 372 ÷ 31 **h** 850 ÷ 25

111

Exercise commentary

The questions assess the objectives on Primary Framework Pages 19, 21 and 69.

Problem solving
Questions 5 and 7 assess the objectives from Primary Framework Page 79.

Group work
Students will benefit from discussing questions 5 and 7 in particular.

Misconceptions
Many students find division difficult.
Use of a multiplication grid will help recall of facts but the method of repeated subtraction can cause problems as there are lots of steps and students tend to lose track.
Encourage structured record keeping and emphasise the need to estimate before calculating and to check each step with the original question.
In question 5 students may count 8 × 8 as two factors and hence not find a number with seven factors.
Encourage them to list the factors rather than the pairs.
In question 6b encourage a logical approach by suggesting they consider 4, 8 then 10 and emphasise the link with finding multiples from N3.3.

Links
Fractions: Primary Framework Page 23.
Estimation: Page 73.

Homework

Ask students to design a poster to explain a written method of division. **N3.6HW** contains hints and suggestions.

Answers

1 **a** 3 **b** 4 **c** 2 **d** 4 **e** 8 **f** 7 **2** **a** 41 **b** 23 **c** 37 **d** 43 **e** 72 **f** 31
3 **a** 105, 161, 378, 84, 126, 266 **b** 78, 162, 378, 84, 126, 132 **c** 162, 261, 378, 126
4 **a** 23 **b** 52 **c** 31 **d** 35 **e** 45 **f** 72
5 **a** Factors of 20: 1, 2, 4, 5, 10, 20
Factors of 60: 1, 2, 3, 4, 5, 6, 10, 12, 15, 20, 30, 60
Factors of 180: 1, 2, 3, 4, 5, 6, 9, 10, 12, 15, 18, 20, 30, 36, 45, 60, 90, 180
b 64 has exactly seven factors: 1, 2, 4, 8, 16, 32, 64
6 **a** Numbers that divide by 5 end in 0 or 5.
7 **a** 4 **b** 5 **c** 14 **d** 17 **8** **a** 14 **b** 17 **c** 15 **d** 19 **e** 12 **f** 23 **g** 12 **h** 34

N3.7 Dividing with remainders

Mental starter

Write this division: $372 \div 11$

Write these possible answers:

40, 361, 363, 33 remainder 9, 33 remainder 12

Discuss which is likely to be the correct answer – make an estimate first. Discuss why a remainder of 12 is impossible if you are dividing by 11.

Useful resources

N3.7OHP contains a repeated subtraction calculation for discussion.

0–9 dice or **R1** digit cards are useful for the further activity described in **N3.7F**.

Introductory activity

Recap the repeated subtraction method.

Use $350 \div 7$ as an example on **N3.7OHP**.

Demonstrate the repeated subtraction method when there is a remainder.

You could use $50 \div 6$ on **N3.7OHP**.

$$\begin{array}{rl} 50 & \\ -30 & 6 \times 5 \\ \hline 20 & \\ -\ 6 & 6 \times 1 \\ \hline 14 & \\ -\ 6 & 6 \times 1 \\ \hline 8 & \\ -\ 6 & 6 \times 1 \\ \hline 2 & \end{array}$$

$6 \times 8 = 48$

$48 + 2 = 50$

$50 \div 6 = 8$ rem 2

Use **N3.7OHP** to discuss the examples in the student book. In the second example, emphasise the importance of estimating first.

Discuss the meaning of a remainder, using a real context.

30 students are to fit into taxis that can hold 4 people.

How many taxis will be completely filled, and how many students will be left over?

Use repeated subtraction to arrive at $4 \times 7 = 28$, and $28 + 2 = 30$. Make the link to $30 \div 4 = 7$ remainder 2.

So 7 taxis will be filled, with two students left over.

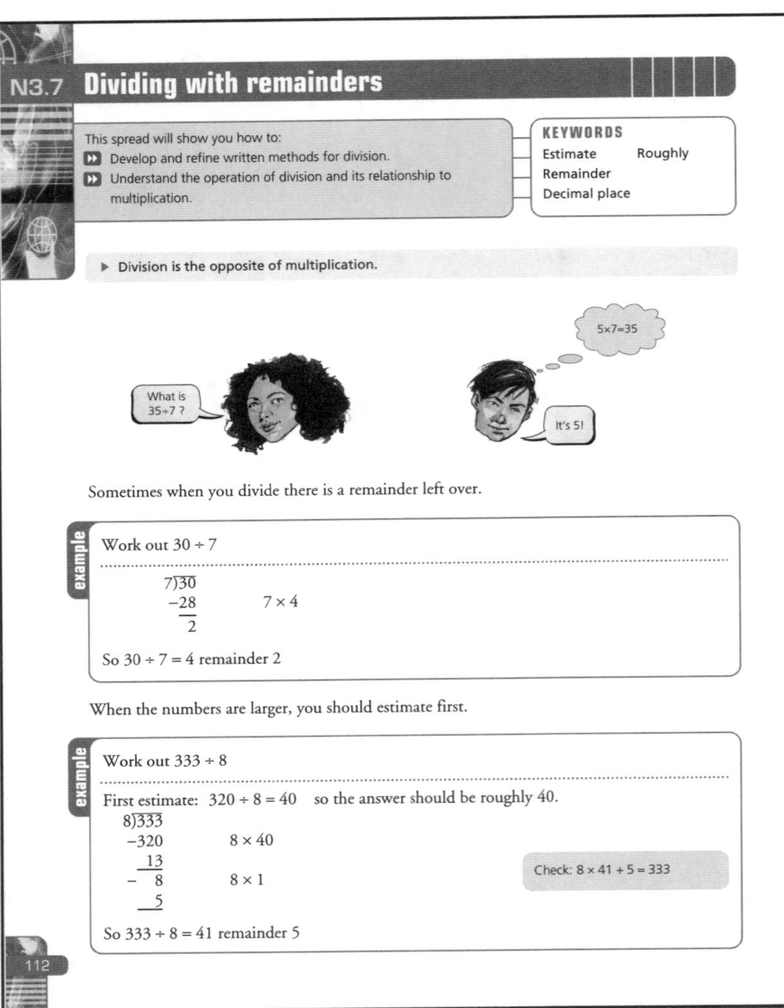

N3.7 Dividing with remainders
This spread will show you how to:
Develop and refine written methods for division.
Understand the operation of division and its relationship to multiplication.
KEYWORDS
Estimate
Roughly
Remainder
Decimal place
Division is the opposite of multiplication.
5×7=35
What is 35÷7 ?
It's 5!
Sometimes when you divide there is a remainder left over.
example
Work out 30 ÷ 7
7)30
−28 7 × 4
2
So 30 ÷ 7 = 4 remainder 2
When the numbers are larger, you should estimate first.
example
Work out 333 ÷ 8
First estimate: 320 ÷ 8 = 40 so the answer should be roughly 40.
8)333
−320 8 × 40
13
− 8 8 × 1
5
Check: 8 × 41 + 5 = 333
So 333 ÷ 8 = 41 remainder 5
112

Plenary

Discuss how you interpret a remainder in real contexts.

In the taxi example, the students will need 8 taxis so you round up the answer.

In other contexts, such as in filling jars in a factory, you would round down. For example, how many 50 g jars of jam can be filled from 406 g of jam?

Further activities

Students can make up word problems for questions 1, 3 and 5.

N3.7F contains a division game for students to practice dividing by 4, 7, 11 and 16. It is recommended for use after students have successfully completed question 5.

Differentiation

Support questions:

- Question 1 revises recall of division facts. Springboard 7, page 338.
- Questions 2 and 3 focus on dividing by a single digit. Springboard 7, pages 339–341.
- Questions 4–6 involve dividing by two-digit numbers and converting improper fractions to mixed numbers with remainders. Springboard 7, page 342.

Core tier: focuses on interpreting a remainder in context, including decimal remainders.

Exercise N3.7

1 Work out these divisions.
Be careful – they all have remainders!

a 18 ÷ 5 **b** 21 ÷ 4 **c** 13 ÷ 4
d 17 ÷ 8 **e** 26 ÷ 9 **f** 35 ÷ 8

2 **Remainder Max Game**
(2 players)

- The object of the game is to have the largest remainder.
- Each player takes it in turns to choose one number from Box A and one from Box B.
- Each number can only be chosen once.

Box A			
38	47	31	56
22	62	49	75

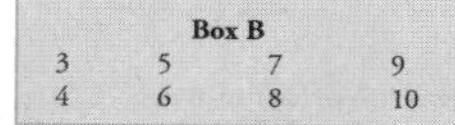

Box B				
3	5		7	9
4	6		8	10

- Divide the number in box A by the number in Box B.
  The player scores the value of the remainder.
- After four turns each the players add up the total.
- The winner is the player with the largest total remainder.

3 These divisions all have remainders.
Calculate:

a 130 ÷ 4 **b** 155 ÷ 3 **c** 241 ÷ 7
d 493 ÷ 8 **e** 310 ÷ 3 **f** 263 ÷ 4
g 430 ÷ 6 **h** 452 ÷ 8 **i** 845 ÷ 4
j 913 ÷ 7 **k** 513 ÷ 8 **l** 823 ÷ 9

4 Identify which of the numbers in the grid are multiples of:
a 12 **b** 15 **c** 13

180	195	228	312	156	104	240	169

5 Calculate the following.
Some of them have remainders.

a 130 ÷ 11 **b** 155 ÷ 12 **c** 238 ÷ 17
d 263 ÷ 15 **e** 420 ÷ 20 **f** 323 ÷ 19
g 208 ÷ 13 **h** 270 ÷ 15 **i** 188 ÷ 14
j 548 ÷ 15 **k** 936 ÷ 18 **l** 517 ÷ 11

6 Convert these improper fractions to mixed numbers.

a $\frac{23}{7}$ **b** $\frac{48}{5}$ **c** $\frac{92}{8}$
d $\frac{107}{4}$ **e** $\frac{128}{7}$ **f** $\frac{163}{10}$

113

Exercise commentary

The questions assess the objectives on Primary Framework Pages 55 and 69.

Problem solving

Question 2 assesses the objectives from Primary Framework Page 79.

Group work

Question 2 is suitable for pair work.

Misconceptions

Many students find division difficult, especially those containing remainders.
Encourage the use of a multiplication grid to find the nearest multiple in simple divisions and use it to illustrate how to find the remainder.
Encourage estimation by approximation and emphasise that in simpler cases this can lead students directly to the answer.
Students need to make the link between multiples and division.
Using real-life problems can help them understand the link, particularly those problems involving money.

Links

Fractions: Primary Framework Page 23.
Estimation: Page 73.

Homework

N3.7HW provides practice at dividing with remainders.

Answers

1 **a** 3 r 3 **b** 5 r 1 **c** 3 r 1 **d** 2 r 1 **e** 2 r 8 **f** 4 r 3

3 **a** 32 r 2 **b** 51 r 2 **c** 34 r 3 **d** 61 r 5 **e** 103 r 1 **f** 65 r 3 **g** 71 r 4 **h** 56 r 4 **i** 211 r 1 **j** 130 r 3 **k** 64 r 1 **l** 91 r 4

4 **a** 180, 228, 312, 156, 240 **b** 180, 195, 240 **c** 195, 312, 156, 104, 169

5 **a** 11 r 9 **b** 12 r 11 **c** 14 **d** 17 r 8 **e** 21 **f** 17 **g** 16 **h** 18 **i** 13 r 6 **j** 36 r 8 **k** 52 **l** 47

6 **a** $3\frac{2}{7}$ **b** $9\frac{3}{5}$ **c** $11\frac{1}{2}$ **d** $26\frac{3}{4}$ **e** $18\frac{2}{7}$ **f** $16\frac{3}{10}$

Mental starter

Write three numbers: 8, 4 and 2.
Students should make as many different answers as they can, by combining them with operators in different ways.
For example, 8 + 4 + 2, 8 + 4 – 2, 8 × 2 – 4 etc.

Ensure that the correct order of operations has been used in each case.

Useful resources

A class set of **calculators** is essential for this lesson.

N3.8OHP shows a standard Casio fx82 scientific calculator.

Introductory activity

Discuss when you would use a calculator rather than your head or a written method. In particular:

- with large numbers e.g. 328 × 34
- with awkward divisions e.g. 70 ÷ 34
- with decimal calculations e.g. 3.2 × 4.4

Recap the correct order of operations with 18 – 3 × 4.
First ask students to work this out in their heads, and then they should work it out on their calculators.
Discuss any different answers and why they occur: students should be familiar with the way in which their own calculator works.

Introduce problems with brackets.
Discuss the first example in the student book. Students should first estimate, and then work it out on their calculators:

- using brackets
- using memory keys.

N3.8OHP shows a scientific calculator to help demonstrate the keys that students should press.

Introduce problems in context.
Discuss the second example in the student book, which is based on sharing a sum of money.
Emphasise approximation first.
Emphasise that the calculator display is not always the final answer; it often needs to be **interpreted**.

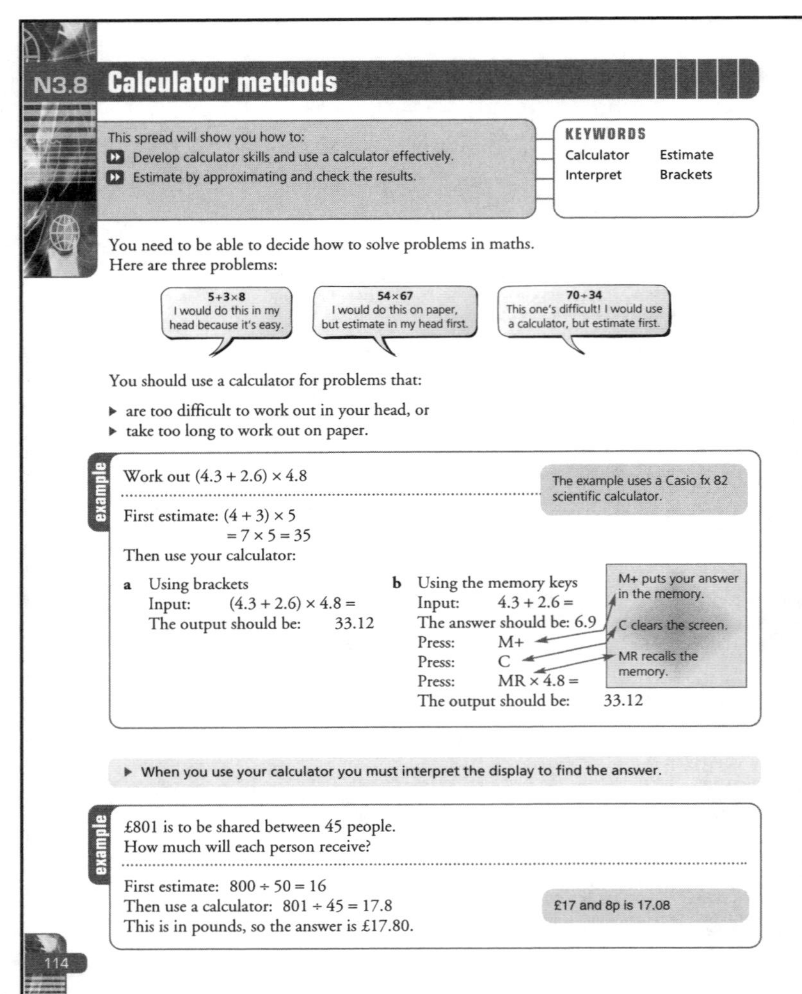

N3.8 **Calculator methods**

This spread will show you how to:
- Develop calculator skills and use a calculator effectively.
- Estimate by approximating and check the results.

KEYWORDS
Calculator, Estimate, Interpret, Brackets

You need to be able to decide how to solve problems in maths.
Here are three problems:

You should use a calculator for problems that:
- are too difficult to work out in your head, or
- take too long to work out on paper.

example

Work out (4.3 + 2.6) × 4.8

The example uses a Casio fx 82 scientific calculator.

First estimate: (4 + 3) × 5
= 7 × 5 = 35
Then use your calculator:

a Using brackets
Input: (4.3 + 2.6) × 4.8 =
The output should be: 33.12

b Using the memory keys
Input: 4.3 + 2.6 =
The answer should be: 6.9
Press: M+
Press: C
Press: MR × 4.8 =
The output should be: 33.12

M+ puts your answer in the memory.
C clears the screen.
MR recalls the memory.

- When you use your calculator you must interpret the display to find the answer.

example

£801 is to be shared between 45 people.
How much will each person receive?

First estimate: 800 ÷ 50 = 16
Then use a calculator: 801 ÷ 45 = 17.8
This is in pounds, so the answer is £17.80.

£17 and 8p is 17.08

114

Plenary

Discuss question 5. Which method did students use for each part, and why?

Discuss question 6, which is a game based on approximation.

- Which calculations were difficult to estimate?
- Which were the easiest?

Further activities

Students can make up word problems for question 5.

Able students can devise a game similar to question 6 but including a division and a subtraction.

Differentiation

Support questions:

- Question 1 is a worked example for students to follow. Springboard 7, page 350.
- Questions 2–4 focus on using the memory and brackets keys in progressively more complex problems. Springboard 7, page 351.
- Question 5 involves a choice of method and question 6 is an activity that generates complex calculations to do. Springboard 7, page 352.

Core tier: focuses on interpreting calculator output to find answers to problems in context.

Exercise N3.8

You will need a scientific calculator for this exercise.

1 This question refers to the keys on a Casio fx82.

a
- Work out 3 + 8 ÷ 2 in your head. (Remember the order of operations.)
- Work out 8 ÷ 2 on your calculator.
- Press the M+ key to store your answer
- Input 3 + MR
- You should have 7 as the answer!

b
- Work out 12 − 3 × 3 in your head.
- Input 3 × 3 =
- Press the M+ key to store your answer.
- Input 12 − MR.
- You should have 3 as the answer.

2 Work out each of these by using the memory keys on your calculator. In each case, first make an estimate.

a 0.9 + 1.6 × 2.1 **b** 2 + 3 × 1.8 **c** 20 − 1.3 × 5
d 9 + 0.7 ÷ 1.4 **e** 11.6 − 10 ÷ 2 **f** 212 − 30.6 ÷ 3

3 Work these out by using the bracket keys where appropriate.

a 5 × (2 + 4) **b** 5 × 2 + 4 **c** 0.2 × (3.6 + 4.4)
d 8 ÷ (1.7 − 0.9) **e** 16.2 × (4.3 + 1.2) **f** 174.8 ÷ (4.2 + 3.4)

4 **a** Each day, John spends £2.65 and Paul spends £3.78 on sweets and comics. How much do they spend altogether in a week?
b Rukshana saves £12.45 per month. How much will she have saved after 3 years?
c Calculate the total cost of:
- 17 rulers at 32p each,
- 64 rubbers at 12p each,
- 14 pairs of compasses at £1.15 each and
- 27 refill pads at £1.99 each.

5 You will need to decide whether you should use a mental, written or calculator method to calculate.

a 12 × 11 **b** 84 ÷ 4 **c** 23 × 25
d 85 ÷ 5 **e** 37 × 23 **f** 0.72 × 100
g 3.8 × 5 **h** 14.2 ÷ 5 **i** 36.4 ÷ 13
j 0.9 + 5 × 0.2 **k** 4362 ÷ 100 **l** 16.4 + 3.6 × 2.8

6 **The Approximation Game**
- Player 1 chooses 3 numbers from the grid.

42.3	14.9	38.4	16.4	7.3	29.2	9.2	23.1

- Player 1 places the 3 numbers into the equation: □ × □ + □ =
- Player 2 gives an estimate of the answer. The difference between the estimate and the real answer is the score for Player 1.
- Player 2 now chooses 3 numbers and Player 1 gives an estimate of the answer.
- The winner is the first player to reach 100.

Exercise commentary

The questions assess the objectives on Primary Framework Pages 71 and 73.

Problem solving

Question 6 assesses Primary Framework Page 79. Question 4 assesses Page 85. Question 5 assesses Page 75.

Group work

Question 6 is suitable for pair work.

Misconceptions

Students tend to use the calculator without thinking what answer to expect and just assume the display is correct.

Encourage the use of an estimate and emphasise that sometimes it is quicker to carry on with the mental method rather than reach for the calculator.

Emphasise that the calculator just calculates and so it is important that students do the thinking.

Students may need reminding of Bidmas before attempting question 3.

In question 4 students need to ensure all the money amounts are in the same units before using a calculator.

Links

Brackets: Primary Framework Page 55.

Homework

N3.8HW is an investigation based on using a calculator.

Answers

1 **a** 7 **b** 3
2 **a** 4.26 **b** 7.4 **c** 13.5 **d** 9.5 **e** 6.6 **f** 201.8
3 **a** 30 **b** 14 **c** 1.6 **d** 10 **e** 89.1 **f** 23
4 **a** £45.01 **b** £448.20 **c** £82.95
5 **a** 132 **b** 21 **c** 575 **d** 17 **e** 851 **f** 72 **g** 19 **h** 2.84 **i** 2.8
j 1.9 **k** 43.62 **l** 26.48

Summary

The Year 6 key teaching objectives are:

- Understand and use the relationships between the four operations (53, 55).
- Derive division facts from known multiplication facts (59).
- Extend mental methods of calculation (67, 69).
- Identify and use appropriate operations to solve word problems (83–89).

Check out commentary

1 Students should be able to answer parts a to g easily. If not they should be set further similar questions based on the multiplication grid at the end of the book. Parts **h** to **l** require an understanding of place value. Students may benefit from using a place value table as on R4.

2 Students tend to work from right to left irrespective of the order. Some students find the number of steps involved confusing and lose track of where they are in calculations.
Encourage students to use the acronym Bidmas to remember that there is a specific order and to set out the working in logical steps underneath each other as in N3.2.

3 Students tend to make mistakes once numbers start to get bigger and they develop multi-step strategies.
Encourage them to use methods that build on successful single-step strategies, in particular emphasise the use of jottings, and encourage them to estimate answers as a check.

4 Word problems can cause many difficulties. Students tend to use all the numbers given in the question and multiply without thinking which operation is needed.
Encourage them to use a logical approach to the questions and simplify the numbers to focus on the operation.

Plenary activity

Ask students to work out:

- the cost of 5 CDs at £10.97 each
- the cost of a kilogram of potatoes when 7 kg cost £3.43
- the total length of 13 pieces of string that are 3.5 cm each
- the weight of cake eaten by each of six people when the whole cake weighs 675 g.

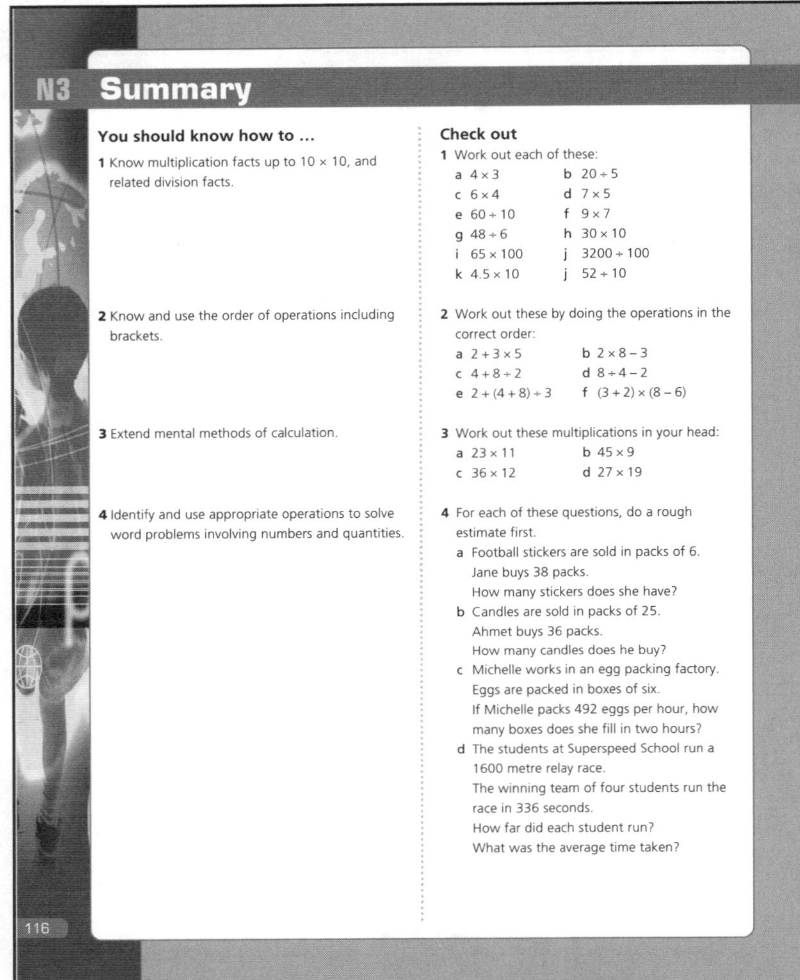

N3 **Summary**

You should know how to ...

1 Know multiplication facts up to 10 × 10, and related division facts.

2 Know and use the order of operations including brackets.

3 Extend mental methods of calculation.

4 Identify and use appropriate operations to solve word problems involving numbers and quantities.

Check out

1 Work out each of these:

a 4×3	b $20 \div 5$
c 6×4	d 7×5
e $60 \div 10$	f 9×7
g $48 \div 6$	h 30×10
i 65×100	j $3200 \div 100$
k 4.5×10	j $52 \div 10$

2 Work out these by doing the operations in the correct order:

a $2 + 3 \times 5$	b $2 \times 8 - 3$
c $4 + 8 \div 2$	d $8 \div 4 - 2$
e $2 + (4 + 8) \div 3$	f $(3 + 2) \times (8 - 6)$

3 Work out these multiplications in your head:

a 23×11	b 45×9
c 36×12	d 27×19

4 For each of these questions, do a rough estimate first.

a Football stickers are sold in packs of 6. Jane buys 38 packs. How many stickers does she have?

b Candles are sold in packs of 25. Ahmet buys 36 packs. How many candles does he buy?

c Michelle works in an egg packing factory. Eggs are packed in boxes of six. If Michelle packs 492 eggs per hour, how many boxes does she fill in two hours?

d The students at Superspeed School run a 1600 metre relay race. The winning team of four students run the race in 336 seconds. How far did each student run? What was the average time taken?

116

Development

Multiplication and division methods are developed in N5 and the order of operations is developed in A4.

Links

Multiplication and division methods are skills used throughout the school curriculum and using the most appropriate method could form part of a whole-school numeracy policy.

Mental starters

Objectives covered in this unit:

- Recognise multiples and use tests of divisibility.
- Know pairs of factors of numbers to 100.
- Know prime numbers less than 20.
- Know squares to at least 10 × 10.

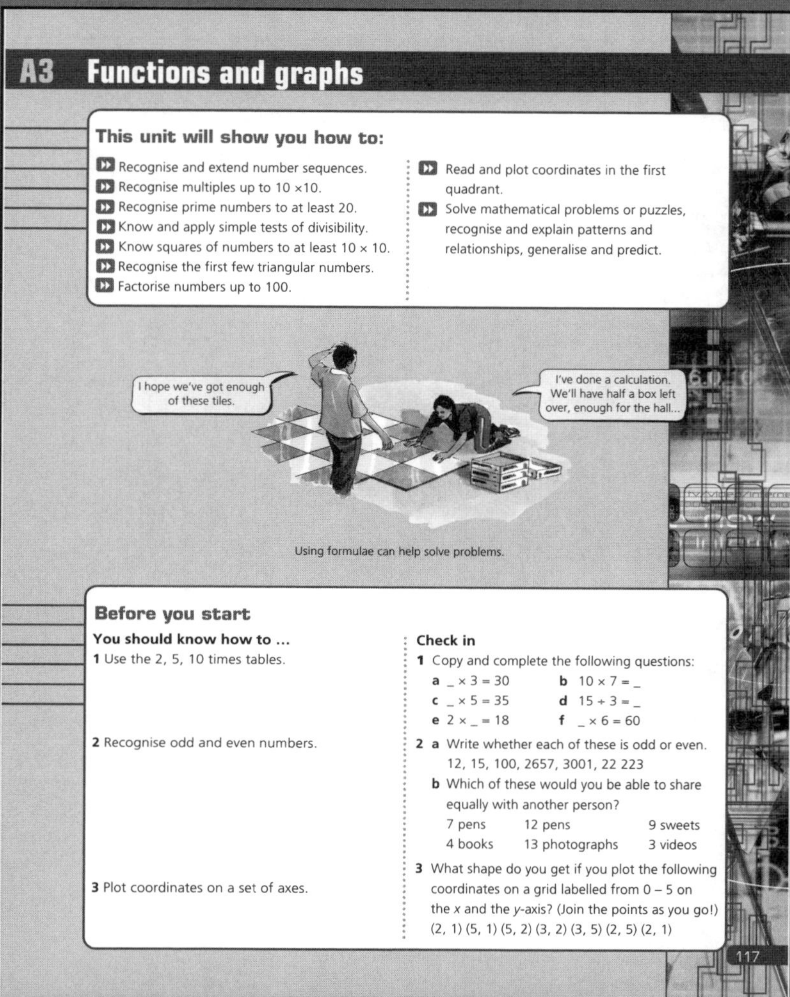

A3 Functions and graphs

This unit will show you how to:

- Recognise and extend number sequences.
- Recognise multiples up to 10 ×10.
- Recognise prime numbers to at least 20.
- Know and apply simple tests of divisibility.
- Know squares of numbers to at least 10 × 10.
- Recognise the first few triangular numbers.
- Factorise numbers up to 100.
- Read and plot coordinates in the first quadrant.
- Solve mathematical problems or puzzles, recognise and explain patterns and relationships, generalise and predict.

I hope we've got enough of these tiles.
I've done a calculation. We'll have half a box left over, enough for the hall...

Using formulae can help solve problems.

Before you start

You should know how to ...	Check in
1 Use the 2, 5, 10 times tables.	1 Copy and complete the following questions: a _ × 3 = 30 b 10 × 7 = _ c _ × 5 = 35 d 15 ÷ 3 = _ e 2 × _ = 18 f _ × 6 = 60
2 Recognise odd and even numbers.	2 a Write whether each of these is odd or even. 12, 15, 100, 2657, 3001, 22 223 b Which of these would you be able to share equally with another person? 7 pens 12 pens 9 sweets 4 books 13 photographs 3 videos
3 Plot coordinates on a set of axes.	3 What shape do you get if you plot the following coordinates on a grid labelled from 0 – 5 on the *x* and the *y*-axis? (Join the points as you go!) (2, 1) (5, 1) (5, 2) (3, 2) (3, 5) (2, 5) (2, 1)

117

Check in activity

Write these sets of numbers on the board and ask students to find the odd one out in each set.
Students can work in groups or pairs and should justify their reasoning.

- 1, 3, 5, 6 (6 – the others are even)
- 3, 9, 11, 15 (11 – the others divide by 3)
- 5, 15, 26, 30 (26 – the others divide by 5)
- 1, 4, 8, 9 (8 – the others are square!)

Resources needed

* class set needed

Essential:
R1* – Digit cards
R21* (OHP) – Multiplication grid
A3.2OHP – Arrangements of 16 and 18
A3.3OHP – Sequence patterns
A3.6OHP – Straight-line graph
Graph or squared paper
Useful:
R7 (OHP) – Function machines
R9 (OHP) – Axes in one quadrant
R17 (OHP) – 100 square
A3.1OHP – Mental starter grid
A3.6ICT* – Using Omnigraph
Multilink cubes

Unit commentary

Aim of the unit

This unit aims to consolidate students' ability to find factors and multiples and use them to find terms of a sequence. It develops to drawing graphs of functions using the input and output pairs from a function machine.

Introduction

Discuss the picture in the student book – how do you work out how many tiles you would need to fit the classroom floor? It depends on the size of the tile – how many would fit along the length and width of the room?

Framework references

This unit focuses on:

- Year 6 teaching objectives pages: 17, 19, 21, 109
- Problem solving objectives page: 79

The unit provides access to:

- Year 7 teaching objectives pages: 52, 56, 108, 146, 160

Differentiation

Core tier develops the idea of the general, *n*th term of a sequence and extends to finding the equation of a straight line.

Springboard 7

Pages 47, 48, 278, 280, 306–316, 394, 395, 493.

Mental starter

Draw a 4 × 4 grid on the board or use **A3.1OHP**.
Fill in the numbers: 12, 25, 7, 40, 36, 15, 20, 10, 18, 3, 9, 24, 30, 27, 5, 8.
Students give multiplication questions that lead to those answers.
Some have more than one question: 12 = 1 × 12, 2 × 6 or 3 × 4.
Some have only one question: 7 = 1 × 7.
Encourage students to find all possible questions for each answer.

Useful resources

A3.1OHP has the grid for the mental starter.

Introductory activity

Refer to the mental starter.
List all the questions for 12 in pairs.
Use a horseshoe shape as in the student book.

Ask students what they call each of the numbers in the questions – factors.
Define factors.

Discuss how you can find the factors of numbers such as 60.
- Ask whether 2 is a factor.
- Students should justify answers.
- Lead to the division rule for 2.
- Repeat for 3, 4, 5 and 10.

Note that 3 is the hardest rule to see and so leave this out with a weak group.
Discuss 6 and 8 if students show interest.

Discuss numbers with exactly two factors such as 7.
Ask students if they know what to call these special numbers – prime.

For each of the numbers from 1 to 10:
- List the number of factors in columns: 1 factor, 2 factors, 3 factors, 4 factors.

Emphasise that a prime number has exactly two factors so 1 is not prime.
Discuss why 2 is the only even prime number.

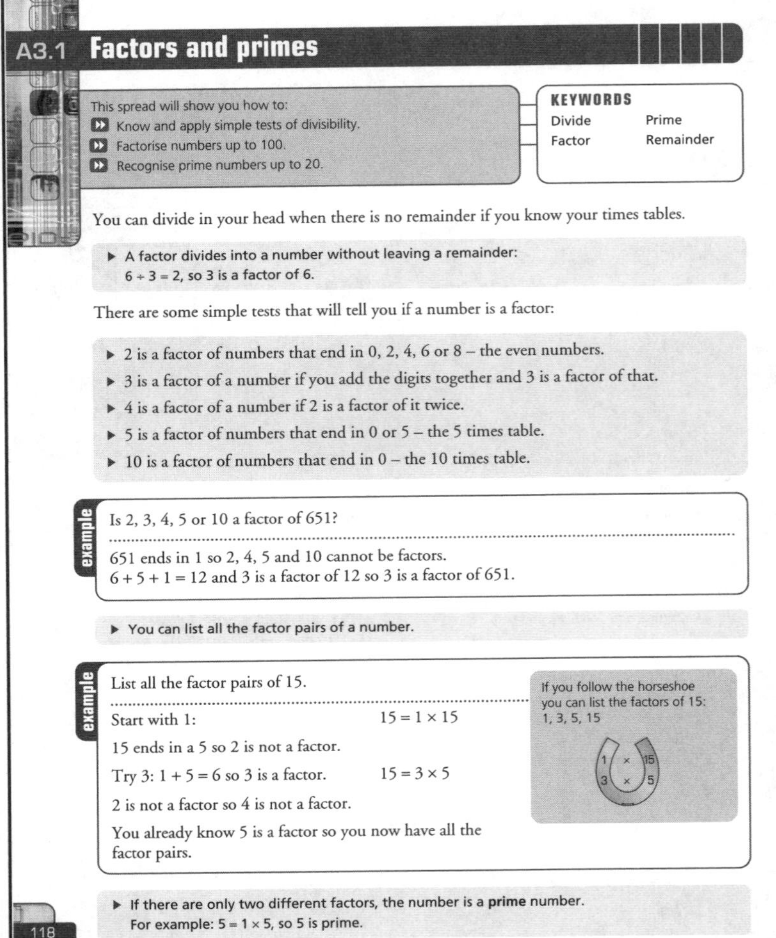

A3.1 **Factors and primes**

This spread will show you how to:
- Know and apply simple tests of divisibility.
- Factorise numbers up to 100.
- Recognise prime numbers up to 20.

KEYWORDS
Divide, Prime, Factor, Remainder

You can divide in your head when there is no remainder if you know your times tables.

- A factor divides into a number without leaving a remainder: 6 ÷ 3 = 2, so 3 is a factor of 6.

There are some simple tests that will tell you if a number is a factor:

- 2 is a factor of numbers that end in 0, 2, 4, 6 or 8 – the even numbers.
- 3 is a factor of a number if you add the digits together and 3 is a factor of that.
- 4 is a factor of a number if 2 is a factor of it twice.
- 5 is a factor of numbers that end in 0 or 5 – the 5 times table.
- 10 is a factor of numbers that end in 0 – the 10 times table.

example

Is 2, 3, 4, 5 or 10 a factor of 651?

651 ends in 1 so 2, 4, 5 and 10 cannot be factors.
6 + 5 + 1 = 12 and 3 is a factor of 12 so 3 is a factor of 651.

- You can list all the factor pairs of a number.

example

List all the factor pairs of 15.

Start with 1: 15 = 1 × 15
15 ends in a 5 so 2 is not a factor.
Try 3: 1 + 5 = 6 so 3 is a factor. 15 = 3 × 5
2 is not a factor so 4 is not a factor.
You already know 5 is a factor so you now have all the factor pairs.

If you follow the horseshoe you can list the factors of 15: 1, 3, 5, 15

- If there are only two different factors, the number is a **prime** number. For example: 5 = 1 × 5, so 5 is prime.

118

Plenary

Discuss strategies for finding factors of numbers.
Emphasise the logical process of starting with 2 then trying 3, then 4 and so on.
Discuss when you can:
- ignore numbers – if 2 isn't then 4 isn't!
- stop – how you know you've got them all.

Move on to finding common factors with good groups.
Emphasise the lowest common factor.

Further activities

Students could devise tests of divisibility for 6 and 8.

Students could try to describe the rule linking the sequences of factors in question 4.

Students could investigate the numbers they find in common in question 8. They could write them in a sequence and try to describe the pattern.

Differentiation

Support questions:

- Questions 1 and 2 involve using simple tests of divisibility. Springboard 7, pages 309, 310.
- Questions 3–5 focus on finding factors. Springboard 7, pages 311, 313, 314.
- Questions 6–8 focus on explaining reasoning with factors and primes. Springboard 7, page 315.

Core tier: focuses on factors and multiples.

Exercise A3.1

1 Is 2, 5 or 10 a factor of:
a 20 **b** 11 **c** 15 **d** 100 **e** 24
f 35 **g** 16 **h** 75 **i** 40 **j** 70

2 Is 2, 3, 4, 5 or 10 a factor of:
a 6 **b** 64 **c** 65 **d** 45 **e** 24
f 25 **g** 12 **h** 60 **i** 26 **j** 11

3 Find all the factor pairs of each of these numbers.
a 10 **b** 15 **c** 20 **d** 22 **e** 13
f 32 **g** 11 **h** 28 **i** 35 **j** 19

4 16 has 5 factors:

They are 1, 2, 4, 8 and 16.
How many factors do each of these numbers have?
List them.
a 10 **b** 15 **c** 20 **d** 22 **e** 13
f 32 **g** 11 **h** 28 **i** 35 **j** 19

5 A prime number has exactly two different factors.
List all the factors of each of these numbers and say whether they are prime or not.
a 9 **b** 14 **c** 17 **d** 21 **e** 23
f 11 **g** 27 **h** 2 **i** 3 **j** 4

6 Is 1 a prime number? Explain your answer.

7 **a** Use your answers to question 5 and 6 to list all the prime numbers between 1 and 20.
b Write down any even prime numbers.
What do you notice?
Explain your answer.

8 **Investigation**
Find a number between 0 and 100 with:
a exactly 3 factors
b exactly 5 factors
c exactly 7 factors

119

Exercise commentary

The questions assess the objectives on Primary Framework Pages 19 and 21.

Problem solving

Questions 6–8 assess Primary Framework Page 79.

Group work

Question 8 is suitable for pair work.

Misconceptions

Students need to have a good recall of multiplication facts and related division facts.

Ensure there is a multiplication grid that students can use as necessary.

Emphasise that students should apply tests of divisibility instead if possible.

Students fail to list all the factors of a number, in particular forgetting $1 \times n$.

Encourage a structured approach, always starting with 1, then 2, then 3 etc.

Emphasise that this is the easiest way to ensure they find all the factors as the tests of divisibility are simple.

Students fail to see 2 as a prime number and assume 1 is prime.

Questions 6 and 7 are designed to highlight this misconception.

Links

Multiplication and division facts: Primary Framework Page 59.

Homework

A3.1HW provides practice at identifying factors and primes.

Answers

1 **a** 2, 5, 10 **b** None **c** 5 **d** 2, 5, 10 **e** 2 **f** 5 **g** 2 **h** 5 **i** 2, 5, 10 **j** 2, 5, 10
2 **a** 2, 3 **b** 2, 4 **c** 5 **d** 3, 5 **e** 2, 3, 4 **f** 5 **g** 2, 3, 4 **h** 2, 3, 4, 5, 10 **i** 2 **j** None
3 **a** 1 × 10, 2 × 5 **b** 1 × 15, 3 × 5 **c** 1 × 20, 2 × 10, 4 × 5 **d** 1 × 22, 2 × 11 **e** 1 × 13 **f** 1 × 32, 2 × 16, 4 × 8 **g** 1 × 11 **h** 1 × 28, 2 × 14, 4 × 7 **i** 1 × 35, 5 × 7 **j** 1 × 19
4 **a** 4: 1, 2, 5, 10 **b** 4: 1, 3, 5, 15 **c** 6: 1, 2, 4, 5, 10, 20 **d** 4: 1, 2, 11, 22 **e** 2: 1, 13 **f** 6: 1, 2, 4, 8, 16, 32 **g** 2: 1, 11 **h** 6: 1, 2, 4, 7, 14, 28 **i** 2: 1, 3 **j** 3: 1, 2, 4
5 **a** 1, 3, 9; no **b** 1, 2, 7, 14; no **c** 1, 17; yes **d** 1, 3, 7, 21; no **e** 1, 23; yes **f** 1, 11; yes **g** 1, 3, 7, 21; no **h** 1, 2; yes **i** 1, 3; yes **j** 1, 2, 4; no
6 No, it only has one factor. **7** **a** 2, 3, 5, 7, 11, 13, 17, 19 **b** 2

A3.2 Patterns in numbers

Mental starter

In your prime!

Students give you a whole number between 0 and 50.
You write the number they give you in one of two columns.
In the first column you write all the prime numbers.
In the other you write all the non-prime numbers (include 1).
Students say what the numbers in the prime column have in common.
Repeat the activity, changing the rule for the first column (e.g. three factors).

Useful resources

A3.2OHP shows rectangular arrangements of 18 and 16.
Multilink cubes

Introductory activity

Revise the previous lesson's work:

- What is a factor?
- Find the factors of 10: list them.

Give out 10 multilink cubes to pairs of students (or demonstrate).
Discuss how they should arrange the cubes to show that $1 \times 10 = 10$.
They should make a long rectangle.
Now discuss how to show $2 \times 5 = 10$.
They should make a 2×5 rectangle.

Emphasise that rectangles give the factors of numbers.
Discuss why this is true (area $= l \times w$).

Start with 2 cubes.
This will make only one rectangle. (Ignore rotations – they are congruent! 1×2 is the same as 2×1.)
That shows that 2 is prime.

Now 3 cubes. This is also prime.

Now 4 cubes. It makes a 1×4 rectangle and a 2×2 square.
Emphasise that 4 has two equal factors: 2 and 2.
Discuss what to call 4 – a square number!
Emphasise that a square number has two equal factors and can be arranged in a square.

Repeat with 5, 6, 7, 8 and 9 cubes.
Discuss arrangements.
A3.2OHP shows rectangular arrangements of 36 which you can use for discussion.

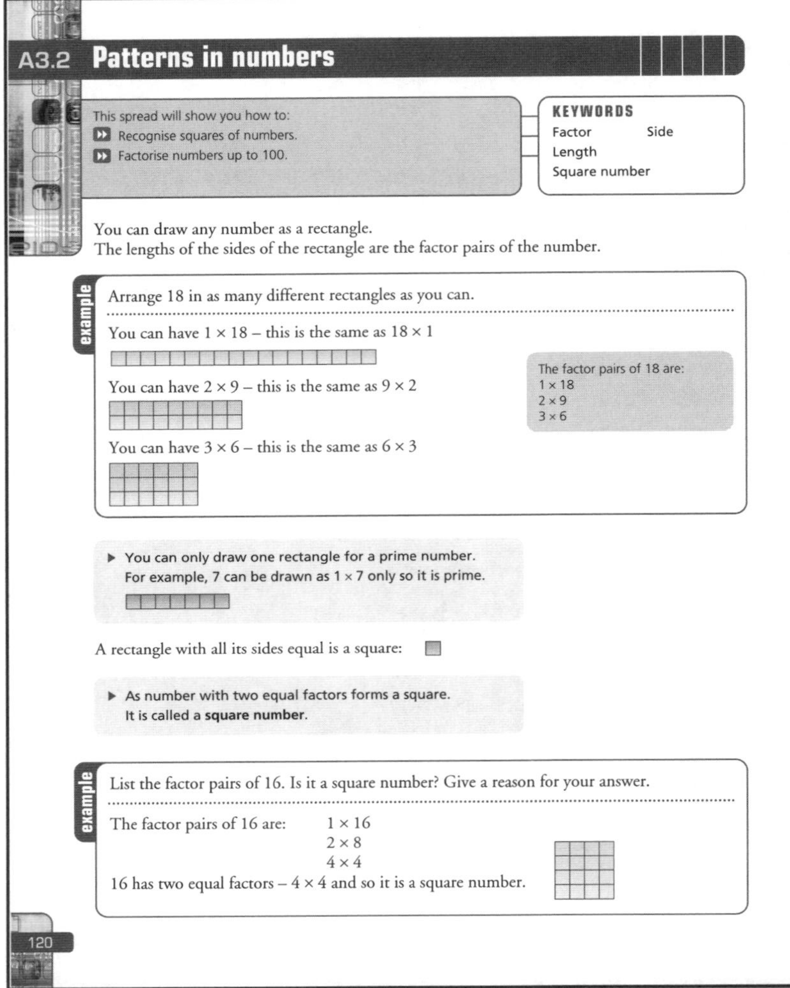

A3.2 **Patterns in numbers**

This spread will show you how to:
- Recognise squares of numbers.
- Factorise numbers up to 100.

KEYWORDS
Factor
Side
Length
Square number

You can draw any number as a rectangle.
The lengths of the sides of the rectangle are the factor pairs of the number.

example

Arrange 18 in as many different rectangles as you can.

You can have 1×18 – this is the same as 18×1

You can have 2×9 – this is the same as 9×2

You can have 3×6 – this is the same as 6×3

The factor pairs of 18 are:
1×18
2×9
3×6

- You can only draw one rectangle for a prime number.
For example, 7 can be drawn as 1×7 only so it is prime.

A rectangle with all its sides equal is a square:

- As number with two equal factors forms a square.
It is called a **square number**.

example

List the factor pairs of 16. Is it a square number? Give a reason for your answer.

The factor pairs of 16 are: 1×16, 2×8, 4×4

16 has two equal factors – 4×4 and so it is a square number.

120

Plenary

More than square

Students use 6 multilink cubes. Ask them to form:

- a rectangle
- a different rectangle
- a square
- a right-angled (isosceles) triangle.

Repeat for 10 cubes.
The next spread uses right-angled isosceles triangles.

Further activities

Students can use multilink cubes to find the first five square numbers.

Able students can list the first five square numbers in a sequence and then describe the pattern and predict the next two square numbers.

Differentiation

Support questions:

- Questions 1 and 2 involve listing factor pairs.
- Questions 3 and 4 focus on rectangular arrangements. Springboard 7, page 316.
- Questions 5–7 focus on finding square numbers and the link to the area of a square.

Core tier: extends to triangular numbers.

Exercise A3.2

1 The factor pairs of 32 are:

$1 \times 32 \qquad 2 \times 16 \qquad 4 \times 8$

a How many factors does 32 have?
b Is 32 a square number?
Explain your answer.

2 Write down all the factor pairs of 24.
Is 24 a square number?
Explain your answer.

3 This rectangle measures 2 cm by 10 cm:

$2 \times 10 = 20$

The area of the rectangle is 20 cm^2.

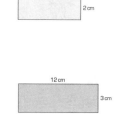

a Draw as many different rectangles as you can with an area of 20 cm^2.
b Write down all the factor pairs of 20.
c Is 20 a square number? Explain your answer.

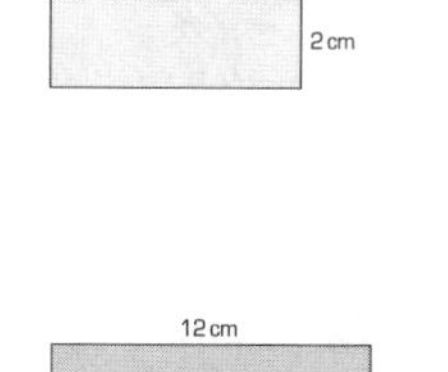

4 This rectangle measures 3 cm by 12 cm:

$3 \times 12 = 36$

The area of the rectangle is 36 cm^2.

a Draw as many different rectangles as you can with an area of 36 cm^2.
b Is 36 a square number? Explain your answer.

5 Draw a square with an **area** of 25 cm^2.
What is the length of each side?

6 Draw a square with an area of 49 cm^2.
What is the length of each side?

7 You find a square number when you multiply a number by itself.

For example: $1 \times 1 = 1$ and $2 \times 2 = 4$ so 1 and 4 are square numbers.

a Find all the square numbers up to 10×10.
b For each square number list all its factors.
c How many factors does each square number have? Explain what you notice.

121

Exercise commentary

The questions assess the objectives on Primary Framework Page 21.

Problem solving

The exercise assesses Primary Framework Page 81 if students are encouraged to generalise.

Group work

Students would benefit from discussing questions 1–4 in pairs.

Misconceptions

Students need to have a good recall of multiplication and division facts.

Some students will need access to a multiplication grid.

Many students will miss the factor pairs of the form $1 \times n$ and also the rectangle with side 1 cm. They also tend to miss the squares where the factors are the same: $m \times m$.

Emphasise a logical approach, always starting with 1, and for students to continue until they come to a pair they have already found.

Area can cause difficulties with students adding instead of multiplying.

Encourage the use of multilink cubes.

Links

Multiplication/division facts: Primary Framework Page 59. Area: Page 97.

Homework

A3.2HW is an investigation that explores factor pairs.

Answers

1 **a** 6 **b** No, no two equal factors. **2** 1×24, 2×12, 3×8, 4×6; no, no two equal factors.
3 **a** 1 cm by 20 cm, 4 cm by 5 cm **b** 1×20, 2×10, 4×5 **c** No, no two equal factors.
4 **a** 1 cm by 36 cm, 2 cm by 18 cm, 3 cm by 12 cm, 4 cm by 9 cm, 6 cm by 6 cm
b Yes, two equal factors: $6 \times 6 = 36$.
5 5 cm **6** 7 cm
7 **a** 1, 4, 9, 16, 25, 36, 49, 64, 81, 100 **b** 1; 1, 2, 4; 1, 3, 9; 1, 2, 4, 8, 16; 1, 5, 25; 1, 2, 3, 4, 6, 9, 12, 18, 36; 1, 7, 49; 1, 2, 4, 8, 16, 32, 64; 1, 3, 9, 27, 81; 1, 2, 4, 5, 10, 20, 25, 50, 100 **c** The number of factors is always an odd number

Mental starter

Squaring the circle

Students may need access to a 100 square or a 10 × 10 multiplication grid.
Draw a circle on the board or OHP.
Students call out a number from 1 to 50 inclusive.
You write square numbers in the circle and non-squares outside.
Ask students for the rule for the numbers inside the circle – they should justify answers. If correct, ask for numbers from 51 to 100 to go inside.

Useful resources

R17 – 100 square
Calculators
A3.3OHP shows square and triangular number sequences
R21 – 10 × 10 multiplication grid for question 5 and plenary.

Introductory activity

Refer to the mental starter.

Ask students how to find square numbers.
Encourage the response and reasoning that they have two equal factors and so you multiply two equal numbers.

Discuss how to write down the sums:

$3 \times 3 = 3$ squared $= 3^2$
$5 \times 5 = 5$ squared $= 5^2$ – the 2 shows you multiply 5 two times.

Discuss the use of a calculator when the numbers get larger.

You can do 11 × 11 or $11x^2$.
Make sure all students can get 121.
Discuss how to say 11^2: eleven squared.

Emphasise that square numbers form a sequence.

A3.3OHP shows the first four square numbers. Use it to discuss how the pattern grows.
Emphasise that the logical development – 1, 2, 3, 4, ... shows up the pattern.

Ask students what the triangular numbers might look like.
Emphasise that triangles come in all shapes and sizes but specifically a triangular number uses a right-angled isosceles triangle so it looks like half a square.
A3.3OHP shows how the triangular numbers develop in a sequence.

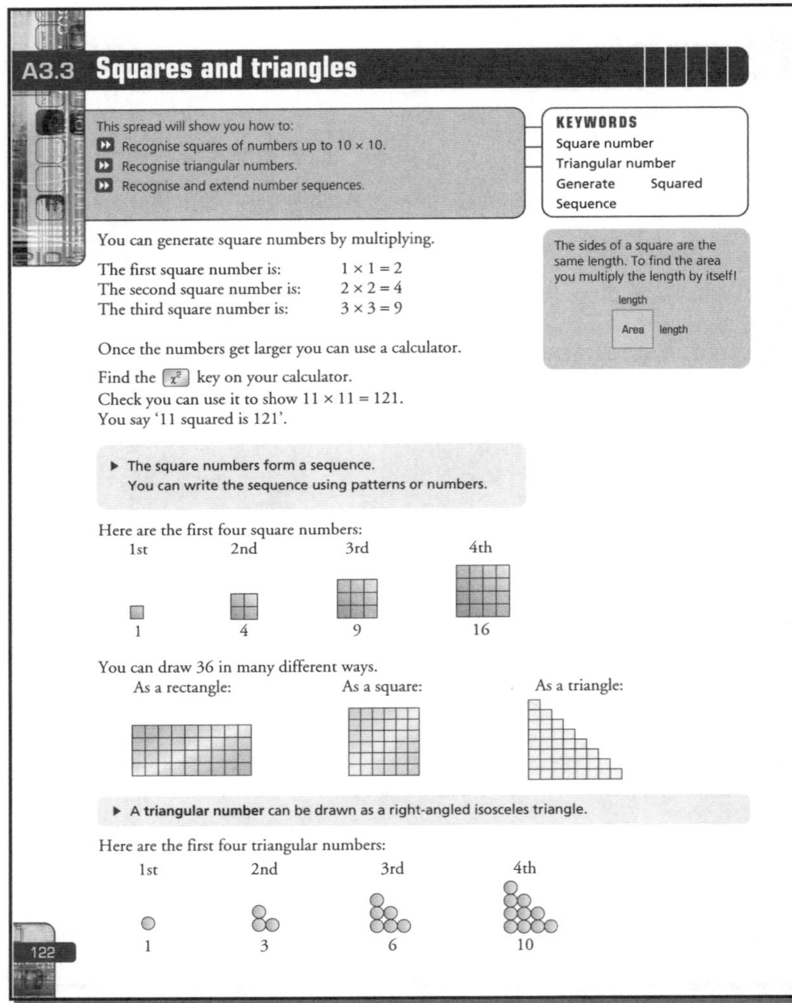

A3.3 Squares and triangles

This spread will show you how to:
- Recognise squares of numbers up to 10 × 10.
- Recognise triangular numbers.
- Recognise and extend number sequences.

KEYWORDS
Square number
Triangular number
Generate
Squared
Sequence

You can generate square numbers by multiplying.

The first square number is: 1 × 1 = 2
The second square number is: 2 × 2 = 4
The third square number is: 3 × 3 = 9

Once the numbers get larger you can use a calculator.

Find the x^2 key on your calculator.
Check you can use it to show 11 × 11 = 121.
You say '11 squared is 121'.

The sides of a square are the same length. To find the area you multiply the length by itself!

▸ The square numbers form a sequence.
You can write the sequence using patterns or numbers.

Here are the first four square numbers:

You can draw 36 in many different ways.

▸ A **triangular number** can be drawn as a right-angled isosceles triangle.

Here are the first four triangular numbers:

122

Plenary

Discuss the pattern formed in question 5.
Students should justify any generalisations.
Use **R21** – 10 × 10 multiplication grid – to show how the pattern builds up. Use coloured pens to fill in the extra squares as you go.
Encourage students to generalise if possible – you add the odd numbers.
Review the use of a calculator.

Further activities

Able students can list the first five square numbers in a sequence and then describe the pattern to help predict the next two square numbers before drawing.

Differentiation

Support questions:

- Question 1 involves finding square numbers.
- Questions 2–4 focus on recognising the sequences of square and triangular numbers. Springboard 7, page 47.
- Question 5 involves describing how the sequence of square numbers grows. Springboard 7, page 48.

Core tier: focuses on the general term of a sequence.

Exercise A3.3

1 Use your calculator to work out the following.

a 7 squared **b** 12 squared **c** 6^2 **d** 13 squared **e** 29^2 **f** 18 squared
g 20^2 **h** 25 squared **i** 30^2 **j** 100 squared **k** 14^2 **l** 27 squared

2 Here are the first four square numbers:

1st 2nd 3rd 4th

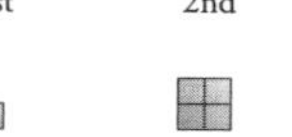
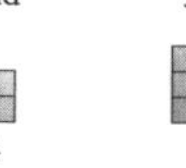
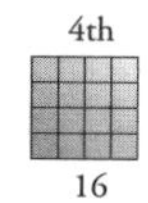

1 4 9 16

Copy and continue the sequence for the first 10 square numbers.

3 Here are the first four triangular numbers:

1st 2nd 3rd 4th

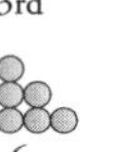
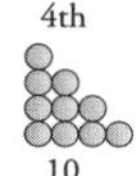

1 3 6 10

Copy and complete the sequence for the first 10 triangular numbers.

4 On a 10 × 10 multiplication grid, shade in the square numbers you found in question 2. Describe any pattern you can see.

5 **a** On this multiplication grid:

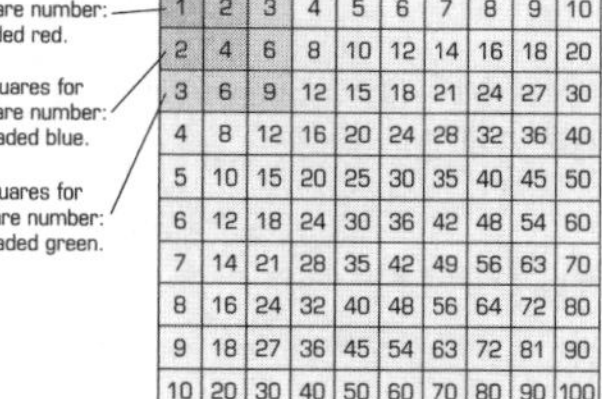
The 1st square number: 1 × 1 is shaded red.
The extra squares for the 2nd square number: 2 × 2 are shaded blue.
The extra squares for the 3rd square number: 3 × 3 are shaded green.

1	2	3	4	5	6	7	8	9	10
2	4	6	8	10	12	14	16	18	20
3	6	9	12	15	18	21	24	27	30
4	8	12	16	20	24	28	32	36	40
5	10	15	20	25	30	35	40	45	50
6	12	18	24	30	36	42	48	54	60
7	14	21	28	35	42	49	56	63	70
8	16	24	32	40	48	56	64	72	80
9	18	27	36	45	54	63	72	81	90
10	20	30	40	50	60	70	80	90	100

Copy and complete the pattern up to the 10th square number.

b Copy and complete this table.

Square number	1st	2nd	3rd	4th	5th	6th
Number of **extra** squares	1	3				

123

Exercise commentary

The questions assess the objectives on Primary Framework Pages 17 and 21.

Problem solving

The exercise assesses Primary Framework Page 81 if students are encouraged to generalise.

Group work

Students would benefit from discussing questions 4 and 5 in pairs.

Misconceptions

The different notation used in question 1 may confuse some students. In particular they think the word 'squared' means the number is already a square.

Use question 1 to highlight this and discuss what '7 squared' means so students can share good ideas.

Poor drawing or sketching skills may cause problems in questions 2 and 3.

Encourage the use of multilink cubes.

Questions 4 and 5 depend on successful completion of question 2.

Encourage students to put results in a table to help them keep track of what the square numbers are.

Links

Multiplication/division facts: Primary Framework Page 59.

Using a calculator: Page 71.

Homework

A3.3HW explores patterns within the sequence of square numbers.

Answers

1 **a** 49 **b** 144 **c** 36 **d** 169
e 841 **f** 324 **g** 400 **h** 625
i 900 **j** 10 000 **k** 196 **l** 729

2 1, 4, 9, 16, 25, 36, 49, 64, 81, 100

3 1, 3, 6, 10, 15, 21, 28, 36, 45, 55

5 **b** Number of extra squares: 1, 3, 5, 7, 9, 11

A3.4 Functions and multiples

Mental starter

Multiply!

Students need two sets of digit cards – **R1**.
Ask a student to give a number between 1 and 20.
You roll the dice.
They multiply the number by the score on the dice and hold it up.
Repeat until all students have had a go.
Compile a list of the multiples under the headings:
1, 2, 3, 4, 5 and 6.

Useful resources

R7 – function machines.
R1 digit cards for the mental starter.

Introductory activity

Refer to the mental starter.
The dice gave the number to multiply by – it gave the function.
Discuss what all the numbers in any one column have in common – they have all been multiplied by the number in the heading.
Emphasise that the numbers are the multiples of 1, 2, 3, 4, 5 and 6.

Remind students about function machines. You input a number, the machine performs a function then outputs the result.
There is a function machine on **R7** that you can show on OHP.

Discuss how you would describe the function of multiplying by 2: ×2.
Use an OHP of R7 to discuss outputs for various input values.

Emphasise the pattern that the output numbers make when you input the counting numbers.
The function ×2 produces multiples of 2 or the 2 times table.

Now ask students for multiples of 5.
They can generate them using a function machine.
Emphasise a logical approach:
- Input 1, 2 and 3
- Multiply by 5
- Output 5, 10 and 15.

These are the first three multiples of 5.

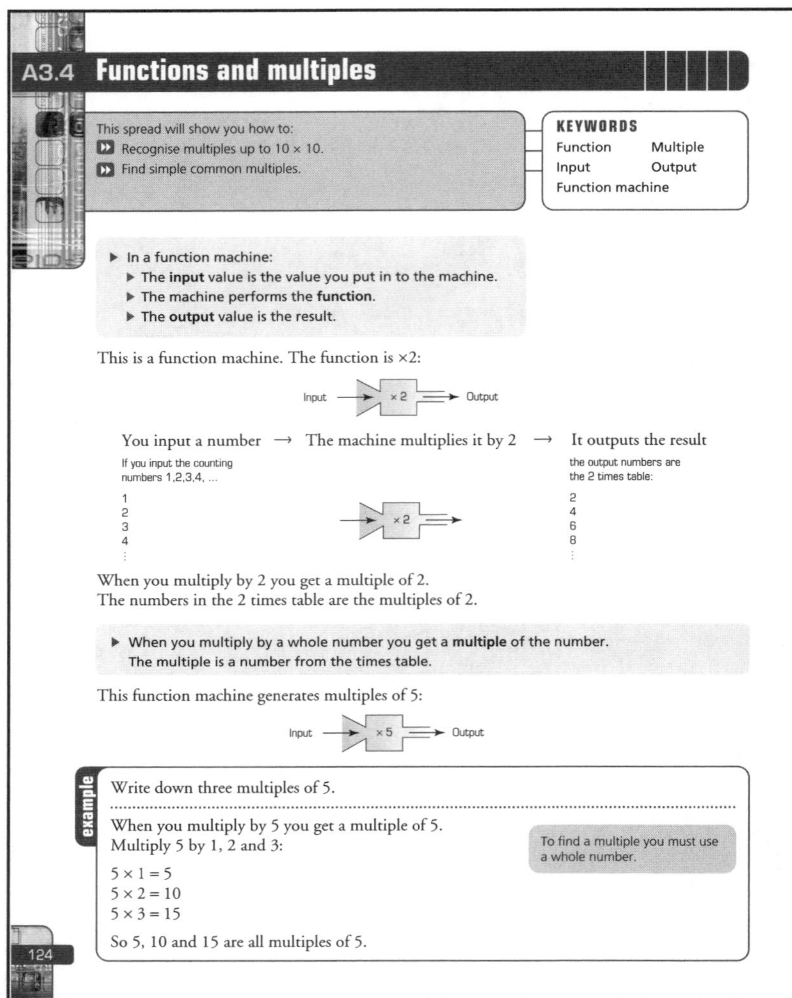
A3.4 Functions and multiples

This spread will show you how to:
- Recognise multiples up to 10 × 10.
- Find simple common multiples.

KEYWORDS
Function, Multiple, Input, Output, Function machine

- In a function machine:
  - The **input** value is the value you put in to the machine.
  - The machine performs the **function**.
  - The **output** value is the result.

This is a function machine. The function is ×2:

Input → ×2 → Output

You input a number → The machine multiplies it by 2 → It outputs the result

If you input the counting numbers 1,2,3,4, ... the output numbers are the 2 times table:

1 → 2
2 → 4
3 → 6
4 → 8
⋮

When you multiply by 2 you get a multiple of 2.
The numbers in the 2 times table are the multiples of 2.

- When you multiply by a whole number you get a **multiple** of the number. The multiple is a number from the times table.

This function machine generates multiples of 5:

Input → ×5 → Output

example

Write down three multiples of 5.

When you multiply by 5 you get a multiple of 5.
Multiply 5 by 1, 2 and 3:

$5 \times 1 = 5$
$5 \times 2 = 10$
$5 \times 3 = 15$

So 5, 10 and 15 are all multiples of 5.

To find a multiple you must use a whole number.

124

Plenary

Discuss the use of function machines to generate multiples:
- Emphasise the logical approach of inputting the counting numbers: 1, 2, 3 shows up patterns.
- Discuss the link between multiples and factors – emphasise the multiple is multiplied!
- Emphasise that the terms only relate to whole numbers. You can't have a multiple of 1.2!

Look at common multiples with good groups.

Further activities

Students devise a function machine that generates multiples of 2, 3, 4, 6 and 8.

You can extend question 5:

- Allow combinations of sizes of tiles.
- Include rectangular-shaped tiles.
- Give students an L-shaped floor to investigate.

Differentiation

Support questions:

- Question 1 involves multiplying numbers to find multiples.
- Questions 2–4 focus on listing multiples of numbers in a logical sequence. Springboard 7, page 306.
- Question 5 combines multiples and factors in a problem solving context. Springboard 7, page 308, 312.

Core tier: focuses on expressing a function as an equation.

Exercise A3.4

1 Copy and complete these multiplication sums.

1 × 3 = 2 × 3 = 3 × 3 = 4 × 3 =

The answers are the first four multiples of 3.

2 Find the first 10 multiples of: **a** 3 **b** 4 **c** 6

3 This function machine generates multiples of 5:

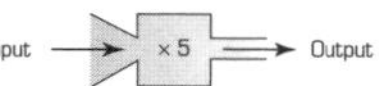

a Input 4 to find the 4th multiple of 5.
b Input 5 to find the 5th multiple of 5.
c Input 6 to find the 6th multiple of 5.
d Find the 8th multiple of 5.

4 The first 10 multiples of 2 are:
2, 4, 6, 8, 10, 12, 14, 16, 18, 20.
The first 10 multiples of 5 are:
5, 10, 15, 20, 25, 30, 35, 40, 45, 50.
The numbers common to both lists are 10 and 20.
Use your results from question 2 to answer these questions.
What numbers are common to the lists of:
a multiples of 3 and multiples of 4
b multiples of 4 and multiples of 6
c multiples of 3 and multiples of 4 and multiples of 6?

10 and 20 are common multiples of 2 and 5.
10 is the lowest common multiple of 2 and 5.

5 A dancefloor measures 12 metres by 12 metres.
Wooden tiles come in these sizes:
1 × 1 2 × 2 3 × 3 4 × 4 5 × 5 6 × 6 8 × 8
If you use 1 × 1 tiles you will need 144 tiles.

How many tiles will you need if you use:
a 2 × 2 tiles **b** 3 × 3 tiles **c** 4 × 4 tiles
d 5 × 5 tiles **e** 6 × 6 tiles **f** 8 × 8 tiles?

Exercise commentary

The questions assess the objectives on Primary Framework Page 19.

Problem solving

Question 5 assesses Primary Framework Page 79.

Group work

Question 5 is suitable for pairs.

Misconceptions

Most students find multiples relatively straightforward so long as they have secure multiplication facts or access to a multiplication grid.

They may find it hard to use the logical approach suggested as there are many steps involved and it is easy to lose track of what the multiplier is.

Encourage students to write the multiplier in the form of a function machine so that they can refer to it throughout the process.

In question 5 it is hard for some students to spot the non-obvious arrangements of tiles.

Discussion in pairs or groups may help as students can compare approaches.

Links

Multiplication/division facts: Primary Framework Page 59. Factors: Page 21. Area: Page 97.

Homework

A3.4HW is an investigation based on multiples and factors.

Answers

1 3, 6, 9, 12
2 **a** 3, 6, 9, 12, 15, 18, 21, 24, 27, 30
b 4, 8, 12, 16, 20, 24, 28, 32, 36, 40
c 6, 12, 18, 24, 30, 36, 42, 48, 54, 60
3 **a** 20 **b** 25 **c** 30 **d** 40
4 **a** 12, 24 **b** 12, 24, 36 **c** 12, 24
5 **a** 36 **b** 16 **c** 9
d 6 **e** 4 **f** 3

A3.5 Graphs of functions

Mental starter

That's my seat!
Arrange students in rows.
The sides of the classroom are the *x* and *y* axes.
Your extreme left is (0, 0).
Each student should have a coordinate for their seat.
Call out a coordinate pair.
The student in that seat should stand up.

Useful resources

R7 – function machine – make an OHP.
R9 blank grid on OHP.
Squared paper for graphs.

Introductory activity

Refer to the mental starter.
Discuss the input and output values and how they form pairs.

Review the use of the term: multiple.
Bring out the fact that the multiples of 3 are the outputs of a ×3 function machine or the 3 times table.
Emphasise that you input whole number values only for multiples.

Emphasise that the multiples of 3 form a pattern.
Ask students how they might best see that pattern – look at the link between the input and output values.
They could:

- draw diagrams/rectangles (spatial)
- explore the numbers (numeric)
- draw a graph (algebraic).

Show **R9** – a blank squared grid.
Ask students what the bold lines are called – axes.
Scale input in 1s and output in 2s.
Now discuss what to call each axis to show the link between the input and output values – input and output.

Develop coordinate pairs from the ×3 function machine.
Emphasise the need to put the input and output value in the same order.

Plot the points and discuss the pattern.
Discuss how to decide what the next point will be and whether this is easier to find on the graph or using the machine.

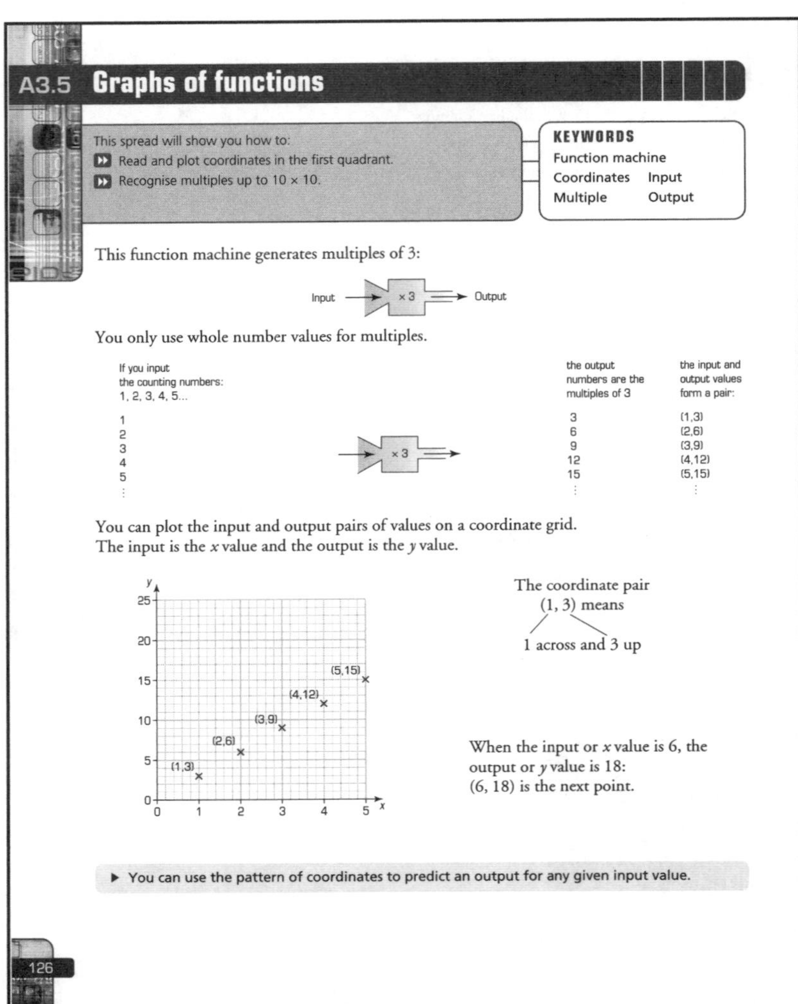

A3.5 Graphs of functions

This spread will show you how to:
- Read and plot coordinates in the first quadrant.
- Recognise multiples up to 10 × 10.

KEYWORDS
Function machine
Coordinates
Input
Multiple
Output

This function machine generates multiples of 3:

You only use whole number values for multiples.

If you input the counting numbers: 1, 2, 3, 4, 5...		the output numbers are the multiples of 3	the input and output values form a pair:
1		3	(1,3)
2		6	(2,6)
3	× 3	9	(3,9)
4		12	(4,12)
5		15	(5,15)
⋮		⋮	⋮

You can plot the input and output pairs of values on a coordinate grid.
The input is the *x* value and the output is the *y* value.

The coordinate pair (1, 3) means 1 across and 3 up

When the input or *x* value is 6, the output or *y* value is 18: (6, 18) is the next point.

▶ You can use the pattern of coordinates to predict an output for any given input value.

126

Plenary

Discuss graphing multiples using questions 4 and 5:

- Generate coordinate pairs – input and output.
- Always put input, output in same order.
- Discuss the use of a scale.
- Plot the points on a grid.
- Do not join the points – why?
- What does a graph show better than the numbers themselves?

Further activities

Students give their coordinates in question 2 and a partner finds their word.

Students can develop question 5 by posing problems for each other to solve based on shapes.

Differentiation

Support questions:

- Questions 1 and 2 focus on reading and plotting coordinates. Springboard 7, page 278.
- Questions 3 and 4 focus on generating and plotting coordinate pairs using a function machine. Springboard 7, page 280.
- Question 5 focuses on completing shapes from geometrical information.

Core tier: focuses on graphs of functions in all four quadrants.

Exercise A3.5

1 Plot these sets of points on a coordinate grid.
Join each set together as you go.

Set A	(1, 8) (1, 10)
Set B	(4, 8) (3, 8) (3, 10)
Set C	(5, 8) (4, 9) (5, 10) (6, 9)
Set D	(6, 10) (7, 8) (8, 10)
Set E	(9, 8) (8, 8) (8, 10) (9, 10)
Set F	(8, 9) (9, 9)
Set G	(1, 4) (1, 7) (2, 6) (3, 7) (3, 4)
Set H	(4, 7) (5, 6) (6, 7)
Set I	(5, 6) (5, 4)

This should spell: I LOVE MY

2 Write a word to complete the sentence in question 1.
For example you might use: DOG, CAT, MUM, BIKE.
Write it on the coordinate grid.
Write down the coordinates to make your word.

3 This function machine generates multiples of 5:

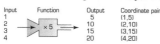

Input	Function	Output	Coordinate pair
1		5	(1,5)
2	× 5	10	(2,10)
3		15	(3,15)
4		20	(4,20)

Plot the pairs on a coordinate grid.
Copy the grid on page 126.

4 This machine generates multiples of 4:

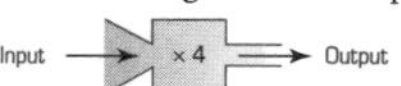

a Input the numbers 1, 2, 3, 4 and 5.
b Write down the coordinate pairs.
c Plot the pairs on a coordinate grid
Copy the grid on page 126.

5 Plot these coordinates on a grid:

(3, 4), (3, 8) and (7, 8).

The coordinates are three corners of a square.
Write down the coordinates of the point that completes the square.

Exercise commentary

The questions assess the objectives on Primary Framework Pages 19 and 109.

Problem solving

Question 5 assesses Primary Framework Page 79.

Group work

The further activity is suitable for pairs.

Misconceptions

Students often get the coordinates mixed up, plotting (y, x).

Question 1 is designed so that students can check their work themselves.

Emphasise that for the first coordinate you count across – *a* for across comes before *u* for up in the alphabet. Some students remember: across the hall then up the stairs, or similar.

Question 4 may cause problems as there are so many steps involved and students find it hard to keep track of four sets of inputs and outputs.

Encourage students to set their work out as for question 3 and emphasise that it is best to work one pair at a time so that each line is completed before moving on to the next one.

Links

2-D shapes: Primary Framework Page 103.

Homework

A3.5HW provides practice at plotting points on a coordinate grid.

Answers

4 **a** 4, 8, 12, 16, 20
b (1, 4), (2, 8), (3, 12), (4, 16), (5, 20)

5 (7, 4)

A3.6 Using a table of values

Mental starter

What's my column?

Draw a grid with three columns on the board or OHP.
Students call out numbers between 1 and 100 and you classify them into the correct column(s) or bin them if they don't match the criteria.
Students must guess the rules for the columns and justify their answers.
Use: multiples of 3, square numbers and prime numbers (or any other classifications depending on the strength of the students).

Useful resources

A3.6OHP shows the graph from the student book.
R7 – function machines.
R9 blank grid on OHP.
Squared paper for graphs.

Introductory activity

Remind students that to see a pattern they could:

- draw diagrams/rectangles (spatial)
- explore the numbers (numeric)
- draw a graph (algebraic).

Emphasise that a graph is a great way to see patterns as it is very easy to extend them – just continue the graph.

Use an example: +3 on a function machine. Discuss how to find the points to draw the graph.
Emphasise the logical approach of using the input numbers 1, 2, 3, …
Emphasise the need to put the input and output values in the same order.

Discuss how to record the pairs of points and encourage the use of a table.

A3.6OHP shows the graph from the student book.
Discuss why the points can be joined and what intermediate points mean.

Re-emphasise the power of using a graph – you can see patterns and pairs of values at a glance.

Discuss how to read points from the graph:

- What input gives an output of … ?
- What output has an input of … ?

Emphasise the need to label the axes so that you start from the right place.

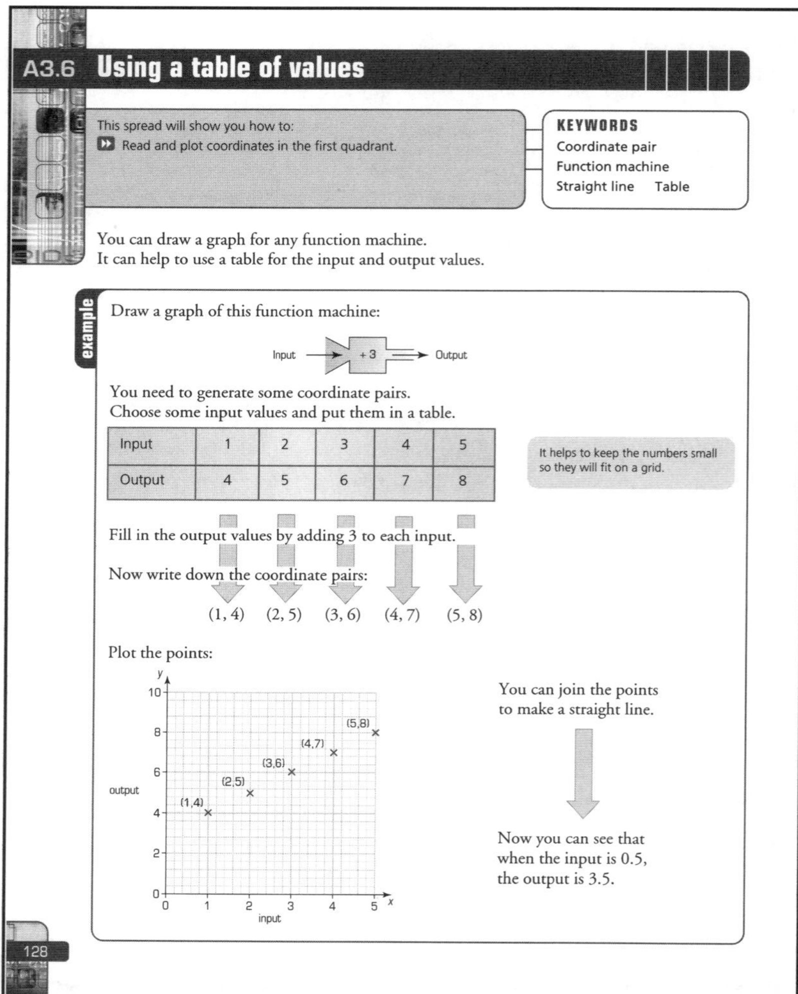

A3.6 **Using a table of values**

This spread will show you how to:
- Read and plot coordinates in the first quadrant.

KEYWORDS
Coordinate pair
Function machine
Straight line
Table

You can draw a graph for any function machine.
It can help to use a table for the input and output values.

example

Draw a graph of this function machine:

Input → +3 → Output

You need to generate some coordinate pairs.
Choose some input values and put them in a table.

Input	1	2	3	4	5
Output	4	5	6	7	8

It helps to keep the numbers small so they will fit on a grid.

Fill in the output values by adding 3 to each input.

Now write down the coordinate pairs:

(1, 4) (2, 5) (3, 6) (4, 7) (5, 8)

Plot the points:

You can join the points to make a straight line.

Now you can see that when the input is 0.5, the output is 3.5.

128

Plenary

On a blank grid on an OHP of **R9**:

- Label the axes: 0 to 8 and 0 to 32.
- Discuss what the small divisions mean.
- Draw three points on the grid (from a straight line).
- Ask students if they can see a pattern.
- Ask for other points that satisfy the pattern.
- Discuss whether you can join the points.

You may want to discuss what the function machine could be.

Further activities

In **A3.6ICT**, students use Omnigraph or Excel to explore graphs of straight lines.

Alternatively

Students can explore the relationship between the coordinate pairs, for example: in question 1 the *x* coordinate is 4 more than the *y* coordinate.

Differentiation

Support questions:

- Question 1 focuses on generating coordinates from a function machine. Springboard 7, page 394.
- Questions 2 and 3 focus on generating and plotting coordinate pairs using a table of values. Springboard 7, page 396.
- In question 4 students make up a table of values to record the results and then use it to plot a graph.

Core tier: focuses on using both positive and negative values of *x* in a table.

Exercise A3.6

1 **a** Copy and complete this function machine:

Input	Function	Output	Coordinate pair
1	+4	5	(1,5)
2			(2,)
3			(3,)
4			(4,)

b Draw the graph of the function machine.
Join the points together. You should get a straight line.

2 This table of values is generated by the function machine:

Input → −2 → Output

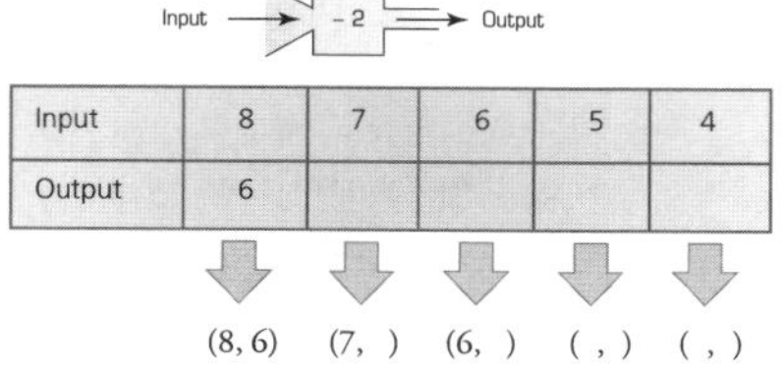

Input	8	7	6	5	4
Output	6				

(8, 6) (7,) (6,) (,) (,)

a Copy and complete the table and the coordinate pairs.
b Plot the pairs on a coordinate grid.
Join the points to make a straight line.

3 **a** Copy and complete this table of values for the function: −1.

Input	5	4	3	2
Output	4	3		

b Write down the coordinate pairs and plot them on a graph.
Join the points to make a straight line.
c What is the output when the input is 3.5?

4 **a** Choose some input values for the function: +2.
b Use the values to generate some coordinate pairs.
c Plot the pairs on a grid and join them to make a straight line.
d What input gives an output of 3.5?

129

Exercise commentary

The questions assess the objectives on Primary Framework Page 109.

Problem solving

The further activity assesses Primary Framework Page 81.

Group work

The exercise is suitable for pairs.

Misconceptions

The number of steps involved in each question can lead to mistakes due to students finding it difficult to keep track of where they are up to. This is particularly obvious when it comes to filling in a table of values and listing coordinate pairs.

The exercise suggest a logical sequence which students should be encouraged to follow and when students have difficulties, refer them to the method of the last successfully answered question.

Students find it hard to read off graphs. Emphasise that they need to find the coordinates of the point on the line and the need to read the question carefully so they understand what to find.

Links

Generalising relationships: Primary Framework Page 81.

Homework

A3.6HW provides practice at drawing a straight-line graph from a table of values.

Answers

1 **a** Missing outputs: 6, 7, 8
Coordinate pairs: (2, 6), (3, 7), (4, 8)
2 **a** (8, 6), (7, 5), (6, 4), (5, 3), (4, 2)
3 **a** Missing outputs: 2, 1
b (5, 4), (4, 3), (3, 2), (2, 1)
c 2.5
4 **d** 1.5

Summary

The Year 5 key teaching objective is:

- Read and plot coordinates (109).

The unit gives access to the Year 7 key teaching objective:

- Plot the graphs of simple linear functions (Secondary Framework 164, 166).

Plenary activity

Students input the numbers 1 to 5 in a ×3 function machine.
Ask questions about the outputs:

- Which numbers are prime? Even? Square? Multiples of 4? etc.

Ask students to list the coordinate pairs and discuss the scales needed to draw the graph on **R9** (OHP).

Check out commentary

1 Most students should be able to use the tests for 2, 5 and 10. The test for 4 may cause more problems as students have to divide twice and may lose track of what they are dividing. Some students may struggle to use the test for 3 – a common problem is not recognising multiples of 3. Emphasise that when dividing by 4 you just divide by 2 twice in a chain – 36 ÷ 2 = ...18 ÷ 2 = ...9 and that for 3 you add the digits but you need to know the multiples of 3 – refer to a multiplication grid.

2 Students need to recognise square numbers. Ensure students see them regularly and start to recognise them easily – a poster can help.
Students having difficulties with factors may refer to the multiplication grid at the back of the book. Students could also use multilink cubes to work out which of the numbers are square then see which rectangular arrangements they can find.

3 Students need to record their results carefully to ensure they list the correct coordinate pairs. They must then remember to plot the input (across) before the output (up) – the initial letters come first in the alphabet.

4 Students find it difficult to answer part c without drawing and tend to mix up the pattern and matchstick numbers. Encourage students to test any theories with patterns 5 and 6 before predicting the 20th term.

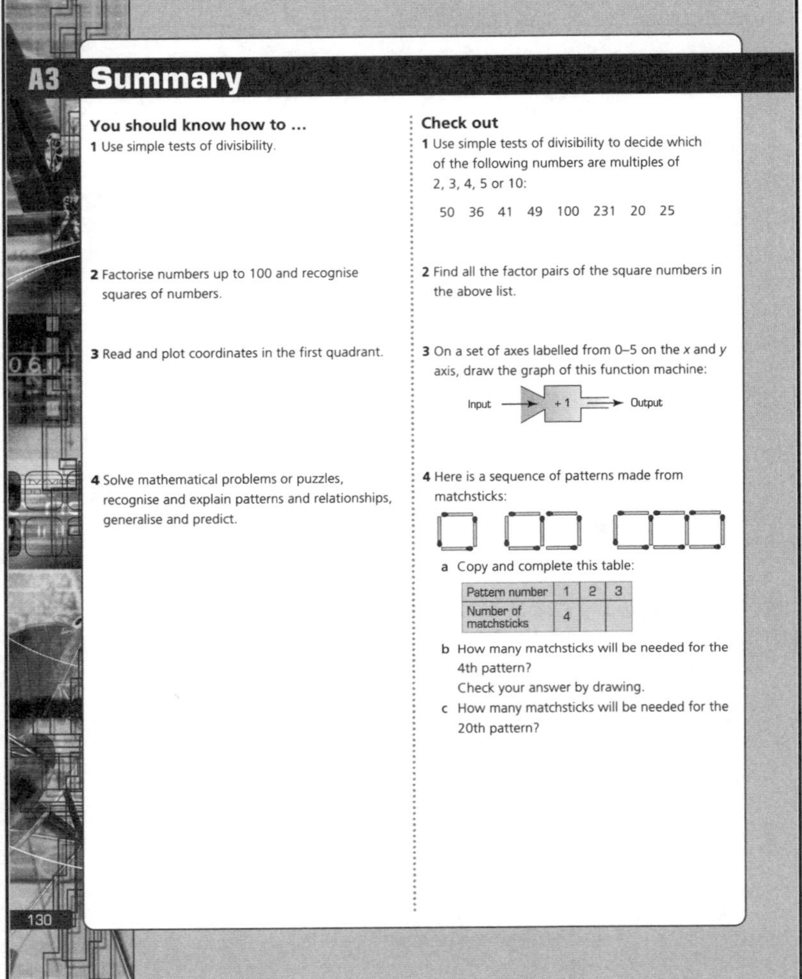

A3 Summary

You should know how to ...

1 Use simple tests of divisibility.

2 Factorise numbers up to 100 and recognise squares of numbers.

3 Read and plot coordinates in the first quadrant.

4 Solve mathematical problems or puzzles, recognise and explain patterns and relationships, generalise and predict.

Check out

1 Use simple tests of divisibility to decide which of the following numbers are multiples of 2, 3, 4, 5 or 10:

50 36 41 49 100 231 20 25

2 Find all the factor pairs of the square numbers in the above list.

3 On a set of axes labelled from 0–5 on the x and y axis, draw the graph of this function machine:

4 Here is a sequence of patterns made from matchsticks:

a Copy and complete this table:

Pattern number	1	2	3
Number of matchsticks	4		

b How many matchsticks will be needed for the 4th pattern?
Check your answer by drawing.

c How many matchsticks will be needed for the 20th pattern?

130

Development

The themes of the unit are developed in A5.

Links

A good knowledge of factors and multiples will help students multiply and divide more successfully and work with area of rectangles more efficiently.

Mental starters

Objectives covered in this unit:

- Visualise, describe and sketch 2-D shapes in different orientations.
- Estimate and order acute and obtuse angles.

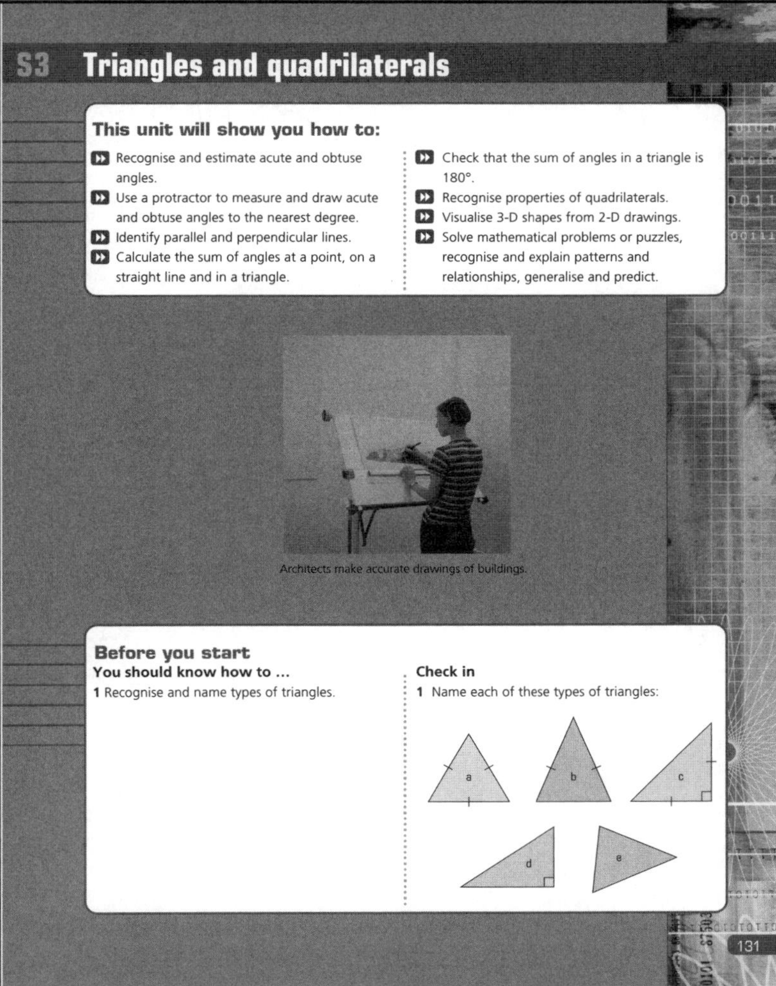

S3 Triangles and quadrilaterals

This unit will show you how to:

- Recognise and estimate acute and obtuse angles.
- Use a protractor to measure and draw acute and obtuse angles to the nearest degree.
- Identify parallel and perpendicular lines.
- Calculate the sum of angles at a point, on a straight line and in a triangle.
- Check that the sum of angles in a triangle is 180°.
- Recognise properties of quadrilaterals.
- Visualise 3-D shapes from 2-D drawings.
- Solve mathematical problems or puzzles, recognise and explain patterns and relationships, generalise and predict.

Architects make accurate drawings of buildings.

Before you start

You should know how to ...

1 Recognise and name types of triangles.

Check in

1 Name each of these types of triangles:

a b c d e

131

Check in activity

Show **R20** on OHP.
Ask students for the angle between two numbers.
Always refer to the clockwise direction.
Emphasise that the order you give the numbers makes a difference: 12 to 3 makes 90° but 3 to 12 makes 270°.
Now ask for the angle between two numbers in both directions: clockwise and anticlockwise.

Resources needed

* means class set needed

Essential:
R12 (OHP) – Protractor
R14 (OHP) – Special triangles
R15 (OHP) – Special quadrilaterals
R17 (OHP) – Ruler
S3.1OHP – Angles to measure
S3.2OHP – Angles in diagrams
S3.4OHP – Triangle diagrams
S3.5OHP – 3-D shapes using cubes
Protractors*

Useful:
R13* – Isometric paper
R20 (OHP) – Analogue clock
S3.3F* – Isosceles triangles
S3.4ICT* – Constructions using interactive geometry
Box of solids, dice, rulers, scissors, glue, coloured pencils, multilink cubes

Unit commentary

Aim of the unit

This unit aims to consolidate and extend students' understanding of angles and shapes. Students measure and draw angles and derive the angle sum of a triangle, using angle facts to solve problems. They then draw 3-D shapes on isometric paper and describe them according to their properties.

Introduction

Discuss who needs to use angles and properties of shapes. Try to build up a diverse range of people from architects and graphic designers to footballers.

Framework references

This unit focuses on:

- Year 6 teaching objectives pages: 103, 105, 111
- Problem solving objectives page: 79

The unit provides access to:

- Year 7 teaching objectives pages: 198, 200, 220, 222, 232

Differentiation

Core tier focuses on constructing triangles and identifying geometric properties of 2-D and 3-D shapes.

Springboard 7

Pages 134, 455–459, 464–466.

S3.1 Measuring angles

Mental starter

More than, less than

You need a clock with moveable hands or use **R20**.

Start at 12. Move one hand through 90° clockwise. Highlight that this makes a corner. Now move it to 6 – this is a straight line.

Make various angles out of the two hands. Students say whether each angle is more than or less than a corner, then a straight line.

Move the hands anticlockwise – discuss which angle to consider.

Useful resources

Protractors.

R12 has a protractor.

A **clock** with moveable hands or **R20**.

S3.1OHP has angles to measure.

Introductory activity

Ask students what they understand by the word angle – a measure of turn.

Discuss when you need to measure or use angles.

Revise what angle facts students already know. Start with 90°.

- What do you call a corner angle?
  right, 90°
- How do you measure it?
  What equipment do you need?
  What is the unit of measure?

Then consider 270° – the rest of the angle – and lead to 360° in a full turn.

Discuss what is meant by the angle on a straight line.

Use the clock to show it is a half turn – it is 180°.

Revise terms: acute and obtuse.

S3.1OHP has some angles to measure.

Ask students to estimate the size first and justify any estimates. Emphasise the need to estimate from known facts – 90°, 180° ...

Now discuss how to measure the angles using a protractor.

Emphasise that the protractor must be placed correctly and then they must choose the right scale.

Students can practise putting a ruler along one of the lines correctly as a step to using a protractor.

You can turn over the OHP to measure the angles again using a different scale.

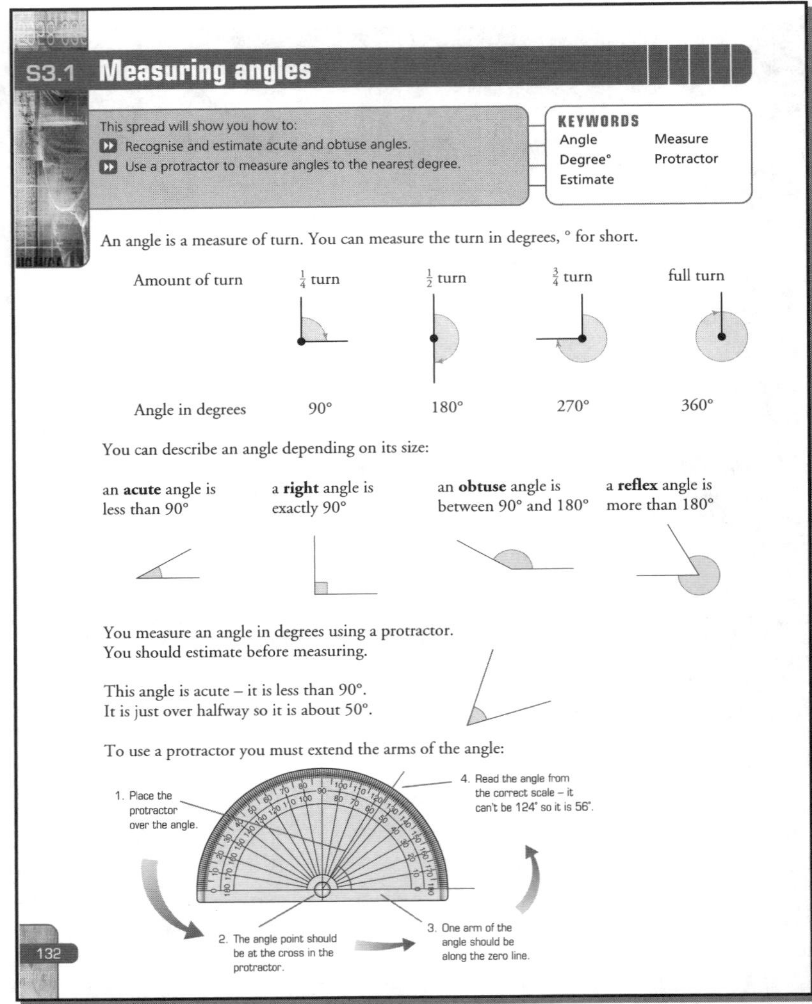

S3.1 **Measuring angles**

This spread will show you how to:

- Recognise and estimate acute and obtuse angles.
- Use a protractor to measure angles to the nearest degree.

KEYWORDS: Angle, Degree°, Estimate, Measure, Protractor

An angle is a measure of turn. You can measure the turn in degrees, ° for short.

Amount of turn	$\frac{1}{4}$ turn	$\frac{1}{2}$ turn	$\frac{3}{4}$ turn	full turn
Angle in degrees	90°	180°	270°	360°

You can describe an angle depending on its size:

an **acute** angle is less than 90°

a **right** angle is exactly 90°

an **obtuse** angle is between 90° and 180°

a **reflex** angle is more than 180°

You measure an angle in degrees using a protractor.
You should estimate before measuring.

This angle is acute – it is less than 90°.
It is just over halfway so it is about 50°.

To use a protractor you must extend the arms of the angle:

1. Place the protractor over the angle.
2. The angle point should be at the cross in the protractor.
3. One arm of the angle should be along the zero line.
4. Read the angle from the correct scale – it can't be 124° so it is 56°.

132

Plenary

Angle bingo

Students choose four numbers between 1 and 360 and place them in a 2 × 2 grid.

The teacher rolls a dice. The six outcomes are:

1 Right angle	2 Acute angle	3 Obtuse angle
4 Reflex angle	5 Half turn	6 Full turn

Students cross off their numbers depending on the dice score.

The first to cross off all four wins.

Further activities

Give students specific angles to draw. You can challenge able students with reflex angles.

Students can draw shapes using a ruler and then measure and label the interior angles.

Differentiation

Support questions:

- Questions 1–5 are straightforward angles to measure as they are all multiples of 5°. Springboard 7, page 457.
- In question 6 the orientation makes measuring more difficult. Springboard 7, pages 455, 456.
- In question 7 there are lots of questions to answer based on the clockwise and anticlockwise scales. Springboard 7, pages 458, 459.

Core tier: focuses on finding missing angles by calculation.

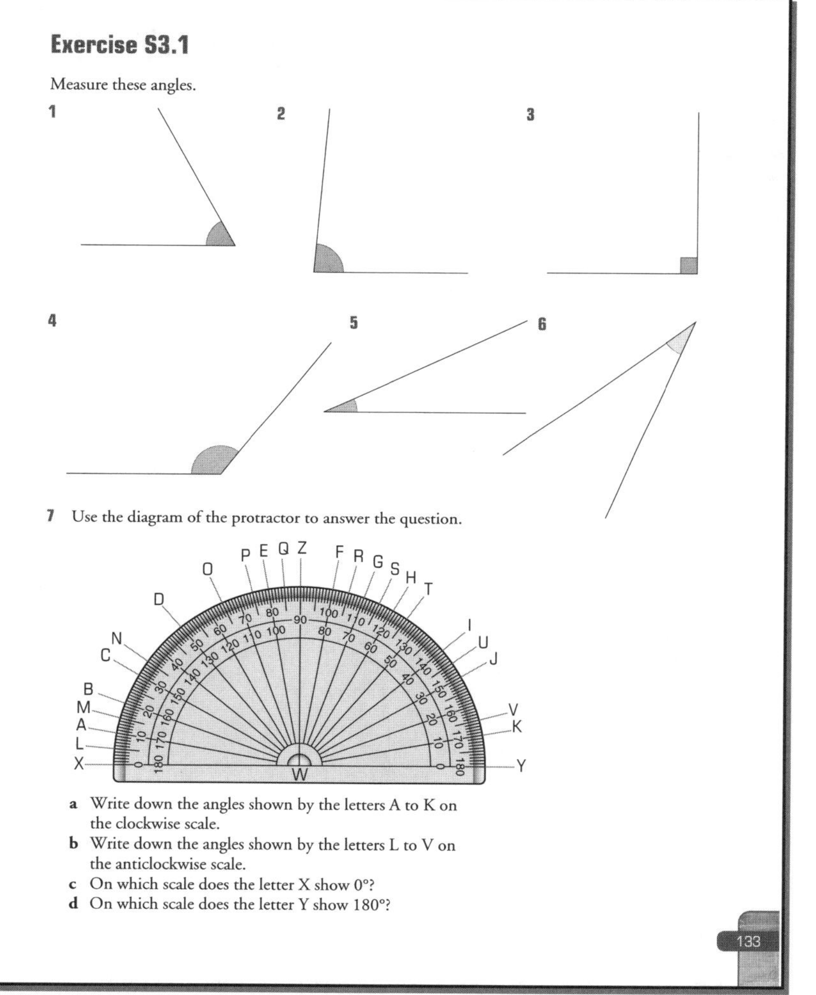

Exercise S3.1

Measure these angles.

1 2 3

4 5 6

7 Use the diagram of the protractor to answer the question.

a Write down the angles shown by the letters A to K on the clockwise scale.
b Write down the angles shown by the letters L to V on the anticlockwise scale.
c On which scale does the letter X show 0°?
d On which scale does the letter Y show 180°?

133

Exercise commentary

The questions assess the objectives on Primary Framework Page 111.

Problem solving
Students could make some general statements about angles based on answers to question 7 which would assess Primary Framework Page 81.

Group work
The further activity is suitable for pairs.

Misconceptions
Students find the protractor difficult to place.
Emphasise the link with a ruler and encourage students to place a ruler carefully along one of the arms then to replace it with the protractor.
Once placed correctly, students must use the correct scale.
When measuring an angle, emphasise that an estimate will help them choose the correct scale.

Links
Estimation: Primary Framework Page 11.

Homework

S3.1HW requires students to estimate angles.

Answers

1 60° 2 86° 3 90°
4 130° 5 26° 6 30°
7 **a** A 10°, B 20°, C 30°, D 50°, E 80°, F 100°, G 110°, H 120°, I 140°, J 150°, K 170° **b** L 175°, M 165°, N 145°, O 115°, P 105°, Q 95°, R 75°, S 65°, T 55°, U 35°, V 15° **c** Clockwise **d** Clockwise

S3.2 Finding angles

Mental starter

What's my pair?
Call out a number.
Students hold up the number that makes it up to 90°.
Move on to 180° then 360°.
Students to use scrap paper or **R1** digit cards to write the number and hold it up.

Useful resources

S3.2OHP has diagrams with missing angles.
Protractors and a board protractor.
R12 shows a protractor.
R1 digit cards for the mental starter.

Introductory activity

Revise what angle facts students know.

- There are 90° on a corner
- 180° on a straight line
- 360° on a full turn.

S3.2OHP has some diagrams which have an angle missing.

- First ask students what the complete angle measures.
- Then ask how much of the angle they already know.
- Finally ask for the missing angle.

The examples develop to use letters to stand for missing angles.

- Reassure students that the letter just stands for a missing angle.
- If the letter is repeated on the same diagram, it means the angles are equal.

Discuss answers. Ask students to justify any working out.

You could ask students to draw the simpler diagrams on the OHP accurately. This will help reinforce the angle facts they are using.
Emphasise the correct use of a protractor:
Place the protractor carefully so that the zero point is in place and the line is along one of the arms.
Count using the correct scale – from 0.

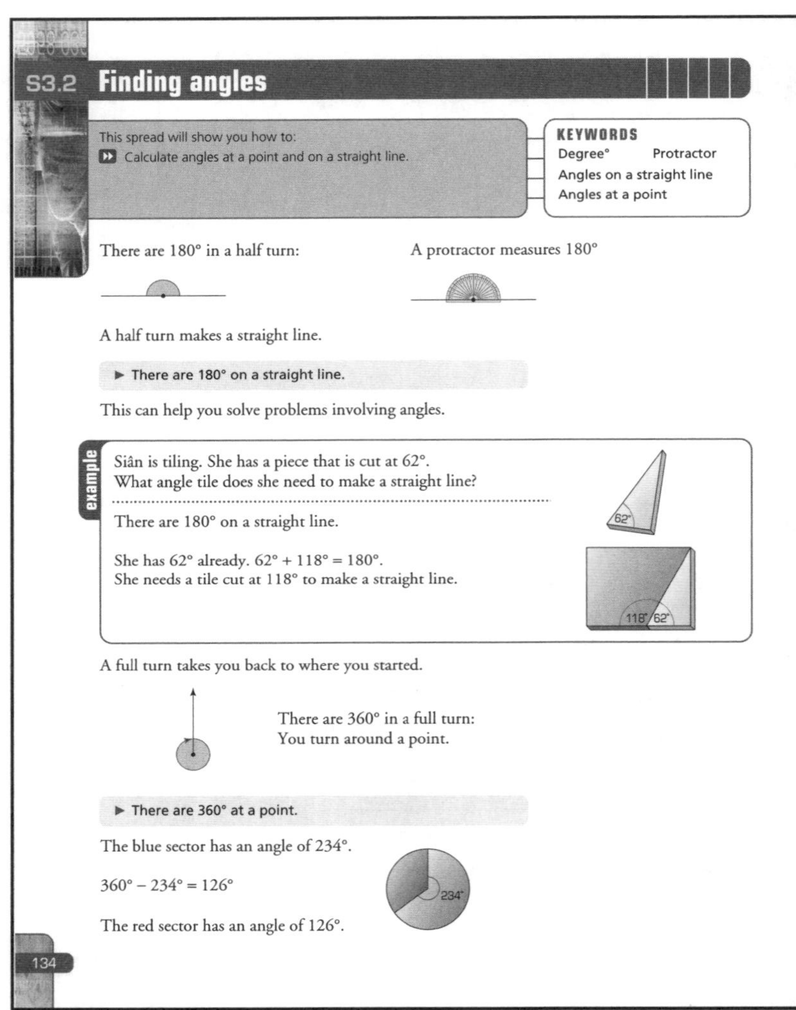

S3.2 Finding angles

This spread will show you how to:
- Calculate angles at a point and on a straight line.

KEYWORDS
Degree°
Protractor
Angles on a straight line
Angles at a point

There are 180° in a half turn:

A protractor measures 180°

A half turn makes a straight line.

► There are 180° on a straight line.

This can help you solve problems involving angles.

example

Siân is tiling. She has a piece that is cut at 62°.
What angle tile does she need to make a straight line?

There are 180° on a straight line.

She has 62° already. 62° + 118° = 180°.
She needs a tile cut at 118° to make a straight line.

A full turn takes you back to where you started.

There are 360° in a full turn:
You turn around a point.

► There are 360° at a point.

The blue sector has an angle of 234°.

360° – 234° = 126°

The red sector has an angle of 126°.

134

Plenary

Corners, lines and points
Call out a number between 0 and 90.
Ask students for the angle that will make a corner.
Move on to numbers up to 180 and line or corner, then numbers up to 360 and line, corner or point.
You can develop this by giving two angles and asking for a third and so on.

Further activities

Challenge students to draw the diagrams in questions 14 and 15 accurately, ensuring all the arms are equal in length. They then join up the ends of each of the arms to form an equilateral triangle and a regular pentagon.
Able students can continue the theme by constructing a regular hexagon and octagon.

Differentiation

Support questions:

- Questions 1–6 focus on angles on a straight line. Springboard 7, page 464.
- Questions 7–11 involve angles at a point. Springboard 7, page 465.
- Questions 13 to 15 involve division of 180° or 360°.

Core tier: focuses on angles in triangles and quadrilaterals.

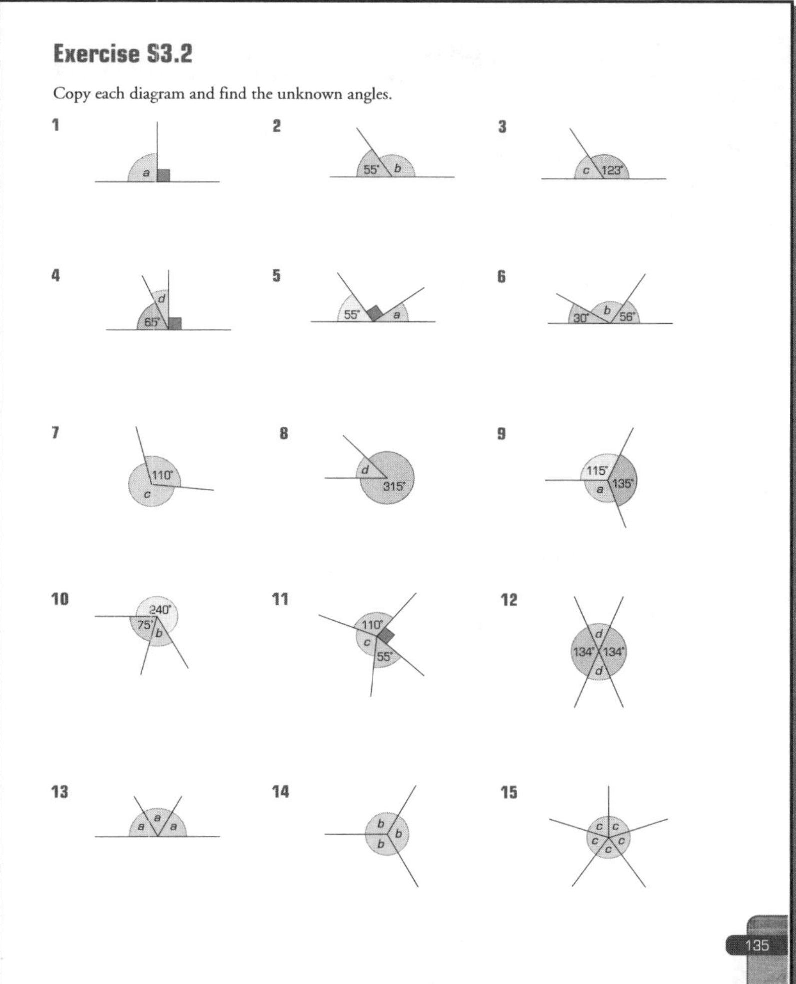

Exercise S3.2

Copy each diagram and find the unknown angles.

Exercise commentary

The questions assess the objectives on Primary Framework Page 111.

Problem solving

Students could be encouraged to make some general statements about angles which would assess Primary Framework Page 81.

Group work

The further activity can be usefully discussed in pairs.

Misconceptions

Students will continue to have the same difficulties with using a protractor as in S2.1.
Emphasise the link with a ruler and the use of an estimate.
Students often measure missing angles rather than calculate.
Emphasise that the diagrams are not drawn to scale.
They often mix up the angle facts.
Emphasise that 180° on a straight line is shown on a protractor and encourage students to start from this fact.

Links

Estimation: Primary Framework Page 11.

Homework

S3.2HW provides practice at finding missing angles on a straight line and at a point.

Answers

1	$a = 90°$	2	$b = 125°$	3	$c = 57°$
4	$d = 25°$	5	$a = 35°$	6	$b = 94°$
7	$c = 250°$	8	$d = 45°$	9	$a = 110°$
10	$b = 45°$	11	$c = 105°$	12	$d = 46°$
13	$a = 60°$	14	$b = 120°$	15	$c = 72°$

Mental starter

Sketch a triangle

Recap on sorts of angles – naming acute, obtuse and right angles.
Draw a right-angled triangle on the board or use the first example **S3.3OHP**.
Ask students the name of each angle.
Give one of the acute angles and ask for the other.
Repeat for isosceles and other scalene triangles.
Ask for the names of the triangles and for missing angles.

Useful resources

Protractors and **rulers**.
R12 protractor.
S3.3OHP has triangles to use in the mental starter.
R14 shows the common triangles.

Introductory activity

Discuss why triangles are important structures – they are difficult to crush as the top is always a point! – they are very strong shapes.

Refer to triangles from the mental starter or use R14.
Ask students to name a triangle with:
- 2 equal sides – isosceles
- 3 equal sides – equilateral
- 0 equal sides – scalene.

For each of the triangles, ask students:
- the number of sides
- the number of angles
- the sum of the angles.

Emphasise that any triangle has: 3 sides; 3 angles; an angle sum of 180°.

Discuss how to draw an angle using just a ruler and protractor.
- Start with the line – why not the angle?
- Place the protractor carefully – imagine it is a ruler!
- Read the protractor using the correct scale – start from zero.
- Mark a point and then join it to the zero mark.

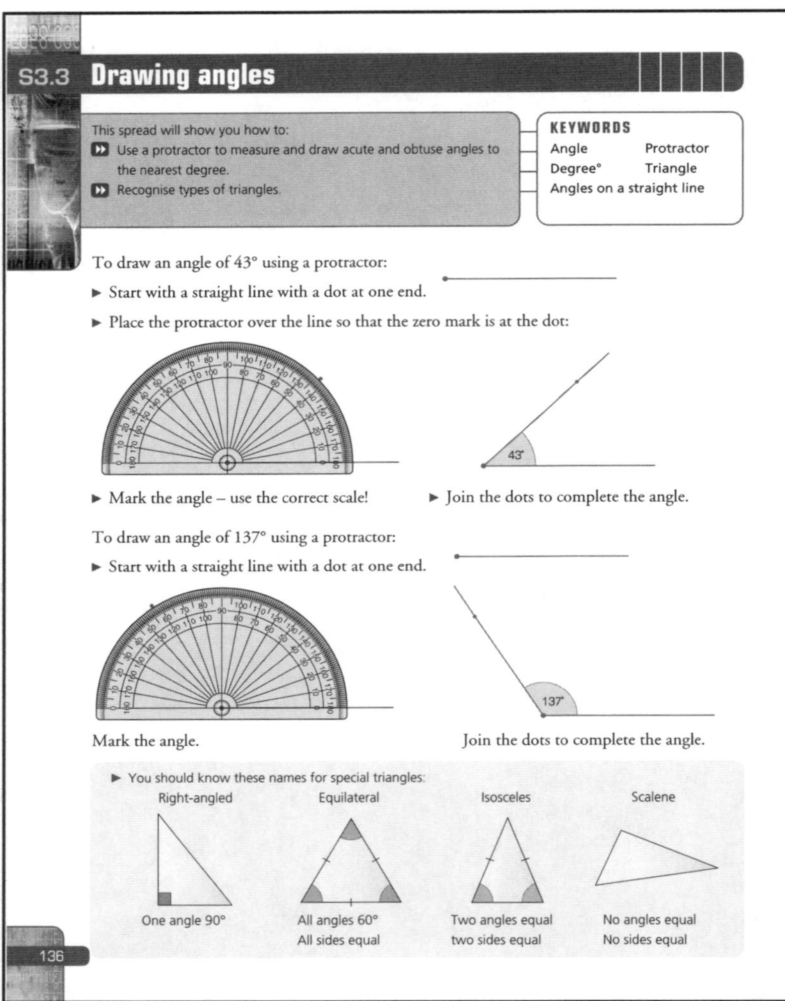

S3.3 Drawing angles
This spread will show you how to:
Use a protractor to measure and draw acute and obtuse angles to the nearest degree.
Recognise types of triangles.
KEYWORDS
Angle
Protractor
Degree°
Triangle
Angles on a straight line
To draw an angle of 43° using a protractor:
Start with a straight line with a dot at one end.
Place the protractor over the line so that the zero mark is at the dot:
43°
Mark the angle – use the correct scale!
Join the dots to complete the angle.
To draw an angle of 137° using a protractor:
Start with a straight line with a dot at one end.
137°
Mark the angle.
Join the dots to complete the angle.
You should know these names for special triangles:
Right-angled
Equilateral
Isosceles
Scalene
One angle 90°
All angles 60°
All sides equal
Two angles equal
two sides equal
No angles equal
No sides equal
136

Plenary

Discuss question 4.
Ask students how they would draw each triangle accurately to find the missing sides.

Further activities

Students can construct the diagrams in exercise S3.2.

S3.3F contains isosceles triangles in different orientations for students to practice recognising which pairs of angles are equal.

Differentiation

Support questions:

- Questions 1a–1d focus on naming and drawing angles to the nearest 5°.
- Questions 1e–1h and 2 focus on constructing angles to the nearest degree.
- Questions 3 and 4 focus on classifying triangles and using their side and angle properties.

Core tier: focuses on properties of triangles and quadrilaterals.

Exercise S3.3

1 Name each of these angles – choose from:
Acute Obtuse Right
Draw them accurately using a protractor.

a 45° **b** 60° **c** 120° **d** 90°
e 56° **f** 29° **g** 132° **h** 176°

2 Draw a line 8 cm long.
At one end, construct an angle of 56°.
At the other end, construct an angle of 32°.
Do your lines meet?

3 What are the names of each of these triangles?

a 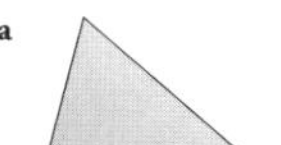

b 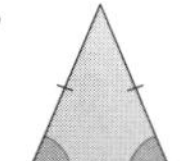

c

d 

4 Find the angles or side lengths.

a Isosceles triangle

angle C
length AB

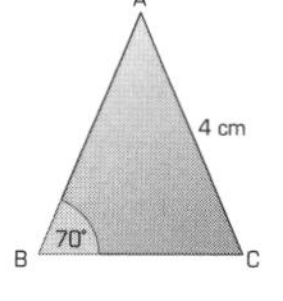

b Right-angled isosceles triangle

angle B
angle A
length BC

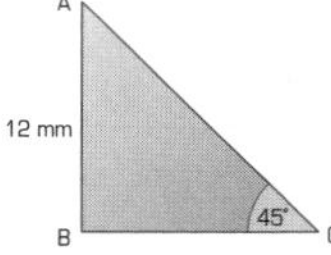

c Equilateral triangle

angle B
angle C
length AB
length AC

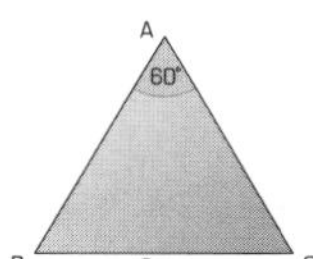

Exercise commentary

The questions assess the objectives on Primary Framework Pages 103 and 111.

Problem solving
Students could be encouraged to make some general statements about angles in a triangle which would assess Primary Framework Page 81.

Group work
Question 2 and the further activity can be usefully discussed in pairs.

Misconceptions
Drawing angles at each end of a line adds complexity to using a protractor.
Emphasise the need to work in a structured way using a sharp pencil so they can still read the diagram!
Students mix up the equal angles in an isosceles triangle and then measure rather than calculate.
Emphasise that the angles link with the equal sides and give students plenty of opportunities to work with different orientations (use **S3.3F**).

Links
Estimation: Primary Framework Page 11.

Homework

S3.3HW provides practice in classifying triangles, and in drawing angles.

Answers

1 **a** Acute **b** Acute **c** Obtuse **d** Right **e** Acute **f** Acute **g** Obtuse **h** Obtuse

3 **a** Scalene **b** Isosceles **c** Right-angled isosceles **d** Equilateral

4 **a** 70°, 4 cm **b** 90°, 45°, 12 mm **c** 60°, 60°, 3 cm, 3 cm

S3.4 Angles in triangles

Mental starter

What's my opposite?

Draw a pair of intersecting lines on the board or OHP.
Tell students the acute angle is 50°.
Ask them what they think the other acute angle is.
Discuss what the obtuse angle is as it makes a straight line.
Then you can see the other acute angle is 50°.
Repeat for other pairs of intersecting lines.

Useful resources

S3.4OHP has diagrams with missing angles

Paper or card, rulers, scissors and coloured pencils

Introductory activity

Refer to the mental starter.

Discuss how you can generalise about the angles formed between two intersecting lines:

- acute angles are equal
- obtuse angles are equal
- acute + obtuse = 180°

Draw a right-angled triangle on the board and ask students its name.
Encourage them to be specific and use technical terms: right angle and acute angle.
Ask students to identify the angles of the triangle (these are the interior angles).
Now ask for estimates of the three angles.
Each student should write down their estimates and add them.
Define the angle sum as the sum of the three angles. The students' estimates should be roughly equal. Discuss this.

Now ask students to draw any triangle on paper using a ruler.
They should:

- colour each angle then
- cut them out carefully and
- place the angles together to make a straight line.

Emphasise that this shows the angle sum of any triangle is 180°.

S3.4OHP has some diagrams which have an angle missing.
Discuss answers. Ask students to justify any working out.

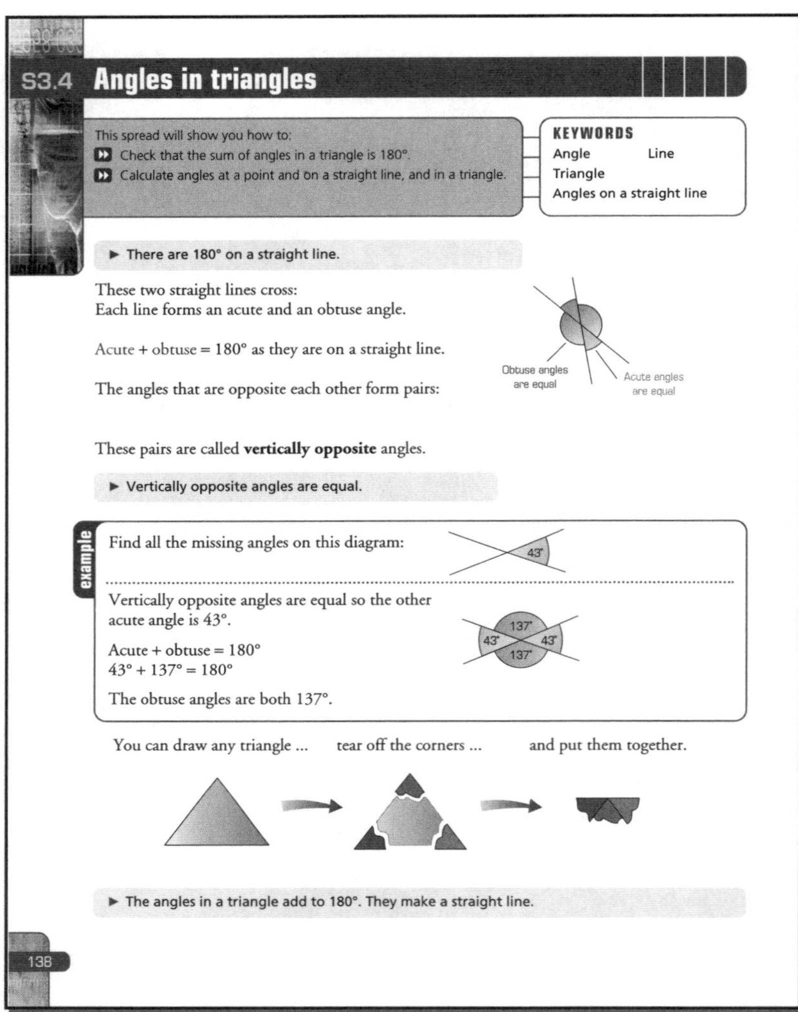

S3.4 **Angles in triangles**

This spread will show you how to:
- Check that the sum of angles in a triangle is 180°.
- Calculate angles at a point and on a straight line, and in a triangle.

KEYWORDS
Angle
Line
Triangle
Angles on a straight line

► There are 180° on a straight line.

These two straight lines cross:
Each line forms an acute and an obtuse angle.

Acute + obtuse = 180° as they are on a straight line.

The angles that are opposite each other form pairs:

These pairs are called **vertically opposite** angles.

► Vertically opposite angles are equal.

example

Find all the missing angles on this diagram:

Vertically opposite angles are equal so the other acute angle is 43°.

Acute + obtuse = 180°
43° + 137° = 180°

The obtuse angles are both 137°.

You can draw any triangle ... tear off the corners ... and put them together.

► The angles in a triangle add to 180°. They make a straight line.

138

Plenary

Go over the problems in the exercise, and the multi-step questions in particular.
Discuss approaches to the questions.
Emphasise that students must learn the facts and then they can use them to solve the problems.

Further activities

In **S3.4ICT**, students use interactive geometry to explore triangle constructions.

Challenge able students to draw accurately each of the different types of triangle.

Students can use questions 9–11 to investigate the relationship between the exterior and interior angles of a triangle.

Differentiation

Support questions:

- Questions 1–3 focus on using angles on a straight line and around a point.
- Questions 4–8 are straightforward questions about the angle sum of a triangle. Springboard 7, page 466.
- Questions 9–15 are more complex requiring multi-step answers.

Core tier: focuses on constructing triangles from geometrical information, and extends to quadrilaterals.

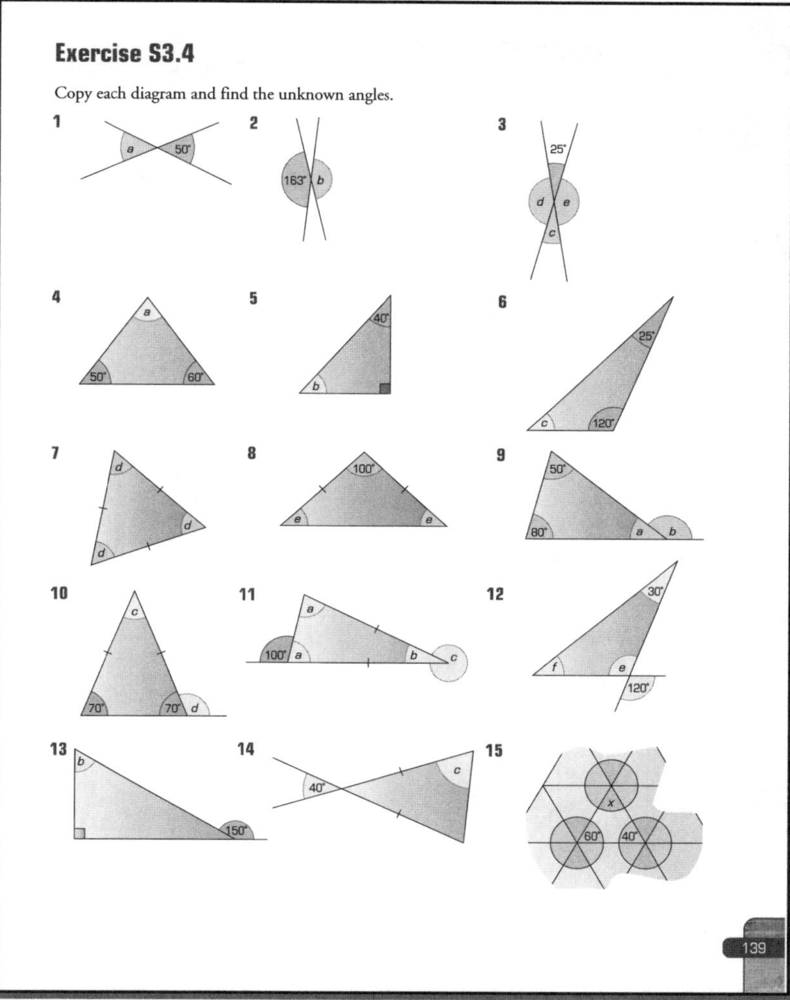

Exercise S3.4
Copy each diagram and find the unknown angles.
139

Exercise commentary

The questions assess the objective on Primary Framework Page 111.

Problem solving

The further activity encourages students to make a general statement about exterior angles which assesses Primary Framework Page 81.

Group work

Questions 9–15 and the further activity can be usefully discussed in pairs.

Misconceptions

Students measure rather than calculate.

Emphasise that calculation is more accurate than measuring as there is rounding involved in the latter (link to continuous data in D2.3).

Students get confused when there are so many facts to remember and use.

Encourage them to remember only two facts: 180° on a straight line which is on a protractor, and 180° in a triangle.

Emphasise the need to work logically and to write all the angles on the diagram as they find them.

Links

Triangles: Primary Framework Page 103.

Homework

S3.4HW provides practice at finding missing angles in a triangle.

Answers

1 $a = 50°$	2 $b = 163°$
3 $c = 25°$, $d = 155°$, $e = 155°$	4 $a = 70°$
5 $b = 50°$	6 $c = 35°$
7 $d = 60°$	8 $e = 40°$
9 $a = 50°$, $b = 130°$	10 $c = 40°$, $d = 110°$
11 $a = 80°$, $b = 20°$, $c = 340°$	12 $e = 120°$, $f = 30°$
13 $b = 60°$	14 $c = 70°$
15 $x = 80°$	

S3.5 2-D drawings of 3-D shapes

Mental starter

Sketch me

Describe a 2-D shape in stages:

- I have four sides, four angles.
- Opposite sides are parallel, equal ...

Students sketch the shape as you describe it.
They name the shape as specifically as possible.

Useful resources

S3.5OHP has some 3-D shapes to describe.
Multilink cubes.
Box of **solids.**
R15 shows special quadrilaterals for the mental starter.
R13 isometric paper.

Introductory activity

Students can work in pairs.
Give out four multilink cubes to each student.

Ask them to describe a cube as accurately as possible. Encourage terms such as equal, square, face.

Discuss the different parts of a cube – the faces, edges and vertices – and encourage students to count them.

Discuss how to draw a cube on paper.
Encourage students to use the method shown in the student book.

Show S3.5OHP.
Ask students to make (using cubes) and then describe the first shape.
Students should sit back to back and one student to describe the shape made as accurately as possible while the other sketches it.
This should prove very difficult.
Discuss how to describe the shape to someone so they can draw it.

Emphasise that they can be drawn accurately on isometric paper.
Use **R17** to discuss how to draw each shape students have made.

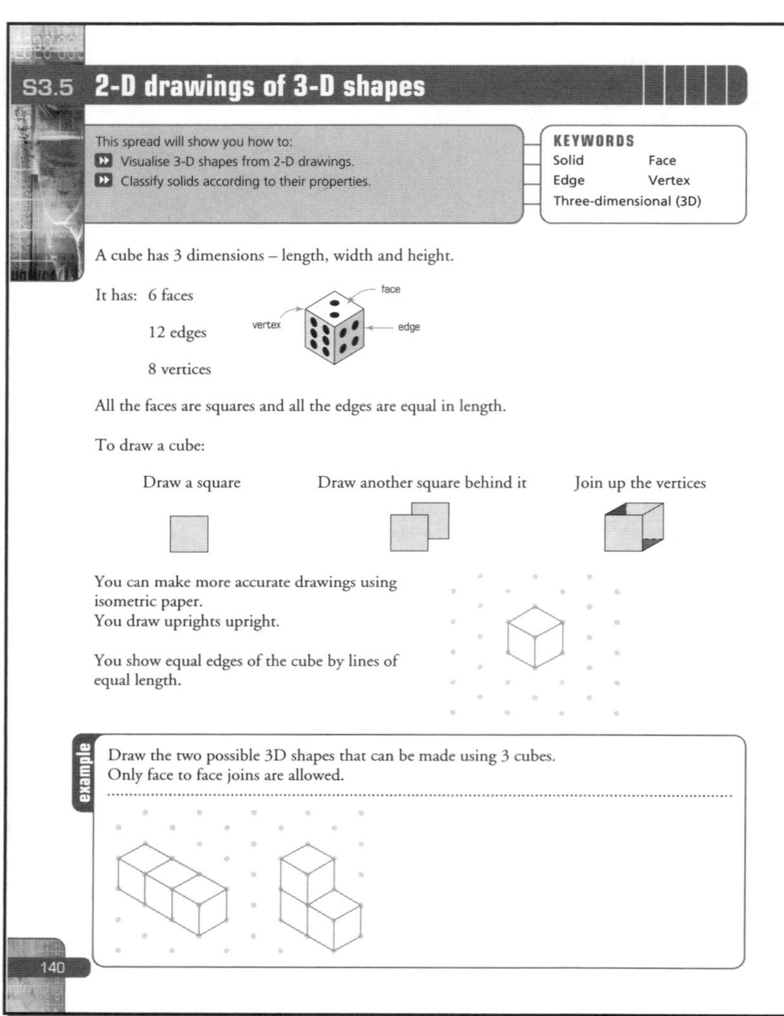

S3.5 2-D drawings of 3-D shapes

This spread will show you how to:
- Visualise 3-D shapes from 2-D drawings.
- Classify solids according to their properties.

KEYWORDS
Solid Face
Edge Vertex
Three-dimensional (3D)

A cube has 3 dimensions – length, width and height.

It has: 6 faces
12 edges
8 vertices

All the faces are squares and all the edges are equal in length.

To draw a cube:

Draw a square — Draw another square behind it — Join up the vertices

You can make more accurate drawings using isometric paper.
You draw uprights upright.

You show equal edges of the cube by lines of equal length.

example

Draw the two possible 3D shapes that can be made using 3 cubes.
Only face to face joins are allowed.

140

Plenary

For each shape students made in question 2, emphasise the different ways of looking at the shape – the different views depending on where you look at it from.
Discuss the view from:

- the top and bottom
- the left and right sides
- the front and back.

Further activities

Question 3 can be developed by asking students how many extra cubes are needed to make the cube in part 2c or a $4 \times 4 \times 4$ cube.

Differentiation

Support questions:

- Questions 1 focuses on classifying solids by the faces, edges and vertices.
- Question 2 focuses on accurately constructing and drawing 3-D shapes. Springboard 7, page 134.
- Question 3 involves visualising 3-D shapes.

Core tier: extends to prisms and pyramids.

Exercise S3.5

1 Write down how many faces, edges and vertices each of these shapes has.

a

b

c

2 **a** How many cubes do you need to make each of these shapes?

A

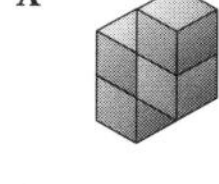

B

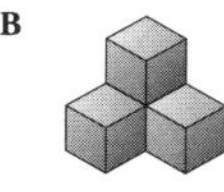

C

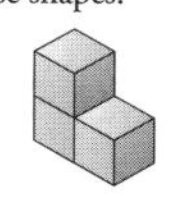

D

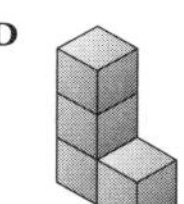

E

F

G

b Draw each shape on isometric paper.

c Make each of the shapes with multilink cubes. Fit them together to make this cube:

3 Find the least number of cubes needed to cover and join the blue faces. Justify your answer.

141

Exercise commentary

The questions assess the objectives on Primary Framework Pages 103 and 105.

Problem solving

Question 3 assesses the objectives on Primary Framework Page 79.

Group work

Questions 2 and 3 can be usefully discussed in pairs.

Misconceptions

Students find visualisation difficult and may only count the visible faces, edges, vertices or cubes.

Using multilink cubes to construct the shapes in questions 2 and 3 can help and it is useful to have a box of solids available for question 1. In question 2 it is unclear whether there is a fourth cube in the shape and you may need to direct students to its existence otherwise they cannot complete the cube in part c.

Some students get confused with faces, edges and vertices.

Have a box of solids available and discuss strategies for remembering as a class so good ideas are shared.

Links

2-D shapes: Primary Framework Page 103.

Homework

S3.5HW is an activity based on isometric drawings of 3-D shapes.

Answers

1 **a** 6, 12, 8 **b** 5, 9, 6 **c** 5, 8, 5

2 A 3, B 4, C 4, D 4, E 4, F 4, G 4, H 4

3 10

Summary

The Year 6 key teaching objective is:

- Use a protractor to measure acute and obtuse angles to the nearest degree (111).

Plenary activity

Ask students to describe properties – parallel and perpendicular lines and angle facts – of various triangles and quadrilaterals from **R14** and **R15**.

Check out commentary

1 This is a straightforward question about using a ruler. Some students will not remember the term 'diagonal' and measure the wrong lengths.
Others may have difficulty placing the ruler on a sloping line.
Encourage students to rotate the page so that the diagonal is horizontal.
Emphasise that the diagonals are equal in length so students should only need to take one measurement.

2 Students use the wrong protractor scale to measure angles.
Encourage them to estimate the angles first so that they know which scale is appropriate.
Students having difficulty placing the protractor properly should be encouraged to place a ruler first and then to use the same principles for placing the protractor.

3 Students mix up angle facts.
Emphasise that they can see 180° on a straight line on a protractor and encourage this as a start point.

4 Students fail to count the unseen cubes.
Using multilink cubes will emphasise that the hidden cubes are necessary to hold the shape together.

5 Many students will only see straightforward rectangles and give the answer as 10. Students will need to use a structured approach to find all the rectangles and may benefit from supportive questioning: how many 1 × 1 rectangles are there? 1 × 2? 1 × 3? 2 × 1? ...

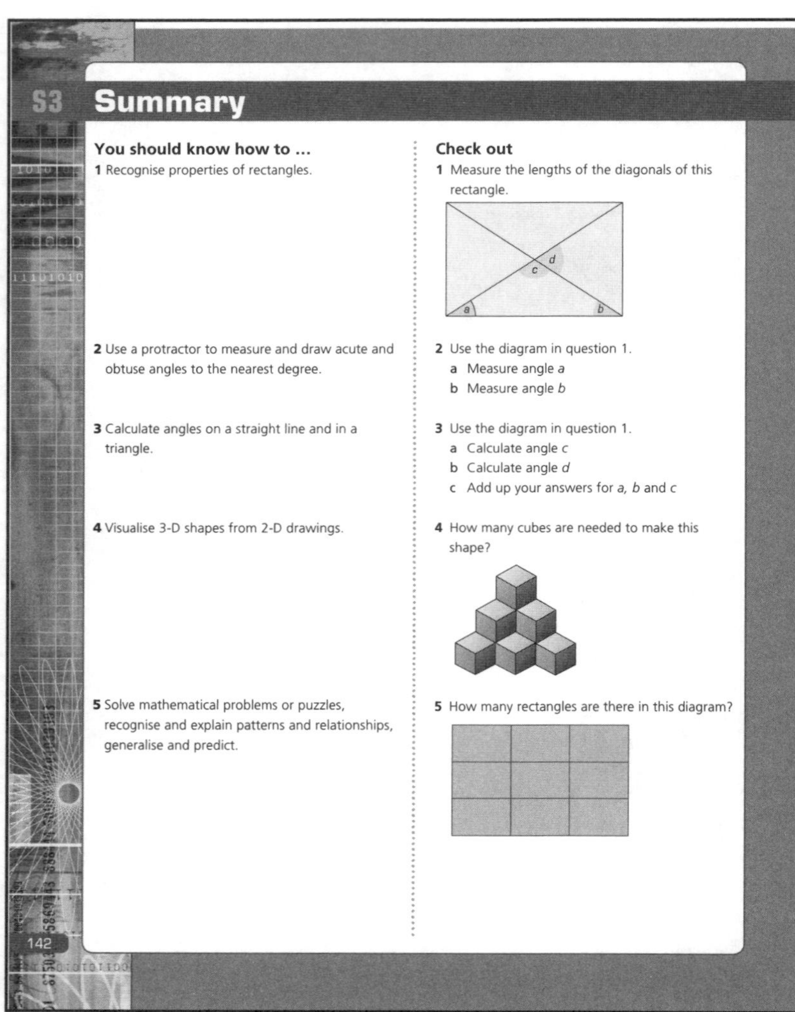

S3 Summary

You should know how to ...	Check out
1 Recognise properties of rectangles.	1 Measure the lengths of the diagonals of this rectangle.
2 Use a protractor to measure and draw acute and obtuse angles to the nearest degree.	2 Use the diagram in question 1. a Measure angle *a* b Measure angle *b*
3 Calculate angles on a straight line and in a triangle.	3 Use the diagram in question 1. a Calculate angle *c* b Calculate angle *d* c Add up your answers for *a*, *b* and *c*
4 Visualise 3-D shapes from 2-D drawings.	4 How many cubes are needed to make this shape?
5 Solve mathematical problems or puzzles, recognise and explain patterns and relationships, generalise and predict.	5 How many rectangles are there in this diagram?

142

Development

The themes of this unit are developed in S5 where students construct shapes with increasing accuracy.

Links

The work in this unit is particularly useful in Technology when designing new products and packaging.

Mental starters

Objectives covered in this unit:

- Multiply and divide decimals by 10, 100, 1000.
- Count on and back in steps.

Resources needed

* means class set needed

Essential:

R6 (OHP) – Number lines

Useful:

R2* – Decimal digit cards
R4 (OHP) – Place value table
N4.5ICT* – Ratio using Excel
Multilink cubes
Counters

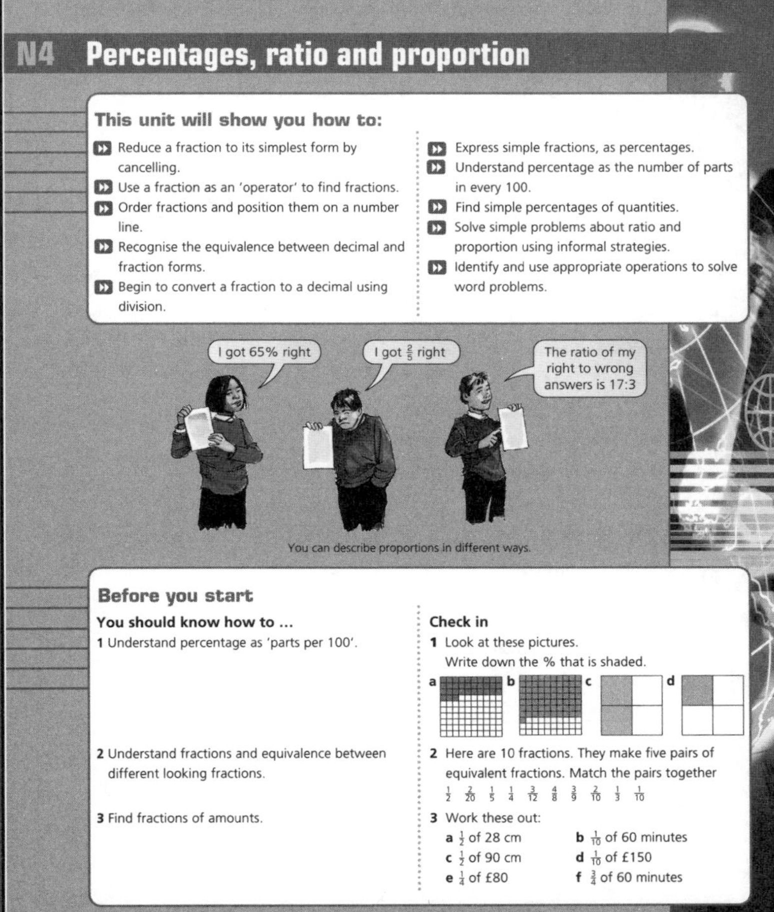

N4 Percentages, ratio and proportion

This unit will show you how to:

- Reduce a fraction to its simplest form by cancelling.
- Use a fraction as an 'operator' to find fractions.
- Order fractions and position them on a number line.
- Recognise the equivalence between decimal and fraction forms.
- Begin to convert a fraction to a decimal using division.
- Express simple fractions, as percentages.
- Understand percentage as the number of parts in every 100.
- Find simple percentages of quantities.
- Solve simple problems about ratio and proportion using informal strategies.
- Identify and use appropriate operations to solve word problems.

You can describe proportions in different ways.

Before you start

You should know how to ...

1 Understand percentage as 'parts per 100'.

2 Understand fractions and equivalence between different looking fractions.

3 Find fractions of amounts.

Check in

1 Look at these pictures.
Write down the % that is shaded.

a b c d

2 Here are 10 fractions. They make five pairs of equivalent fractions. Match the pairs together

$\frac{1}{2}$ $\frac{2}{20}$ $\frac{1}{5}$ $\frac{1}{4}$ $\frac{3}{12}$ $\frac{4}{8}$ $\frac{3}{9}$ $\frac{2}{10}$ $\frac{1}{3}$ $\frac{1}{10}$

3 Work these out:

a $\frac{1}{2}$ of 28 cm　　b $\frac{1}{10}$ of 60 minutes
c $\frac{1}{2}$ of 90 cm　　d $\frac{1}{10}$ of £150
e $\frac{1}{4}$ of £80　　f $\frac{3}{4}$ of 60 minutes

143

Unit commentary

Aim of the unit

This unit aims to build on the work of unit N2, consolidating students' ability to calculate with simple percentages. The unit then introduces the ideas of ratio and proportion.

Introduction

Discuss the picture in the student book:

- Which student did best in the test?
- What are the similarities and differences of the different forms?

Framework references

This unit focuses on:

- Year 6 teaching objectives pages: 23, 25, 27, 31, 33
- Problem solving objectives page: 83, 85, 87, 89

The unit provides access to:

- Year 7 teaching objectives pages: 64, 66, 70, 72, 74, 78, 80

Check in activity

Fraction Bingo

Write these ten questions on the board:

$\frac{1}{3}$ of 90, $\frac{1}{2}$ of 50, $\frac{1}{4}$ of 60, $\frac{1}{2}$ of 90, $\frac{1}{3}$ of 60,
$\frac{2}{3}$ of 60, $\frac{1}{10}$ of 50, $\frac{1}{4}$ of 200, $\frac{1}{5}$ of 50, $\frac{1}{2}$ of 70

Students choose 4 questions and place them in a 2 × 2 grid.

Call out the answers: 5, 10, 15, 20, 25, 30, 35, 40, 45, 50.

Students cross out correct questions, justifying their choices.

Differentiation

Core tier focuses on the equivalence between fractions, decimals, percentages, ratio and proportion, and calculating with fractions and percentages.

Springboard 7

Pages 423–428, 430–434, 436–439.

Mental starter

×/÷ 10 and 100 bingo

- Give a start number: 9
- Students multiply by 10: 90
- Students multiply by 100: 900
- Include decimals: 9.1, 91, 910
- Include divisions: 96, 9.6, 0.96

Useful resources

R6 is a number line marked into tenths, for use with the plenary.
R4 is a place value table which you may find useful in the mental starter.

Introductory activity

Recap the meaning of percentages.
Ask students what 48% means:
48 parts for every 100.

Check by asking questions that students understand:

- A percentage can be written as a fraction e.g. $48\% = \frac{48}{100}$
- A percentage can be written as a decimal e.g. $62\% = 0.62$
- A decimal can be written as a percentage e.g. $0.34 = 34\%$
- A fraction can be written as a decimal e.g. $\frac{3}{5} = 0.6$

Introduce the terms 'convert' and 'conversion'.
Explain that being able to convert between the three forms makes calculations easier.

Demonstrate with an example that percentage to fraction conversions should be simplified.
E.g. $25\% = \frac{25}{100} = \frac{1}{4}$
Give the students some simple examples to try.

Discuss the equivalences that students should know.
Draw a 0–1 number line, or use **R6**. Build it up steadily, discussing with students where particular percentages, decimals and fractions should go.
There are some common equivalences shown in the student book.

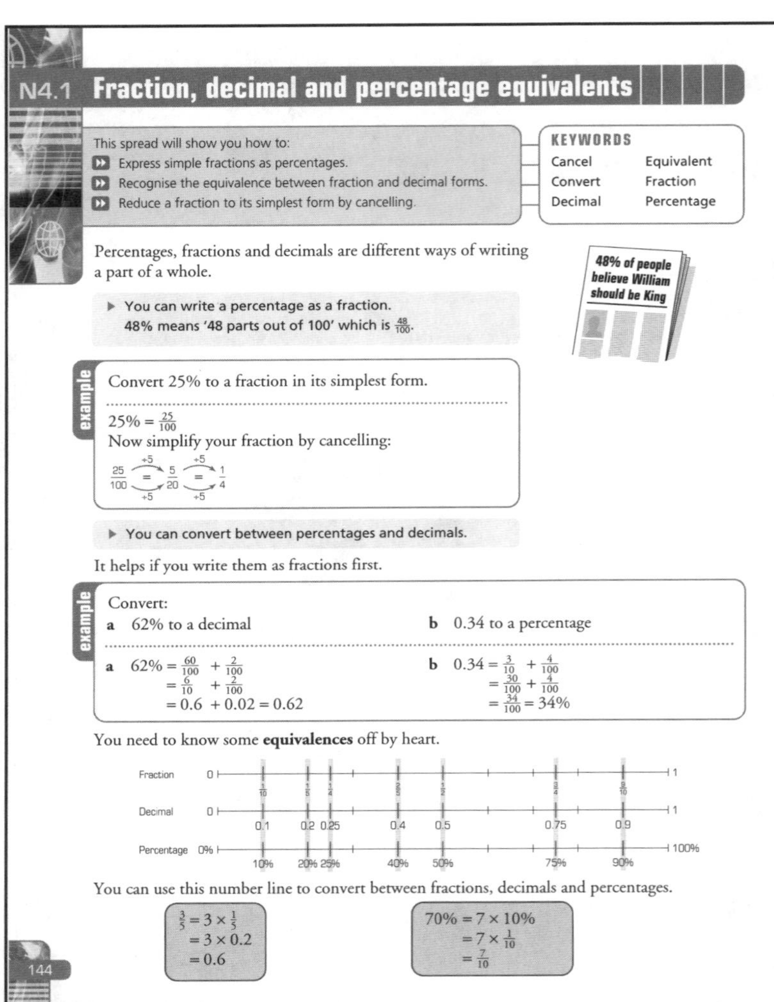

N4.1 **Fraction, decimal and percentage equivalents**

This spread will show you how to:

- Express simple fractions as percentages.
- Recognise the equivalence between fraction and decimal forms.
- Reduce a fraction to its simplest form by cancelling.

KEYWORDS
Cancel, Equivalent, Convert, Fraction, Decimal, Percentage

Percentages, fractions and decimals are different ways of writing a part of a whole.

- You can write a percentage as a fraction.
48% means '48 parts out of 100' which is $\frac{48}{100}$.

example
Convert 25% to a fraction in its simplest form.

$25\% = \frac{25}{100}$
Now simplify your fraction by cancelling:

$\frac{25}{100} = \frac{5}{20} = \frac{1}{4}$ (÷5, ÷5)

- You can convert between percentages and decimals.

It helps if you write them as fractions first.

example
Convert:
a 62% to a decimal
b 0.34 to a percentage

a $62\% = \frac{60}{100} + \frac{2}{100} = \frac{6}{10} + \frac{2}{100} = 0.6 + 0.02 = 0.62$

b $0.34 = \frac{3}{10} + \frac{4}{100} = \frac{30}{100} + \frac{4}{100} = \frac{34}{100} = 34\%$

You need to know some **equivalences** off by heart.

You can use this number line to convert between fractions, decimals and percentages.

$\frac{3}{5} = 3 \times \frac{1}{5} = 3 \times 0.2 = 0.6$

$70\% = 7 \times 10\% = 7 \times \frac{1}{10} = \frac{7}{10}$

144

Plenary

- Draw a 0–2 number line on the board, or use **R6**.
- Ask students to label these points on the line:
$32\%, \frac{3}{10}, \frac{3}{7}, 169\%, 1\frac{2}{3}, 1.6, \frac{11}{47}, 20\%, 0.19$
- Ask students to justify their reasons
- Correct as necessary, with reasons, and ask students to copy the correct version.

Further activities

Students can place all the percentages in question 1 on a number line.

Give students these numbers in a magic square as in question 8, reading from right to left:
240%, 0.3, $\frac{18}{10}$, $\frac{270}{100}$, $\frac{3}{2}$, 210%, $1\frac{1}{5}$, $\frac{18}{20}$, 0.6
Just swap $\frac{270}{100}$ and $\frac{18}{20}$ to make the square magic again.

Differentiation

Support questions:

- Questions 1 and 2 focus on percentage and decimal conversions. Springboard 7, page 430.
- Questions 3–7 focus on the equivalence of fractions, decimals and percentages. Springboard 7, pages 431–433.
- Questions 8 and 9 involve relating fractions to division and hence comparing fractions and decimals. Springboard 7, page 434.

Core tier: focuses on converting between fractions, decimals and percentages by calculation.

Exercise N4.1

1 Convert these percentages into decimals.
a 63% **b** 48% **c** 22% **d** 130% **e** 70% **f** 7% **g** 113% **h** 12%

2 Convert these decimals into percentages.
a 0.28 **b** 0.73 **c** 1.25 **d** 0.8 **e** 0.04 **f** 0.4 **g** 0.43 **h** 0.01

3 Copy and complete this table.

Percentage	Fraction	Decimal
60%	—	0.6
30%	$\frac{3}{10}$	—
—	—	0.1

Percentage	Fraction	Decimal
—	$\frac{7}{100}$	—
80%	—	—
—	—	0.35

4 Work out which is the biggest number in each question by changing the fraction into a percentage.
a 63% $\frac{1}{2}$ **b** $\frac{1}{4}$ 20% **c** 72% $\frac{3}{4}$ **d** 40% $\frac{3}{10}$ **e** $\frac{1}{4}$ 35%

5 Write these percentages as fractions in their simplest form.
a 60% **b** 42% **c** 51% **d** 72% **e** 135% **f** 18% **g** 4% **h** 30%

6 Write these numbers in order, starting with the smallest.
a 0.2 $\frac{1}{4}$ 22% **b** 0.7 73% $\frac{3}{4}$ **c** 38% 0.4 $\frac{4}{100}$ **d** $\frac{33}{100}$ 0.3 31%

7 Convert these fractions into percentages.
a $\frac{21}{50}$ **b** $\frac{37}{50}$ **c** $\frac{24}{25}$ **d** $\frac{8}{25}$ **e** $\frac{15}{20}$ **f** $\frac{7}{20}$ **g** $\frac{9}{75}$ **h** $\frac{15}{80}$

8 $\frac{1}{8} = 0.125$ and $\frac{3}{8} = 0.375$
a Use a calculator to work out $1 \div 8$.
Write down what you notice.
b Use a calculator to work out $3 \div 8$.
Write down what you notice.
c Use your calculator to work out:
$5 \div 8$, $1 \div 4$ and $7 \div 8$.
d Write down the decimal equivalents of:
$\frac{5}{8}$, $\frac{1}{4}$ and $\frac{7}{8}$.
e Find the decimal equivalents of $\frac{1}{3}$, $\frac{1}{9}$ and $\frac{1}{11}$.

9 **Challenge**
In this magic square each row, column and diagonal adds up to 3.
Unfortunately someone has muddled up the numbers.
Can you rearrange the numbers to make the square magic again?

1	0.6	$\frac{1}{5}$
1.8	$\frac{4}{10}$	$1\frac{1}{5}$
1.6	$\frac{140}{100}$	$\frac{80}{100}$

145

Exercise commentary

The questions assess the objectives on Primary Framework Pages 23, 31 and 33.

Problem solving

Questions 8 and 9 assess the objective from Primary Framework Page 79.

Group work

Students would benefit from discussing questions 8 and 9 in pairs or groups.

Misconceptions

Many students will write 113% = 0.113 and 0.8 as 8%.
Encourage students to start from facts they already know and to use a number line to estimate before writing down the answer.
It helps to have an equivalence line available or on the classroom wall.
Encourage students to refer to it until they have a firm grasp of equivalences.
Students may also benefit from having a copy of a place value table so they can see how the place value changes.
So many different forms in the same exercise can be overwhelming for weak students so do encourage them to focus on one conversion at a time.

Links

Division: Primary Framework Page 57.
Place value: Page 7.

Homework

N4.1HW requires students to place fractions, decimals and percentages on a number line.

Answers

1 **a** 0.63 **b** 0.48 **c** 0.22 **d** 1.3 **e** 0.7 **f** 0.07 **g** 1.13 **h** 0.12
2 **a** 28% **b** 73% **c** 125% **d** 80% **e** 4% **f** 40% **g** 43% **h** 1%
3 60%, 30%, 10%, 7%, 80%, 35%; $\frac{3}{5}$, $\frac{3}{10}$, $\frac{1}{10}$, $\frac{7}{100}$, $\frac{4}{5}$, $\frac{7}{20}$; 0.6, 0.3, 0.1, 0.07, 0.8, 0.35
4 **a** 63% **b** $\frac{1}{4}$ **c** $\frac{3}{4}$ **d** 40% **e** 35%
5 **a** $\frac{3}{5}$ **b** $\frac{21}{50}$ **c** $\frac{51}{100}$ **d** $\frac{18}{25}$ **e** $1\frac{7}{20}$ **f** $\frac{9}{50}$ **g** $\frac{1}{25}$ **h** $\frac{3}{10}$
6 **a** 0.2, 22%, $\frac{1}{4}$ **b** 0.7, 73%, $\frac{3}{4}$ **c** $\frac{4}{100}$, 38%, 0.4 **d** 0.3, 31%, $\frac{33}{100}$
7 **a** 42% **b** 74% **c** 96% **d** 32% **e** 75% **f** 35% **g** 12% **h** 18.75%
8 **a** 0.125 **b** 0.375 **c** 1.6, 0.25, 0.875 **d** 1.6, 0.25, 0.875 **e** $0.\dot{3}$, $0.\dot{1}$, $0.0\dot{9}$

N4.2 Finding simple percentages

Mental starter

Stand up

- Go around the class giving students a number: 10, 20, 30, 40, 10, 20, 30, 40, ...
- Call out fraction questions and explain that if their number is the answer they should stand up. For example, read out '$\frac{1}{2}$ of 60' and expect all the 30s to stand up.
- You could include questions like: 'Stand up if you are smaller than $\frac{1}{4}$ of 80.'

Useful resources

R6 contains number lines which may be useful for visualisation.

Introductory activity

Refer to the mental starter.

Recap how to find a fraction of an amount.

You could use the examples in the student book, but stick to simple fractions and numbers.

Include a non-unitary fraction.

All calculations should be done using a mental method but encourage students to explain their methods and help them to formalise their working.

Discuss percentages of amounts.

In particular you could discuss:

- What does 50% of 80 mean?
- How could you calculate it?

Coax out different methods;

some may say that it is 80 ÷ 2, others may say it is half of 80.

Encourage students to realise that these are the same.

Emphasise that you can find a percentage of an amount by changing it into a fraction first.

- Remind students about the equivalences they learned last lesson.
- Go through an example, for instance 10% of 40.
- Give students a few to try, sticking to 50%, 10%, 25% and 75% (you will probably need to go through a 75% example, as this is a non-unitary fraction and will involve first dividing by 4 and then multiplying by 3).

Students should use mental methods.

Emphasise that you should include units if they are indicated in the amount.

E.g. 10% of 30 cm is 3 cm, not 3.

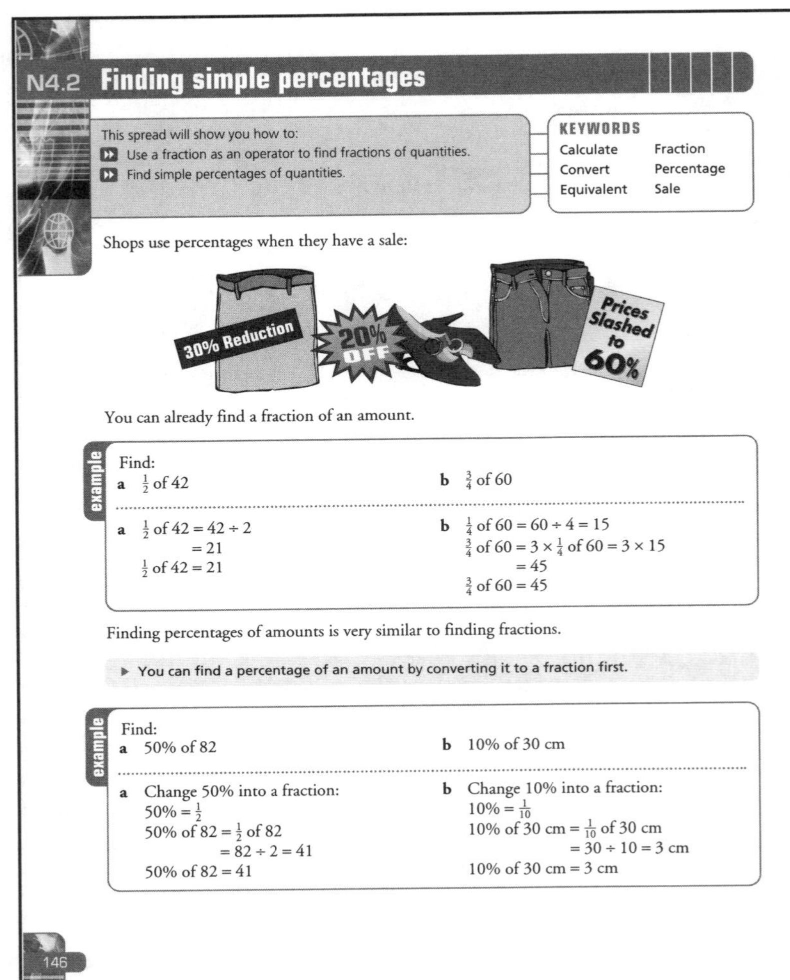

N4.2 **Finding simple percentages**

This spread will show you how to:

- Use a fraction as an operator to find fractions of quantities.
- Find simple percentages of quantities.

KEYWORDS

Calculate	Fraction
Convert	Percentage
Equivalent	Sale

Shops use percentages when they have a sale:

You can already find a fraction of an amount.

example

Find:

a $\frac{1}{2}$ of 42 b $\frac{3}{4}$ of 60

a $\frac{1}{2}$ of $42 = 42 \div 2$
$= 21$
$\frac{1}{2}$ of $42 = 21$

b $\frac{1}{4}$ of $60 = 60 \div 4 = 15$
$\frac{3}{4}$ of $60 = 3 \times \frac{1}{4}$ of $60 = 3 \times 15$
$= 45$
$\frac{3}{4}$ of $60 = 45$

Finding percentages of amounts is very similar to finding fractions.

- You can find a percentage of an amount by converting it to a fraction first.

example

Find:

a 50% of 82 b 10% of 30 cm

a Change 50% into a fraction:
$50\% = \frac{1}{2}$
50% of $82 = \frac{1}{2}$ of 82
$= 82 \div 2 = 41$
50% of 82 = 41

b Change 10% into a fraction:
$10\% = \frac{1}{10}$
10% of 30 cm = $\frac{1}{10}$ of 30 cm
$= 30 \div 10 = 3$ cm
10% of 30 cm = 3 cm

146

Plenary

- Put a number on the board, for example 8.
- Students should make up percentage questions with 8 as the answer, such as 50% of 16 etc.
- Discuss how they formed their questions.
- Students pose similar 'answers' for the class, challenging them to find the questions.

Further activities

Challenge students to find a percentage calculation for every number in the 5 times table, for example:
3 × 5 = 15, 50% of 30 = 15
Able students can repeat this with the 6 and 7 times tables.

Differentiation

Support questions:

- Questions 1–3 focus on finding simple percentages. Springboard 7, pages 423, 424.
- Questions 4–7 focus on finding percentages of amounts in context and using them to order quantities. Springboard 7, page 425.
- Question 8 involves devising calculations which requires a good understanding of percentages. Springboard 7, page 427.

Core tier: focuses on finding harder percentages of an amount.

Exercise N4.2

1 Work out these percentages.
a 50% of £20 **b** 50% of £28 **c** 50% of £80
d 50% of 64 cm **e** 50% of 32 km **f** 50% of 52 mm

2 Work out these percentages.
a 25% of £40 **b** 25% of £20 **c** 25% of £80
d 25% of 44 mm **e** 25% of 32 cm **f** 25% of 56 m

3 Now work out these percentages.
a 75% of £40 **b** 75% of £80 **c** 75% of £44
d 75% of 16 km **e** 75% of 36 cm **f** 75% of 52 m

4 Work out each percentage in these questions.
Write down which one gives the biggest answer.
a 50% of 30, 25% of 48 **b** 50% of 70, 25% of 120
c 25% of 24, 75% of 16 **d** 50% of 38, 75% of 28
e 75% of 60, 25% of 200 **f** 25% of 40, 10% of 80

5 Here are some lengths of rope. Find 10% of each length.
a 50 m **b** 30 cm **c** 800 cm
d 45 m **e** 95 cm **f** 18.5 m

6 Copy and complete these questions.
a 10% of £80 = £____ **b** 50% of £66 = £____
c 50% of £____ = £32 **d** 25% of £____ = £14
e ____% of £64 = £16 **f** ____% of £84 = £63

7 Three of the four percentages in each grid give the same answer.
Work out each answer and write down the odd one out.

a

25% of 40	10% of 100
50% of 20	75% of 12

b

10% of 200	75% of 16
25% of 48	50% of 24

c

75% of 28	25% of 84
10% of 120	50% of 42

d

10% of 90	25% of 32
50% of 18	75% of 12

8 Write down three percentage questions that give these answers. The first one is done for you.
a 4
50% of 8, 25% of 16, 10% of 40.
b 10 **c** 7 **d** 9

147

Exercise commentary

The questions assess the objectives on Primary Framework Pages 25 and 33.

Problem solving

Questions 1–3 and 5 and 6 assess Primary Framework Page 85. Question 7 assesses Page 79 and question 8 assesses Page 75.

Group work

Students would benefit from discussing questions 7 and 8 in pairs or groups.

Misconceptions

Some students struggle to apply finding 25% of an amount to finding 75%. Emphasise that 25% is $\frac{1}{4}$ and 75% is $\frac{3}{4}$ so once you've found 25% you only need to multiply by 3. Alternatively students can take 25% away from the whole – discuss this strategy as a class to see whether they think this seems easier. The key is to find the strategy that gives the most success – which is easier for students, ×3 or −25%?
In question 7 one small mistake will cause big problems.
Encourage students to discuss the work in pairs to help accuracy.

Links

Division: Primary Framework Page 57.
Place value: Page 7.

Homework

In N4.2HW, students are asked to draw spider diagrams showing percentages of an amount.

Answers

1 **a** £10 **b** £14 **c** £40 **d** 32 cm **e** 16 km **f** 26 mm
2 **a** £10 **b** £5 **c** £20 **d** 11 mm **e** 8 cm **f** 14 m
3 **a** £30 **b** £60 **c** £33 **d** 12 km **e** 27 cm **f** 39 m
4 **a** 15, 12, 50% of 30 **b** 35, 30, 50% of 70 **c** 6, 12, 75% of 16
d 19, 21, 75% of 28 **e** 45, 50, 25% of 200 **f** 10, 8, 25% of 40
5 **a** 5 m **b** 3 cm **c** 80 cm **d** 4.5 m **e** 9.5 cm **f** 1.85 m
6 **a** £8 **b** £33 **c** £64 **d** £56 **e** 25% **f** 75%
7 **a** 75% of 12 = 4 **b** 10% of 200 = 20 **c** 10% of 120 = 12 **d** 25% of 32 = 8

Mental starter

Stand up

- Give students a multiple of 10: 10, 20, 30, 40, 10, 20, 30, 40, ...
- Call out statements like '10% of 200'.
- Students stand up if their number is the answer.

Useful resources

R6 contains number lines which may help visualisation.

Introductory activity

Refer to the mental starter activity.

Check by asking questions that students can find 10% of a number.

Start with simple multiples of 10, and then try with money. Give students some examples to try.

Emphasise that you can start with a known quantity (10%) and then find other percentages:

- 5% is half of 10%
- 20% is 10% + 10%, or 2 × 10%
- 35% = 3 × 10% + 5% etc.

Ask students how they would work out 55% of 80: 50% + 5% = 50% + $\frac{1}{10}$ of 50%.

Give some examples in context, using units.

You can make up examples based on:

- sale reductions
- increases in bus fares
- increases in height, e.g. Laila was 120 cm a year ago and has grown 15% taller. How much taller has she grown?

With these types of question you do not need to ask for the new value, just the increase or decrease.

Stick to easy numbers.

Students should explain the mental methods they use and you can help them formalise those methods by writing down the steps in their working.

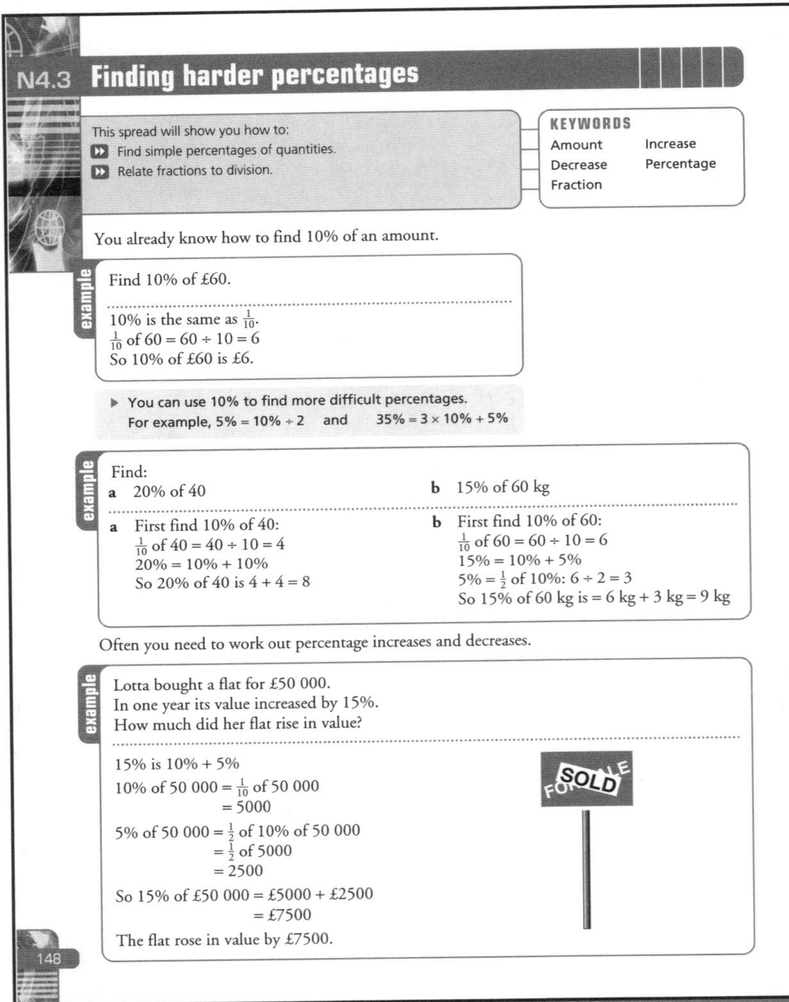

N4.3 Finding harder percentages

This spread will show you how to:

- Find simple percentages of quantities.
- Relate fractions to division.

KEYWORDS: Amount, Decrease, Fraction, Increase, Percentage

You already know how to find 10% of an amount.

example

Find 10% of £60.

10% is the same as $\frac{1}{10}$.
$\frac{1}{10}$ of 60 = 60 ÷ 10 = 6
So 10% of £60 is £6.

- You can use 10% to find more difficult percentages. For example, 5% = 10% ÷ 2 and 35% = 3 × 10% + 5%

example

Find:
a 20% of 40
b 15% of 60 kg

a First find 10% of 40:
$\frac{1}{10}$ of 40 = 40 ÷ 10 = 4
20% = 10% + 10%
So 20% of 40 is 4 + 4 = 8

b First find 10% of 60:
$\frac{1}{10}$ of 60 = 60 ÷ 10 = 6
15% = 10% + 5%
5% = $\frac{1}{2}$ of 10%: 6 ÷ 2 = 3
So 15% of 60 kg is = 6 kg + 3 kg = 9 kg

Often you need to work out percentage increases and decreases.

example

Lotta bought a flat for £50 000.
In one year its value increased by 15%.
How much did her flat rise in value?

15% is 10% + 5%
10% of 50 000 = $\frac{1}{10}$ of 50 000
= 5000
5% of 50 000 = $\frac{1}{2}$ of 10% of 50 000
= $\frac{1}{2}$ of 5000
= 2500
So 15% of £50 000 = £5000 + £2500
= £7500
The flat rose in value by £7500.

148

Plenary

- Put a number on the board, for example 10.
- Students should make up percentage questions with 10 as the answer, such as 5% of 200 etc.
- Encourage them to use the percentages that they have worked with this lesson (multiples of 5, not just 10).
- Discuss how they formed their questions.
- Students pose similar 'answers' for the class, challenging them to find the questions.

Further activities

Give students a number or quantity, say £12, and challenge them to find as many different percentage calculations as they can with that answer.

Challenge able students to find 17.5% of an amount using a mental method and jottings.

Differentiation

Support questions:

- Question 1 focuses on finding 10% of an amount.
- Questions 2–6 focus on finding other percentages of an amount based on 10%. Springboard 7, page 428.
- Questions 7 and 8 involve percentages with fractional parts.

Core tier: focuses on expressing an amount as a percentage of another amount.

Exercise N4.3

1 Find 10% of these amounts.
  a £20 b £30 c £60
  d £120 e £65 f £43

2 Work out the answers to these.
  a 20% of £30 b 20% of £40
  c 5% of £20 d 5% of £60
  e 30% of £30 f 30% of £20
  g 40% of £40 h 40% of £30
  i 15% of £40 j 15% of £60

3 Calculate these percentages.
  a 40% of £10 b 5% of £3
  c 5% of £3.20 d 20% of £8.40
  e 20% of £2.10 f 15% of £2.20
  g 15% of £6.60 h 35% of £6.60

4 Sarah earns £280 a week.
She gets a rise of 10%.
Find 10% of £280 to find out how much more she will earn a week.

5 Will earns £360 a week.
He gets a rise of 5%.
Find 5% of £360 to find out how much more he will earn.

6 Jane bought a house for £30 000.
In one year its value increased by 15%.
Work out 15% of £30 000 to find out how much the value of the house went up.

7 Work out each of these amounts and put them in order, starting with the smallest.
  a 20% of 60 15% of 50 $\frac{1}{4}$ of 40 35% of 40
  b 45% of 160 35% of 180 15% of 700 $\frac{1}{4}$ of 300

8 You know that 5% is half of 10%. You should also know that $2\frac{1}{2}$% is half of 5%. Use this fact to work out:
  a $2\frac{1}{2}$% of £40 b $12\frac{1}{2}$% of £40
  c $7\frac{1}{2}$% of £60 d $12\frac{1}{2}$% of £80
  e $7\frac{1}{2}$% of £120 f $17\frac{1}{2}$% of £160

149

Exercise commentary

The questions assess the objectives on Primary Framework Pages 31 and 33.

Problem solving

Questions 1–6 and 8 assess Primary Framework Page 85.

Group work

Students would benefit from discussing questions 7 and 8 in pairs or groups.

Misconceptions

Some students struggle to work out percentages such as 15% as there are a few steps involved.

Encourage the use of a structured approach and the use of jottings.

Emphasise that students are always starting from a fact they know – how to find 10% – and so the calculations are not difficult, rather they are complex.

In question 3 students need to change units in order to find the answer. This may lead to difficulty in interpreting the decimal part of a money amount.

Encourage students to change the amount into something easier to divide (pence) before doing the calculation.

In question 8, the use of $\frac{1}{2}$% will increase the number of decimals to work with which may cause problems.

Use this to reinforce the fact that you line up the units in decimal calculations.

Links

Division: Primary Framework Page 57.

Homework

In **N4.3HW**, students are asked to calculate harder percentages of an amount.

Answers

1 a £2 b £3 c £6 d £12 e £6.50 f £4.30
2 a £6 b £8 c £1 d £3 e £9 f £6 g £16 h £12 i £6 j £9
3 a £4 b 15p c 16p d £1.68 e 42p f 33p g 99p h £2.31
4 £28 5 £18 6 £4500
7 a 15% of 50 = 7.5, $\frac{1}{4}$ of 40 = 10, 20% of 60 = 12, 35% of 40 = 14
  b 35% of 180 = 63, 45% of 160 = 72, $\frac{1}{4}$ of 300 = 75, 15% of 700 = 105
8 a £1 b £5 c £4.50 d £10 e £9 f £28

Mental starter

Quick-fire questions

Ask the students a series of quick-fire mental calculation questions.
For example:

- Which decimal is equivalent to $\frac{1}{4}$? 0.25
- Which percentage is equivalent to $\frac{1}{2}$? 50%
- Which fraction is equivalent to 75%? $\frac{3}{4}$
- Which decimal is equivalent to 40%? 0.4

Useful resources

Multilink cubes are useful to demonstrate proportion in the introductory activity.
R2 digit cards are useful for the mental starter.

Introductory activity

Introduce the concept of a proportion.
Discuss with students what the word 'proportion' means to them, and where they may have heard it before in different contexts.
For example:

- art and design
- cookery
- chemistry.

Use multilink cubes of different colours to compare the size of a part with the size of the whole: use 2 red and 6 blue.

- Start by expressing the proportion as a fraction: $\frac{2}{8}$ are red.
- Add on mutlilink cubes to alter the proportion: add 1 red – include fractions that can be simplified: $\frac{3}{9}$ are red.

You may need to recap how to simplify a fraction.
Use the multilink cubes to illustrate that the proportions $\frac{3}{9}$ and $\frac{1}{3}$ are the same.

Emphasise that you can write a proportion as a fraction, decimal or percentage.
Give a real-life example; you could use the example in the student book, or think of a similar example within your classroom (if you do, make sure that the numbers are easy – no recurring decimals).

- Start by expressing the proportion as a fraction.
- Convert the fraction to a decimal.
- Convert the fraction (or decimal) to a percentage.

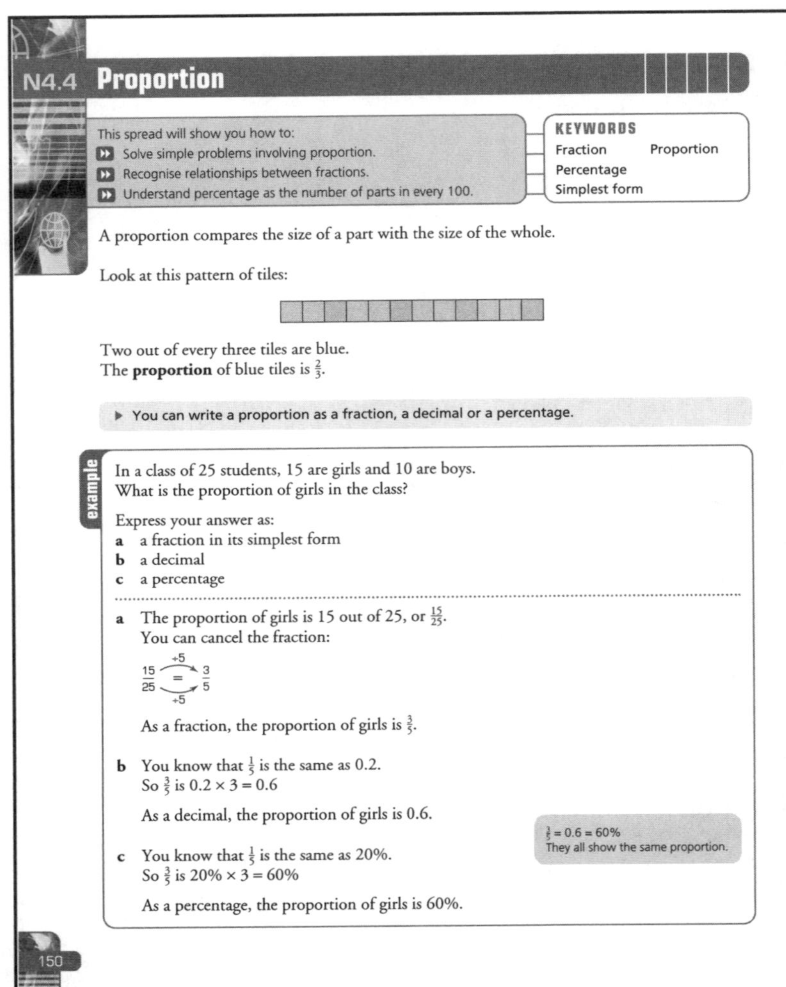

N4.4 **Proportion**

This spread will show you how to:

- Solve simple problems involving proportion.
- Recognise relationships between fractions.
- Understand percentage as the number of parts in every 100.

KEYWORDS
Fraction
Proportion
Percentage
Simplest form

A proportion compares the size of a part with the size of the whole.

Look at this pattern of tiles:

Two out of every three tiles are blue.
The **proportion** of blue tiles is $\frac{2}{3}$.

- You can write a proportion as a fraction, a decimal or a percentage.

example

In a class of 25 students, 15 are girls and 10 are boys.
What is the proportion of girls in the class?

Express your answer as:
a a fraction in its simplest form
b a decimal
c a percentage

a The proportion of girls is 15 out of 25, or $\frac{15}{25}$.
You can cancel the fraction:

$$\frac{15}{25} \overset{\div 5}{=} \frac{3}{5}$$

As a fraction, the proportion of girls is $\frac{3}{5}$.

b You know that $\frac{1}{5}$ is the same as 0.2.
So $\frac{3}{5}$ is $0.2 \times 3 = 0.6$
As a decimal, the proportion of girls is 0.6.

c You know that $\frac{1}{5}$ is the same as 20%.
So $\frac{3}{5}$ is $20\% \times 3 = 60\%$
As a percentage, the proportion of girls is 60%.

$\frac{3}{5} = 0.6 = 60\%$
They all show the same proportion.

150

Plenary

Put a proportion on the board, say $\frac{3}{4}$.
Then put decimals and percentages on the board, asking which quantities go with the fraction:
3.4, 75%, 34%, 0.34, 43%, 0.25, 0.75
Discuss students' responses.

Further activities

Students make a 3 × 4 grid on squared paper and shade in the squares using three different colours. They then challenge a partner to write down the proportion of each colour.
Repeat with 3 × 5 and 3 × 6 grids.

Differentiation

Support questions:

- Questions 1 and 2 revise Year 4 objectives. Springboard 7, page 436.
- Questions 3–6 focus on writing proportions as fractions in their simplest form. Springboard 7, page 426.
- Question 7 has no visual prompts making it harder to see the proportions.

Core tier: focuses on expressing measures as proportions, and extends to direct proportion.

Exercise N4.4

1 Look at this pattern of tiles:
  a What proportion of the tiles is yellow?
  b What proportion of the tiles is purple?

2 Look at this pattern of tiles:
  a What proportion of the tiles is yellow?
  b What proportion of the tiles is black?

3 Look at this pattern of tiles:
  a What proportion of the tiles is green?
  b What proportion of the tiles is black?
  c Write the proportions in **a** and **b** in their simplest form.

4 Look at this pattern:
  a How many black tiles are there?
  b How many orange tiles are there?
  c What proportion of the tiles is black?
  d What proportion of the tiles is orange?
  e Write your answers to **c** and **d** in their simplest form.

5 Write these proportions in their simplest form.
  a $\frac{3}{6}$ b $\frac{4}{10}$ c $\frac{8}{16}$
  d $\frac{5}{25}$ e $\frac{4}{16}$ f $\frac{3}{15}$
  g $\frac{6}{9}$ h $\frac{8}{12}$ i $\frac{12}{18}$

6 Look at this grid:
  a What proportion of the tiles is:
    i green
    ii yellow
    iii purple?
  b Write your answers to **a** in their simplest form.

7 Calculate the proportion of black cats in each of the following cat families.
  Express each proportion in its simplest form.
  a 3 white; 2 black; 5 tortoiseshell
  b 6 white; 4 black; 4 tabbies
  c 4 white; 7 black; 1 tabby; 3 tortoiseshell
  d 11 white; 3 black; 6 tabbies

151

Exercise commentary

The questions assess the objectives on Primary Framework Page 27.

Problem solving

Question 7 assesses Primary Framework Page 83.

Group work

The further activity is suitable for pair work but weaker students will benefit from discussing all the questions in pairs.

Misconceptions

Students may get confused about what they are comparing, saying for example that the proportion of yellow tiles in question 1 is 3 out of 1. They may also confuse the numbers to use in the fractions, expressing the fraction of yellow as $\frac{3}{1}$ and the fraction of purple as $\frac{1}{3}$.
Emphasise that 'in every' refers to a proportion and encourage students to look at the totals first. Some students will benefit from supportive questioning:

- How many tiles are there altogether?
- How many of them are yellow?
- What proportion is yellow?

Students will also benefit from using tiles or multilink cubes to model the patterns.

Links

Fractions: Primary Framework Page 23.
Percentages: Page 33.

Homework

N4.4HW provides practice in finding proportions.

Answers

1 a $\frac{3}{4}$ b $\frac{1}{4}$
2 a $\frac{2}{5}$ b $\frac{3}{5}$
3 a $\frac{12}{18}$ b $\frac{6}{18}$ c $\frac{2}{3}, \frac{1}{3}$
4 a 5 b 10 c $\frac{5}{15}$ d $\frac{10}{15}$ e $\frac{1}{3}, \frac{2}{3}$
5 a $\frac{1}{2}$ b $\frac{2}{5}$ c $\frac{1}{2}$ d $\frac{1}{5}$ e $\frac{1}{4}$ f $\frac{1}{5}$ g $\frac{2}{3}$ h $\frac{2}{3}$ i $\frac{2}{3}$
6 a i $\frac{5}{12}$ ii $\frac{4}{12}$ iii $\frac{3}{12}$ b i $\frac{5}{12}$ ii $\frac{1}{3}$ iii $\frac{1}{4}$
7 a $\frac{1}{5}$ b $\frac{2}{7}$ c $\frac{7}{15}$ d $\frac{3}{20}$

N4.5 Introducing ratio

Mental starter

- Give a start number and a rule, for example 'start with 21 and add 15'.
- Go around the class; students keep adding 15 until you decide to change the rule.
- Try to keep this fairly lively – it is an exercise that students should already be familiar with.

Useful resources

Multilink cubes are useful in the introductory activity.
Students may wish to use multilink cubes or **counters** to help in the exercise.

Introductory activity

Introduce the term 'ratio'.
Ask where students have heard this term before, and what it means.
Ratio, like proportion, is used in lots of different contexts so be prepared for unexpected responses.

Demonstrate ratio with a row of multilink cubes.

- Use two different colours, say three blue to one red.
- Write down the ratio 3 : 1 on the board.
- Add an extra red cube to the row, and ask for the ratio of blue to red now.
- Show that this can be cancelled like fractions.
- Discuss what the ratio of red to blue looks like.

Emphasise the difference between a ratio and a proportion.

- The ratio is '1 **in every** 4'.
- The proportion is '1 **for every** 4'.

Set a problem in context.
As a variation on the example in the student book, there are 30 students in a class and there are four girls for every boy.
How many girls and boys are there in the class?
You could use rows of multilink cubes to solve this problem visually, adding on rows until you reach 30.
This approach links to the tile diagrams referred to in the student book.

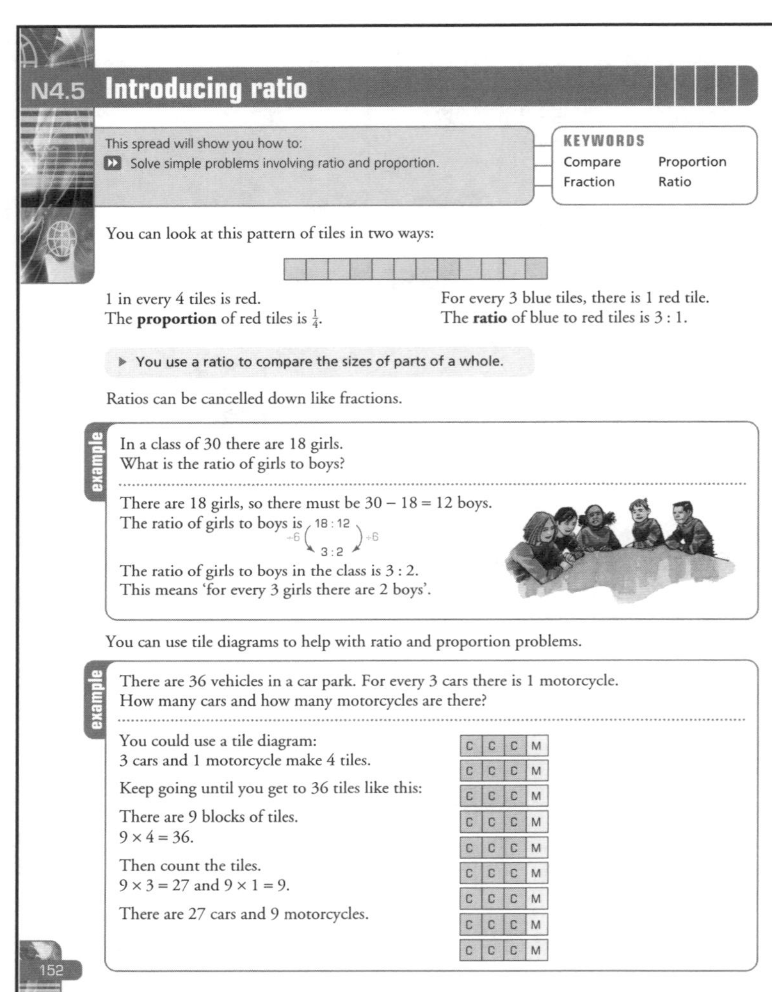

N4.5 **Introducing ratio**

This spread will show you how to:
- Solve simple problems involving ratio and proportion.

KEYWORDS
Compare
Fraction
Proportion
Ratio

You can look at this pattern of tiles in two ways:

1 in every 4 tiles is red.
The **proportion** of red tiles is $\frac{1}{4}$.

For every 3 blue tiles, there is 1 red tile.
The **ratio** of blue to red tiles is 3 : 1.

- You use a ratio to compare the sizes of parts of a whole.

Ratios can be cancelled down like fractions.

example

In a class of 30 there are 18 girls.
What is the ratio of girls to boys?

There are 18 girls, so there must be 30 – 18 = 12 boys.
The ratio of girls to boys is 18 : 12 (÷6) → 3 : 2 (÷6)
The ratio of girls to boys in the class is 3 : 2.
This means 'for every 3 girls there are 2 boys'.

You can use tile diagrams to help with ratio and proportion problems.

example

There are 36 vehicles in a car park. For every 3 cars there is 1 motorcycle.
How many cars and how many motorcycles are there?

You could use a tile diagram:
3 cars and 1 motorcycle make 4 tiles.
Keep going until you get to 36 tiles like this:
There are 9 blocks of tiles.
9 × 4 = 36.
Then count the tiles.
9 × 3 = 27 and 9 × 1 = 9.
There are 27 cars and 9 motorcycles.

C	C	C	M
C	C	C	M
C	C	C	M
C	C	C	M
C	C	C	M
C	C	C	M
C	C	C	M
C	C	C	M
C	C	C	M

152

Plenary

Discuss the sharing problems (questions 6 to 10) in the exercise.
Try to introduce a more formal method, such as:
'How much per share?'

Further activities

In **N4.5ICT**, students build a spreadsheet that they can use to solve simple ratio problems.

Give students a supermarket problem to solve:
Potatoes cost 24p per kg.
- Work out the cost of 2 kg, 3 kg, 5 kg, 10 kg.
- How many kg can you buy for £3.60? with a £5 note?

Differentiation

Support questions:
- Questions 1 and 2 focus on extending tile patterns. Springboard 7, page 437.
- Questions 3–8 focus on solving problems using ratio and direct proportion. Springboard 7, page 438.
- Questions 9 and 10 focus on harder ratio problems. Springboard 7, page 439.

Core tier: extends to sharing a quantity in a given ratio.

Exercise N4.5

Use the tile diagram shown in each question to help answer questions 1–5.

1 There are 20 pupils in a class.
There are 2 boys for every 3 girls.
Copy and continue the tile diagram to work out how many boys and how many girls there are in the class.

B	B	G	G	G

2 In a different class there are 24 pupils.
There is 1 girl for every 2 boys.
Copy and continue the tile diagram and work out how many boys and how many girls there are in the class.

B	B	G

3 1 kg of potatoes costs 35p.
How much will 5 kg of potatoes cost?

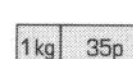

4 1 kg of broccoli costs £1.25.
How much does 6 kg of broccoli cost?

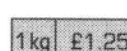

5 A bag of apples costs 63p.
How many bags could you buy if you had £5.12?

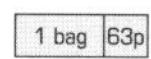

You can use tile diagrams for questions 6–10.

6 Jack has 15 sweets. He gives his brother Ewan 2 sweets for every 3 sweets that he takes.
How many sweets do they each get?

7 A painter mixes 1 tin of blue paint with 3 tins of white paint.
He needs 12 tins altogether.
How many tins of each colour will he need?

8 A gardener puts 2 spades of manure into his wheelbarrow for each 3 spades of soil.
The wheelbarrow holds 60 spadefuls in total.
How many are manure and how many are soil?

9 Kathy and Sharon put their money together and buy a raffle ticket for £1.
Kathy put in 30p and Sharon put in 70p.
They win the 1st prize of £25.
They share the prize in the ratio 30 : 70.
How much do they each get?

10 In a box of chocolates, the ratio of soft centres to hard centres is 2 : 5.
There are 42 chocolates in the box.
a How many have soft centres?
b How many have hard centres?

Exercise commentary

The questions assess the objectives on Primary Framework Page 27.

Problem solving

The exercise assesses Primary Framework Pages 83–87.

Group work

Weaker students will benefit from discussing all the questions in pairs.

Misconceptions

Students tend to think that 20 shared in the ratio 2:3 is 20 ÷ 2 and 20 ÷ 3.
Encourage students to find the total number of parts first and then to find what one part is worth.
Students will just multiply the numbers given without thinking about the question and so will get question 5 wrong.
Refer back to the tile diagrams and encourage students to continue this until they can see the pattern: 2 kg costs 126p, 3 kg costs 189p...
Students find visualisation difficult in questions 6–10.
Encourage students to use tiles or multilink cubes to build up the pattern.

Links

Multiplication: Primary Framework Page 59.

Homework

N4.5HW provides practice in finding ratios.

Answers

1 8 boys, 12 girls **2** 16 boys, 8 girls **3** £1.75
4 £7.50 **5** 8 **6** Jack gets 9 sweets, Ewan gets 6 sweets
7 3 tins of blue paint, 9 tins of white paint
8 24 spades of manure, 36 spades of soil
9 Kathy gets £7.50, Sharon gets £17.50
10 a 12 **b** 30

Summary

The Year 6 key teaching objectives are:

- Reduce a fraction to its simplest form by cancelling (23).
- Solve simple problems involving ratio and proportion (27).
- Understand percentage as the number of parts in every 100 (33).
- Find simple percentages of small whole-number quantities (33).
- Identify and use appropriate operations to solve word problems (83–89).

Check out commentary

1 Most students will be able to write a percentage as a fraction out of 100 but the other way round may cause difficulties, especially parts **i** – students tend to write 5% – and **j**.
Encourage students to place the fractions on a 0 to 1 number line and then to estimate the percentage before writing it.

2 Students may need to refer back to the idea of equivalent rectangles, perhaps by using a 100 square, to understand that they need to divide both parts of the fraction by the same number to cancel.

3 These questions are straightforward although students may try to use an alogorithm instead of an intuitive approach based on 10%.
They may also forget to use the units in their answers.
Emphasise the need to go back and read the questions ensuring they use the correct units and that the answer is reasonable.

4 The distinction between ratio and proportion can cause confusion.
Emphasise that ratio is 'for every' and proportion 'in every'.

5 Students find these problems difficult, tending to use all the numbers given rather than considering the information needed to find the answer.
Students will benefit from supportive questioning: What proportion/fraction of the people are men?

Plenary activity

Discuss the picture on the first page of the unit again: page 143.
Discuss how to compare the results:

- Work out the number of correct answers if there were 40 questions.
- Change all the results to percentages!

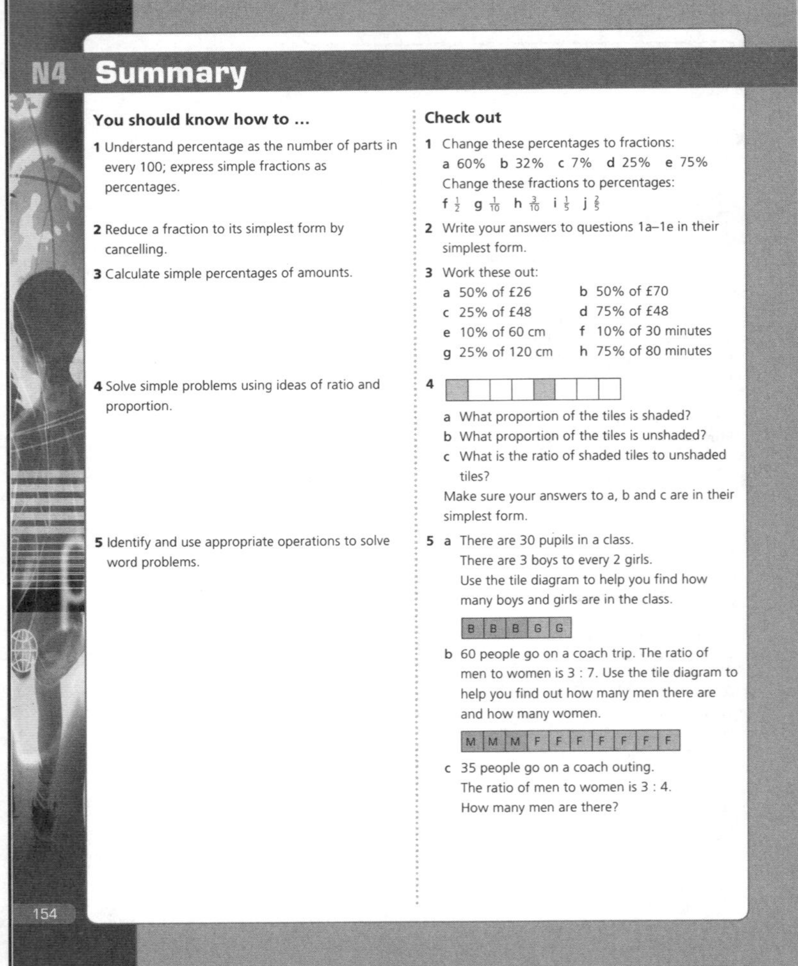

N4 **Summary**

You should know how to ...

1 Understand percentage as the number of parts in every 100; express simple fractions as percentages.

2 Reduce a fraction to its simplest form by cancelling.

3 Calculate simple percentages of amounts.

4 Solve simple problems using ideas of ratio and proportion.

5 Identify and use appropriate operations to solve word problems.

Check out

1 Change these percentages to fractions:
a 60% b 32% c 7% d 25% e 75%
Change these fractions to percentages:
f $\frac{1}{2}$ g $\frac{1}{10}$ h $\frac{3}{10}$ i $\frac{1}{5}$ j $\frac{2}{5}$

2 Write your answers to questions 1a–1e in their simplest form.

3 Work these out:
a 50% of £26 b 50% of £70
c 25% of £48 d 75% of £48
e 10% of 60 cm f 10% of 30 minutes
g 25% of 120 cm h 75% of 80 minutes

4
a What proportion of the tiles is shaded?
b What proportion of the tiles is unshaded?
c What is the ratio of shaded tiles to unshaded tiles?
Make sure your answers to a, b and c are in their simplest form.

5 a There are 30 pupils in a class.
There are 3 boys to every 2 girls.
Use the tile diagram to help you find how many boys and girls are in the class.
B B B G G
b 60 people go on a coach trip. The ratio of men to women is 3 : 7. Use the tile diagram to help you find out how many men there are and how many women.
M M M F F F F F F F
c 35 people go on a coach outing.
The ratio of men to women is 3 : 4.
How many men are there?

154

Development

The relationship between fractions, decimals and percentages is developed further in N5.

Links

The use of proportion can link to using formulae in algebra (A5). Fractions are used in probability (D4) and percentages in data handling (D3).

Mental starters

Objectives covered in this unit:

- Recall multiplication and division facts to 10 × 10.
- Derive answers to calculations.

Resources needed

* means class set needed

Essential:

A4.3OHP – Putting in brackets

Useful:

R1* – Digit cards

R7 (OHP) – Function machines

A4.3ICT* – Expanding brackets in Excel

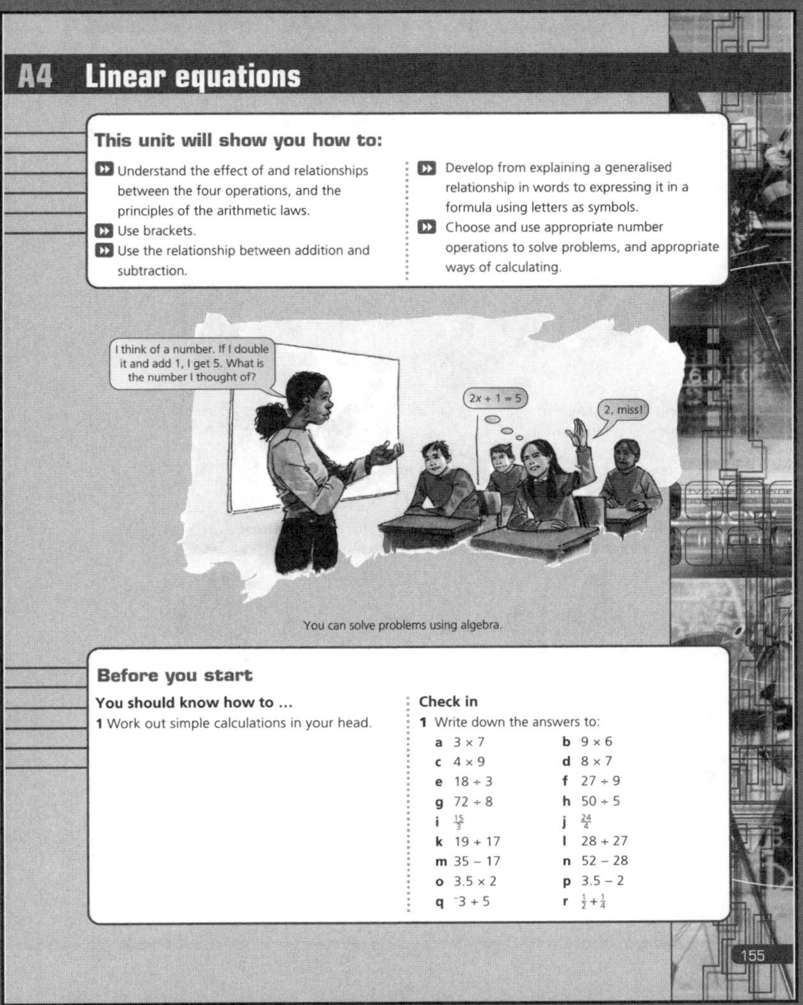

A4 Linear equations

This unit will show you how to:

- Understand the effect of and relationships between the four operations, and the principles of the arithmetic laws.
- Use brackets.
- Use the relationship between addition and subtraction.
- Develop from explaining a generalised relationship in words to expressing it in a formula using letters as symbols.
- Choose and use appropriate number operations to solve problems, and appropriate ways of calculating.

I think of a number. If I double it and add 1, I get 5. What is the number I thought of?
2x + 1 = 5
2, miss!

You can solve problems using algebra.

Before you start

You should know how to ...

1 Work out simple calculations in your head.

Check in

1 Write down the answers to:

a	3 × 7	**b**	9 × 6
c	4 × 9	**d**	8 × 7
e	18 ÷ 3	**f**	27 ÷ 9
g	72 ÷ 8	**h**	50 ÷ 5
i	$\frac{15}{3}$	**j**	$\frac{24}{4}$
k	19 + 17	**l**	28 + 27
m	35 − 17	**n**	52 − 28
o	3.5 × 2	**p**	3.5 − 2
q	$^{-}3 + 5$	**r**	$\frac{1}{2} + \frac{1}{4}$

155

Unit commentary

Aim of the unit

This unit aims to consolidate students' understanding of the rules of number, in particular the relationships between the operations and the convention order of using them. Throughout the unit students are encouraged to use letters to generalise relationships, eventually solving simple equations by working backwards.

Introduction

Discuss scenarios when the exact number is unknown: hairs on your head, people at an event, and when they have used letters to stand for numbers in other subject areas such as science.

Framework references

This unit focuses on:

- Year 6 teaching objectives pages: 43, 53, 55
- Problem solving objectives pages: 81, 83, 85, 87, 89

The unit provides access to:

- Year 7 teaching objectives pages: 112, 114, 116, 122

Check in activity

Ask a series of quick-fire questions with whole-number answers based on multiplication and division facts to 10 × 10 and simple addition and subtraction problems using mental methods.

Try to ask the questions in pairs: 3 × 8, then 8 × 3.

Students use **R1** digit cards to show answers.

Discuss any difficulties.

Differentiation

Core tier focuses on constructing equations and solving and expanding brackets in algebra.

Springboard 7

Pages 238, 488, 494.

A4.1 Using algebraic expressions

Mental starter

Assign each student a number – start with 1 and go round the class. Now ask them to perform various functions:
$+ 2$, $\times 4$, $\times 3$, $+ 1$, $\times 2$ and $+ 1$, $\times 3$ and $- 2$, and so on.
Students show their answers on cards or paper or whiteboards.
After each function, ask how you would write down what they just did. You start with their specific examples: $1 + 2$, $3 + 2$, $7 + 2$ ... but lead up to the general: $n + 2$.

Useful resources

R1 – digit cards for the mental starter.

Introductory activity

Refer to the mental starter.
Each student performed a function on a number.
You can generalise for the whole class to show what they did.
Use n to stand for the number.

Discuss when to use letters to stand for numbers or quantities.

- When the quantity is variable – as in the starter.

Emphasise that variable means the value can vary and discuss what things in the classroom can vary – length of time left in the lesson!

- When the quantity is unknown – the number of hairs on your head!

Emphasise that unknown quantities can have a value – the hairs on your head can be counted precisely – but it is difficult to do and not necessary.

Tell students that x stands for a number of students.
Ask them to make up stories for:
$x + 4$: (some students are playing football and then 4 more join in)
$x - 3$: (three students go home early)
$5x$: (5 classes of students in assembly)
and so on.

Talk through the book examples:

- How many biscuits are in a jar?
- How many left when you eat 3?
- How many grains of rice in a bag?
- How many in 2 bags?

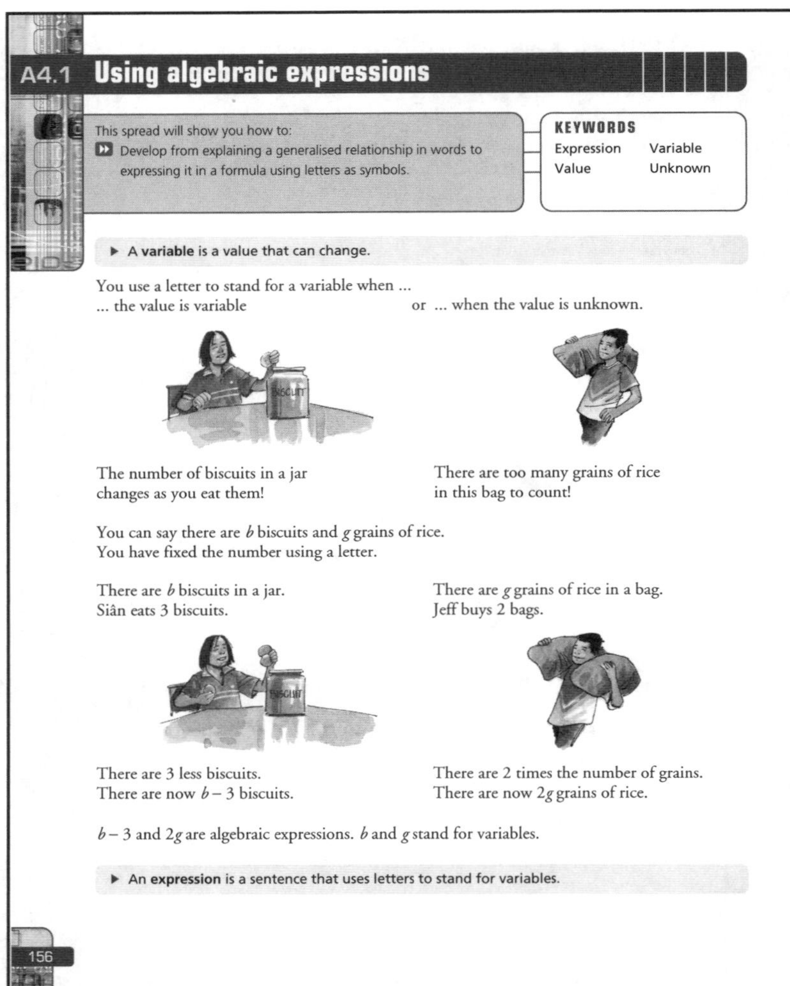

A4.1 Using algebraic expressions

This spread will show you how to:
- Develop from explaining a generalised relationship in words to expressing it in a formula using letters as symbols.

KEYWORDS
Expression Variable
Value Unknown

- A **variable** is a value that can change.

You use a letter to stand for a variable when ...
... the value is variable or ... when the value is unknown.

The number of biscuits in a jar changes as you eat them!

There are too many grains of rice in this bag to count!

You can say there are b biscuits and g grains of rice.
You have fixed the number using a letter.

There are b biscuits in a jar.
Siân eats 3 biscuits.

There are g grains of rice in a bag.
Jeff buys 2 bags.

There are 3 less biscuits.
There are now $b - 3$ biscuits.

There are 2 times the number of grains.
There are now $2g$ grains of rice.

$b - 3$ and $2g$ are algebraic expressions. b and g stand for variables.

- An **expression** is a sentence that uses letters to stand for variables.

156

Plenary

Discuss question 3.

- Encourage students to work in logical steps.
- Discuss how to combine the x's to make $4x$.
- Emphasise that $4x$ means $4 \times x$.
(So $4x$ generates multiples of 4!)
- $4 \times 5 = 20$ so the sides must be 5 cm.

Further activities

Students can make up problems similar to those in questions 1 and 2 for partners to solve. They will need to think carefully about how to describe the unknown term – using a letter or just 'lots of'.

Give students some expressions and ask them to make up stories.

Differentiation

Support questions:

- Question 1 focuses on writing expressions involving unknown terms.
- Question 2 focuses on choosing a letter to stand for an unknown number.
- Question 3 involves using algebra in the context of perimeter.

Core tier: focuses on forming and solving simple equations using number towers.

Exercise A4.1

1 Write an algebraic expression for each of these sentences.
 a There are x fleas on a dog.
 12 jump off onto a cat.
 How many fleas are left on the dog?
 b There are f fish in a pond.
 20 fish are added to the pond.
 How many fish are there now?
 c There are 22 players on a pitch.
 Some get sent off.
 How many are left?
 d Add 5 to an unknown number, x.
 e Subtract 3 from an unknown number, y.
 f Divide an unknown number, z, by 3.
 g Add two unknown numbers, r and s, together.

2 Write an algebraic expression for each of these sentences.
 a There are lots of dogs at a show.
 2 more dogs arrive.
 How many dogs are there at the show now?
 b There are lots of flowers in Ruby's garden.
 She picks 8 flowers.
 How many flowers are there in the garden now?
 c Some students go to Blackpool on a coach.
 2 students get left behind.
 How many students are on the coach home?
 d There are lots of videos in a rental shop.
 They lend 25 videos out on Saturday.
 How many videos are left?
 e There are lots of books in the library.
 20 people return a book and 5 people borrow a book.
 How many books are there now?
 f There are lots of cars in the car park.
 Each car has 4 wheels.
 How many wheels are there altogether?
 g Jules has lots of sweets.
 She shares them equally with a friend.
 How many sweets do they each have?

3 On this square, all the edges are x cm long.
 The distance around the edge of the square is the perimeter.
 Write an expression for the perimeter of the square.

157

Exercise commentary

The questions assess the objectives on Primary Framework Page 81.

Problem solving
The exercises assesses Primary Framework Page 81.

Group work
The further activity is suitable for pair work.

Misconceptions
Students tend to use a letter to stand for an object rather than the number of objects. Encourage the use of n or x instead of more descriptive lettering.
In question 2 students may find it difficult to decide which operation is involved. Encourage students to think about the question as if they know the number: 10 dogs or 10 flowers, and to work out what operation they would use.
Emphasise that, in general, 'more' means add, 'left' means less, 'each' means multiply and 'share' means divide.

Links
Perimeter: Primary Framework Page 97.

Homework

A4.1HW provides practice at forming expressions and equations.

Answers

1 **a** $x - 12$ **b** $f + 20$ **c** $22 - s$
 d $x + 5$ **e** $y - 3$ **f** $\frac{z}{3}$ **g** $r + s$
2 **a** $d + 2$ **b** $f - 8$ **c** $s - 2$
 d $v - 25$ **e** $b + 15$ **f** $4w$ **g** $\frac{s}{2}$
3 $4x$

A4.2 Algebraic operations

Mental starter

Make my number
Ask students for pairs of numbers that will add to 20.
In each case, students keep going until they have given you all the pairs which you write on the board or OHP.
Encourage the pairs written both ways: 3 + 17 and 17 + 3.
Repeat with multiplying numbers to 20.
Change the target number to 50 then 100.

Useful resources

R1 contains digit cards for the mental starter.
R7 contains function machines which you may find useful.

Introductory activity

Refer to the mental starter.
You can add and multiply numbers together in any order.
Discuss how to write this rule:
Give the first number a letter (a), then the second number (b).

- $a + b = b + a$
- $a \times b = b \times a$

Introduce the word 'term'. a and b are both terms. They are parts of the sentence or expression.

Emphasise that in algebra there are conventions used when you mix letter and number terms together.
Write the:

- letter first when you add
- number first when you multiply.

Discuss how to write an example using the letter x. Use your example to show that the letter x can get confused with the multiplication sign ×, so the sign is usually left out.

Remind students of the work they did with function machines. (You can show one using **R7** on OHP.)

- Use the function: + 5.
- Give inputs and ask for outputs.
- Then give some outputs and ask for the inputs.

Students should explain their reasoning.
Encourage the fact that +5 is opposite to –5 (+ undoes the –)
Emphasise that from one fact you can see three other facts: 8 + 5 = 13 and so on from the student book.

- Repeat for × and ÷

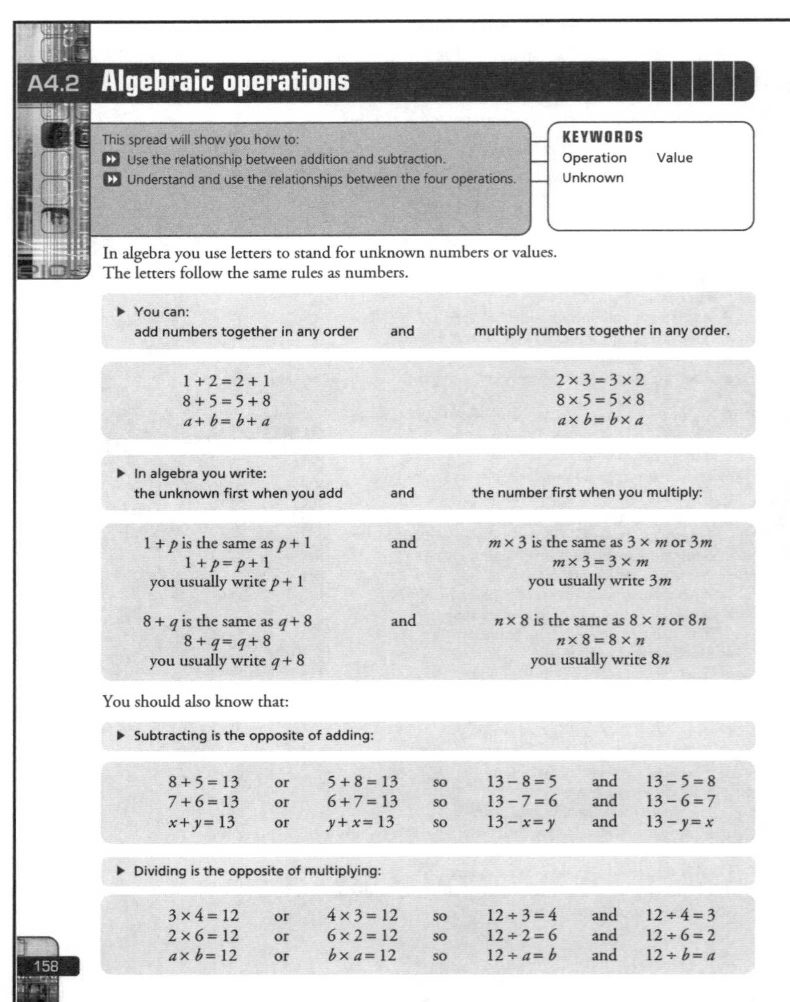

A4.2 **Algebraic operations**

This spread will show you how to:
- Use the relationship between addition and subtraction.
- Understand and use the relationships between the four operations.

KEYWORDS
Operation
Value
Unknown

In algebra you use letters to stand for unknown numbers or values.
The letters follow the same rules as numbers.

- You can:
add numbers together in any order and multiply numbers together in any order.

$1 + 2 = 2 + 1$	$2 \times 3 = 3 \times 2$
$8 + 5 = 5 + 8$	$8 \times 5 = 5 \times 8$
$a + b = b + a$	$a \times b = b \times a$

- In algebra you write:
the unknown first when you add and the number first when you multiply:

$1 + p$ is the same as $p + 1$ $1 + p = p + 1$ you usually write $p + 1$	and	$m \times 3$ is the same as $3 \times m$ or $3m$ $m \times 3 = 3 \times m$ you usually write $3m$
$8 + q$ is the same as $q + 8$ $8 + q = q + 8$ you usually write $q + 8$	and	$n \times 8$ is the same as $8 \times n$ or $8n$ $n \times 8 = 8 \times n$ you usually write $8n$

You should also know that:

- Subtracting is the opposite of adding:

$8 + 5 = 13$	or	$5 + 8 = 13$	so	$13 - 8 = 5$	and	$13 - 5 = 8$
$7 + 6 = 13$	or	$6 + 7 = 13$	so	$13 - 7 = 6$	and	$13 - 6 = 7$
$x + y = 13$	or	$y + x = 13$	so	$13 - x = y$	and	$13 - y = x$

- Dividing is the opposite of multiplying:

$3 \times 4 = 12$	or	$4 \times 3 = 12$	so	$12 \div 3 = 4$	and	$12 \div 4 = 3$
$2 \times 6 = 12$	or	$6 \times 2 = 12$	so	$12 \div 2 = 6$	and	$12 \div 6 = 2$
$a \times b = 12$	or	$b \times a = 12$	so	$12 \div a = b$	and	$12 \div b = a$

158

Plenary

Write $3w = 15$ on the board.
Discuss what the expression means – make up a sentence.
Ask students for the three other facts they can write down from $3w = 15$.
Emphasise that one of the facts gives the value of w.
Repeat for other expressions.

Further activities

Students work in pairs – one gives a simple sum, the partner finds three equivalent sums as in questions 3 and 4.

Differentiation

Support questions:

- Questions 1 and 2 focus on the commutative law for addition and multiplication.
- Question 3 focuses on addition as the inverse of subtraction. Springboard 7, page 238.
- Question 4 focuses on multiplication as the inverse of division.

Core tier: focuses on formulating and solving simple equations using 'Hot Crosses'.

Exercise A4.2

1 Copy and complete these addition sums.

a $3+4 = 4+\square$
b $6+9 = 9+\square$
c $8+3 = 3+\square$
d $7+1 = 1+\square$
e $4+9 = \square+\square$
f $3+5 = \square+\square$
g $x+2 = 2+\square$
h $y+4 = 4+\square$
i $a+b = b+\square$
j $c+\square = d+\square$

2 Copy and complete these multiplication sums.

a $3\times4 = 4\times\square$
b $6\times9 = 9\times\square$
c $8\times3 = 3\times\square$
d $7\times1 = 1\times\square$
e $4\times9 = \square\times\square$
f $3\times5 = \square\times\square$
g $x\times2 = 2\times\square$
h $y\times4 = 4\times\square = 4y$
i $a\times b = b\times\square = ab$
j $c\times\square = d\times\square = \square$

3 Copy and complete these sums.

a $3+8=11$ or $8+3=11$ so $11-3=\square$ and $11-8=\square$
b $4+5=9$ or $5+\square=\square$ so $9-4=\square$ and $9-\square=\square$
c $2+6=\square$ or $6+\square=\square$ so $8-2=\square$ and $8-\square=\square$
d $x+y=7$ or $y+x=7$ so $7-x=\square$ and $7-y=\square$
e $p+q=8$ or $q+\square=\square$ so $8-p=\square$ and $8-\square=\square$

4 Copy and complete these sums.

a $3\times8=24$ or $8\times3=24$ so $24\div3=\square$ and $24\div8=\square$
b $4\times5=20$ or $5\times\square=\square$ so $20\div4=\square$ and $20\div\square=\square$
c $2\times6=12$ or $6\times\square=\square$ so $12\div2=\square$ and $12\div\square=\square$
d $x\times y=7$ or $y\times x=7$ so $7\div x=\square$ and $7\div y=\square$
e $p\times q=8$ or $q\times\square=\square$ so $8\div p=\square$ and $8\div\square=\square$

159

Exercise commentary

The questions assess the objectives on Primary Framework Pages 43, 53 and 55.

Problem solving

The exercise assesses Primary Framework Page 81.

Group work

Weak students will benefit from discussing questions in pairs.

Misconceptions

This work is quite difficult to conceptualise and so students may have problems. In particular they may just write down the numbers in any order, not knowing why, and not be able to spot patterns.

It is important that they get a feel for the rules using the number examples before moving on to use letters and so you may want to direct students to just these questions.

It may help if students work in pairs and for them to work out the numeric examples in each form and refer to a multiplication grid to help emphasise that × and ÷ , and + and – are inverse operations.

Links

Multiplication and division facts: Primary Framework Page 59.

Homework

A4.2HW provides practice at using operations in algebra.

Answers

1 **a** 3 **b** 6 **c** 8 **d** 7 **e** $9+4$ **f** $5+3$ **g** x **h** y **i** a **j** $c+d=d+c$
2 **a** 3 **b** 6 **c** 8 **d** 7 **e** 9×4 **f** 5×3 **g** x **h** y **i** a **j** $c\times d=d\times c=cd$
3 **a** $11-3=8, 11-8=3$ **b** $5+4=9, 9-4=5, 9-5=4$
c $2+6=8, 6+2=8, 8-2=6, 8-6=2$ **d** $7-x=y, 7-y=x$
e $q+p=8, 8-p=q, 8-q=p$
4 **a** $24\div3=8, 24\div8=3$ **b** $5\times4=20, 20\div4=5, 20\div5=4$
c $6\times2=12, 12\div2=6, 12\div6=2$ **d** $7\div x=y, 7\div y=x$
e $q\times p=8, 8\div p=q, 8\div q=p$

Mental starter

Work it out

- Students perform a simple calculation: 4 × 8.
- Now ask for related facts: 40 × 8, 4 × 0.8, 40 × 80 etc.
- Students justify their answers.
- Repeat with other pairs of numbers.

Useful resources

R2 digit cards are useful for the mental starter.

A4.3OHP shows the expression from the student book for you to add the brackets.

Introductory activity

Refer to the last lesson.

You can add and multiply numbers together in any order.

Discuss whether it is true when you have a combination of operations:

- 2 + 3 × 4 + 1

Can you do them in any order?

Ask students to give their answers to the question.

They should describe their method.

There are four possible answers. Ask students for the sequence of working out to get any they don't spot.

A4.3OHP contains the expression for students to show their working.

Encourage students to suggest which is the true answer.

- For that answer, discuss the sequence of operations – what do you do first?

For each of the answers, discuss the sequence – what do you do first?

Tell students the correct sequence:

- multiply first, then
- add and subtract in any order.

Show you can add or subtract in any order.

Discuss what you can do to the sentence to show you want to override this sequence. You use brackets.

Discuss how you would use brackets to show how to group the parts together to get the other outcomes.

Emphasise the order when there is a division:

- multiply or divide first, then
- add or subtract.

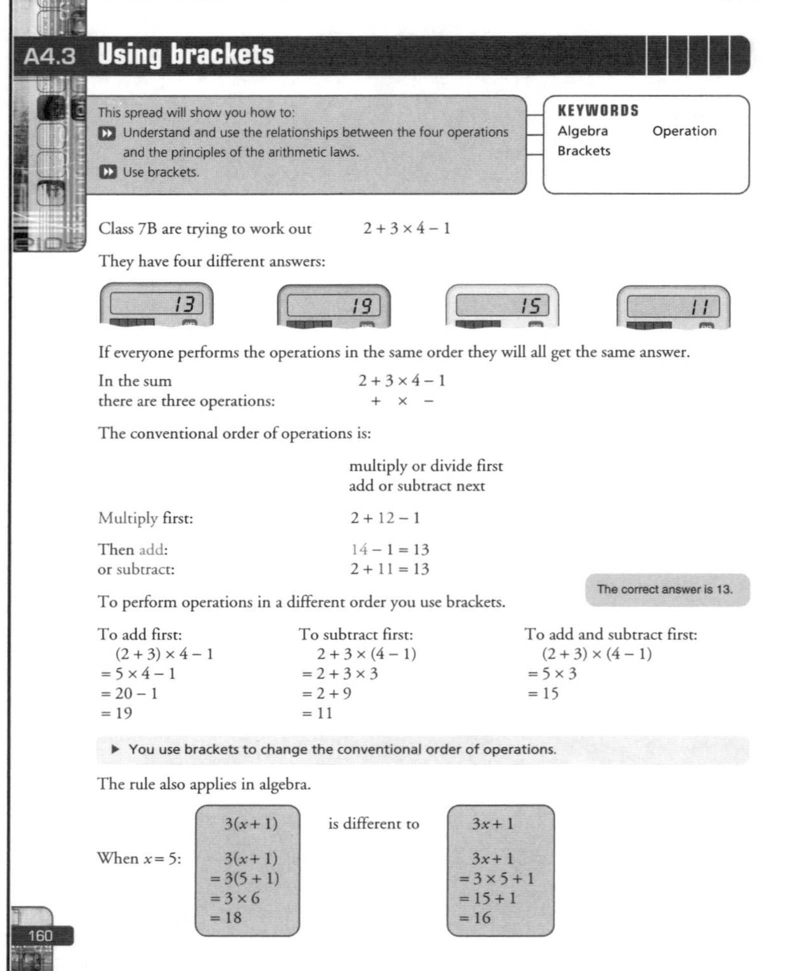

A4.3 **Using brackets**

This spread will show you how to:
- Understand and use the relationships between the four operations and the principles of the arithmetic laws.
- Use brackets.

KEYWORDS
Algebra
Brackets
Operation

Class 7B are trying to work out 2 + 3 × 4 − 1

They have four different answers:

13 19 15 11

If everyone performs the operations in the same order they will all get the same answer.

In the sum 2 + 3 × 4 − 1
there are three operations: + × −

The conventional order of operations is:

multiply or divide first
add or subtract next

Multiply first: 2 + 12 − 1

Then add: 14 − 1 = 13
or subtract: 2 + 11 = 13

The correct answer is 13.

To perform operations in a different order you use brackets.

To add first:	To subtract first:	To add and subtract first:
(2 + 3) × 4 − 1	2 + 3 × (4 − 1)	(2 + 3) × (4 − 1)
= 5 × 4 − 1	= 2 + 3 × 3	= 5 × 3
= 20 − 1	= 2 + 9	= 15
= 19	= 11	

- You use brackets to change the conventional order of operations.

The rule also applies in algebra.

$3(x + 1)$ is different to $3x + 1$

When $x = 5$:

$3(x + 1)$
$= 3(5 + 1)$
$= 3 \times 6$
$= 18$

$3x + 1$
$= 3 \times 5 + 1$
$= 15 + 1$
$= 16$

160

Plenary

- Discuss question 3.
- Ask students to do these calculations: 3 + (6 ÷ 3 − 1) and (3 + 6 ÷ 3) − 1
- Discuss the need for brackets in these expressions.
- Ask for all the different answers to question 2 if brackets can be used.

Further activities

In **A4.3ICT**, students use a spreadsheet to show that $a(b + c) = ab + ac$ using numerical values, building on the grid method.

Students make up problems as in question 3 for partners to solve. They give the solution they want and the partner must show how to use brackets to make it the answer.

Differentiation

Support questions:

- Questions 1 and 2 focus on the order of operations.
- Question 3 focuses on using brackets.
- Question 4 introduces the use of brackets in algebra. Springboard 7, page 488.

Core tier: focuses on expanding brackets.

Exercise A4.3

1 Copy and complete the working out for these sums.

a 3 + 4 × 6 − 2
= 3 + 24 − 2
= ☐ − 2
= ☐

b 2 + 9 ÷ 3 − 1
= 2 + ☐ − 1
= ☐ − 1
= ☐

c 12 − 8 ÷ 2 + 5
= ☐ − ☐ + 5
= ☐ + 5
= ☐

2 Work out these sums.
Remember: multiply or divide first, then add or subtract.
a $7 + 2 \times 3 - 4$
b $5 + 8 \div 2 - 7$
c $8 \div 2 + 1 - 3$
d $9 - 2 + 4 \times 3$

3 $3 + 6 \div 3 - 1 = 4$
Use brackets to show how to make these answers.
a $3 + 6 \div 3 - 1 = 2$
b $3 + 6 \div 3 - 1 = 6$
c $3 + 6 \div 3 - 1 = 4.5$

4 Use $x = 2$ to find the value of:
a $2(x + 3)$
b $2x + 3$
Are $2(x + 3)$ and $2x + 3$ the same or different?
Explain your answer.

161

Exercise commentary

The questions assess the objectives on Primary Framework Pages 53 and 55.

Problem solving
Question 4 assesses Primary Framework Page 81.

Group work
Questions 3 and 4 and the further activity are suitable for discussion in pairs.

Misconceptions
Students tend to work from left to right regardless of the correct order.
The acronym Bidmas may help students remember the conventional order. Discuss other ways.
Performing a string of operations can lead to errors, particularly when the order of operations is changed.
Encourage students to use plenty of space and to set out their work as in question 1 so they can keep track of their working.
Students tend to misuse brackets, using them unnecessarily.
Emphasise that they are only used to override the conventional order and otherwise add needless complexity.

Links
Long multiplication using the grid method: Primary Framework Page 67.

Homework

A4.3HW provides practice at using brackets in algebra.

Answers

1 **a** $27 - 2 = 25$
b $2 + 3 - 1 = 5 - 1 = 4$
c $12 - 4 + 5 = 8 + 5 = 13$
2 **a** 9 **b** 2 **c** 2 **d** 19
3 **a** $(3 + 6) \div 3 - 1 = 2$
b $3 + 6 \div (3 - 1) = 6$
4 **a** 10 **b** 7
The answers are different because the expressions are not equivalent.

A4.4 Solving equations

Mental starter

Express yourself!

Write some simple expressions on the board:

1. $d - 3$ 2. $5d$ 3. $d + 2$ 4. $d + 5$ 5. $2d + 1$ 6. $3d$

Roll a dice. That gives the expression students must use.

Roll it again. That gives the value of *d*.

Students substitute in the value of *d* and hold up the answer.

Useful resources

R1 digit cards for the mental starter and plenary.

Introductory activity

Ask students what they understand the term expression to mean.

It is a collection of terms.

Refer to the mental starter.

Emphasise that substituting a value of *d* into the expression is finding the value of the expression – this is evaluating the expression.

Repeat the substitution activity.

Ask students to:

- Imagine the dice score is 3
- Explain how to evaluate each of the expressions.

Discuss how to write substitutions on paper and encourage students to set out their work in logical steps.

Now pose the question differently.

- Using expression 4 you get an outcome of 10.
- What was the score on the dice?

Students should justify solutions.

Encourage students to work backwards rather than use trial and error to find the dice score.

Emphasise that you 'undo' + with –.

Discuss how to write that down on paper:

$$d + 5 = 10$$
$$d = 10 - 5 = 5$$

Discuss what to call a sentence like $d + 5 = 10$.

Emphasise it has an equals sign and so is called an equation.

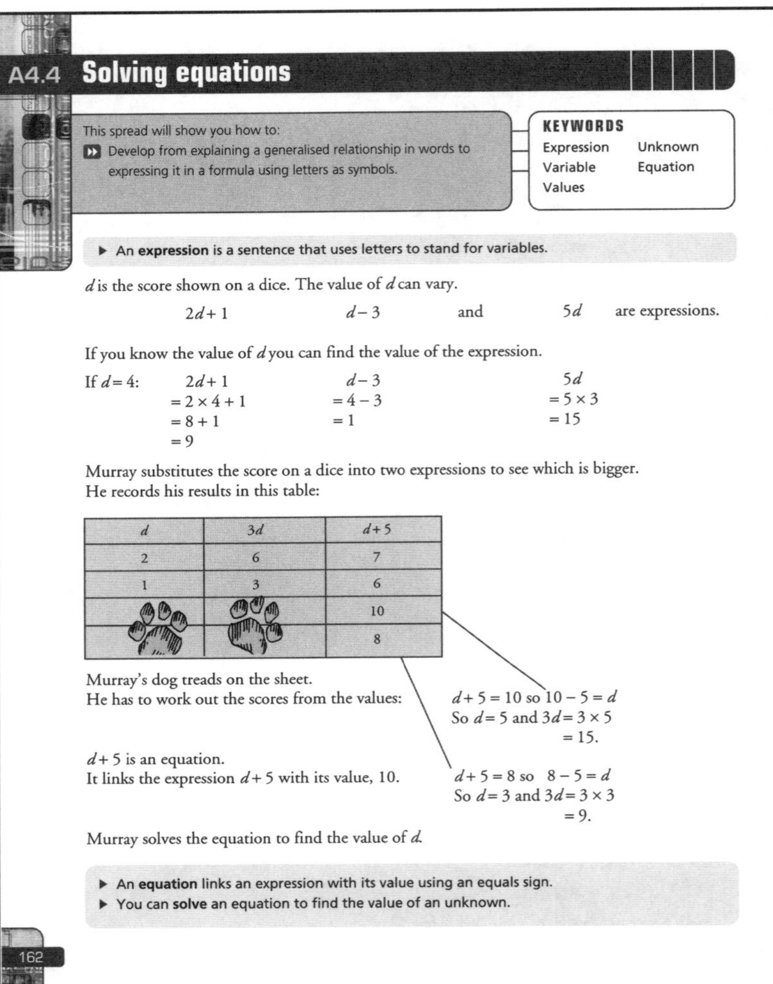

A4.4 **Solving equations**

This spread will show you how to:

- Develop from explaining a generalised relationship in words to expressing it in a formula using letters as symbols.

KEYWORDS
Expression, Unknown, Variable, Equation, Values

- An **expression** is a sentence that uses letters to stand for variables.

d is the score shown on a dice. The value of *d* can vary.

$2d + 1$ $d - 3$ and $5d$ are expressions.

If you know the value of *d* you can find the value of the expression.

If $d = 4$:

$2d + 1 = 2 \times 4 + 1 = 8 + 1 = 9$

$d - 3 = 4 - 3 = 1$

$5d = 5 \times 3 = 15$

Murray substitutes the score on a dice into two expressions to see which is bigger.
He records his results in this table:

d	$3d$	$d+5$
2	6	7
1	3	6
		10
		8

Murray's dog treads on the sheet.
He has to work out the scores from the values:

$d + 5 = 10$ so $10 - 5 = d$
So $d = 5$ and $3d = 3 \times 5 = 15$.

$d + 5 = 8$ so $8 - 5 = d$
So $d = 3$ and $3d = 3 \times 3 = 9$.

$d + 5$ is an equation.
It links the expression $d + 5$ with its value, 10.

Murray solves the equation to find the value of *d*.

- An **equation** links an expression with its value using an equals sign.
- You can **solve** an equation to find the value of an unknown.

162

Plenary

Repeat the mental starter activity.

- This time, do not tell students the value of *d*. Give them the answer and ask for the value of *d*.
- Students should justify their answers.
- Encourage the use of logical steps.

Further activities

Students give a solution and a partner must devise the equation, for example: the dice score was 6 and the answer was 12. What was the question? ($2d$ or $d + 6$)

Students make up equations for partners to solve as in question 6.

Differentiation

Support questions:

- Question 1 focuses on substituting values into an expression.
- Questions 2–5 focus on solving simple equations.
- Question 6 involves more complex equations to solve. Springboard 7, page 494.

Core tier: focuses on forming an equation from context and then solving it.

Exercise A4.4

1 Substitute $d = 3$ into each of these expressions.

a $2d$
b $d + 2$
c $2d + 1$
d $3d - 2$

2 Work out the value of d that makes these results true. The first one is done for you.

a $d + 5 = 6$
$1 + 5 = 6$
so $d = 1$
b $d + 5 = 7$
c $d + 5 = 9$
d $d + 5 = 11$

3 Find the value of d when:

a $3d = 6$
b $3d = 12$
c $3d = 18$
d $3d = 3$

4 Find the value of d that makes these equations true.

a $d + 1 = 7$ b $d + 4 = 5$
c $d + 8 = 11$ d $d + 6 = 8$
e $3 + d = 5$ f $4 + d = 7$
g $d - 1 = 3$ h $d - 2 = 4$
i $d - 3 = 2$ j $d - 5 = 0$

5 Find the value of d that makes these equations true.

a $3d = 9$ b $4d = 8$
c $2d = 12$ d $3d = 15$
e $7d = 14$ f $5d = 25$
g $2 = 2d$ h $12 = 4d$
i $8 = 2d$ j $24 = 8d$

6 Find the value of x that makes these equations true.

a $x + 3 = 9$ b $x + 7 = 24$
c $x - 11 = 12$ d $x - 9 = 7$
e $2x = 16$ f $3x = 30$
g $\frac{x}{2} = 5$ h $\frac{x}{5} = 3$
i $2x + 1 = 5$ j $3x - 1 = 14$

Exercise commentary

The questions assess the objectives on Primary Framework Pages 43, 53 and 55.

Problem solving

The exercise assesses Primary Framework Page 81.

Group work

Weak students would benefit from discussing questions in pairs.

Misconceptions

Students may make many mistakes in solving equations as the ideas are hard to conceptualise.

In particular it is common to write $3d = 6$ so $d = 18$ or $d + 1 = 7$ so $d = 8$.

The exercise is grounded in a context of a dice score to help students overcome this difficulty and start to see how easy it is to solve an equation by working backwards.

Emphasise that the answers to questions 2–5 must be between 1 and 6 and encourage students to think of the equations as sentences: 3 times a number is 6 and 3×2 is 6, so the number is 2.

Links

Students use these techniques when using formulae such as for area of a rectangle: Primary Framework Page 97.

Homework

A4.4HW provides practice at solving simple linear equations.

Answers

1 a 6 b 5 c 7 d 7
2 b 2 c 4 d 6
3 a 2 b 4 c 6 d 1
4 a 6 b 1 c 3 d 2 e 2 f 3 g 4 h 6 i 5 j 5
5 a 3 b 2 c 6 d 5 e 2 f 5 g 1 h 3 i 4 j 3
6 a 6 b 17 c 23 d 16 e 8 f 10 g 10 h 15 i 2 j 5

Summary

The Year 6 key teaching objective is:

- Identify and use appropriate operations to solve word problems (83, 85, 87, 89).

Plenary activity

Give students a 'think of a number' problem to solve:

- I think of a number. Add 3. Multiply by 2.
  The answer is 16. What did I think of?

Students justify reasoning – help them to use algebra by discussing how to write the equation and then solve it.
Students can then take it in turns to pose similar questions for the class to solve.

Check out commentary

1 Students should have a secure understanding of the conventions of algebra before attempting to solve equations. Parts **a** to **h** should highlight any difficulties and it is important students check their answers to these before attempting the rest of the question. Students with difficulties should move on to question 2.
Parts **i** and **j** are assessing Year 7 objectives although students should have enough of an understanding of multiplication and division facts to answer the questions. Refer them to the multiplication grid at the back of the book to help.
It is intended that students take an intuitive approach to solving equations at this level, although a more formal approach would be useful for later work on solving equations. Students should be encouraged to explain how they worked out their answers even of they do not set the working out formally.

2 This question will show whether students have a firm grasp of using letters to stand for numbers in a variety of situations. Emphasise that the letter stands for an unknown or immeasurable value and encourage students to use actual examples discussed at the beginning of the unit (hairs on your head, people at an event, grains of rice in a bag, etc).

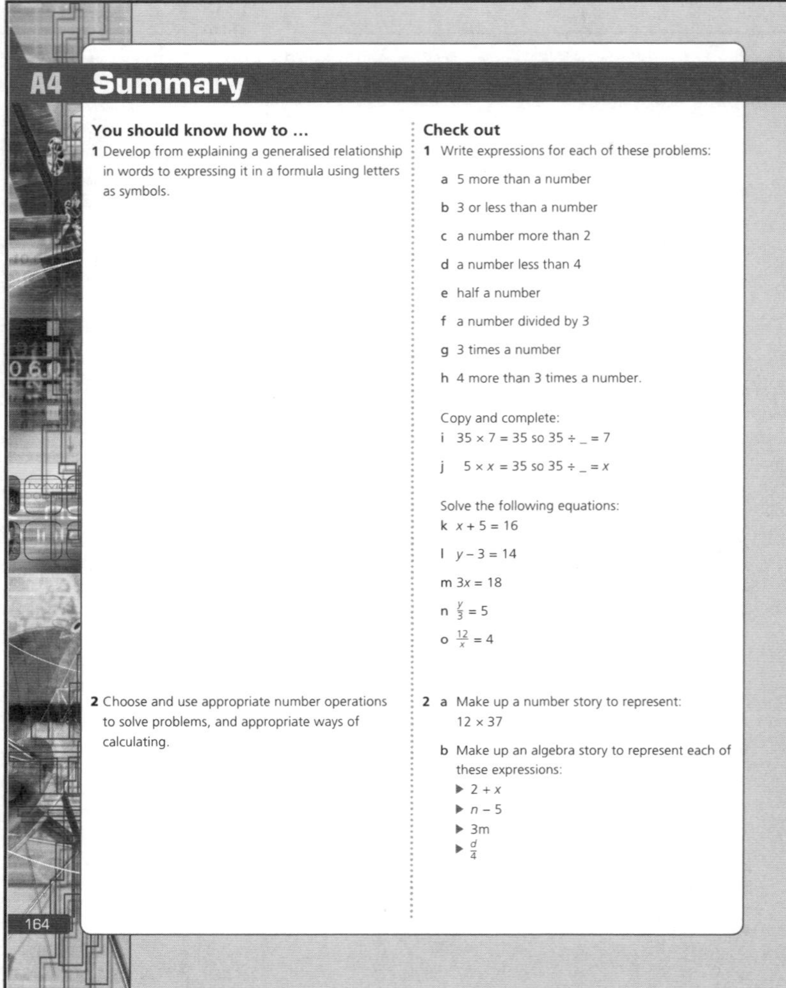

A4 Summary

You should know how to ...	Check out
1 Develop from explaining a generalised relationship in words to expressing it in a formula using letters as symbols.	**1** Write expressions for each of these problems: a 5 more than a number b 3 or less than a number c a number more than 2 d a number less than 4 e half a number f a number divided by 3 g 3 times a number h 4 more than 3 times a number. Copy and complete: i $35 \times 7 = 35$ so $35 \div \_ = 7$ j $5 \times x = 35$ so $35 \div \_ = x$ Solve the following equations: k $x + 5 = 16$ l $y - 3 = 14$ m $3x = 18$ n $\frac{y}{3} = 5$ o $\frac{12}{x} = 4$
2 Choose and use appropriate number operations to solve problems, and appropriate ways of calculating.	**2** a Make up a number story to represent: 12×37 b Make up an algebra story to represent each of these expressions: ▸ $2 + x$ ▸ $n - 5$ ▸ $3m$ ▸ $\frac{d}{4}$

164

Development

The work of this unit is developed in Year 8 in unit A2.

Links

Students form and solve simple equations to find missing angles in shape. Expanding brackets links to the grid method for multiplying large numbers (N5).

Mental starters

Objectives covered in this unit:

- Visualise and describe 2-D shapes.

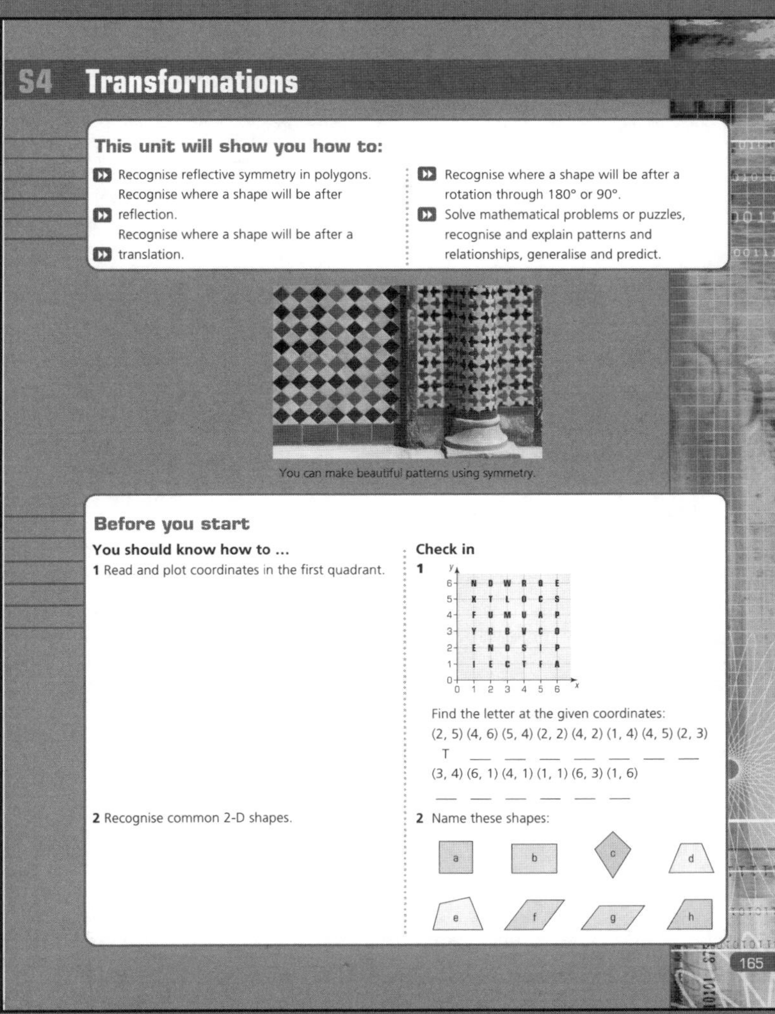

S4 Transformations

This unit will show you how to:

- Recognise reflective symmetry in polygons.
- Recognise where a shape will be after reflection.
- Recognise where a shape will be after a translation.
- Recognise where a shape will be after a rotation through 180° or 90°.
- Solve mathematical problems or puzzles, recognise and explain patterns and relationships, generalise and predict.

You can make beautiful patterns using symmetry.

Before you start

You should know how to …	Check in
1 Read and plot coordinates in the first quadrant.	1 Find the letter at the given coordinates: (2, 5) (4, 6) (5, 4) (2, 2) (4, 2) (1, 4) (4, 5) (2, 3) T ___ ___ ___ ___ ___ ___ ___ (3, 4) (6, 1) (4, 1) (1, 1) (6, 3) (1, 6) ___ ___ ___ ___ ___ ___
2 Recognise common 2-D shapes.	2 Name these shapes:

Check in activity

Show **R15** on OHP and ask students for the names of the quadrilaterals.

Challenge students to describe one of the shapes to a partner using its geometric properties. The partner should have their back to the OHP and should name (or sketch) the shape as soon as they recognise it.

Resources needed

* class set needed

Essential:

R8* (OHP) – Coordinate grid
R9* (OHP) – Axes in one quadrant
R15 (OHP) – Special quadrilaterals
S4.2OHP – Reflecting shapes
S4.4OHP – Translating shapes
S4.5OHP – Rotated shapes
S4.6OHP – Transformations on a grid
Mirrors, scissors, squared paper

Useful:

R20 (OHP) – Analogue clock face
S4.1OHP – Letters of the alphabet
N1.2OHP – Negative number thermometers
S4.1F* – Symmetry game
S4.2ICT* – Reflections using interactive geometry
S4.6ICT* – Transformations using interactive geometry
Dice

Unit commentary

Aim of the unit

This unit aims to develop students' ability to recognise and draw reflections. It introduces coordinates in all four quadrants and students then tranlsate and reflect shapes on a grid. They also make patterns using simple rotations through 90°.

Introduction

Discuss the pattern shown in the student book. Encourage students to describe how the patterns are made.

Discuss any similar local patterns made from tessellating shapes. Link to graphic design work.

Framework references

This unit focuses on:

- Year 6 teaching objectives pages: 107, 109, 111
- Problem solving objectives page: 79

The unit provides access to:

- Year 7 teaching objectives pages: 202–212, 218

Differentiation

Core tier focuses on transformations on a coordinate grid and identifying symmetry properties of 2-D shapes.

Springboard 7

Pages 279, 451–453, 461.

Mental starter

Naming shapes

Sketch a quadrilateral on the board.

Ask students to name the shape.

Repeat for special quadrilaterals in different orientations.

Useful resources

S4.1OHP – letters

R15 – special quadrilaterals

Blank sheet of paper

Mirrors

R9 – axes in one quadrant

Scissors

Introductory activity

Ask students what they understand by the word symmetry.

Ask them for shapes they can see that have symmetry.

Emphasise that if you can fold a shape in half it has reflection symmetry.

Illustrate using a rectangular piece of paper. Show that there are only two possible fold lines.

Ask the name of the fold line – line of symmetry.

Use S4.1OHP to discuss the lines of symmetry for letters of the alphabet.

Emphasise that the shape must fit onto itself after a fold and an S will not.

Students can cut out the letters and fold them to check if you make copies.

Discuss the word 'reflection'.

Emphasie the link to using a mirror.

Encourage students to use a mirror to check for lines of symmetry on letters and on shapes.

R15 shows all the special quadrilaterals which you can use for discussion.

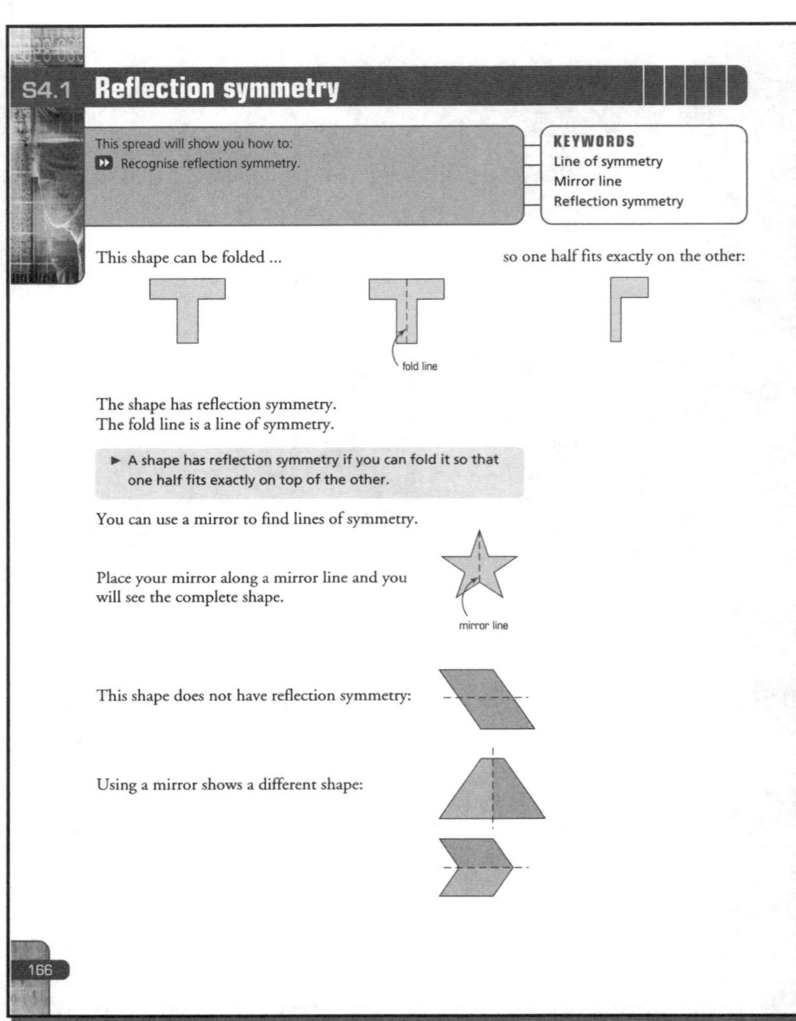

S4.1 Reflection symmetry
This spread will show you how to:
Recognise reflection symmetry.
KEYWORDS
Line of symmetry
Mirror line
Reflection symmetry
This shape can be folded ...
so one half fits exactly on the other:
fold line
The shape has reflection symmetry.
The fold line is a line of symmetry.
A shape has reflection symmetry if you can fold it so that one half fits exactly on top of the other.
You can use a mirror to find lines of symmetry.
Place your mirror along a mirror line and you will see the complete shape.
mirror line
This shape does not have reflection symmetry:
Using a mirror shows a different shape:
166

Plenary

How many lines?

Give students the name of a shape: use special quadrilaterals and triangles.

Students give the number of lines of symmetry.

Ask students to justify their answers – they should sketch the shape on the board and then draw in the lines.

Then ask them to sketch any shape with 0, 1, 2, 3, 4 ... lines of symmetry.

Further activities

S4.1F contains a game for two players based on lines of symmetry. Students will need a dice.

Differentiation

Support questions:
All of the questions are of a similar nature and the differentiation occurs by outcome:

- Spotting horizontal or vertical lines of symmetry.
- Spotting diagonal lines of symmetry.
- Spotting all the lines of symmetry. Springboard 7, page 451.

Core tier: focuses on reflecting shapes in vertical and horizontal mirror lines.

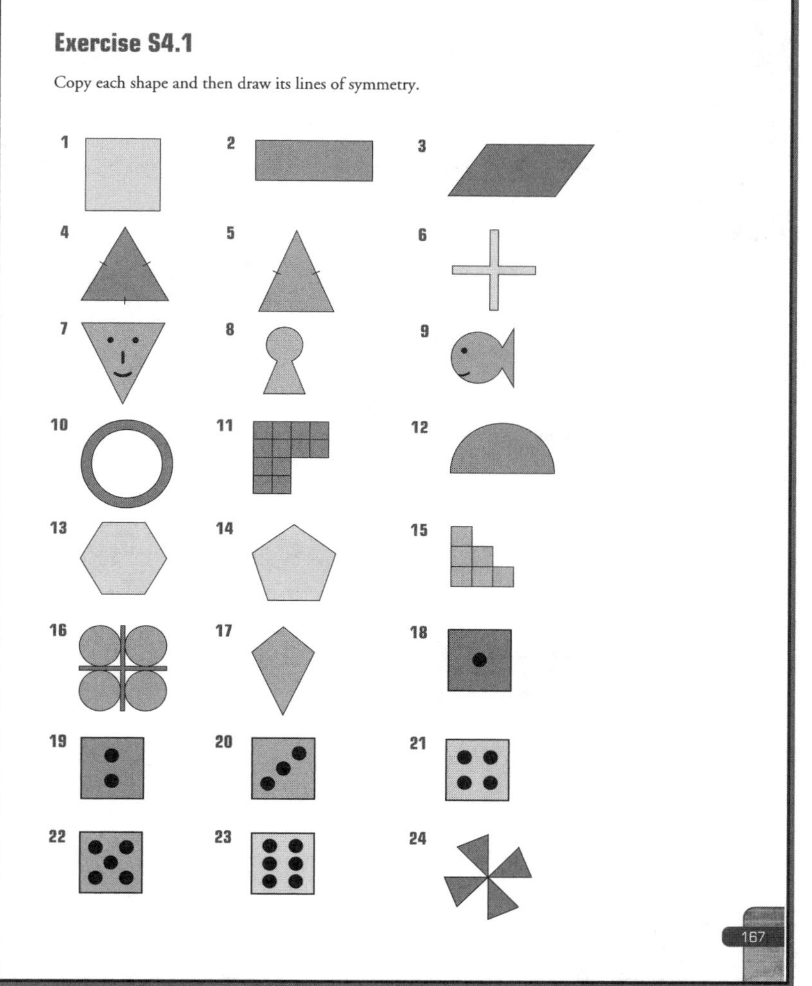

Exercise S4.1

Copy each shape and then draw its lines of symmetry.

1 2 3 4 5 6 7 8 9 10 11 12 13 14 15 16 17 18 19 20 21 22 23 24

167

Exercise commentary

The questions assess the objectives on Primary Framework Page 107.

Problem solving
Students could be encouraged to make general statements about the symmetry properties of specific shapes which assesses Primary Framework Page 81.

Group work
The further activity is suitable for pair work.

Misconceptions
Most students can spot a vertical line of symmetry although many will also find symmetry in a parallelogram.
Encourage the use of mirrors to check lines and emphasise that students can turn the page to see if they can spot any further lines. Using a cut-out of a parallelogram and folding it may help some students see it has no reflection symmetry.
The rectangle also causes particular difficulty with students drawing in diagonal lines.
Again, cut-out shapes or mirrors can help overcome this.

Links
2-D shapes: Primary Framework Page 103.

Homework

S4.1HW provides practice in identifying lines of symmetry.

Answers

Number of lines of symmetry:

1	4	2	2	3	None	4	3
5	1	6	4	7	1	8	1
9	None	10	∞	11	1	12	1
13	6	14	5	15	1	16	4
17	1	18	4	19	2	20	2
21	4	22	4	23	2	24	4

Mental starter

What's the point?

Students need a coordinate grid marked from 0 to 8 on both axes.
Call out a coordinate pair. Ask students to plot the point.
Each time they must join the point to the last point.
They plot these points: (4, 2) (6, 1) (5, 3) (6, 5) (4, 4) (3, 6) (2, 4) (0, 5) (1, 3) (0, 1) (2, 2) (3, 0)

It will make a six-pointed star.

Useful resources

R9 is a coordinate grid
Mirrors
S4.2OHP of a shape to be reflected on a grid

Introductory activity

Revise the work from the previous lesson on symmetry of shapes.
Emphasise that if you can fold a shape in half it has reflection symmetry.

Remind students that you see your reflection in a mirror.
Discuss what happens when you look in a mirror:
- You see the opposite of yourself.
- The further away you hold the mirror, the further away you seem.

Now draw a shape on a blank squared grid (use **R9**) and then a dotted line a distance from the shape.
Ask students to draw the reflection in the mirror line.

Emphasise that:
- **the shape looks 'opposite'**
- **corresponding points are the same distance either side of the mirror line.**

Revise the use of coordinate axes.
Refer to the mental starter.
There is a coordinate grid and a shape to reflect on **S4.2OHP**.
Ask students to reflect the shape in the given lines.
Encourage students to write down the coordinates of the vertices of the reflected shape.

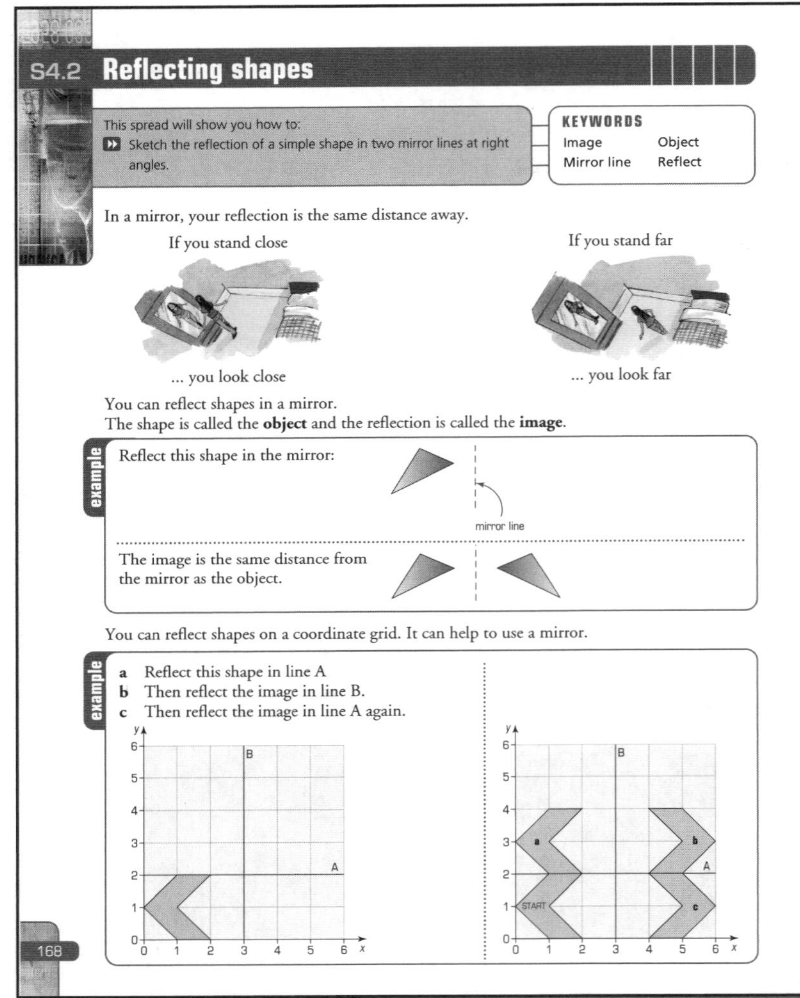

Plenary

Mirror me

Show a copy of **S4.2OHP**.
Give a coordinate pair.
Ask students to write down the coordinates of the point when it is reflected in each of the lines A and B.
You can give examples that will need to use negative coordinates and discuss how you would continue the axes to allow you to plot the points – this is covered on the next spread.

Further activities

In S4.2ICT, students use an interactive geometry package to reflect shapes in mirror lines.

Students can devise their own patterns like those in question 10, challenging a partner to draw the completed pattern.

Differentiation

Support questions:

- Questions 1–3 revise Year 4 objectives.
- Questions 4–9 focus on reflecting a shape in an axis. Springboard 7, page 452.
- Question 10 involves reflecting a shape in two axes. Springboard 7, page 453.

Core tier: focuses on reflecting shapes in diagonal mirror lines.

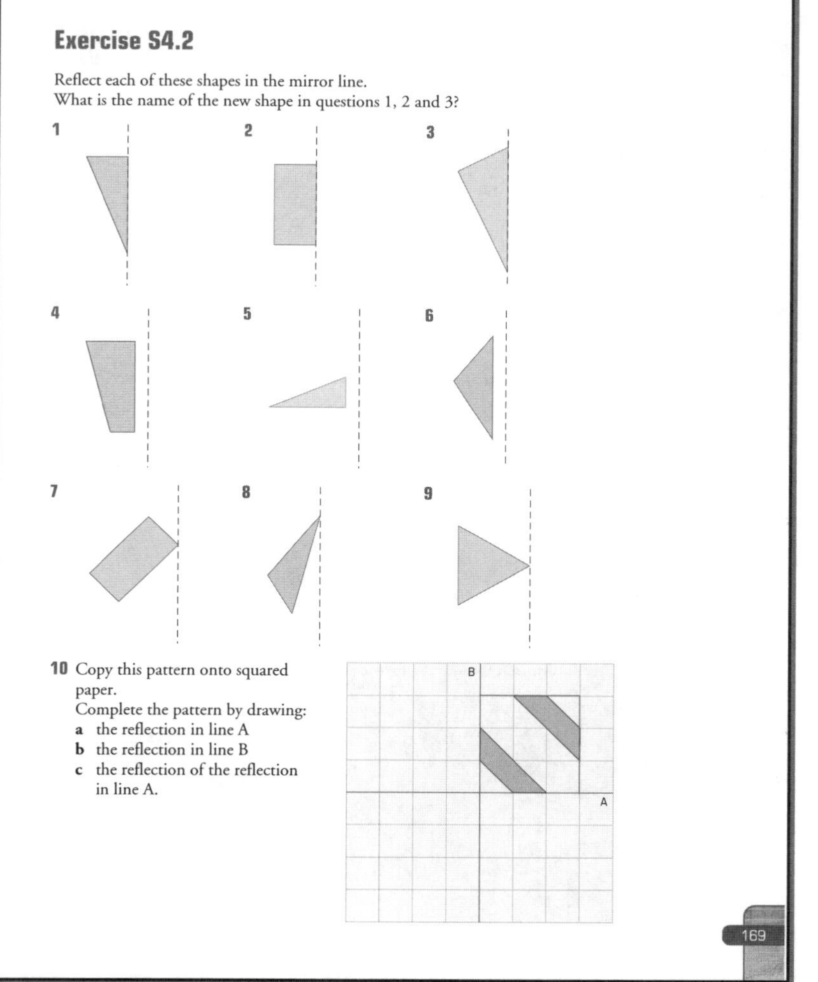

Exercise S4.2

Reflect each of these shapes in the mirror line.
What is the name of the new shape in questions 1, 2 and 3?

1 2 3

4 5 6

7 8 9

10 Copy this pattern onto squared paper.
Complete the pattern by drawing:
a the reflection in line A
b the reflection in line B
c the reflection of the reflection in line A.

Exercise commentary

The questions assess the objectives on Primary Framework Page 107.

Problem solving

Students could be encouraged to make general statements about the symmetry properties of specific shapes which assesses Primary Framework Page 81.

Group work

The further activity is suitable for pair work.

Misconceptions

Most students find reflecting shapes in vertical mirrors straightforward. However when the shape is some distance away from the line or just touching at a point, it becomes harder to see where the image should be placed, and the main error is translating the shape rather than reflecting it.

Emphasise that the image will be the same distance away from the mirror line and encourage the use of mirrors or folding as a check.

Links

2-D shapes: Primary Framework Page 103.

Homework

S4.2HW provides practice in reflecting shapes on a square grid in a mirror line.

Answers

1	Isosceles triangle
2	Square
3	Kite

Mental starter

Mirror me again

Recap reflecting points in a mirror line and extend to consider the need for negative numbers.

Show a copy of S4.2OHP. Give a coordinate pair.

Ask students to write down the coordinates of the point reflected in A.

Give examples that will need to use negative coordinates.

Discuss how you would continue the axes to plot these points.

Useful resources

R8 is a coordinate grid in all four quadrants – copy this for students.

Squared paper

S4.2OHP can be used for the mental starter.

N1.2OHP shows thermometers.

Introductory activity

Use the mental starter to revise the work from the previous spread on reflecting shapes in mirror lines.

The mental starter highlights the need to extend the axes into all four quadrants.

Emphasise that you can reflect the points as you can see the reflections in a mirror but that you can't describe the new position until the lines are extended.

Discuss how to label each of the lines backwards and downwards.

Link this to negative numbers on thermometers for the vertical then the horizontal axis.

N1.2OHP shows a horizontal and vertical thermometer for dicussion.

Once you have labelled the lines, discuss how to put them together – you can put any of the numbers together, e.g. ($^{-}1$, $^{-}1$), as the origin but putting the 0s together makes it easiest to count.

Use R8 to discuss naming and drawing points.

Emphasise that the horizontal number goes first and then the vertical – across the hall then up the stairs.

Draw a triangle in the top left quadrant and ask students to reflect it in each axis and give the coordinates of the reflected shapes.

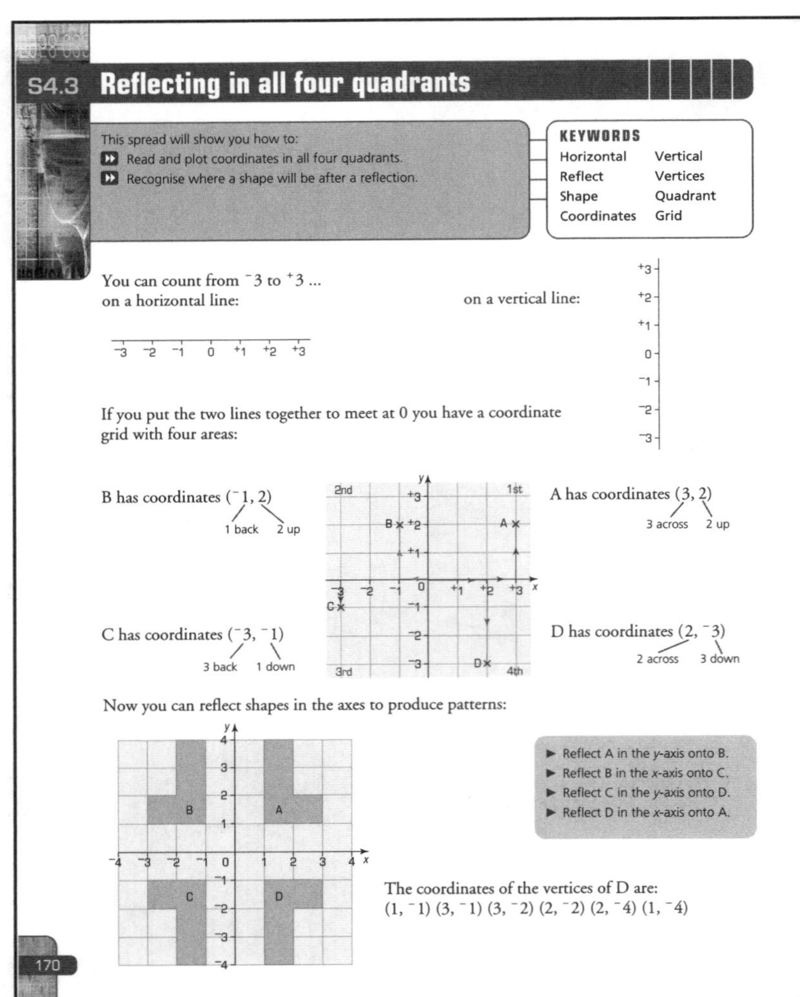

S4.3 Reflecting in all four quadrants

This spread will show you how to:
- Read and plot coordinates in all four quadrants.
- Recognise where a shape will be after a reflection.

KEYWORDS: Horizontal, Reflect, Shape, Coordinates, Vertical, Vertices, Quadrant, Grid

You can count from $^{-}3$ to $^{+}3$ ...
on a horizontal line: on a vertical line:

If you put the two lines together to meet at 0 you have a coordinate grid with four areas:

B has coordinates ($^{-}1$, 2) — 1 back, 2 up

A has coordinates (3, 2) — 3 across, 2 up

C has coordinates ($^{-}3$, $^{-}1$) — 3 back, 1 down

D has coordinates (2, $^{-}3$) — 2 across, 3 down

Now you can reflect shapes in the axes to produce patterns:

- Reflect A in the y-axis onto B.
- Reflect B in the x-axis onto C.
- Reflect C in the y-axis onto D.
- Reflect D in the x-axis onto A.

The coordinates of the vertices of D are:
(1, $^{-}1$) (3, $^{-}1$) (3, $^{-}2$) (2, $^{-}2$) (2, $^{-}4$) (1, $^{-}4$)

170

Plenary

Round and round

On **R8** plot a point, e.g. ($^{-}3$, 4).

Ask students to reflect the point in the x-axis then the y-axis then the x-axis again – until the point is back where it started.

Students should write down the coordinates of the point in each quadrant.

Discuss what they notice – that the points use the same numbers.

Repeat until they can spot any patterns.

Further activities

Challenge students to consider the coordinates of the vertices of the object and the image following a reflection in the *x*- or *y*-axis and to generalise if possible.

Differentiation

Support questions:

All questions have a similar level of difficulty if completed. The differentiation depends on how far you go with each question.

- Plotting the points and naming the shapes in questions 1, 2 and 7 is Year 5 work. Springboard 7, page 279.
- Plotting the points then reflecting the shapes is the main focus of the spread.
- Completing all the tasks for all the questions provides a link to the work in the Core book.

Core tier: focuses on recognising and drawing translations.

Exercise S4.3

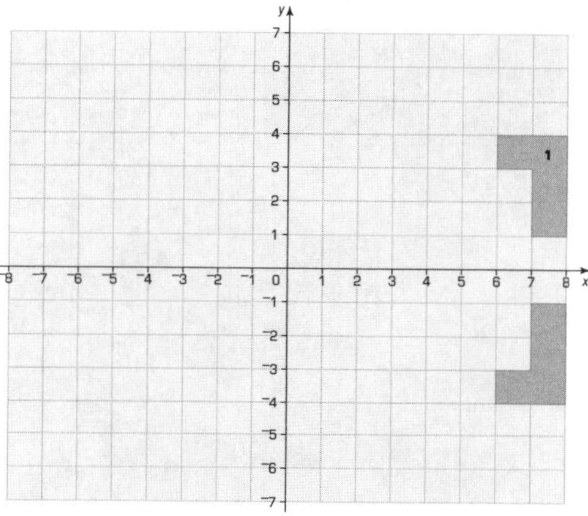

Each question gives the coordinates of the vertices of a shape.

- Copy the grid.
- Plot each set of points and join them to form a shape.
- Name the shape.
- Reflect it in the *x*-axis.
- Write down the coordinates of each point of the reflection.

The first one is started for you.

1 (8, 1) (8, 4) (6, 4) (6, 3) (7, 3) (7, 1) (8, 1) → (8, $^-1$) (8, $^-4$) ...

2 (1, 1) (3, 1) (1, 4) (1,1)

3 ($^-1$, 1) ($^-4$, 1) ($^-3$, 3) ($^-1$, 3) ($^-1$, 1)

4 (6, $^-2$) (5, $^-3$) (4, $^-2$) (5, $^-1$) (6, $^-2$)

5 ($^-4$, $^-2$) ($^-5$, $^-4$) ($^-4$, $^-6$) ($^-3$, $^-4$) ($^-4$, $^-2$)

6 (1, $^-5$) (2, $^-7$) ($^-2$, $^-7$) ($^-3$, $^-5$) (1, $^-5$)

7 (7, 5) (7, 7) (4, 7) (4, 5) (7, 5)

8 ($^-5$, 1) ($^-5$, 3) ($^-8$, 2) ($^-5$, 1)

9 (3, $^-2$) (3, $^-4$) (5, $^-4$) (3, $^-2$)

10 ($^-7$, 3) ($^-6$, 6) ($^-7$, 7) ($^-8$, 6) ($^-7$, 3)

171

Exercise commentary

The questions assess Primary Framework Pages 107 and 109.

Problem solving

The further activity assesses Primary Framework Page 81.

Group work

The further activity is suitable for pair work.

Misconceptions

Students plot (*y*, *x*) instead of (*x*, *y*). Emphasise that *x* comes before *y* in the alphabet and similarly *a* for across comes before *u* for up so plot *x* then *y*.

Students also have difficulty plotting points on the axes: (0, *y*) and (*x*, 0). Discuss strategies as a group so students can share good ideas.

Negative coordinates can cause difficulties, especially when the axes are not numbered. Practice counting on and back past 0.

Students put the shape in the wrong place after a reflection.

Encourage the use of a mirror to check.

Links

2-D shapes: Primary Framework Page 103.

Negative numbers: Page 15.

Homework

S4.3HW provides practice at reflecting shapes in the *y*-axis.

Answers

1 Hexagon; (8, $^-1$), (8, $^-4$), (6, $^-4$), (6, $^-3$), (7, $^-3$), (7, $^-1$), (8, $^-1$)
2 Right-angled triangle; (1, $^-1$), (3, $^-1$), (1, $^-4$), (1, $^-1$)
3 Right-angled trapezium; ($^-1$, $^-1$), ($^-4$, $^-1$), ($^-3$, $^-3$), ($^-1$, $^-3$), ($^-1$, $^-1$)
4 Square; (6, 2), (5, 3), (4, 2), (5, 1), (6, 2) 5 Rhombus; ($^-4$, 2), ($^-5$, 4), ($^-4$, 6), ($^-3$, 4), ($^-4$, 2) 6 Parallelogram; (1, 5), (2, 7), ($^-2$, 7), ($^-3$, 5), (1, 5)
7 Rectangle; (7, $^-5$), (7, $^-7$), (4, $^-7$), (4, $^-5$), (7, $^-5$)
8 Isosceles triangle; ($^-5$, $^-1$), ($^-5$, $^-3$), ($^-8$, $^-2$), ($^-5$, $^-1$)
9 Right-angled isosceles triangle; (3, 2), (3, 4), (5, 4), (3, 2)
10 Kite; ($^-7$, $^-3$), ($^-6$, $^-6$), ($^-7$, $^-7$), ($^-8$, $^-6$), ($^-7$, $^-3$)

S4.4 Translating shapes

Mental starter

Who's in the chair?

Start with a student. Ask her or him to stand up.

Define the direction 'up' as in front of them and 'right' as to their right.

Then give an instruction – 2 to your right and 4 up – and ask the student to stand up. The first person sits down.

Continue giving instructions so that everyone has a go at standing up.

Each time start with left or right then up or down.

Useful resources

S4.4OHP – a shape and its translation

R8 is a coordinate grid in all four quadrants

Squared paper

Introductory activity

Use R8 to revise naming and plotting points in all four quadrants.

Use two cut-outs of a right-angled triangle 2 cm by 4 cm. Place one on the grid. Ask students to place the other to show a reflection in the *x*- or *y*-axis.

Emphasise that for a reflection you flip the shape over.

Now place one of the triangles on the grid. Then place the second shape so that it is translated by 4 units across and 5 units up.

Discuss how to describe the movement of the triangle. Emphasise that it is a sliding movement.

Introduce the term 'translation'.

Discuss how to describe the exact movement. Encourage use of across, and up or along the axis.

Emphasise that in a coordinate pair you write the across coordinate first. Discuss the benefits of using the same order for a translation – everyone knows the order and so can follow your instructions.

Place the triangle on the grid again and ask students to move it a given translation. Ask them to write down the coordinates of the vertices.

S4.4OHP shows the example from the student book for discussion.

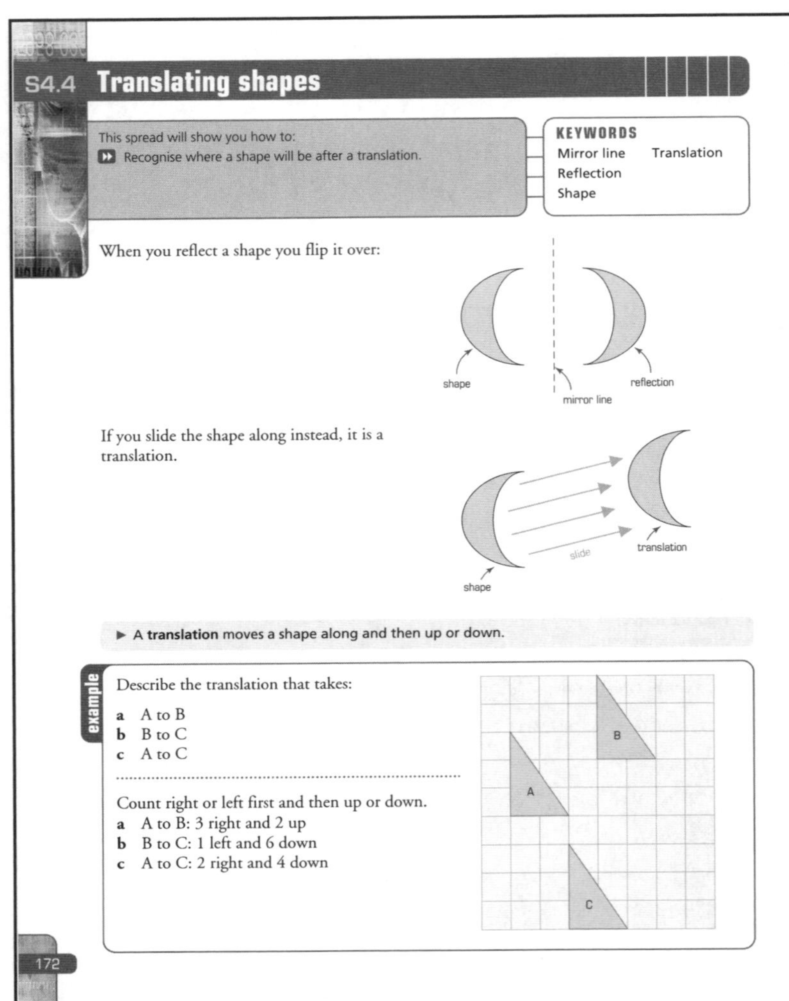

S4.4 Translating shapes

This spread will show you how to:

- Recognise where a shape will be after a translation.

KEYWORDS
Mirror line
Translation
Reflection
Shape

When you reflect a shape you flip it over:

If you slide the shape along instead, it is a translation.

► A **translation** moves a shape along and then up or down.

example

Describe the translation that takes:

a A to B
b B to C
c A to C

Count right or left first and then up or down.

a A to B: 3 right and 2 up
b B to C: 1 left and 6 down
c A to C: 2 right and 4 down

172

Plenary

Repeat the mental starter.

Give students an instruction and ask that person to stand. They must give the instruction that would go back to the original chair.

Write the instructions in pairs to help students spot the pattern.

Further activities

Students create their own diagrams as in question 2 but using all four quadrants and challenge a partner to translate the shape a given distance and direction.

Challenge students to consider the coordinates of the vertices of the object and the image following a translation and to generalise if possible.

Differentiation

Support questions:

- Question 1 involves recognising translations.
- Question 2 focuses on plotting points and translating shapes.
- The further activity focuses on translating shapes in all four quadrants.

Core tier: focuses on rotation.

Exercise S4.4

1 Describe these translations.
The first one is done for you.

a A→B $\begin{pmatrix}\text{6 right}\\ \text{1 up}\end{pmatrix}$
b D→B
c G→D
d E→F
e H→I
f I→H
g A→F
h F→D
i F→G
j A→D
k B→C

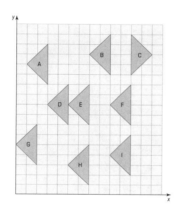

2 On squared paper draw: the x-axis from $x = 0$ to $x = 13$
the y-axis from $y = 0$ to $y = 13$
Plot each shape on the same grid.

- Name each shape.
- Translate each shape.
- Write down the coordinates of the translated shape.

A	(3, 12) (6, 13) (6, 11) (3, 12)	Translate A $\begin{pmatrix}\text{1 to the left}\\ \text{5 down}\end{pmatrix}$
B	(0, 9) (0, 11) (6, 11) (6, 9) (0, 9)	Translate B $\begin{pmatrix}\text{5 to the right}\\ \text{3 down}\end{pmatrix}$
C	(0, 6) (1, 6) (1, 8) (0, 6)	Translate C $\begin{pmatrix}\text{4 to the right}\\ \text{0 up}\end{pmatrix}$
D	(0, 2) (1, 2) (1, 3) (2, 3) (2, 1) (0, 1) (0, 2)	Translate D $\begin{pmatrix}\text{4 to the right}\\ \text{3 up}\end{pmatrix}$
E	(3, 2) (5, 3) (3, 1) (3, 2)	Translate E $\begin{pmatrix}\text{8 to the right}\\ \text{6 up}\end{pmatrix}$
F	(5, 1) (5, 2) (6, 2) (6, 3) (7, 3) (7, 1) (5, 1)	Translate F $\begin{pmatrix}\text{4 to the right}\\ \text{3 up}\end{pmatrix}$

173

Exercise commentary

The questions assess Primary Framework Page 107.

Problem solving

The further activity assesses Primary Framework Page 81.

Group work

The further activity is suitable for pair work.

Misconceptions

Students plot (y, x) instead of (x, y).
Emphasise that x comes before y in the alphabet and similarly a for across comes before u for up so plot x then y.
The common error with translations is to translate by the wrong amount, typically getting vertices mixed up.
Encourage students to focus on one particular vertex to decide where to place the shape. If necessary they can then repeat with another vertex.
Tracing the shapes and moving the paper can help students to spot errors.

Links

2-D shapes: Primary Framework Page 103.

Homework

S4.4HW provides practice in translating shapes.

Answers

1 **b** 4 right and 5 up **c** 3 right and 4 up **d** 4 right **e** 4 right and 1 up
f 4 left and 1 down **g** 8 right and 4 down **h** 6 left
i 9 left and 4 down **j** 2 right and 4 down **k** Not a translation

2 **A** Isosceles triangle; (2, 7), (5, 8), (5, 6), (2, 7)
B Rectangle; (5, 6), (5, 8), (11, 8), (11, 6), (5, 6)
C Right-angled triangle; (4, 6), (5, 6), (5, 8), (4, 6)
D Hexagon; (4, 5), (5, 5), (5, 6), (6, 6), (6, 4), (4, 4), (4, 5)
E Scalene triangle; (11, 8), (13, 9), (11, 7), (11, 8)
F Hexagon; (9, 4), (9, 5), (10, 5), (10, 6), (11, 6), (11, 4), (9, 4)

Mental starter

What's the time?

You need a clock face or use **R20**.
Start at 12. Ask students the angle you need to move the hand to 3. (You can tell them this is 90°.)
Ask for the turn from 6 to 9, 3 to 6, 9 to 12 – all 90°.
Now consider 3 to 12, 9 to 6, 6 to 3, 12 to 9 – all 90° (or 270°).
Emphasise the need to use clockwise or anticlockwise.

Useful resources

R20 for the mental starter.
Squared paper.
S4.5OHP shows a shape that has been rotated.

Introductory activity

Review the transformations covered so far: a reflection is a flip, a translation is a slide.

Define a rotation as a turn.
Ask students where they have heard the term before – a rota means you take it in turns.

Refer to the mental starter.
Discuss the angle made when the hand rotates clockwise.
Define clockwise as the direction the clock works in.
Emphasise that the hand moves to a different place when the turn is anticlockwise through the same angle.
Ask students whether there is any information needed other than the turn and the direction.

Emphasise the pivot point in the centre of the clock that the hand rotates through.
Make the link with an angle – you measure the turn from the point where the arms meet.

Discuss how to rotate shapes clockwise or anticlockwise.
You need an angle and a point to turn it from.

Put a cut-out shape on the board and show how you can rotate it about a vertex or its centre. You can use **S4.5OHP** which shows the example from the student book.

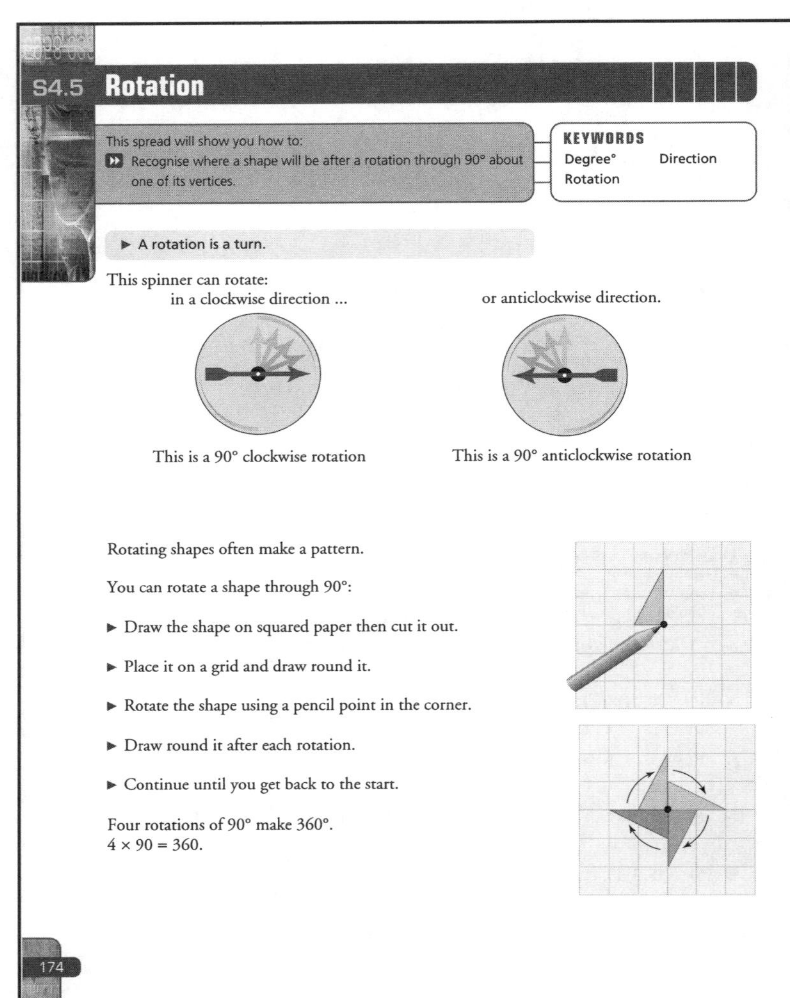

S4.5 Rotation

This spread will show you how to:
- Recognise where a shape will be after a rotation through 90° about one of its vertices.

KEYWORDS
Degree° Direction
Rotation

- A rotation is a turn.

This spinner can rotate:
in a clockwise direction … or anticlockwise direction.

This is a 90° clockwise rotation

This is a 90° anticlockwise rotation

Rotating shapes often make a pattern.

You can rotate a shape through 90°:

- Draw the shape on squared paper then cut it out.
- Place it on a grid and draw round it.
- Rotate the shape using a pencil point in the corner.
- Draw round it after each rotation.
- Continue until you get back to the start.

Four rotations of 90° make 360°.
4 × 90 = 360.

174

Plenary

Use the mental starter again.
You need a clock face or students imagine a clock face.
Start at 2. Ask students the angle you need to move the hand to 5. (You can tell them this is 90°.)
Ask for other turns of 90° – e.g. 1 to 4, 7 to 4.
Emphasise the need to use clockwise or anticlockwise.

Further activities

Question 2 can be extended to consider other turns.

Question 4 can be developed to include isometric paper.

Challenge students to draw a shape with coordinates:
(0, 0), (0, 2) and (2, 0)
and to find the coordinates after different rotations, generalising if possible.

Differentiation

Support questions:

- Question 1 focuses on simple turns.
- Questions 2 and 3 focus on rotating through 90° and 180°.
- Question 4 introduces the idea of rotating through 45°. Springboard 7, page 461.

Core tier: focuses on classifying shapes according to their symmetry properties.

Exercise S4.5

1 Give the angle and direction of each of these rotations.

a b c d

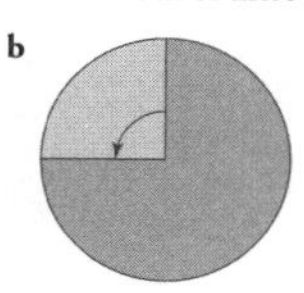

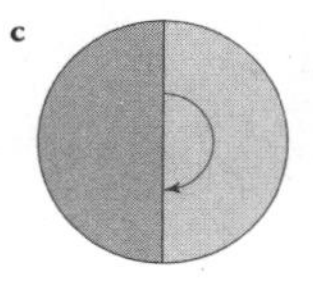

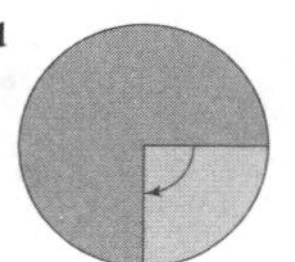

2 Copy and complete this table.

	Start	Finish	Angle and direction
a	12	3	
b	6	3	
c	1	4	
d	9		90° clockwise
e	8		180°
f	7		90° clockwise
g		6	90° anticlockwise
h		10	180°
i		4	180°

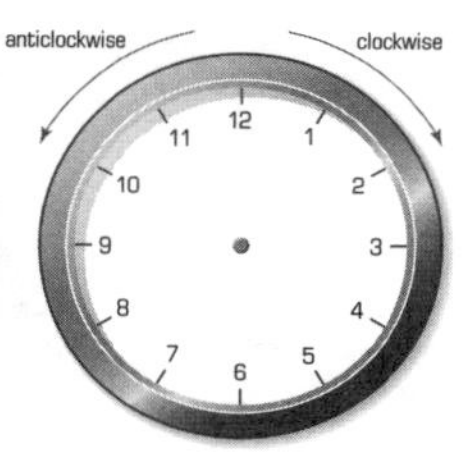

3 Copy and rotate these shapes about the dot through the angle given.

a 90° clockwise **b** 90° clockwise **c** 180° **d** 90° anticlockwise

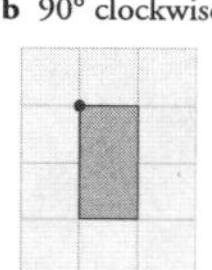

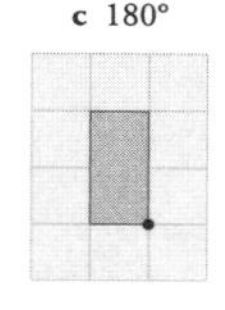

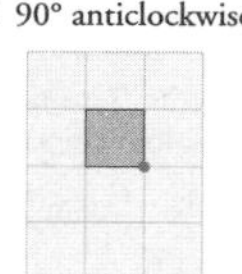

4 When a right-angled triangle is rotated, these are the results.

Draw similar rotations for:
a an isosceles right-angled triangle
b a square

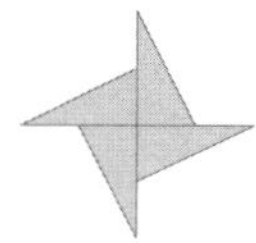

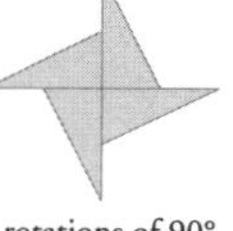

rotations of 90°

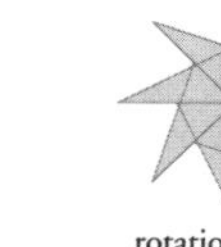

rotations of 45°

175

Exercise commentary

The questions assess Primary Framework Page 111.

Problem solving

The further activity assesses Primary Framework Page 81 if students generalise.

Group work

The further activity is suitable for pair work.

Misconceptions

Students find rotations difficult to visualise and draw.

Encourage them to turn the page so that they can see what the rotated shape will look like.

The use of tracing paper is essential so that students can place the resulting rotation – students can use a pencil point to hold the centre of rotation in place while they turn the paper.

Some students will confuse clockwise and anticlockwise turns.

Emphasise that clockwise turns go the same way as the hands of a clock. Have a clock on the wall for reference.

Links

2-D shapes: Primary Framework Page 103.
Angles: Page 111.

Homework

In **S4.5HW** students are asked to identify angles associated with the directions of a compass. Students are also required to rotate shapes on a grid.

Answers

1 **a** 90° clockwise **b** 90° anticlockwise
c 180° clockwise **d** 90° clockwise

2 **a** 90° clockwise **b** 90° anticlockwise
c 90° clockwise **d** 12
e 2 **f** 10 **g** 9 **h** 4 **i** 10

Mental starter

Which turn?

Show **S4.1OHP** of the letters of the alphabet.

- Ask which letters have reflection symmetry. Remind students this means they fold in half.
- Rotate the OHP through 180°.
- Ask students which letters are the same upside-down.
- Define this as rotational symmetry.

Useful resouces

S4.6OHP has various transformations of a shape on a grid.

S4.1OHP shows the letters of the alphabet for the mental starter.

Introductory activity

Review the transformations:

- a reflection is a flip
- a translation is a slide
- a rotation is a turn.

Emphasise that any of these movements leave the shape unchanged in terms of size.

Define shapes that are exactly the same shape and size as congruent.

Discuss meaning of the word congruent – if shapes are congruent then they will fit exactly on top of each other when you cut them out.

Discuss what actually changes – the position of the shape.

Introduce the term 'transformation' as a word that describes any of the three movements.

S4.6OHP has a grid with congruent shapes.

Use the grid to ask students to describe the transformation that moves one shape onto another.

Encourage full descriptions:

- Reflection – give the mirror line
- Translation – give the across and up distances
- Rotation – give the angle, direction and centre.

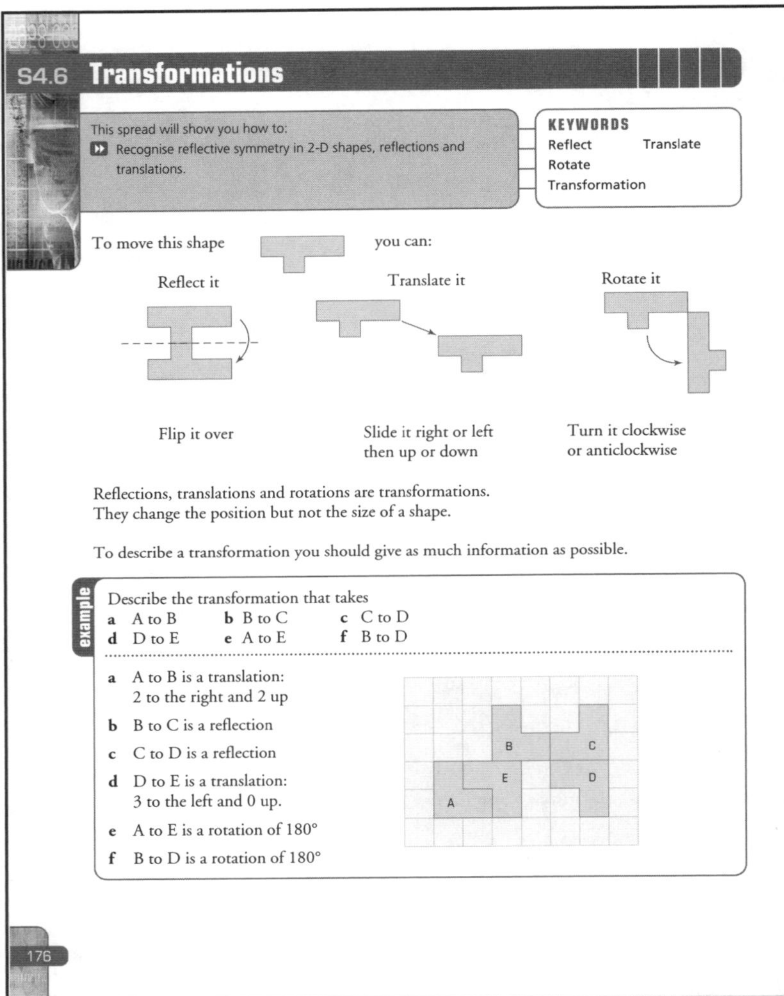

S4.6 Transformations
This spread will show you how to:
Recognise reflective symmetry in 2-D shapes, reflections and translations.
KEYWORDS
Reflect
Translate
Rotate
Transformation
To move this shape
you can:
Reflect it
Translate it
Rotate it
Flip it over
Slide it right or left then up or down
Turn it clockwise or anticlockwise
Reflections, translations and rotations are transformations.
They change the position but not the size of a shape.
To describe a transformation you should give as much information as possible.
example
Describe the transformation that takes
a A to B b B to C c C to D
d D to E e A to E f B to D
a A to B is a translation: 2 to the right and 2 up
b B to C is a reflection
c C to D is a reflection
d D to E is a translation: 3 to the left and 0 up.
e A to E is a rotation of 180°
f B to D is a rotation of 180°
B
C
E
D
A
176

Plenary

Use **S4.6OHP** – various transformations of a shape.

Discuss the transformation that moves one shape to another and also the inverse transformation that moves the shape back to where it started.

Encourage full descriptions.

Further activities

In **S4.6ICT**, students use an interactive geometry package to solve transformation problems.

Students can create wallpaper (or wrapping paper) patterns using reflections, translations and rotations. This could link with work in technology.

Differentiation

Support questions:

- Question 1 focuses on reflections.
- Questions 2 and 3 focus on describing rotations and translations.
- Questions 4 and 5 are harder questions involving coordinates in all four quadrants.

Core tier: focuses on describing transformations of congruent shapes.

Exercise S4.6

1 Reflect each of these shapes in the mirror line.
What is the name of each new shape?

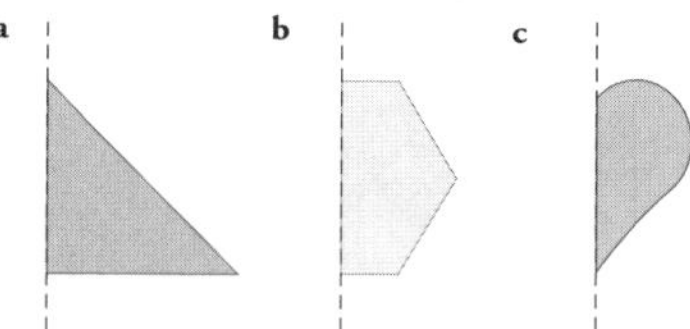

2 Copy and complete this table.

	Start	Finish	Angle and direction
a	N	E	
b	NE	NW	
c	SE	NW	
d	W		90° anticlockwise
e	SW		180°
f	S	SW	

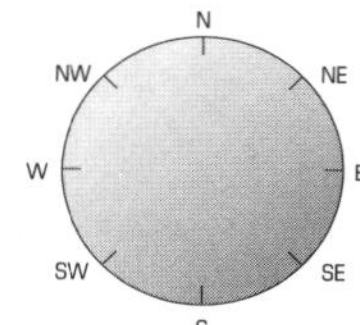

3 A shape is translated 2 units to the right, 3 units down and 4 units to the left.
Describe this translation with only two instructions.

4 Copy this grid and the triangle.
Rotate the triangle:
a through 90° clockwise about the point (0, 3)
b through 90° anticlockwise about the point (2, 0)

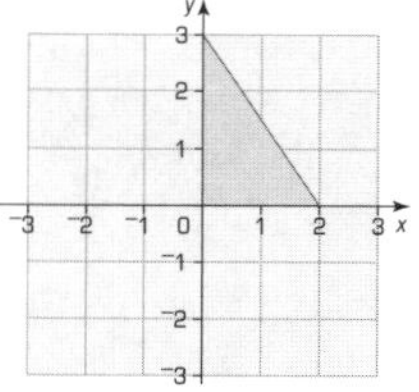

5 Translate the triangle in question 4 using the instructions in question 3.
What are the coordinates of the translated shape?

Exercise commentary

The questions assess Primary Framework Pages 107, 109 and 111.

Problem solving

Questions 3 and 5 assess Primary Framework Page 81 if students generalise.

Group work

Some students would benefit from discussing question 4 in pairs.

Misconceptions

The misconceptions identified throughout the unit will apply here too, in particular:

- Rotations are hard to visualise
- Mixing up direction of turns
- Translating the wrong distance

It is important to have tracing paper and mirrors available to help students check their diagrams.

In addition, students tend to see all congruent shapes as translations, confusing the terms translation and transformation. Discuss ways of remembering that a translation is a slide as a class to share good ideas.

Links

2-D shapes: Primary Framework Page 103.
Angles: Page 111.

Homework

S4.6HW provides practice at identifying transformations of congruent shapes.

Answers

1 **a** Isosceles triangle **b** Regular hexagon **c** Heart
2 **a** 90° clockwise **b** 90° anticlockwise **c** 180°
d S **e** NE **f** 45° clockwise
3 2 units left and 3 units down
5 ($^-2$, 0), ($^-2$, $^-3$), (0, $^-3$)

Summary

The Year 6 key teaching objective is:

- Read and plot coordinates in all four quadrants (109).

Plenary activity

On S4.6OHP:

- Describe transformations and ask students to draw the image you describe.

Check out commentary

1 The inclusion of negative coordinates can confuse students.
Emphasise that for the first coordinate you count across (a comes first in the alphabet) and that the lines are numbered which makes it easier to see where the negative coordinates are.

2 Students tend to see all transformations as translations, taking 'translate' to mean move.
Emphasise that a turn and a flip are moves. Encourage students to describe how the right angle of the shape moves to the new position and then to check their definition works with another vertex.
Emphasise the need to describe the transformation as fully as possible and to check with a partner whether the definition works.

3 Students need to take a structured approach to this problem, ensuring they consider all possibilities.
Using multilink cubes may help students to visualise the different orientations possible.
Some students will confuse line symmetry with rotational symmetry. Encourage students to draw the completed shapes on squared paper and to use a mirror to check lines of symmetry.

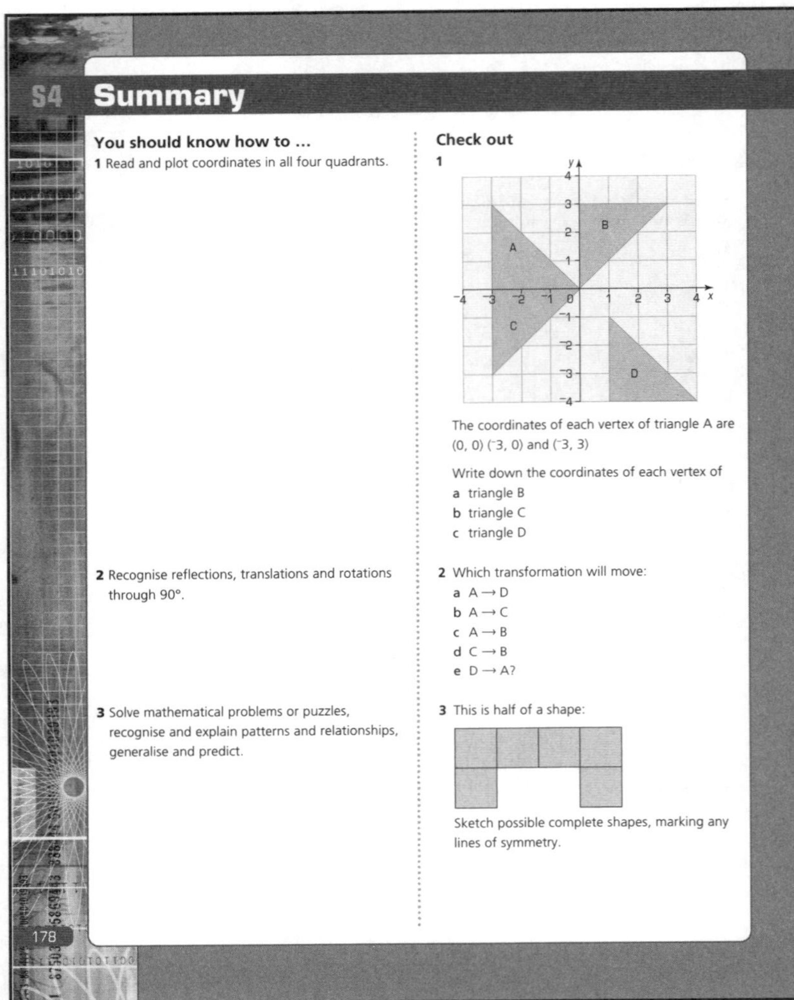

S4 **Summary**

You should know how to ...

1 Read and plot coordinates in all four quadrants.

2 Recognise reflections, translations and rotations through 90°.

3 Solve mathematical problems or puzzles, recognise and explain patterns and relationships, generalise and predict.

Check out

1

The coordinates of each vertex of triangle A are (0, 0) (⁻3, 0) and (⁻3, 3)

Write down the coordinates of each vertex of

a triangle B
b triangle C
c triangle D

2 Which transformation will move:

a A → D
b A → C
c A → B
d C → B
e D → A?

3 This is half of a shape:

Sketch possible complete shapes, marking any lines of symmetry.

178

Development

The themes of the unit are developed in S5 where students study symmetry properties of shapes.

Links

Students use coordinates in all four quadrants in A5.
Transformations of congruent shapes are used to produce patterns in Technology (Graphic Design).

Mental starters

Objectives covered in this unit:

- Multiply and divide by 10, 100.
- Round numbers.
- Recall multiplication and division facts to 10 × 10.
- Use doubling and halving to calculate.
- Use factors to multiply mentally.
- Derive answers to calculations.
- Multiply a two-digit number by a one-digit number.

Resources needed * class set needed

Essential:
N5.2OHP – Rectangular arrays
N5.3OHP – Dividing by factors
N5.4OHP – Grid method
N5.5OHP – Repeated subtraction
N5.6OHP – Fraction equivalences
N5.8OHP – Fractions of 60
Calculators

Useful:
R1* – Digit cards
R3 – Fraction cards
R4 (OHP) – Place value table
R6 (OHP) – Number lines
R17 (OHP) – Ruler
A3.2OHP – Arrangements of 36
N5.1ICT* – Rounding in Excel
Rulers

N5 More number calculations

This unit will show you how to:

- Round positive whole numbers to the nearest 10, 100 or 1000 and decimals to the nearest whole number or one decimal place.
- Recognise multiples up to 10 ×10.
- Recognise prime numbers to at least 20.
- Factorise numbers up to 100.
- Reduce a fraction to its simplest form by cancelling common factors.
- Use a fraction as an operator.
- Compare and order simple fractions.
- Use decimal notation for tenths and hundredths.
- Find simple percentages of quantities.
- Recognise the equivalence of fraction and decimal forms.
- Understand the effect of and relationships between the four operations, and the principles of the arithmetic laws as they apply to multiplication.
- Approximate first. Use informal pencil and paper methods to support, record, or explain multiplications and divisions.
- Extend written methods of multiplication and division.
- Use the vocabulary of estimation and approximation.
- Consolidate and extend mental calculation strategies.
- Explain methods and reasoning.

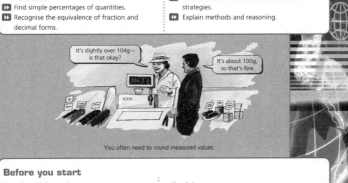

It's slightly over 104g – is that okay?

It's about 100g, so that's fine.

104.3 g

You often need to round measured values.

Before you start

You should know how to …

1 Recall 10 × 10 time table facts.

2 Convert between fractions and percentages.

Check in

1 Work out:
 a 5 × 5 **b** 6 × 6 **c** 30 ÷ 6
 d 28 ÷ 7 **e** 9 × 8 **f** 81 ÷ 9

2 Change these fractions to percentages:
 a $\frac{1}{2}$ **b** $\frac{1}{4}$ **c** $\frac{3}{4}$ **d** $\frac{1}{10}$ **e** $\frac{7}{10}$ **f** $\frac{1}{5}$
 Change these fractions to percentages:
 g $\frac{31}{100}$ **h** $\frac{63}{100}$ **i** $\frac{7}{100}$ **j** $\frac{1}{2}$ **k** $\frac{1}{4}$ **l** $\frac{1}{10}$

179

Unit commentary

Aim of the unit

This unit consolidates the number work studied in this book. Students find factors, multiples and primes, and use them to simplify mental calculations including those involving fractions, decimals and percentages. Students practice written methods of calculation and choose to use them appropriately, estimating answers.

Introduction

Discuss when measures or quantities can be estimated or approximated and when they need to be given exactly. This will depend on the context: you need to know exactly how much you will earn but only roughly how many people were at the match.

Framework references

This unit focuses on:

- Year 6 teaching objectives pages: 11, 13, 19, 21, 23, 25, 29, 31, 33, 53, 55, 59, 61, 63, 65, 67, 69
- Problem solving objectives page: 77

The unit provides access to:

- Year 7 teaching objectives pages: 52, 54, 88–106, 110

Check in activity

Ask students for the odd one out of these groups of four:

$\frac{1}{4}$, $\frac{3}{12}$, 25%, 0.4
$\frac{3}{5}$, $\frac{6}{10}$, 60%, 35%
$\frac{3}{10}$, 3%, 30%, $\frac{6}{20}$
15%, $\frac{1}{15}$, $\frac{3}{20}$, 0.15

Differentiation

Core tier focuses on extending mental and written methods including using fractions, decimals and percentages.

Springboard 7

Pages 307, 344–348, 475–480, 482–486, 493.

N5.1 Rounding

Mental starter

Rounding stand up

Go around the class giving each student a number, such as 100, 200, 300, 100, 200, 300 ...

Call out some numbers, such as 242.

Students stand up if this number rounds to them, to the nearest 100.

You can vary the numbers and the degree of accuracy.

Useful resources

R6 may be useful to discuss rounding.

Rulers may be useful for rounding decimals.

R17 has a ruler to use for ordering decimals.

Introductory activity

Ask students what they understand by the word 'rounding'.

When would you use it?

Have any of the students used rounding or estimation before?

Write a football match crowd attendance on the board, for example 8357.

Ask students for the attendance:

- to the nearest 1000
- to the nearest 100
- to the nearest 10.

It might help if you use a number line. **R6** contains number lines which you can use to zoom in to the nearest 10, 100 or 1000.

Discuss the idea of halfway being rounded up.

Extend the discussion to decimals.

Keep these to 1 decimal place, and demonstrate with a number line marked in units (you could use R6).

You could also demonstrate decimals with a ruler. For example, 3.7 cm is clearly closer to 4 cm when you look at a ruler – use **R17**.

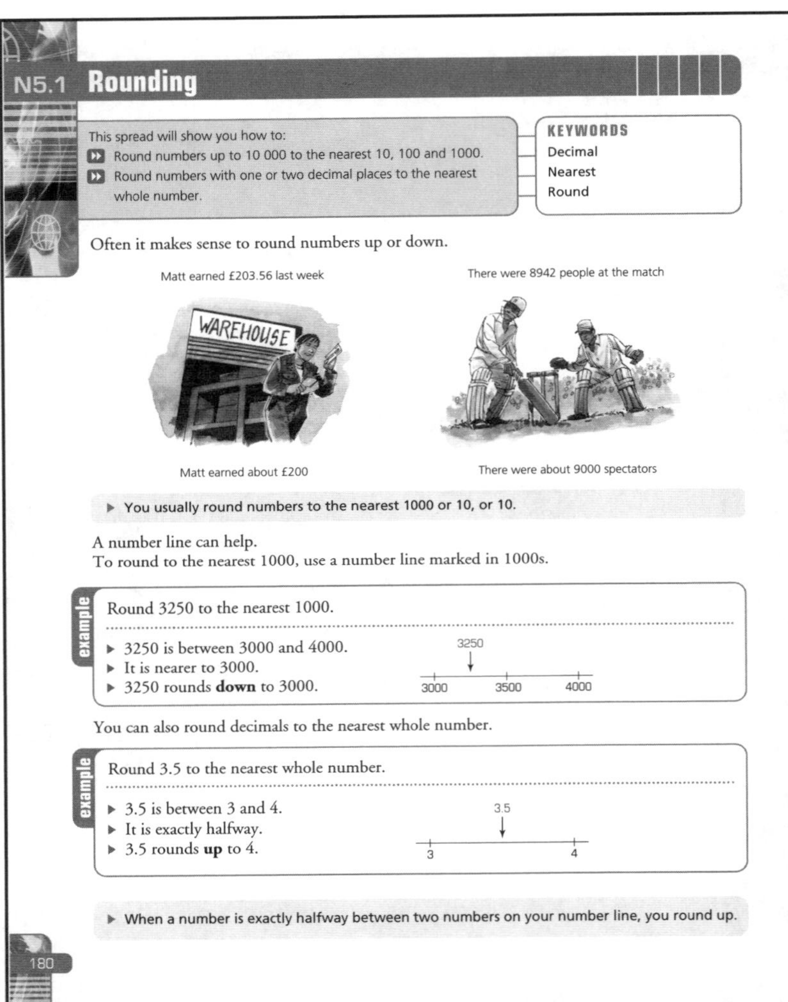

N5.1 **Rounding**

This spread will show you how to:

- Round numbers up to 10 000 to the nearest 10, 100 and 1000.
- Round numbers with one or two decimal places to the nearest whole number.

KEYWORDS
Decimal
Nearest
Round

Often it makes sense to round numbers up or down.

Matt earned £203.56 last week

There were 8942 people at the match

Matt earned about £200

There were about 9000 spectators

- You usually round numbers to the nearest 1000 or 10, or 10.

A number line can help.
To round to the nearest 1000, use a number line marked in 1000s.

example

Round 3250 to the nearest 1000.

- 3250 is between 3000 and 4000.
- It is nearer to 3000.
- 3250 rounds **down** to 3000.

You can also round decimals to the nearest whole number.

example

Round 3.5 to the nearest whole number.

- 3.5 is between 3 and 4.
- It is exactly halfway.
- 3.5 rounds **up** to 4.

- When a number is exactly halfway between two numbers on your number line, you round up.

180

Plenary

Play 'Rounding stand up' again, but this time with rounding to the nearest whole number from 1 dp.

Use the context of money to round amounts to the nearest £1.

Further activities

In **N5.1ICT**, students use Excel to round numbers and are shown how to use the rounded values to produce estimates.

Differentiation

Support questions:

- Questions 1 –3 focus on whole number rounding. Springboard 7, page 307.
- Questions 3–7 focus on rounding using decimals and in context. Springboard 7, page 344.
- Question 8 focuses on finding numbers that will round to give a particular answer. Springboard 7, pages 345, 346.

Core tier: focuses on rounding to the nearest whole number and 1 dp.

Exercise N5.1

1 Round these numbers to the nearest 10.

a 21	**b** 53	**c** 67	**d** 89	**e** 55	**f** 45
g 99	**h** 127	**i** 253	**j** 3	**k** 7	**l** 1563

2 Round these numbers to the nearest 100.

a 167	**b** 293	**c** 832	**d** 749	**e** 350	**f** 150
g 907	**h** 951	**i** 1371	**j** 82	**k** 31	**l** 2593

3 Round these numbers to the nearest 1000.

a 5200	**b** 5907	**c** 1350	**d** 2795	**e** 12 302	**f** 950
g 3500	**h** 7500	**i** 172	**j** 3962	**k** 9563	**l** 29 807

4 Round these numbers to the nearest whole number.

a 3.2	**b** 7.8	**c** 4.5	**d** 12.3	**e** 18.59	**f** 3.8
g 21.5	**h** 0.8	**i** 0.2	**j** 9.8	**k** 29.3	**l** 99.5

5 Round the heights of these people to the nearest 10 cm.

6 These are the results of a 400 m race.

1st	Jim	48.3 secs	2nd	Joe	48.8
3rd	Bill	49.2	4th	Mac	49.4
5th	Samir	49.9	6th	Nick	50.1
7th	David	53.5	8th	Tom	54.1

Round each of the times to the nearest second.

7 The crowd at a football match was 3752. Round this number to the nearest 1000.

8 For each question use the numbers only once. You do not have to use them all.

6 9 3 7 5

a Make a number that will round to 690 to the nearest 10.
b Make as many numbers as you can that will round to 570 to the nearest 10.
c Make as many numbers as you can that will round to 5700 to the nearest 100.

181

Exercise commentary

The questions assess the objectives on Primary Framework Pages 13 and 31.

Problem solving
Question 8 assesses Primary Framework Page 79.

Group work
Question 8 is suitable for pair work.

Misconceptions
Students get confused when rounding, looking at the wrong place, for example: 127 = 200 because 7 > 5.
Encourage students to use a number line rather than an algorithm.
A place value table can help students look at the number in a structured way.
Another common error is to round down, for example: 53 rounds down to 40.
Again the use of a number line can help.
Choosing the correct numbers to place on the number line is vital to success.
Supportive questioning can help:

- How many thousands are there in 5200?
- Is it more or less than 5000?
- What should the labels on the line be?

Links
Place value: Primary Framework Page 7.

Homework

N5.1HW provides practice at rounding in context.

Answers

1 **a** 20 **b** 50 **c** 70 **d** 90 **e** 60 **f** 50 **g** 100 **h** 130 **i** 250 **j** 0 **k** 10 **l** 1560
2 **a** 200 **b** 300 **c** 800 **d** 700 **e** 400 **f** 200 **g** 900 **h** 1000 **i** 1400 **j** 100 **k** 0 **l** 2600 **3** **a** 5000 **b** 6000 **c** 1000 **d** 3000 **e** 12 000 **f** 1000 **g** 4000 **h** 8000 **i** 0 **j** 4000 **k** 10 000 **l** 30 000
4 **a** 3 **b** 8 **c** 5 **d** 12 **e** 19 **f** 4 **g** 22 **h** 1 **i** 0 **j** 10 **k** 29 **l** 100
5 Baby Jack: 80 cm, Sarah: 110 cm, Ewan: 110 cm, Middle Jack: 140 cm, Esther: 140 cm, Big Jack: 180 cm **6** 48, 49, 49, 49, 50, 50, 54, 54 **7** 4000
8 **a** 693 **b** 573, 567, 569 **c** 5673, 5679, 5693, 5697, 5736, 5739

N5.2 Factors, multiples and primes

Mental starter

Areas

- Sketch a rectangle on the board.
- Tell students you will give them the length and width and they must find the area.
- Use easy numbers to check understanding.
- Ask for the length given the area and width.

Useful resources

N5.2OHP shows factors as rectangular arrays for discussion.
A3.2OHP shows rectangular arrays of 36.

Introductory activity

Recap the 8 times table.
Emphasize that 8, 16, 24 etc. are multiples of 8.

Ask for the first four multiples of 6.
Emphasise that the 4th multiple of 6 means 4 × 6.

Introduce the term 'factor'.
Write the statement □ × □ = 16.

- Ask what could go in the boxes.
- Write down the multiplications.
- List the factors 1, 2, 4, 8, 16.

Ask for the factors of:
a 12 **b** 11

Refer to the mental starter.
Discuss the link between the area and lengths of a rectangle, and a number and its factors.

Illustrate the factors of 12 and 11 with rectangular patterns of dots.
You could use **N5.2OHP**.
Point out that you can make three rectangles with 12 but only one with 11, because it only has two factors.

Explain that 11 is a prime number.
Define a prime number as a number that has just two factors: 1 and itself.

Ask for other prime numbers.
Ask if 87 is a prime number, and how you could tell.
A3.2OHP shows arrays of 36 and can be used to reinforce factors or to introduce square numbers.

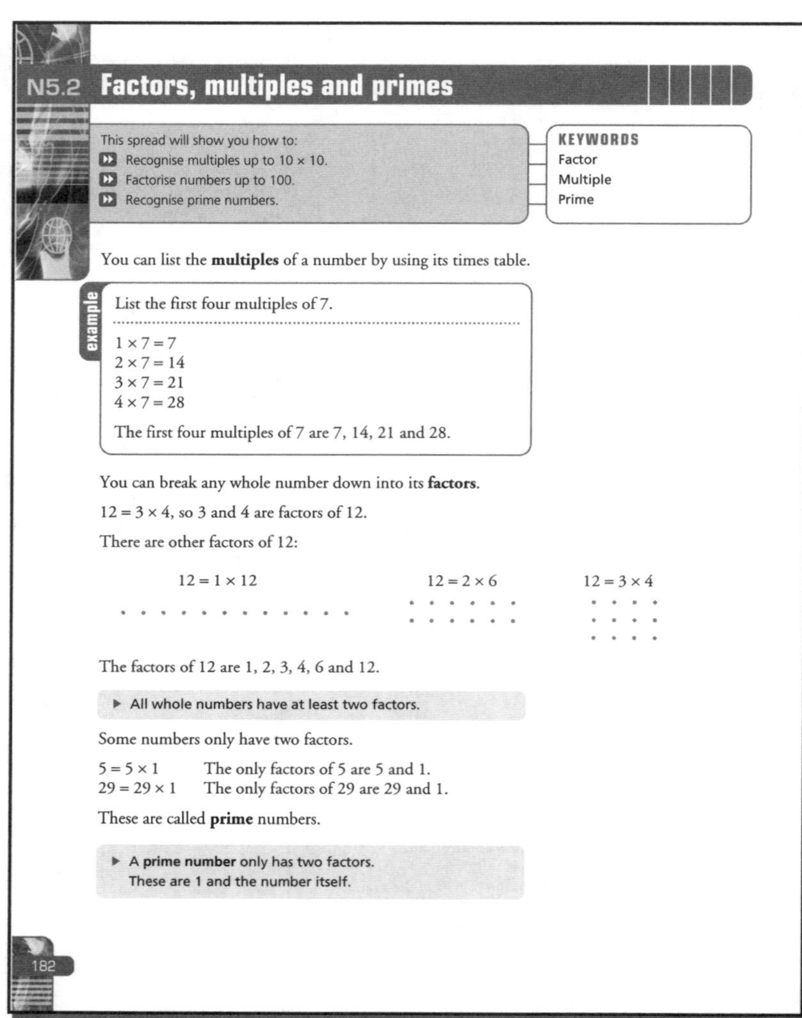

N5.2 **Factors, multiples and primes**

This spread will show you how to:
- Recognise multiples up to 10 × 10.
- Factorise numbers up to 100.
- Recognise prime numbers.

KEYWORDS
Factor
Multiple
Prime

You can list the **multiples** of a number by using its times table.

example

List the first four multiples of 7.

1 × 7 = 7
2 × 7 = 14
3 × 7 = 21
4 × 7 = 28

The first four multiples of 7 are 7, 14, 21 and 28.

You can break any whole number down into its **factors**.

12 = 3 × 4, so 3 and 4 are factors of 12.

There are other factors of 12:

12 = 1 × 12   12 = 2 × 6   12 = 3 × 4

The factors of 12 are 1, 2, 3, 4, 6 and 12.

- All whole numbers have at least two factors.

Some numbers only have two factors.

5 = 5 × 1   The only factors of 5 are 5 and 1.
29 = 29 × 1   The only factors of 29 are 29 and 1.

These are called **prime** numbers.

- A **prime number** only has two factors. These are 1 and the number itself.

182

Plenary

Write the whole numbers from 30 to 50 on the board.

- Ask students to identify the prime numbers.
- Students justify their answers.
- Encourage them to use the key words in their discussion: multiple, factor, prime.

Further activities

Extend question 7 by asking for numbers with 3, 7, 8 and 9 factors.
Encourage students to be systematic and to look at numbers over 100.

Differentiation

Support questions:

- Question 1 revises Year 4 and 5 objectives.
- Questions 2–5 focus on recognising factors, multiples and prime numbers.
- Questions 6 and 7 require a good understanding of how to find multiples and factors.

Core tier: focuses on HCF and LCM.

Exercise N5.2

1 Write down the first five multiples and the 10th multiple of:
a 2 **b** 5 **c** 6 **d** 3 **e** 9 **f** 8

2 Write down all the factors of:
a 7 **b** 6 **c** 8 **d** 12 **e** 15
f 11 **g** 20 **h** 21 **i** 30

3 Think of the numbers on a dice.
Which numbers are :
a Multiples of 2
b Prime numbers
c Factors of 9
d Factors of 24?

4 Look at this list of numbers.
8, 9, 10, 11, 12, 13, 14, 15, 16, 17, 18, 19, 20
Which numbers are:
a Multiples of 4
b Multiples of 6
c Prime numbers
d Multiples of both 3 and 4
e Multiples of both 2 and 5
f Factors of both 6 and 15?

5 Look at this list of numbers.
19, 20, 21, 22, 23, 24, 25, 26, 27, 28, 29, 30
Which numbers are:
a Multiples of 3
b Multiples of 4
c Multiples of both 3 and 4
d Factors of 60
e Prime numbers?

6 Work out what these numbers are and place them in order starting with the smallest.
a The 5th multiple of 7
b The 4th multiple of 8
c The 9th multiple of 3
d The 2nd multiple of 10

7 **Investigation**
Find a number that has
a 4 factors **b** 5 factors **c** 6 factors **d** 10 factors

183

Exercise commentary

The questions assess the objectives on Primary Framework Pages 19 and 21.

Problem solving

Questions 3–5 assess Primary Framework Page 77 if students are encouraged to explain their reasoning.

Group work

Question 7 is suitable for pair work.

Misconceptions

Students often leave out 1 and the number when listing factors.
Encourage a systematic approach always starting with 1.
Students find it difficult to spot factors when the numbers are large, missing out 3 as a factor of 48.
Emphasise that any number in the list such as 6 and 12 will have factors that should also be in the list. This develops to the idea of breaking a number down into its prime factors.
In question 3 students will often list 1 as a prime number.
Emphasise the definition of a prime number and have a list of them displayed in the classroom for reinforcement.

Links

Multiplication and division: Primary Framework Page 59.

Homework

N5.2HW is an activity entitled 'Sieve of Eratosthenes', which enables students to identify all the prime numbers up to 100.

Answers

1 **a** 2, 4, 6, 8, 10, 20 **b** 5, 10, 15, 20, 25, 50 **c** 6, 12, 18, 24, 30, 60
d 3, 6, 9, 12, 15, 30 **e** 9, 18, 27, 36, 45, 90 **f** 8, 16, 24, 32, 40, 80
2 **a** 1, 7 **b** 1, 2, 3, 6 **c** 1, 2, 4, 8 **d** 1, 2, 3, 4, 6, 12 **e** 1, 3, 5, 15
f 1, 11 **g** 1, 2, 4, 5, 10, 20 **h** 1, 3, 7, 21 **i** 1, 2, 3, 5, 6, 10, 15, 30
3 **a** 2, 4, 6 **b** 2, 3, 5 **c** 1, 3 **d** 1, 2, 3, 4, 6
4 **a** 8, 12, 16, 20 **b** 12, 18 **c** 11, 13, 17, 19 **d** 12 **e** 10, 20 **f** 1, 3
5 **a** 21, 24, 27, 30 **b** 20, 24, 28 **c** 24 **d** 20, 30 **e** 19, 23, 29
6 **a** 35 **b** 32 **c** 27 **d** 20, 20, 27, 32, 35

Mental starter

Write these questions on the board and ask students to give the answers to the ones they can do. They can show their answers using **R1** digit cards, or verbally.

2×4	20×4	2×40	20×40
2×400	20×400	200×40	200×4

Discuss how they get their answers.

Useful resources

R1 digit cards for student response in the mental starter.

N5.3OHP shows the factor and partition methods.

Introductory activity

Build from the mental starter by writing down the product 32 × 30.

Ask how students would work this out in their heads.

Discuss any strategies that they suggest.

Encourage use of the factor method.

Illustrate it with the example:

$32 \times 30 = 32 \times 10 \times 3$

$= 320 \times 3$

$= 960$

Emphasise that you have made the problem simpler by splitting one of the numbers into its factors.

Discuss how you can use the factor method with division.

Try $96 \div 16$:

$96 \div 2 = 48 \qquad 48 \div 8 = 6$

Illustrate the partition method with a variation of the initial example, 32 × 12.

Discuss strategies with students.

Write down and explain:

$32 \times 12 = 32 \times 10 + 32 \times 2$

You could include the factor method as well with 32×20.

Show how the partition method can be used for division.

This will lead into N5.5.

You could illustrate with example **b** at the foot of the student page.

This is an extension of the repeated subtraction method from N3.6.

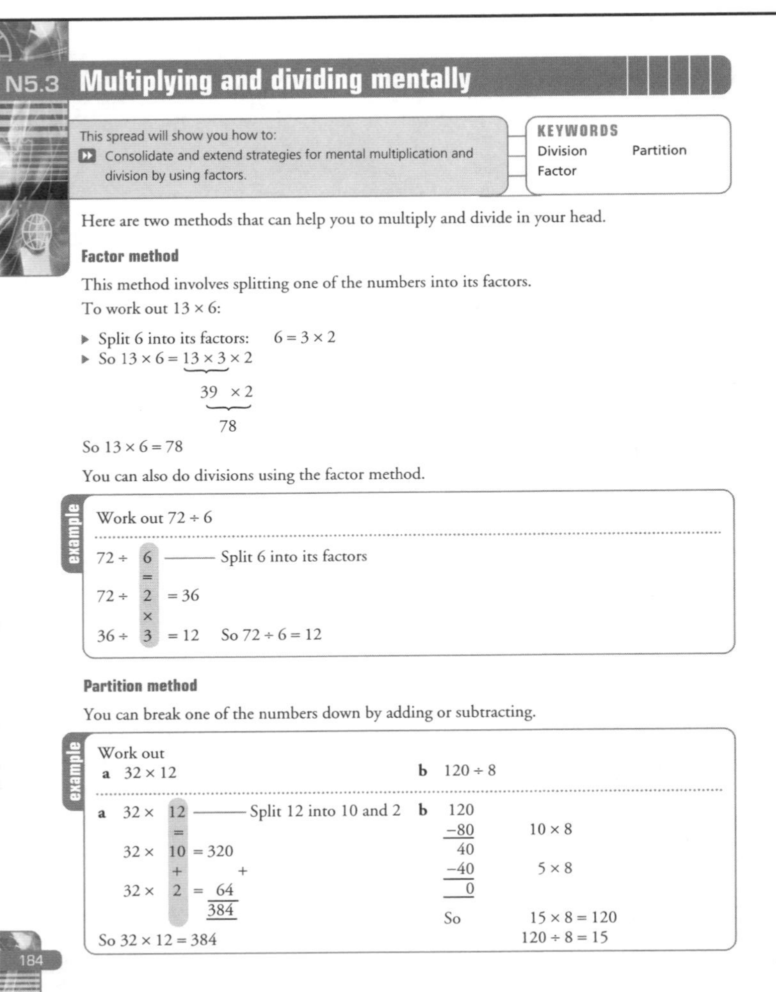

N5.3 Multiplying and dividing mentally

This spread will show you how to:

- Consolidate and extend strategies for mental multiplication and division by using factors.

KEYWORDS: Division, Partition, Factor

Here are two methods that can help you to multiply and divide in your head.

Factor method

This method involves splitting one of the numbers into its factors.

To work out 13×6:

- Split 6 into its factors: $6 = 3 \times 2$
- So $13 \times 6 = 13 \times 3 \times 2$

39×2

78

So $13 \times 6 = 78$

You can also do divisions using the factor method.

example

Work out $72 \div 6$

$72 \div 6$ — Split 6 into its factors ($6 = 2 \times 3$)

$72 \div 2 = 36$

$36 \div 3 = 12 \qquad$ So $72 \div 6 = 12$

Partition method

You can break one of the numbers down by adding or subtracting.

example

Work out

a 32×12 **b** $120 \div 8$

a 32×12 — Split 12 into 10 and 2 ($12 = 10 + 2$)

$32 \times 10 = 320$

$32 \times 2 = 64$

$320 + 64 = 384$

So $32 \times 12 = 384$

b

120	
−80	10 × 8
40	
−40	5 × 8
0	

So $15 \times 8 = 120$

$120 \div 8 = 15$

184

Plenary

Put a product on the board such as 22×18.

Ask students how they would do it.

Some will choose the factor method and others may choose the partition method.

Encourage students to suggest $(22 \times 20) - (22 \times 2)$.

Emphasise that you can partition by subtraction as well as addition.

Further activities

Students work in pairs to find 56×9, one using $56 \times 3 \times 3$ and the other using $56 \times 10 - 56 \times 1$. Students then compare methods and decide which is the easiest and most successful one and why.

Differentiation

Support questions:

- Question 1 revises multiplying by single digits and multiples of 10. Springboard 7, page 475.
- Questions 2 – 6 focus on consolidating mental methods of multiplication and division. Springboard 7, pages 476, 478.
- Questions 7 – 10 focus on applying methods in a problem solving context. Springboard 7, pages 477, 479.

Core tier: focuses on multiplying decimals and using divisibility tests.

Exercise N5.3

Do questions 1–3 using the factor method.

1 a 23×20 $(20 = 2 \times 10)$
b 31×30 $(30 = 3 \times 10)$
c 25×6 $(6 = 2 \times 3)$
d 32×8
e 43×20
f 45×30

2 a $84 \div 8$ $(\div 2 \text{ then } \div 4)$
b $96 \div 6$ $(\div 3 \text{ then } \div 2)$
c $252 \div 12$ $(\div 3 \text{ then } \div 4)$
d $288 \div 9$
e $126 \div 6$
f $372 \div 12$

3 a 42×4 b $156 \div 6$ c 3.5×20
d 4.2×30 e $330 \div 15$ f 5.3×40

Do questions 4–6 using the partition method.

4 a 21×12 b 24×13 c 33×12
d 22×22 e 51×14 f 3.5×21

5 a $390 \div 13$ b $264 \div 12$ c $1331 \div 11$
d $433 \div 13$ e $467 \div 15$ f $450 \div 14$

6 a 55×13 b $417 \div 14$ c 4.5×31
d 27×22 e 121×14 f $609 \div 12$

In questions 7–10 choose the most appropriate method to UK.

7 Eight people go on a coach trip for the day.
They each pay £63.
How much do they pay in total?

8 Jim buys 20 pizzas at £2.25 each.
How much does he spend in total?

9 Harry buys 21 CDs at £12 each.
How much does he spend in total?

10 Gina buys 8 CDs at £10.99 each.
How much does she spend in total?

185

Exercise commentary

The questions assess the objectives on Primary Framework Pages 61 and 63.

Problem solving

Questions 7–10 assess Primary Framework Page 77 if students explain their reasoning, and Page 85.

Group work

The further activity is suitable for pairs.

Misconceptions

Students find it hard to keep track when there are a few steps in the working.

It is important to encourage students to make jottings (that can lead to formal written methods) and lay their work out in a logical way.

Students also fail to choose easy factors or multiples to work with, or use the factors in an order that doesn't simplify the work.

Encourage students to think about facts they know or can work out mentally and then to find a way to build on them.

In questions 7–10 students need to choose the best method to use.

Emphasise that a good method is successful and brief.

Links

Multiplication and division facts: Primary Framework Page 59.

Tests of divisibility: Page 19.

Homework

N5.3HW provides practice at multiplying and dividing mentally.

Answers

1 a 460 b 930 c 150 d 256 e 860 f 1350
2 a 10.5 b 16 c 21 d 32 e 21 f 31
3 a 168 b 26 c 70 d 126 e 22 f 212
4 a 252 b 312 c 396 d 484 e 714 f 73.5
5 a 30 b 22 c 121 d 33 r 4 e 31 r 2 f 32 r 2
6 a 715 b 29 r 11 c 139.5 d 594 e 1694 f 50 r 9
7 £504 8 £45 9 £252 10 £87.92

Mental starter

Two times one

- Ask students to work out 2-digit × 1-digit calculations in their heads: 91 × 5.
- Discuss successful strategies.
- Emphasise partitioning.

Useful resources

N5.4OHP contains blank grids for use in explaining the grid method.
R1 digit cards for the mental starter.

Introductory activity

The mental starter recaps the previous lesson, particularly the different ways of multiplying.
Explain that the focus of this lesson will be written methods of multiplication.

Ask how students would solve 23 × 24.
First ask for an estimate.
In this case it could be 20 × 20 = 400
Discuss strategies, and suggest a written method based on partitioning.

- Draw a grid:

×	20	3
20		
4		

- Ask a student to show how they would fill it in.
- Discuss why you add them up at the end.

Ask why the estimate (400) is quite a bit lower than the answer (552).
Encourage the response that both the estimated numbers were lower than the originals.

Extend the grid method to 3-digit numbers.
You can use the example in the student book.
N5.4OHP contains blank grids for use with different-sized numbers.

Extend the grid method to decimals.
You could refer to the example in the student book.
Encourage students to check their answers.

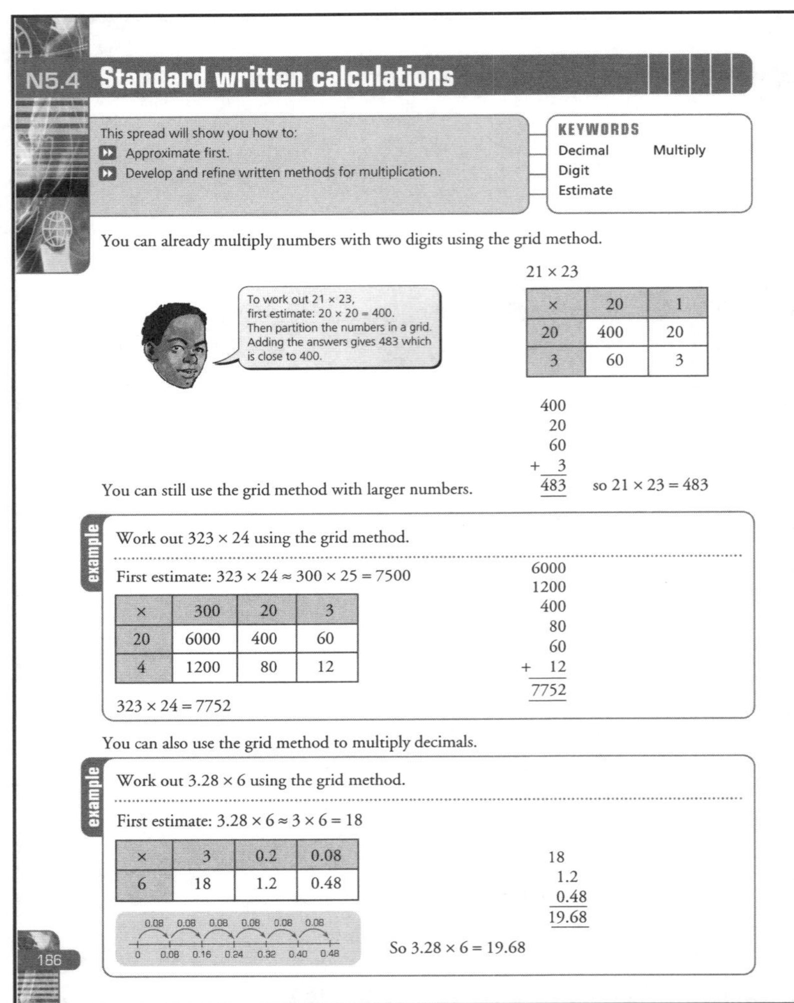

N5.4 **Standard written calculations**

This spread will show you how to:
- Approximate first.
- Develop and refine written methods for multiplication.

KEYWORDS
Decimal
Digit
Estimate
Multiply

You can already multiply numbers with two digits using the grid method.

To work out 21 × 23,
first estimate: 20 × 20 = 400.
Then partition the numbers in a grid.
Adding the answers gives 483 which
is close to 400.

21 × 23

×	20	1
20	400	20
3	60	3

400
20
60
+ 3
483 so 21 × 23 = 483

You can still use the grid method with larger numbers.

example

Work out 323 × 24 using the grid method.

First estimate: 323 × 24 ≈ 300 × 25 = 7500

×	300	20	3
20	6000	400	60
4	1200	80	12

6000
1200
400
80
60
+ 12
7752

323 × 24 = 7752

You can also use the grid method to multiply decimals.

example

Work out 3.28 × 6 using the grid method.

First estimate: 3.28 × 6 ≈ 3 × 6 = 18

×	3	0.2	0.08
6	18	1.2	0.48

18
1.2
0.48
19.68

So 3.28 × 6 = 19.68

186

Plenary

Write down a question and offer four possible answers.
Question: 31.3 × 5
Answers: 156.5, 1565, 15.65, 15.7

Discuss how you could find the correct answer without doing the calculation.
Encourage responses connected with estimation, and even a last-digit check.

Further activities

Challenge students to find the three-digit by two-digit multiplication that gives the closest answer to 5000 using the digits: 1, 2, 3, 4, 5.

Differentiation

Support questions:

- Question 1 focuses on two-digit by one- or two-digit calculations.
- Questions 2–4 focus on three-digit by two-digit whole-number problems. Springboard 7, page 482.
- Questions 5–8 include decimals and complex problems. Springboard 7, page 483.

Core tier: focuses on multiplying with decimals to 2 dp.

Exercise commentary

The questions assess the objectives on Primary Framework Pages 67 and 69.

Problem solving

Questions 3, 4 and 6 assess Primary Framework Page 85. Question 7 assesses Pages 77 and 79. Question 8 and the further activity assess Page 79.

Group work

Questions 7 and 8 and the further activity are suitable for pair or group work.

Misconceptions

Students place the numbers on the grid wrongly or add the numbers up wrongly. Using a place value table may help students see how to partition the numbers. Supportive questioning will help:

- How many digits does 217 have?
- So how many columns will you need?

Encourage students to estimate before calculating and emphasise that this often leads to the first number in the table!

Students may multiply successfully for most of the problem but then add to find the bottom right answer.

Encourage students to check answers with a calculator and to find where the error is when a mistake is made.

Links

Multiplication facts: Primary Framework Page 59. Estimation: Page 11. Checking calculations: Page 73.

Exercise N5.4

1 Use the grid method to work out these questions.

a	21 × 4	b	35 × 4
c	42 × 5	d	83 × 4
e	72 × 5	f	81 × 6
g	22 × 32	h	25 × 23
i	32 × 34	j	56 × 38
k	37 × 26	l	95 × 78

2 Work out the answers to these questions.

a	217 × 31	b	315 × 24
c	422 × 25	d	153 × 35
e	325 × 42	f	527 × 31
g	325 × 38	h	577 × 27
i	627 × 35	j	895 × 56
k	343 × 32	l	415 × 26

3 A school trip costs £325.
25 pupils go on the trip.
How much do the pupils pay in total?

4 The head gardener of a park buys 375 trees each costing £27.
How much does he pay for the trees in total?

5 Work out the answers to these using the grid method.

a	32.5 × 7	b	25.7 × 8	c	2.75 × 6	d	8.25 × 3
e	2.91 × 9	f	8.35 × 7	g	2.32 × 7	h	52.1 × 8
i	43.5 × 4	j	4.13 × 8	k	35.7 × 7	l	29.2 × 6

6 A record shop owner buys 85 CDs each costing £5.75.
How much does he pay in total for the CDs?

7 One of these numbers is the answer to 347 × 27:

8249 899 9369 3642 134 799 1439

a Write down which number you think is the answer.
b Work out 347 × 27 by the grid method to check whether you are correct.

8 In each question, three of the four multiplications give the same answer.
Find the odd one out.

a

52 × 86	104 × 43
63 × 74	26 × 172

b

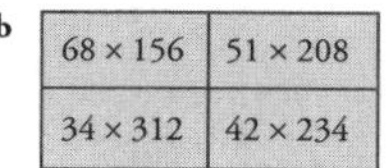

68 × 156	51 × 208
34 × 312	42 × 234

187

Homework

N5.4HW is a problem-solving activity based on multiplying decimals.

Answers

1 a 84 b 140 c 210 d 332 e 360 f 486 g 704
h 575 i 1088 j 2128 k 962 l 7410
2 a 6727 b 7560 c 10 550 d 5355 e 13 650 f 16 337
g 12 350 h 15 579 i 21 945 j 50 120 k 10 976 l 10 790
3 £8125 4 £10 125
5 a 227.5 b 205.6 c 16.5 d 24.75 e 26.19 f 58.45
g 16.24 h 416.8 i 174 j 33.04 k 249.9 l 175.2
6 £488.75 7 b 9369 8 a 63 × 74 b 42 × 234

Mental starter

How many ...?

- Give students a 2-digit ÷ 1-digit calculation to do quickly in their heads. You could ask: how many 3s in 24?
- Discuss successful strategies.
- Emphasise recognising factors and the relationship between × and ÷.
- Encourage use of tests of divisibility when factors are not recognised.

Useful resources

N5.5OHP illustrates the repeated subtraction method for use in the introductory activity.
R1 digit cards for the mental starter.

Introductory activity

Refer to the mental starter.
Discuss the relationship between division and multiplication.
Illustrate with an example that division is the opposite of multiplication.
Discuss how you can use this fact to divide mentally with small numbers.

Emphasise that this lesson will focus on a written method of division.

Introduce or recap the repeated subtraction method.
Use the example 120 ÷ 8 on **N5.5OHP**, and go through each stage in the subtraction.

```
8)120
   80      10 × 8
   40
   40       5 × 8
    0
           15 × 8 = 120
```

Show **N5.5OHP**, which shows how 120 has been split into two chunks comprising 15 lots of 8, or 15 × 8.

Explain that this is equivalent to
120 ÷ 8 = 15

Introduce a problem involving a remainder.
You could just adapt the previous problem by making it 121 ÷ 8.
Make necessary alterations to the working and add to the OHP if used.
N5.5OHP shows the example from the student book.

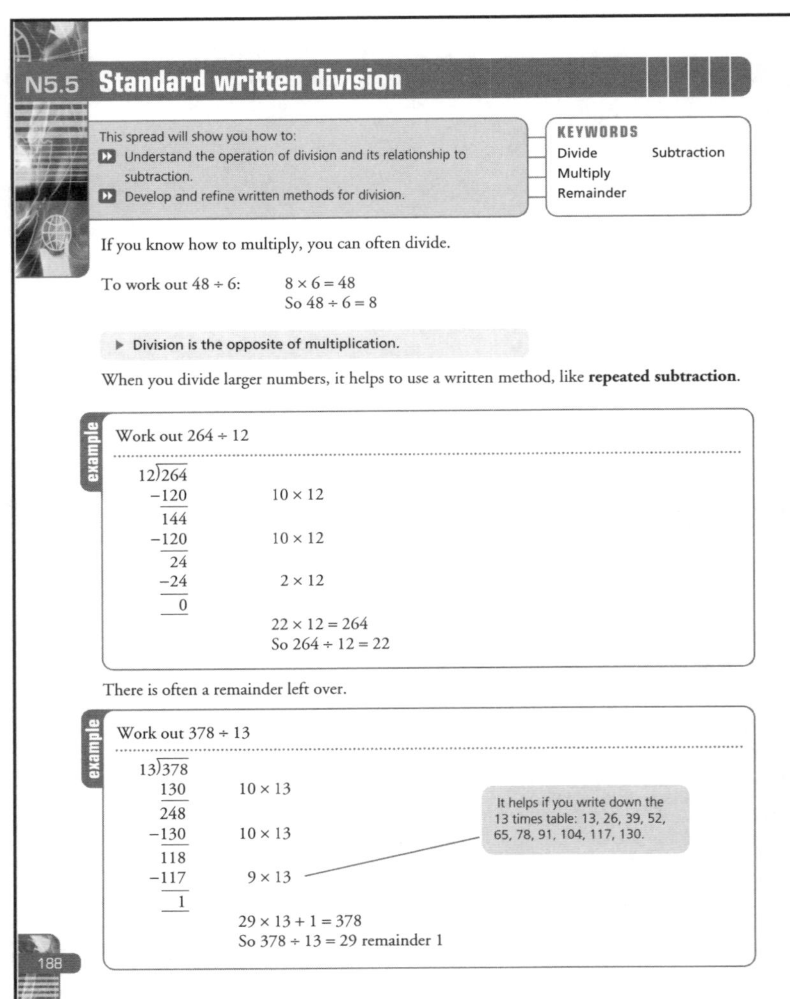

N5.5 **Standard written division**

This spread will show you how to:
- Understand the operation of division and its relationship to subtraction.
- Develop and refine written methods for division.

KEYWORDS
Divide, Subtraction, Multiply, Remainder

If you know how to multiply, you can often divide.

To work out 48 ÷ 6: 8 × 6 = 48
So 48 ÷ 6 = 8

- Division is the opposite of multiplication.

When you divide larger numbers, it helps to use a written method, like **repeated subtraction**.

example

Work out 264 ÷ 12

```
12)264
  −120      10 × 12
   144
  −120      10 × 12
    24
   −24       2 × 12
     0
            22 × 12 = 264
            So 264 ÷ 12 = 22
```

There is often a remainder left over.

example

Work out 378 ÷ 13

```
13)378
   130      10 × 13
   248
  −130      10 × 13
   118
  −117       9 × 13
     1
            29 × 13 + 1 = 378
            So 378 ÷ 13 = 29 remainder 1
```

It helps if you write down the 13 times table: 13, 26, 39, 52, 65, 78, 91, 104, 117, 130.

188

Plenary

Write down the problem: A computer costs £835.
If you pay back £18 per week, how many weeks would it take to pay off the £835?

Discuss the strategies that students use.
This will lead into the homework.

Further activities

Give students a number such as 594 and ask them to find which numbers in the 20s divide into it exactly.

Differentiation

Support questions:

- Questions 1a–1f have whole-number answers.
- Questions 1g–7 focus on division. Springboard 7, pages 484, 485.
- Questions 5–7 include decimals and complex problems. Springboard 7, page 486.

Core tier: focuses on dividing with decimals to 2 dp.

Exercise N5.5

1 Do these division questions. Write out the times table by the side of each question to help you.

a 170 ÷ 5	**b** 204 ÷ 4	**c** 384 ÷ 6
d 258 ÷ 3	**e** 504 ÷ 9	**f** 304 ÷ 8
g 609 ÷ 7	**h** 405 ÷ 6	**i** 648 ÷ 7
j 457 ÷ 8	**k** 336 ÷ 6	**l** 774 ÷ 9

2 Now do these division questions. Again, write out the times table by the side to help you.

a 336 ÷ 12	**b** 473 ÷ 11	**c** 675 ÷ 15
d 592 ÷ 16	**e** 416 ÷ 16	**f** 728 ÷ 14
g 444 ÷ 17	**h** 743 ÷ 16	**i** 953 ÷ 15
j 623 ÷ 18	**k** 728 ÷ 13	**l** 703 ÷ 19

3 A football player wins the 'Man of the Match' award of £375. He shares the money equally with the other 10 members of the team.

a How much does each player get?
b How much money is left over?
c Suppose the two substitutes are included as well. How much does each player get now?

4 James buys 32 graphic calculators at a total cost of £576. How much does each calculator cost?

5 Freja has £835 to spend on graphic calculators. Each calculator costs £18.

a How many calculators can she buy?
b How much money will she be left with?

6 18 friends spend £612 on a school reunion dinner. They split the cost equally between them. How much do they each pay?

7 In each of these questions, three of the four divisions give the same answer. Find the odd one out.

a

504 ÷ 12	756 ÷ 18
688 ÷ 16	630 ÷ 15

b

441 ÷ 7	832 ÷ 13
945 ÷ 15	756 ÷ 12

189

Exercise commentary

The questions assess the objectives on Primary Framework Pages 55 and 69.

Problem solving

Questions 3–6 assess Primary Framework Page 85. Question 7 assesses Page 79.

Group work

Question 7 and the further activity are suitable for pair or group work.

Misconceptions

Students may have poor recall of multiplication facts which leads to errors.
Ensure they have a multiplication grid for reference and that they know how to use it.
In question 3, students may divide by 10 instead of 11.
Emphasise that they need to read the question carefully.
Students find long division very hard to follow and tend to make mistakes in recording, losing track of the divisor.
Encourage them to work in logical steps and to build on successful mental strategies, starting from facts they know.
Encourage students to check their answers by multiplying or if the link is hard for them to understand, they could use a calculator.

Links

Multiplication facts: Primary Framework Page 59. Estimation: Page 11.
Checking calculations: Page 73.

Homework

N5.5HW is an activity requiring students to calculate with real data from newspapers or magazines.

Answers

1 **a** 34 **b** 51 **c** 64 **d** 86 **e** 56 **f** 38
g 87 **h** 67 r 3 **i** 92 r 4 **j** 57 r 1 **k** 56 **l** 86
2 **a** 28 **b** 43 **c** 45 **d** 37 **e** 26 **f** 52
g 26 r 2 **h** 46 r 7 **i** 63 r 8 **j** 34 r 11 **k** 56 **l** 37
3 **a** £34 **b** £1 **c** £28
4 £18 5 **a** 46 **b** £7
6 £34 7 **a** 688 ÷ 16 **b** 832 ÷ 13

N5.6 Using equivalent fractions

Mental starter

Give me a number …

… that is a:

- multiple of 2 and a multiple of 3
- multiple of 2 and a factor of 12
- multiple of 3 and a factor of 24
- the lowest possible multiple of 3 and 6.

Useful resources

N5.6OHP demonstrates the equivalence of $\frac{2}{3}$ and $\frac{6}{9}$ and of $\frac{2}{5}$ and $\frac{4}{10}$.

R1 digit cards for the mental starter.

Introductory activity

Revise the use of fractions.

Ask the students what $\frac{1}{2}$ means:

1 out of 2 shares.

Discuss whether it is better to have $\frac{1}{2}$ or $\frac{2}{4}$ of a bar or chocolate.

Emphasise that $\frac{1}{2}$ and $\frac{2}{4}$ are equivalent.

N5.6OHP shows equivalent fractions using diagrams.

Write down the statement:

$\frac{2}{3} = \frac{6}{9}$

Emphasise that $\frac{2}{3}$ and $\frac{6}{9}$ are equivalent fractions.

Discuss how to get from one to the other – multiply by 3.

Emphasise that you multiply to find equivalent fractions.

You may need to recap the terms numerator and denominator.

Introduce the term 'common denominator' by using an example.

For example, you could use $\frac{3}{5}$ and $\frac{5}{9}$.

Refer to the mental starter.

Discuss how to find:

- a multiple of 5 and 9
- equivalent fractions
- which fraction is larger and why.

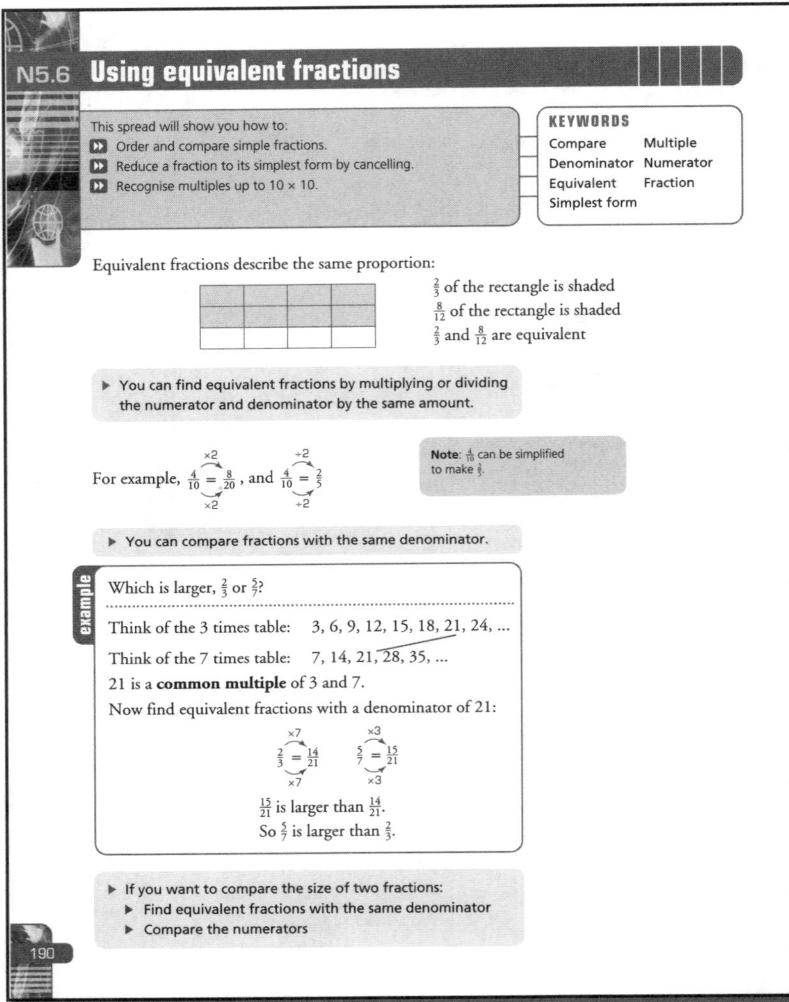

N5.6 **Using equivalent fractions**

This spread will show you how to:

- Order and compare simple fractions.
- Reduce a fraction to its simplest form by cancelling.
- Recognise multiples up to 10 × 10.

KEYWORDS

Compare, Multiple, Denominator, Numerator, Equivalent, Fraction, Simplest form

Equivalent fractions describe the same proportion:

$\frac{2}{3}$ of the rectangle is shaded

$\frac{8}{12}$ of the rectangle is shaded

$\frac{2}{3}$ and $\frac{8}{12}$ are equivalent

- You can find equivalent fractions by multiplying or dividing the numerator and denominator by the same amount.

For example, $\frac{4}{10} \overset{\times 2}{=} \frac{8}{20}$, and $\frac{4}{10} \overset{\div 2}{=} \frac{2}{5}$

Note: $\frac{4}{10}$ can be simplified to make $\frac{2}{5}$.

- You can compare fractions with the same denominator.

example

Which is larger, $\frac{2}{3}$ or $\frac{5}{7}$?

Think of the 3 times table: 3, 6, 9, 12, 15, 18, 21, 24, …

Think of the 7 times table: 7, 14, 21, 28, 35, …

21 is a **common multiple** of 3 and 7.

Now find equivalent fractions with a denominator of 21:

$\frac{2}{3} \overset{\times 7}{=} \frac{14}{21}$ $\quad$ $\frac{5}{7} \overset{\times 3}{=} \frac{15}{21}$

$\frac{15}{21}$ is larger than $\frac{14}{21}$.

So $\frac{5}{7}$ is larger than $\frac{2}{3}$.

- If you want to compare the size of two fractions:
  - Find equivalent fractions with the same denominator
  - Compare the numerators

190

Plenary

Write some fractions on blank sheets of A4 paper using a marker pen.

Just write one fraction on each sheet.

Select students to take a sheet and stand at the front.

The class discusses how to arrange them in order.

Further activities

Students can find equivalent fractions for the fractions on **R3**. Able students can arrange them in order of size, explaining their reasoning.

Differentiation

Support questions:

- Questions 1 and 2 are straightforward equivalence problems.
- Questions 3–6 focus on comparing two fractions with different denominators.
- Questions 7–10 are more complex problems involving more than two fractions.

Core tier: focuses on adding fractions with different denominators.

Exercise commentary

The questions assess the objectives on Primary Framework Pages 19 and 23.

Problem solving

Questions 4–10 assess Primary Framework Page 77 if students explain reasoning.

Group work

Questions 9 and 10 and the further activity are suitable for pair or group work. Weak students would benefit from discussing questions 3–8.

Misconceptions

Students make many different mistakes when dealing with fractions, especially:

- Adding instead of multiplying to find equivalences.
- Only multiplying the numerators.
- Multiplying both denominators by the same number.

Questions 1–3 should help set a structured approach for weaker students.
Encourage students to think about drawing rectangles to illustrate answers so they can visualise what is happening.
Encourage the use of a number line or fraction wall with the main fractions marked on it to help students gain a feel for the size of a fraction.
Students may also struggle to recognise the common denominator to use.
Emphasise the use of multiples.

Links

Tests of divisibility and multiples: Primary Framework Page 19.

Exercise N5.6

1 Copy and complete these equivalent fraction problems.

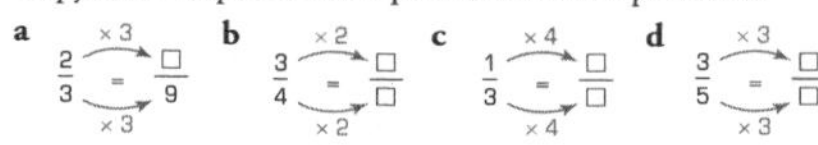

2 Copy and complete these simplifying problems.

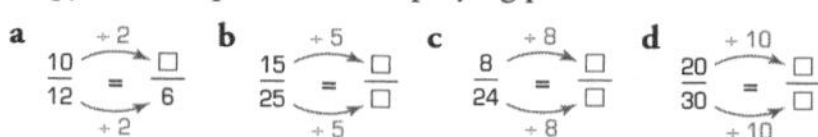

3 Copy and complete this question.
Which is bigger:
$\frac{3}{5}$ or $\frac{5}{7}$?

4 Which is bigger: $\frac{2}{3}$ or $\frac{7}{10}$?

5 Which is smaller: $\frac{3}{10}$ or $\frac{1}{3}$?

6 Which is bigger: $\frac{5}{11}$ or $\frac{3}{7}$?

7 Put these fractions in order, starting with the smallest first.
$\frac{3}{10}, \frac{2}{5}, \frac{7}{15}, \frac{13}{20}$
You need to find equivalent fractions to do this.

8 Put these fractions in order, starting with the smallest first.
$\frac{2}{3}, \frac{5}{6}, \frac{1}{2}, \frac{5}{7}$

9 Look at these fractions:
$\frac{2}{6}, \frac{4}{10}, \frac{3}{9}, \frac{5}{15}, \frac{20}{30}$
Find which two of them are not equivalent to $\frac{1}{3}$.

10 Look at these fractions:
$\frac{6}{10}, \frac{18}{25}, \frac{30}{50}, \frac{9}{15}, \frac{20}{35}$
Find which two of them are not equivalent to $\frac{3}{5}$.

191

Homework

N5.6HW is a puzzle based on reducing fractions to their simplest form.

Answers

1 **a** $\frac{6}{9}$ **b** $\frac{6}{8}$ **c** $\frac{4}{12}$ **d** $\frac{9}{15}$ **2** **a** $\frac{5}{6}$ **b** $\frac{3}{5}$ **c** $\frac{1}{3}$ **d** $\frac{2}{3}$

3 $\frac{3}{5} = \frac{21}{35}$, $\frac{5}{7} = \frac{25}{35}$, so $\frac{5}{7}$ is bigger **4** $\frac{2}{3} = \frac{20}{30}$, $\frac{7}{10} = \frac{21}{30}$, so $\frac{7}{10}$ is bigger

5 $\frac{3}{10} = \frac{9}{30}$, $\frac{1}{3} = \frac{10}{30}$, so $\frac{3}{10}$ is smaller **6** $\frac{5}{11} = \frac{35}{77}$, $\frac{3}{7} = \frac{33}{77}$, so $\frac{5}{11}$ is bigger

7 $\frac{3}{10}, \frac{2}{5}, \frac{7}{15}, \frac{13}{20}$ **8** $\frac{1}{2}, \frac{2}{3}, \frac{5}{7}, \frac{5}{6}$

9 $\frac{4}{10}, \frac{20}{30}$ **10** $\frac{18}{25}, \frac{20}{35}$

N5.7 Converting fractions, decimals and percentages

Mental starter

×, ÷ by 10, 100

Give students a start number: 63

Ask them to × by 10, 100: 630, 6300

Ask them to ÷ by 10, 100: 6.3, 0.63

Repeat for other numbers.

Include 3-digits and 1 dp.

Useful resources

R4 contains a place value table for the mental starter and decimal conversion.

R6 contains number lines to help order numbers.

Calculators

Introductory activity

Look at a division sign ÷.

Point out that it looks a bit like a fraction, where the numbers have been replaced by dots.

Emphasise that you can think of a fraction as being a division.

So $\frac{63}{100} = 63 \div 100$.

Discuss what 63 ÷ 100 is as a decimal.

This should link to the mental starter, and encourage the response 0.63.

Emphasise that you convert a fraction to a decimal by dividing the numerator by the denominator.

Offer some simple examples.

Encourage students to use mental methods to recall facts.

Avoid recurring decimals at this stage.

Emphasise that you can change percentages to decimals by changing to fractions first.

Give a few percentages and ask for the corresponding decimals.

Discuss rounding decimals.

You could use $\frac{3}{7}$ as an example (as in the student book).

Ask students to:

- perform the calculation 3 ÷ 7 on their calculators
- write down the answer on the screen.

Recap rounding to 1 decimal place and extend to 3 decimal places.

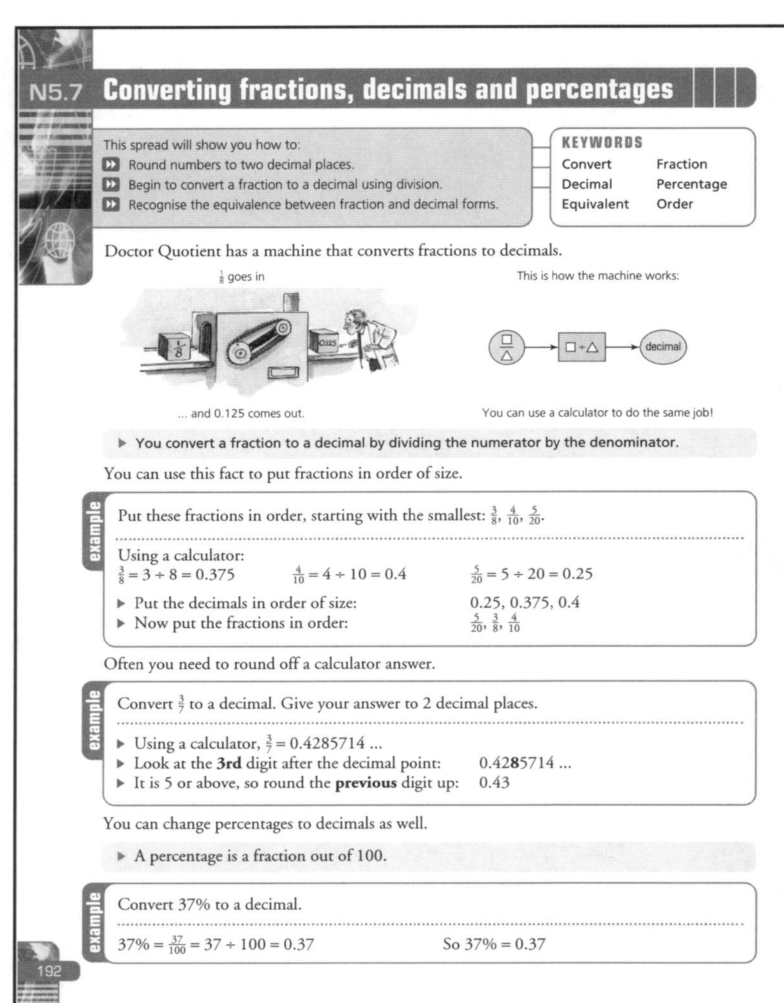

N5.7 **Converting fractions, decimals and percentages**

This spread will show you how to:
- Round numbers to two decimal places.
- Begin to convert a fraction to a decimal using division.
- Recognise the equivalence between fraction and decimal forms.

KEYWORDS
Convert, Fraction, Decimal, Percentage, Equivalent, Order

Doctor Quotient has a machine that converts fractions to decimals.

$\frac{1}{8}$ goes in
This is how the machine works:
$\frac{\square}{\triangle}$
□÷△
decimal
... and 0.125 comes out.
You can use a calculator to do the same job!

- **You convert a fraction to a decimal by dividing the numerator by the denominator.**

You can use this fact to put fractions in order of size.

example

Put these fractions in order, starting with the smallest: $\frac{3}{8}, \frac{4}{10}, \frac{5}{20}$.

Using a calculator:
$\frac{3}{8} = 3 \div 8 = 0.375$ $\quad \frac{4}{10} = 4 \div 10 = 0.4$ $\quad \frac{5}{20} = 5 \div 20 = 0.25$

- Put the decimals in order of size: 0.25, 0.375, 0.4
- Now put the fractions in order: $\frac{5}{20}, \frac{3}{8}, \frac{4}{10}$

Often you need to round off a calculator answer.

example

Convert $\frac{3}{7}$ to a decimal. Give your answer to 2 decimal places.

- Using a calculator, $\frac{3}{7} = 0.4285714$ ...
- Look at the **3rd** digit after the decimal point: 0.42**8**5714 ...
- It is 5 or above, so round the **previous** digit up: 0.43

You can change percentages to decimals as well.

- A percentage is a fraction out of 100.

example

Convert 37% to a decimal.

$37\% = \frac{37}{100} = 37 \div 100 = 0.37$ $\quad$ So 37% = 0.37

192

Plenary

Write six different percentages, fractions and decimals on separate pieces of A4 paper. Use 23%, $\frac{1}{5}$, 0.21, $\frac{2}{7}$, 0.206, $\frac{3}{13}$.

Give the papers out to six students and ask them to stand at the front. The class discusses which order these students should be in.

Further activities

Give students a list of three fractions as in question 3 but they must order them without using a calculator or doing a calculation – i.e. they must use estimation and their knowledge of fractions.

Differentiation

Support questions:

- Questions 1 and 2 relate fractions to division. Springboard 7, page 480.
- Questions 3–7 focus on converting between fractions, decimals and percentages.
- Question 8 involves using all three forms. Springboard 7, page 493.

Core tier: focuses on converting between forms, and extends to addition and subtraction problems.

Exercise N5.7

1 Use a calculator to change these fractions into decimals.

a $\frac{1}{2}$ **b** $\frac{3}{6}$ **c** $\frac{5}{10}$
d $\frac{1}{4}$ **e** $\frac{2}{8}$ **f** $\frac{5}{20}$
g $\frac{1}{5}$ **h** $\frac{3}{15}$ **i** $\frac{10}{50}$

2 Use a calculator to change these fractions into decimals. (Only write down the first three decimal places.)

a $\frac{1}{3}$ **b** $\frac{3}{9}$ **c** $\frac{5}{15}$
d $\frac{1}{9}$ **e** $\frac{4}{9}$ **f** $\frac{7}{9}$
g $\frac{3}{7}$ **h** $\frac{4}{7}$ **i** $\frac{6}{7}$

3 Put these fractions in order, smallest first, by changing them into decimals.

a $\frac{5}{7}, \frac{13}{16}, \frac{18}{25}$ **b** $\frac{13}{23}, \frac{7}{13}, \frac{25}{48}$ **c** $\frac{13}{41}, \frac{21}{53}, \frac{18}{49}$
d $\frac{21}{32}, \frac{9}{13}, \frac{16}{23}$ **e** $\frac{15}{18}, \frac{7}{8}, \frac{12}{13}$ **f** $\frac{27}{83}, \frac{13}{51}, \frac{83}{127}$

4 Rewrite these percentages as fractions out of 100.

a 67% **b** 83% **c** 29%
d 8% **e** 35% **f** 42%
g 19% **h** 81% **i** 90%

5 Rewrite these fractions as percentages.

a $\frac{21}{100}$ **b** $\frac{63}{100}$ **c** $\frac{38}{100}$
d $\frac{49}{100}$ **e** $\frac{32}{100}$ **f** $\frac{99}{100}$
g $\frac{69}{100}$ **h** $\frac{3}{100}$ **i** $\frac{5}{100}$

6 Rewrite these fractions as percentages.

a $\frac{1}{2}$ **b** $\frac{1}{4}$ **c** $\frac{3}{4}$
d $\frac{1}{10}$ **e** $\frac{3}{10}$ **f** $\frac{7}{10}$
g $\frac{1}{5}$ **h** $\frac{3}{5}$ **i** $\frac{4}{5}$

7 Change these percentages into fractions then decimals.

a 18% **b** 53% **c** 59%
d 71% **e** 77% **f** 23%
g 28% **h** 39% **i** 43%

8 Put these percentages, fractions and decimals in order, starting with the smallest first.

a $\frac{2}{3}$, 65%, 0.62 **b** 32%, 0.4, $\frac{3}{8}$
c $\frac{2}{9}$, 20%, 0.02 **d** 62%, 0.7, $\frac{5}{8}$

Exercise commentary

The questions assess the objectives on Primary Framework Pages 29, 31 and 33.

Problem solving

Question 8 assesses Primary Framework Page 77 if students explain reasoning.

Group work

Weak students would benefit from discussing all questions.

Misconceptions

Students tend to try to use algorithms wrongly, leading to errors.

Encourage the intuitive approach, starting from facts they already know.

Encourage students to focus on one conversion at a time. Have an equivalence line available or on the classroom wall and encourage students to refer to it until they have a firm grasp of equivalences.

Students will see 0.3 < 0.41 as 3 < 41.

Encourage the use of a number line to place the decimals. Using a place value table may help some students.

Students make mistakes in rounding decimals, finding it hard to know which digit to look at.

Encourage the use of a number line and a place value table.

Links

Rounding: Primary Framework Page 31.

Homework

Ask students to search through newspapers, magazines or the internet for percentages. N5.7HW offers hints and suggestions.

Answers

1 **a** 0.5 **b** 0.5 **c** 0.5 **d** 0.25 **e** 0.25 **f** 0.25 **g** 0.2 **h** 0.2 **i** 0.2

2 **a** 0.333 **b** 0.333 **c** 0.333 **d** 0.111 **e** 0.444 **f** 0.777 **g** 0.428 **h** 0.571 **i** 0.857

3 **a** $\frac{5}{7}, \frac{18}{25}, \frac{13}{16}$ **b** $\frac{25}{48}, \frac{7}{13}, \frac{13}{23}$ **c** $\frac{13}{41}, \frac{18}{49}, \frac{21}{53}$ **d** $\frac{21}{32}, \frac{9}{13}, \frac{16}{23}$ **e** $\frac{15}{18}, \frac{7}{8}, \frac{12}{13}$ **f** $\frac{13}{51}, \frac{27}{83}, \frac{83}{127}$

4 **a** $\frac{67}{100}$ **b** $\frac{83}{100}$ **c** $\frac{29}{100}$ **d** $\frac{8}{100}$ **e** $\frac{35}{100}$ **f** $\frac{42}{100}$ **g** $\frac{19}{100}$ **h** $\frac{81}{100}$ **i** $\frac{90}{100}$

5 **a** 21% **b** 63% **c** 38% **d** 49% **e** 32% **f** 99% **g** 69% **h** 3% **i** 5%

6 **a** 50% **b** 25% **c** 75% **d** 10% **e** 30% **f** 70% **g** 20% **h** 60% **i** 80%

7 **a** $\frac{18}{100}$, 0.18 **b** $\frac{53}{100}$, 0.53 **c** $\frac{59}{100}$, 0.59 **d** $\frac{71}{100}$, 0.71 **e** $\frac{77}{100}$, 0.77 **f** $\frac{23}{100}$, 0.23 **g** $\frac{28}{100}$, 0.28 **h** $\frac{39}{100}$, 0.39 **i** $\frac{43}{100}$, 0.42

8 **a** 0.62, 65%, $\frac{2}{3}$ **b** 32%, $\frac{3}{8}$, 0.4 **c** 0.02, 20%, $\frac{2}{9}$ **d** 62%, $\frac{5}{8}$, 0.7

Mental starter

Doubles and halves

Select a starting number and a rule, then go around the classroom asking each student to respond in turn.

- For example, 5 and double it: 10, 20, 40, 80, 160, 320
- Now halve it: 160, 80, 40, 20, 10, 5, 2.5
- Try different numbers, keeping the same doubling and halving rule.

Useful resources

R1 digit cards for the mental starter.
R6 number lines to illustrate working.
N5.8OHP has 60 buttons to share.

Introductory activity

Discuss with students how to find $\frac{1}{2}$ of something.

- Encourage the response ÷ 2.
- Then ask how to find $\frac{1}{4}$ of something.
- Build this into a rule, keeping to unitary fractions.

Now discuss how to find $\frac{3}{10}$ of something.

- Explain that you divide by 10 as previously.
- Emphasise that it is **three** tenths.
- Encourage students to suggest multiplying by 3.
- Build this into a general rule for finding a fraction of an amount.
- Offer some further examples, including quantities with units.

Use a number line to illustrate the totals and the fractions.

Discuss how to find a percentage of an amount.

- Emphasise that it is a fraction out of 100.
- You may need to revise changing percentages to fractions and reducing fractions to a simpler form.

Emphasise the importance of 10%.

Discuss, with examples, how you can use 10% to find other more difficult percentages of amounts.

Encourage the use of number lines. Mark either end 0% and 100% and also mark on the amounts they represent.

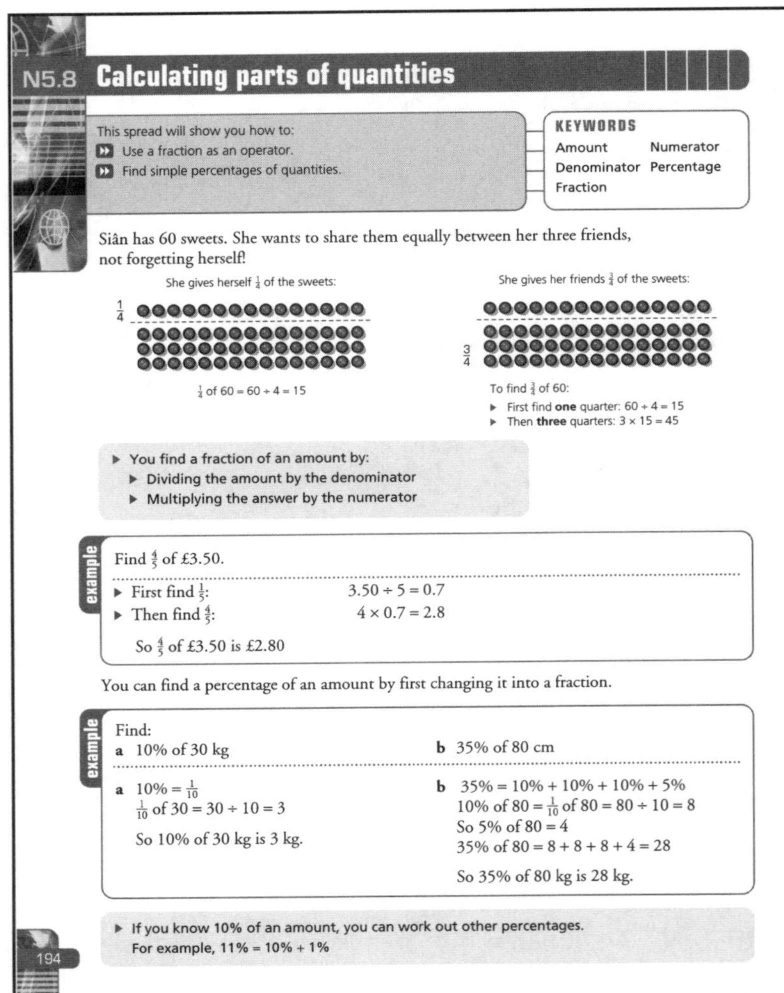

N5.8 **Calculating parts of quantities**

This spread will show you how to:
- Use a fraction as an operator.
- Find simple percentages of quantities.

KEYWORDS
Amount, Numerator, Denominator, Percentage, Fraction

Siân has 60 sweets. She wants to share them equally between her three friends, not forgetting herself!

She gives herself $\frac{1}{4}$ of the sweets:

$\frac{1}{4}$ of 60 = 60 ÷ 4 = 15

She gives her friends $\frac{3}{4}$ of the sweets:

To find $\frac{3}{4}$ of 60:
- First find **one** quarter: 60 ÷ 4 = 15
- Then **three** quarters: 3 × 15 = 45

- You find a fraction of an amount by:
  - Dividing the amount by the denominator
  - Multiplying the answer by the numerator

example

Find $\frac{4}{5}$ of £3.50.

- First find $\frac{1}{5}$: 3.50 ÷ 5 = 0.7
- Then find $\frac{4}{5}$: 4 × 0.7 = 2.8

So $\frac{4}{5}$ of £3.50 is £2.80

You can find a percentage of an amount by first changing it into a fraction.

example

Find:
a 10% of 30 kg
b 35% of 80 cm

a 10% = $\frac{1}{10}$
$\frac{1}{10}$ of 30 = 30 ÷ 10 = 3
So 10% of 30 kg is 3 kg.

b 35% = 10% + 10% + 10% + 5%
10% of 80 = $\frac{1}{10}$ of 80 = 80 ÷ 10 = 8
So 5% of 80 = 4
35% of 80 = 8 + 8 + 8 + 4 = 28
So 35% of 80 kg is 28 kg.

- If you know 10% of an amount, you can work out other percentages.
For example, 11% = 10% + 1%

194

Plenary

Suggest a percentage problem such as 65% of 80.
Ask students how they would work it out.

Discuss their strategies, for example:

- 50% + 10% + 5%
- 75% − 10%
- 6 × 10% + 5%

Further activities

Weak students could find $\frac{1}{2}$, $\frac{1}{3}$, $\frac{1}{4}$, $\frac{1}{5}$, $\frac{1}{6}$ and $1\frac{1}{7}$ of 420 and use the answers to try to order the fractions.

Discuss how to find 1% of a quantity given 10%.
Challenge students to find:
11%, 12%, 13% ... of 800.

Differentiation

Support questions:

- Questions 1 and 2 involve simple fractions and 10%. Springboard 7, page 480.
- Questions 3–8 focus on finding fractions and percentages of amounts.
- Questions 9 and 10 are more complex, requiring a good understanding of percentage. Springboard 7, page 493.

Core tier: focuses on proportions of an amount using a variety of contexts and units.

Exercise N5.8

1 Work out the following amounts.

a	$\frac{1}{2}$ of 84 cm	**b**	$\frac{1}{2}$ of 28 g
c	$\frac{1}{3}$ of 60 minutes	**d**	$\frac{2}{3}$ of 30 minutes
e	$\frac{1}{4}$ of £8	**f**	$\frac{3}{4}$ of £8
g	$\frac{2}{5}$ of 30p	**h**	$\frac{7}{10}$ of 50p

2 Work out the following amounts.

a	10% of £40	**b**	10% of £80
c	10% of 60 cm	**d**	10% of 20 minutes
e	10% of £4	**f**	10% of 65p
g	10% of 950 cm	**h**	10% of 9 m

3 Now work out these amounts.

a	20% of 90p	**b**	20% of 50p
c	20% of 20 minutes	**d**	5% of 40 metres
e	5% of 60 minutes	**f**	30% of 30 litres
g	30% of 50p	**h**	40% of 25 minutes

4 Which is bigger:
$\frac{2}{3}$ of 63 metres or $\frac{2}{5}$ of 100 metres?

5 Which is bigger:
$\frac{5}{7}$ of 35 minutes or $\frac{3}{4}$ of 44 minutes?

6 Which is bigger:
$\frac{1}{3}$ of 60p or 20% of 80p?

7 Which is longer:
$\frac{2}{5}$ of 35 metres or 20% of 60 metres?

8 Which is heavier:
5% of 600 g or $\frac{3}{10}$ of 90 g?

9 Find three different ways of calculating the following.
a 25% of 60
b 35% of 60
c 15% of 60

10 Find three different ways of calculating 120% of 80.

195

Exercise commentary

The questions assess the objectives on Primary Framework Pages 25 and 33.

Problem solving

Questions 1–8 assess Primary Framework Pages 83–87.
Questions 9 and 10 assess Page 79.

Group work

Questions 9 and 10 are suitable for pair work.

Misconceptions

Students need good recall of multiplication and division facts or access to a multiplication grid.
When calculating with fractions, students forget to multiply by the numerator.
Encourage the use of jottings and emphasise the intuitive approach: $\frac{1}{7}$ is 5 so $\frac{5}{7}$s is 5×5.
Some students find using rectangles to break up the amounts helps them keep track of the calculation.
To find 20% students divide by 20.
This is due to trying to follow an algorithm.
Encourage students to start with facts they know or can derive: 10%.
Finding 10% of £4 can cause problems.
Encourage students to convert into units that are easy to use: 400p.

Links

Multiplication and division facts: Primary Framework Page 59. Place value: Page 7.
Measures: Page 91.

Homework

N5.8HW explores different techniques in calculating a percentage of an amount.

Answers

1 **a** 42 cm **b** 14 g **c** 20 minutes **d** 20 minutes **e** £2 **f** £6 **g** 12p **h** 35p
2 **a** £4 **b** £8 **c** 6 cm **d** 2 minutes **e** 40p **f** 6.5p **g** 95 cm **h** 90 cm
3 **a** 18p **b** 10p **c** 4 minutes **d** 2 metres **e** 3 minutes **f** 9 litres **g** 15p **h** 10 minutes
4 $\frac{2}{3}$ of 63 m **5** $\frac{3}{4}$ of 44 minutes
6 $\frac{1}{3}$ of 60p **7** $\frac{2}{5}$ of 35 m **8** 5% of 600 g
9 **a** 15 **b** 21 **c** 9 **10** 96

Summary

The Year 6 key teaching objectives are:

- Convert a fraction to its simplest form by cancelling (23).
- Use a fraction as an operator to find fractions of numbers or quantities (25).
- Find simple percentages of whole number quantities (33).
- Extend written methods of multiplication and division (67, 69).

Check out commentary

1 Students often confuse which number to round, writing 2732 as 2300 to the nearest 100.
Encourage the use of a number line. The process of marking the ends appropriately reinforces the significance of the digits and leads to fewer mistakes.

2 Students should be encouraged to estimate answers before calculating and to use a written method that is firmly based on a successful mental method. They can then revert to the mental method using jotting in cases of difficulty.

3 The mixture of forms and use of units may overwhelm weaker students who should be encouraged to focus on parts **a** to **f**. Other students should be encouraged to develop the successful mental strategies they have used in parts **a** to **f** in answering parts **g** to **j**.

4 These questions should be relatively straightforward. More students may lose track of a calculation so encourage them to set their working out in logical steps and to say the steps out loud: one third is 30 litres so two thirds is 60 litres.

5 The aim of this question is to ensure that students choose an appropriate method. Students' explanations should highlight why they chose their method.
6 Students may need to be reminded that they divide both numbers to cancel. They may also still find decimal to fraction conversions hard. Encourage the use of a place value table.

Plenary activity

Write 37×29 in a 2×2 multiplication grid. Fill out the grid properly but put the wrong answer in the 7×9 box: 16 instead of 63.
Ask students to decide whether the answer is correct and if not where the mistake is.

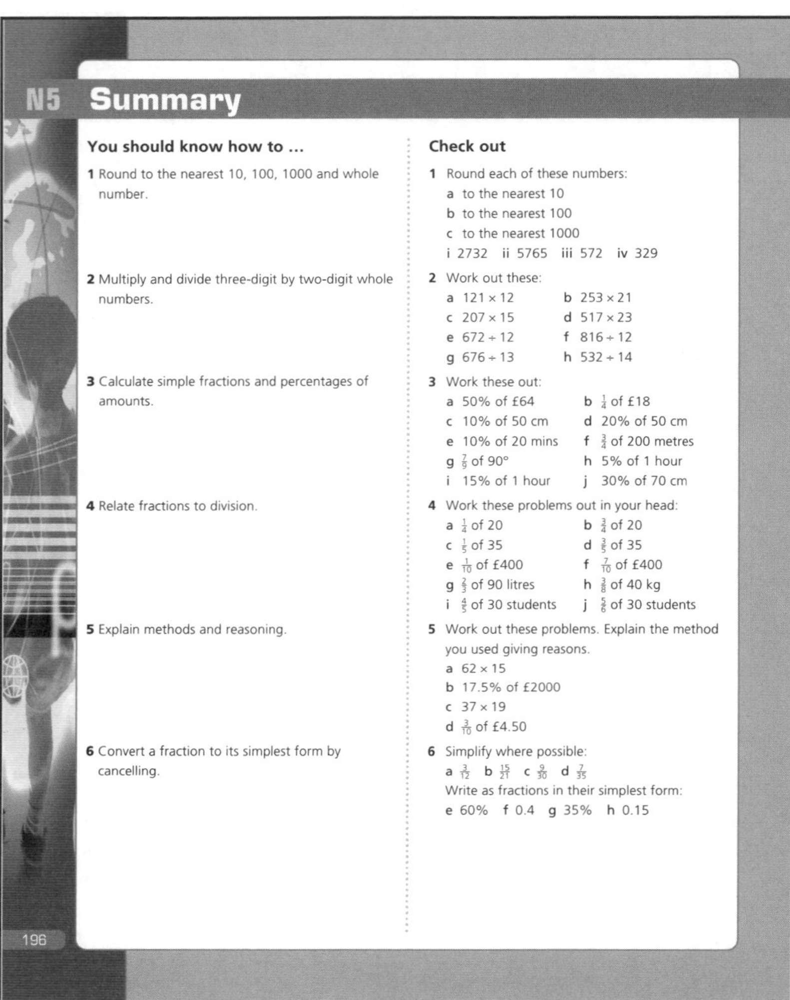

N5 Summary

You should know how to …

1 Round to the nearest 10, 100, 1000 and whole number.

2 Multiply and divide three-digit by two-digit whole numbers.

3 Calculate simple fractions and percentages of amounts.

4 Relate fractions to division.

5 Explain methods and reasoning.

6 Convert a fraction to its simplest form by cancelling.

Check out

1 Round each of these numbers:
a to the nearest 10
b to the nearest 100
c to the nearest 1000
i 2732 ii 5765 iii 572 iv 329

2 Work out these:
a 121×12 b 253×21
c 207×15 d 517×23
e $672 \div 12$ f $816 \div 12$
g $676 \div 13$ h $532 \div 14$

3 Work these out:
a 50% of £64 b $\frac{1}{4}$ of £18
c 10% of 50 cm d 20% of 50 cm
e 10% of 20 mins f $\frac{3}{4}$ of 200 metres
g $\frac{7}{9}$ of 90° h 5% of 1 hour
i 15% of 1 hour j 30% of 70 cm

4 Work these problems out in your head:
a $\frac{1}{4}$ of 20 b $\frac{3}{4}$ of 20
c $\frac{1}{5}$ of 35 d $\frac{3}{5}$ of 35
e $\frac{1}{10}$ of £400 f $\frac{7}{10}$ of £400
g $\frac{2}{3}$ of 90 litres h $\frac{3}{8}$ of 40 kg
i $\frac{4}{5}$ of 30 students j $\frac{5}{6}$ of 30 students

5 Work out these problems. Explain the method you used giving reasons.
a 62×15
b 17.5% of £2000
c 37×19
d $\frac{3}{10}$ of £4.50

6 Simplify where possible:
a $\frac{3}{12}$ b $\frac{15}{21}$ c $\frac{9}{30}$ d $\frac{7}{35}$
Write as fractions in their simplest form:
e 60% f 0.4 g 35% h 0.15

196

Development

Students will need to work with fractions and percentages in D3 and D4.

Links

Students should be encouraged to choose efficient methods and check calculations whenever they are faced with number problems and so this is ideal for inclusion in a whole-school numeracy policy.

Mental starters

Objectives covered in this unit:

- Round numbers to one decimal place.
- Order numbers.
- Find the mean of a set of numbers.
- Convert between metric and common imperial units.
- Discuss and interpret graphs.

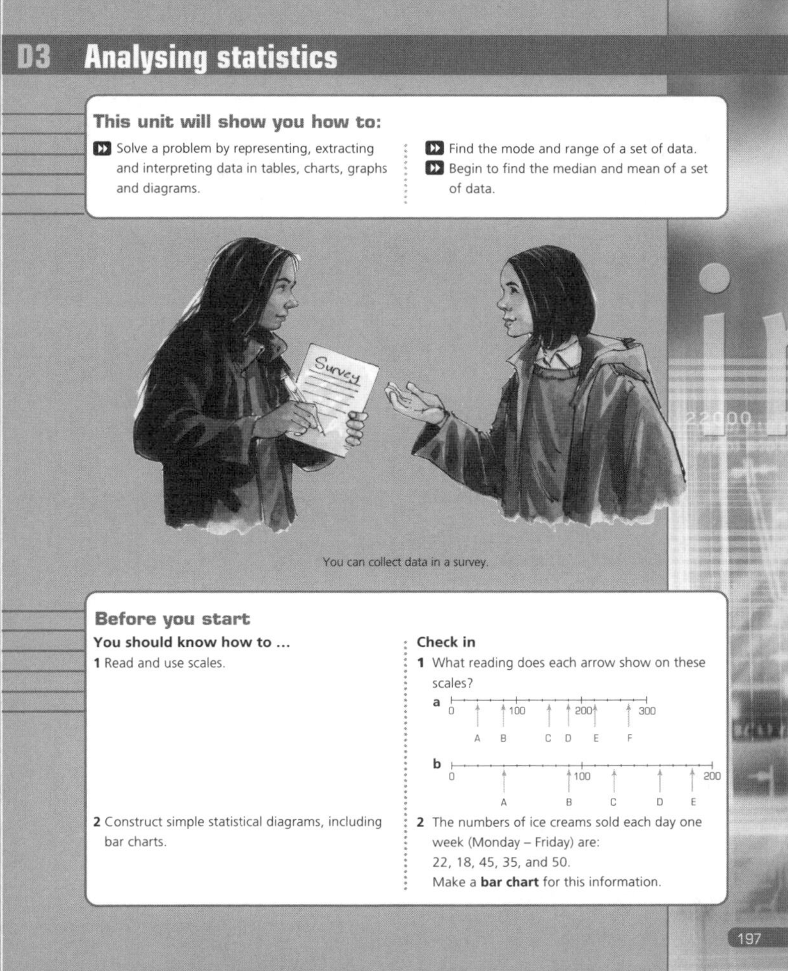

D3 Analysing statistics

This unit will show you how to:

- Solve a problem by representing, extracting and interpreting data in tables, charts, graphs and diagrams.
- Find the mode and range of a set of data.
- Begin to find the median and mean of a set of data.

You can collect data in a survey.

Before you start

You should know how to ...	Check in
1 Read and use scales.	1 What reading does each arrow show on these scales?
2 Construct simple statistical diagrams, including bar charts.	2 The numbers of ice creams sold each day one week (Monday – Friday) are: 22, 18, 45, 35, and 50. Make a **bar chart** for this information.

197

Check in activity

Discuss the steps involved in undertaking a statistical enquiry. Refer back to work done in D2 as appropriate.

1. Highlight issues – not trivial ones – and plan.
2. Collect or find relevant data.
3. Display the results using relevant diagrams and calculate relevant statistics.
4. Summarise the findings and what they show about the original enquiry.

Resources needed

* means class set needed

Essential:

D3.1OHP – Ski data
D3.2OHP – Statistical diagrams
D3.3OHP – Comparative charts
Squared paper

Useful:

R1* – Digit cards
R2* – Decimal digit cards
R9* (OHP) – Axes in one quadrant
R11 (OHP) – Tally chart
D3.4OHP – Snowfall data
D3.5OHP – Statistical report
D3.2ICT* – Creating statistical diagrams in Excel and importing them into Word

Unit commentary

Aim of the unit

This unit consolidates the learning from D2, aiming to develop students' ability to form hypotheses, collect relevant data, and communicate and interpret results. It is intended that the unit is used to support students' own project work, possibly an extension of the enquiry started in D2.

Introduction

Discuss what kind of data students might collect in a survey and emphasise this is primary data.

Discuss examples of secondary data and where you might find it.

Framework references

This unit focuses on:

- Year 6 teaching objectives pages: 115, 117
- Problem solving objectives page: 77

The unit provides access to:

- Year 7 teaching objectives pages: 248–252, 256, 258, 264, 268–272

Differentiation

Core tier focuses on comparing sets of data using diagrams and statistics.

D3.1 Planning the data collection

Mental starter

Revise the vocabulary of statistics.
Students write five numbers on pieces of paper: 6, 4, 8, 3, 9.
Use **R1** digit cards to answer quick-fire questions:
Which is the smallest/largest number? What is the range?
What is the middle value?
Repeat for other sets of five numbers.

Useful resources

D3.1OHP shows the data for the ski resort – use it to discuss the relevance of the data and to criticise the data collection sheet.

Introductory activity

Ask students what they think is meant by the word 'data'.

Set the scene of the ski trip and ask what data would be relevant to a study of the weather.
How would it be different/similar to the data they would collect for their local area?

Discuss how students could find the data that they have suggested.
Brainstorm the class for practical suggestions, and encourage the class to analyse them critically.
For each suggestion ask:

- Is it a practical way to collect the data?
- How will it help the enquiry?

Introduce the terms 'primary data' and 'secondary data'.

- Have any students heard of these terms before?
- Try to categorise their suggestions for data collection into these groups.

Discuss sources of secondary data:

- Library
- Internet
- Magazines ...

Discuss how to record data.
Show **D3.1OHP** as an example of a data collection sheet.
Invite the students to comment on it and criticise it.
Emphasise that when you collect secondary data you should always acknowledge where it has come from.

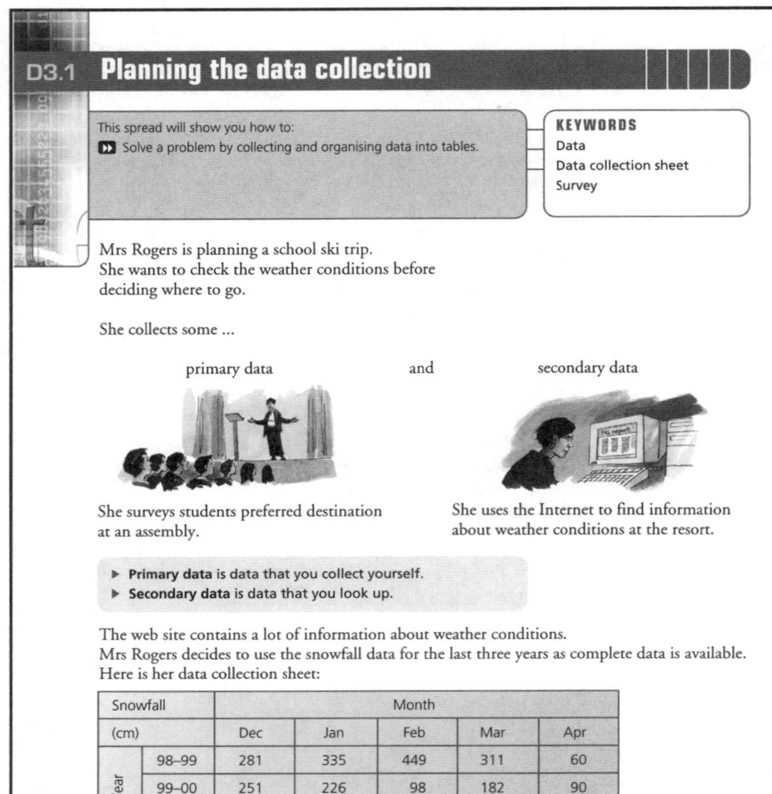

D3.1 **Planning the data collection**

This spread will show you how to:
- Solve a problem by collecting and organising data into tables.

KEYWORDS
Data
Data collection sheet
Survey

Mrs Rogers is planning a school ski trip.
She wants to check the weather conditions before deciding where to go.

She collects some ...

primary data and secondary data

She surveys students preferred destination at an assembly.

She uses the Internet to find information about weather conditions at the resort.

- **Primary data** is data that you collect yourself.
- **Secondary data** is data that you look up.

The web site contains a lot of information about weather conditions.
Mrs Rogers decides to use the snowfall data for the last three years as complete data is available.
Here is her data collection sheet:

Snowfall		Month				
(cm)		Dec	Jan	Feb	Mar	Apr
Year	98–99	281	335	449	311	60
	99–00	251	226	98	182	90
	00–01	171	163	53	124	137

Source: The Whistler Blackcomb ski resort: www.whistler-blackcomb.com/weather/stats/index/asp

- To collect the right data for your enquiry:
  1. Decide which data is relevant
  2. Research possible sources of the data
  3. Plan and design a data collection sheet.

198

Plenary

Recap the stages to go through before you collect data for an enquiry:

1 Decide which data is relevant.
2 Research possible data sources.
3 Plan and design a data collection sheet.

Further activities

Students should be encouraged to develop their own projects to carry through in this unit. There are some examples on Pages 248 and 250 of the Secondary Framework that can provoke useful discussion, alternatively there are examples throughout this unit.

Differentiation

Support questions:

- Question 1 focuses on classifying data.
- Questions 2 and 5 focus on identifying sources on data.
- Questions 3–5 involve designing a data capture sheet to collect relevant data.

Core tier: focuses on designing a questionnaire and a data capture sheet.

Exercise D3.1

1 Copy this table:

Primary Data	Secondary Data

Put each of these sources of data into the correct column:

- A reference book in a library
- A survey you do in your class
- A Web Site on the Internet
- An experiment you do in a science lesson
- A newspaper artical
- This week's football league table

2 Here are some questions that could be investigated.

- Do boys spend more time than girls playing computer games?
- What is your class's favourite television programme?
- Is there more rain in London or in Liverpool?

Explain where you could find information to help you answer each question.
Explain whether the information would be *primary* or *secondary* data.

3 Design a questionnaire or a data collection sheet for one of the three questions given in Question 2.

4 Design a data collection sheet to collect these sets of data:

a Number of vehicles of different types (car, van...) in a car park.
b Lengths of the world's five longest rivers, in kilometres and miles.
c How often people in your class use the Internet to help with homework.
d Attendance at the UK's top five tourist attractions over the past 10 years.

5 For each part of question 4:

- Explain whether you would need to collect *primary* data or *secondary* data.
- Describe a *source* for the data required.

Exercise commentary

The questions assess the objective on Primary Framework Page 115.

Problem solving

Questions 2 and 5 assess the objective on Primary Framework Page 77 as students are encouraged to explain reasoning.

Group work

The exercise is suitable for pair work.

Misconceptions

The distinction between discrete and continuous data can cause problems. Emphasise that continuous data has been measured rather than counted.

Designing a questionnaire will be difficult for some students as it is quite an open-ended activity.

Emphasise that questions need to be relevant, easy to answer and avoid repetition. Students working in pairs can test questions out on each other as in a pilot enquiry.

Links

Students will need to collect data in other areas of the school curriculum such as geography or leisure and tourism.

Homework

D3.1HW requires students to collect data.

Answers

1. Primary data: a survey you do in your class; an experiment you do in a science lesson.
   Secondary data: a reference book in a library; a website on the internet; a newspaper article; this week's football league table.
2. The first two questions could be answered using a class survey; this would be primary data. The third question could be answered using reference books or the internet; this would be secondary data.

Mental starter

Show the diagrams on **D3.2OHP**.
Ask for simple questions about the graphs:

- What fraction of Y10 are beginners?
- What fraction of Y11 students prefer downhill?
- Which month had the lowest temperature?

Useful resources

D3.2OHP shows the diagrams from the student book for discussion.

Introductory activity

Refer to the mental starter.
Emphasise the use of charts and diagrams to display data as they help show trends and make it easier to see the overall picture.

Brainstorm the types of diagram students know and what they know about each one.
Explain that you use:

- pie charts for displaying a few categories
- line graphs for measured data
- bar charts for displaying either.

D3.2OHP contains all the charts from the student book for discussion.
Use the OHP to:
Discuss how to draw each type of chart and in particular how to use the scales on a line graph.
There is no need to go into detail about how to construct a pie chart as this will not be required.

Emphasise that you should use the best diagram for a particular set of data.
Emphasise that:

- A pie chart can get too difficult to use if there are lots of categories.
- A line graph may sometimes be misleading, as the lines in between the data points do not always have meaning.

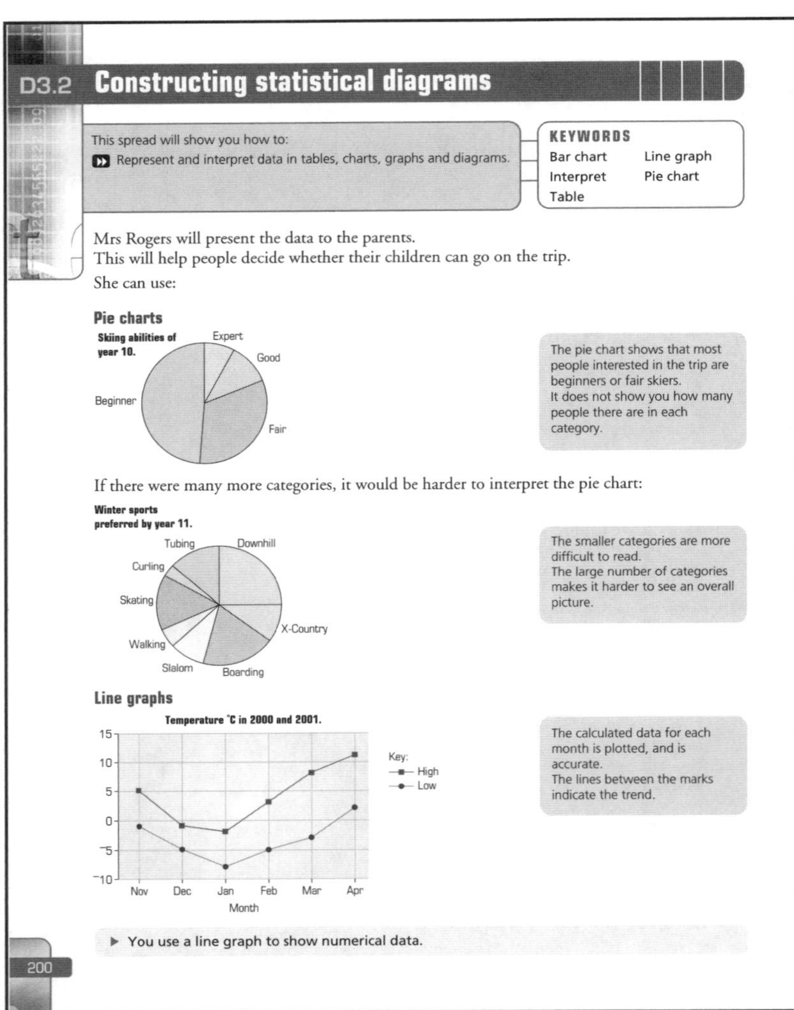

D3.2 **Constructing statistical diagrams**

This spread will show you how to:
- Represent and interpret data in tables, charts, graphs and diagrams.

KEYWORDS
Bar chart
Interpret
Table
Line graph
Pie chart

Mrs Rogers will present the data to the parents.
This will help people decide whether their children can go on the trip.
She can use:

Pie charts

The pie chart shows that most people interested in the trip are beginners or fair skiers.
It does not show you how many people there are in each category.

If there were many more categories, it would be harder to interpret the pie chart:

The smaller categories are more difficult to read.
The large number of categories makes it harder to see an overall picture.

Line graphs

The calculated data for each month is plotted, and is accurate.
The lines between the marks indicate the trend.

- You use a line graph to show numerical data.

200

Plenary

- Discuss the best diagram to use in questions 2 and 3. Emphasise that students should only use the diagram that best displays the data in the context of the enquiry.
- Discuss use of scales on line graphs in question 4.

Further activities

In **D3.2ICT**, students use a spreadsheet to draw pie charts and paste them into documents.

Students should construct relevant diagrams – using ICT – to illustrate the data they collect for their own projects.

Students can redraw diagrams from the exercise in alternative forms and discuss the pros and cons of each representation.

Differentiation

Support questions:

- Questions 1 and 2 focus on reading bar charts.
- Question 3 focuses on interpreting a pie chart.
- Question 4 focuses on interpretation of a line graph.

Core tier: focuses on interpreting and critically analysing a variety of diagrams.

Exercise D3.2

1 The bar chart shows the number of times Sophie's computer crashed one week.

a How many times did Sophie's computer crash on Monday?
b On which day of the week did Sophie's computer not crash at all?
c How many times did her computer crash altogether?

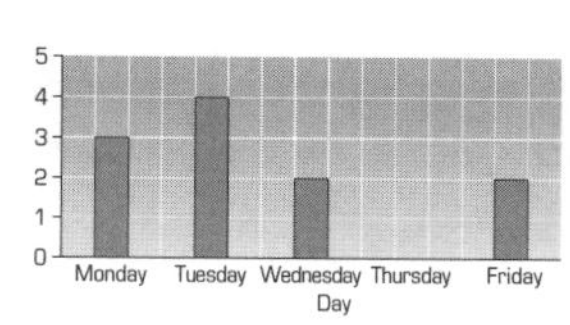

2 The chart shows the number of people attending a club each month.
Copy and complete the table using the data from the chart.

Month	Attendance
January	10
February	
March	
April	
May	
June	

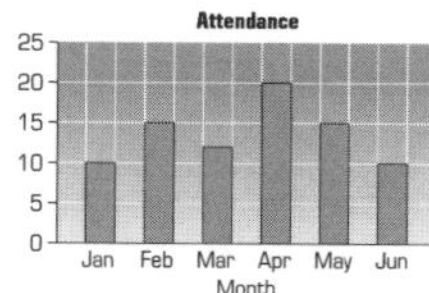

3 The pie chart shows the colours of 14 cars.

a What was the most popular car colour?
b Copy and complete the table using the data from the pie chart.

Colour	Frequency
Red	4
Blue	
Green	
Yellow	
White	

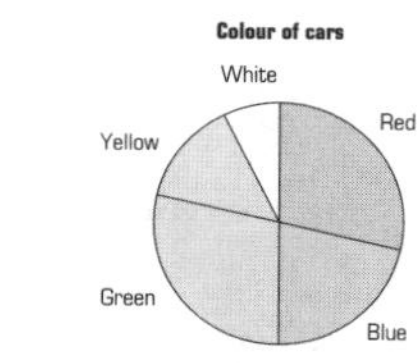

4 The line graph shows the temperature at midday each day one week.

a Which day was the hottest?
b Which day was the coldest?
c What was the range of temperatures during the week?

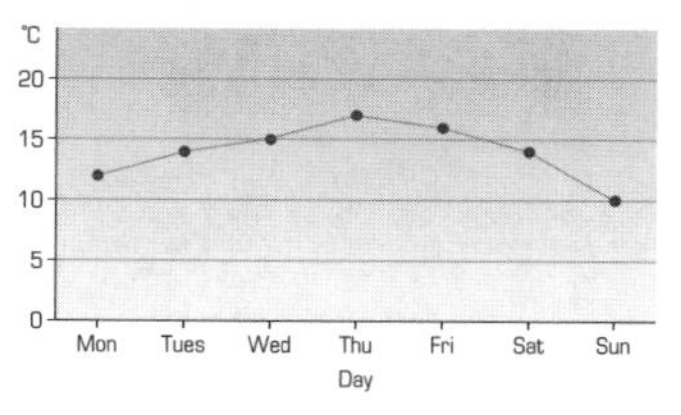

201

Exercise commentary

The questions assess the objectives on Primary Framework Pages 115 and 117.

Problem solving

The further activity assesses the objective on Primary Framework Page 77 as students explain reasoning.

Group work

The further activity is suitable for pairs.

Misconceptions

Students sometimes treat the various statistical diagrams as alternatives which add variety to a project.

Emphasise the purpose of each diagram, for example: pie charts show proportions of a whole, line graphs show variation over time etc.

Encourage students to use the diagram that is most appropriate to what they are trying to show. They must always interpret any graph or chart they show (they will focus on this in D3.3).

The use of scales can cause difficulties. Encourage students to consider the scale before answering questions.

Links

Scales: Primary Framework Page 95.

Homework

In **D3.2HW**, students are asked to illustrate data that they have collected.

Answers

1 **a** 3 **b** Thursday **c** 11
2 January: 10, February: 15, March: 12, April: 20, May: 15, June: 10
3 **a** Red and green
b Red: 4, Blue: 3, Green: 4, Yellow: 2, White 1
4 **a** Thursday **b** Sunday **c** 7 °C

Mental starter

Convert!

Explain that there are approximately 2.5 cm to an inch.

It may help if you show a ruler with cm and inches.

Ask students:

- How many cm in 2 inches? 5 inches? 12 inches?
- 10 cm of rain fell one month. How many inches is this?

Students could show their responses using **R2** digit cards.

Useful resources

D3.3OHP shows the diagrams from the student book for discussion.

Squared paper for bar charts and line graphs.

R9 has axes to draw a line graph on.

R2 digit cards for the mental starter.

Introductory activity

Discuss why it is useful to draw diagrams.

Ask students which is better to see patterns: a set of data, or a diagram?

Introduce the term 'trend' and apply it in the context of seasonal patterns.

Discuss which one students think is better to display monthly snowfall: a line graph or a bar chart?

D3.3OHP shows the diagrams from the student book.

Discuss the need to compare the snowfall data for different years.

Ask students how they would compare two sets of data using a diagram.

Emphasise the effectiveness of using just one diagram to compare data sets.

Encourage students to consider how to compare data on a line graph.

Emphasise that the data must use the same scale in order to fit on the same graph.

Illustrate this using the comparative graphs on D3.3OHP.

Look at the line graphs comparing snowfall on D3.3OHP.

Discuss what they show, and which graph better displays the data.

- The line graph shows the trend more clearly.

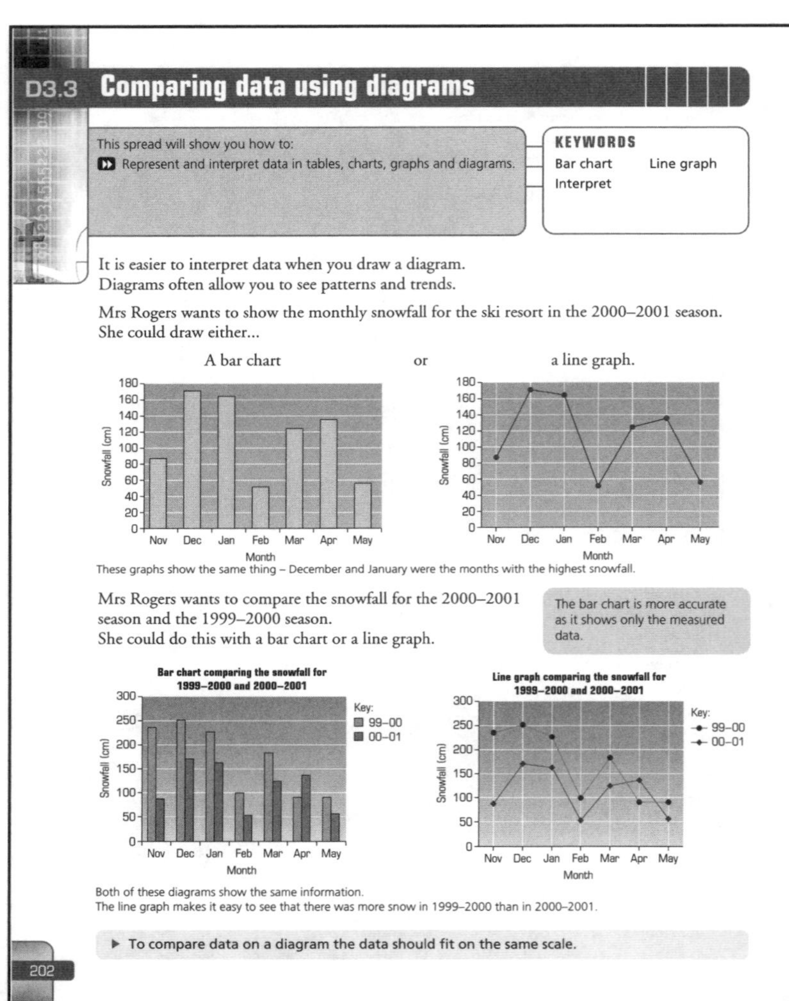

D3.3 **Comparing data using diagrams**

This spread will show you how to:

- Represent and interpret data in tables, charts, graphs and diagrams.

KEYWORDS: Bar chart, Line graph, Interpret

It is easier to interpret data when you draw a diagram.
Diagrams often allow you to see patterns and trends.

Mrs Rogers wants to show the monthly snowfall for the ski resort in the 2000–2001 season.
She could draw either...

A bar chart or a line graph.

These graphs show the same thing – December and January were the months with the highest snowfall.

Mrs Rogers wants to compare the snowfall for the 2000–2001 season and the 1999–2000 season.
She could do this with a bar chart or a line graph.

The bar chart is more accurate as it shows only the measured data.

Both of these diagrams show the same information.
The line graph makes it easy to see that there was more snow in 1999–2000 than in 2000–2001.

- To compare data on a diagram the data should fit on the same scale.

202

Plenary

Review use of statistical diagrams through the exercise:

- Information is often clearer on a diagram.
- Pie charts use a circle split into sectors representing proportions.
- Bar charts use heights of bars to represent proportions.
- You can compare data on a single diagram.

Further activities

Students should construct relevant diagrams to illustrate the data they collect for their own projects.

Students can redraw diagrams from the exercise in alternative forms and discuss the pros and cons of each representation.

Differentiation

Support questions:

- Questions 1 focuses on reading a comparative bar chart.
- Question 2 focuses on drawing a comparative bar chart.
- Question 3 focuses on interpretation of a line graph.

Core tier: focuses on comparing data using comparative and component bar charts.

Exercise D3.3

1 The graph shows the number of absences for two classes last week.

- **a** How many people in 7A were absent on Tuesday?
- **b** How many people were absent altogether on Monday?
- **c** On which day was *nobody* absent in 7B?
- **d** Jack was away all week. Which class is he in?
- **e** What was the total number of absences, for both classes, for the whole week?

Key: 7A, 7B

Monday Tuesday Wednesday Thursday Friday

Day

2 Students at Piltdown School are awarded Gold Certificates for outstanding work.
The table shows the number of certificates awarded to boys and girls last year.

	Certificates Awarded	
Term	**Boys**	**Girls**
Autum	5	6
Spring	8	7
Summer	12	14

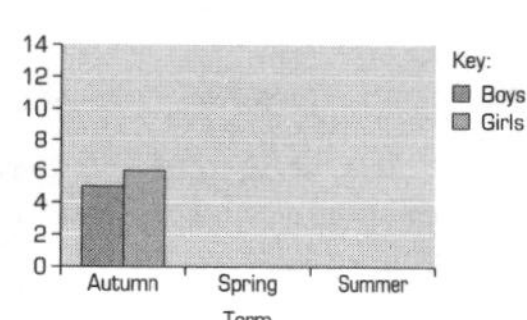

Copy and complete the bar chart to show these data.

3 A club has a pool table and a pinball machine.
The chart shows how many times they were played last year.

- **a** Which game was most popular? Explain your answer.
- **b** The pool table was out of order for a while. Which month did this breakdown happen in?
- **c** The club decides to get the machines serviced next year. They will be out of action for about a week. What would be the best month to do this?

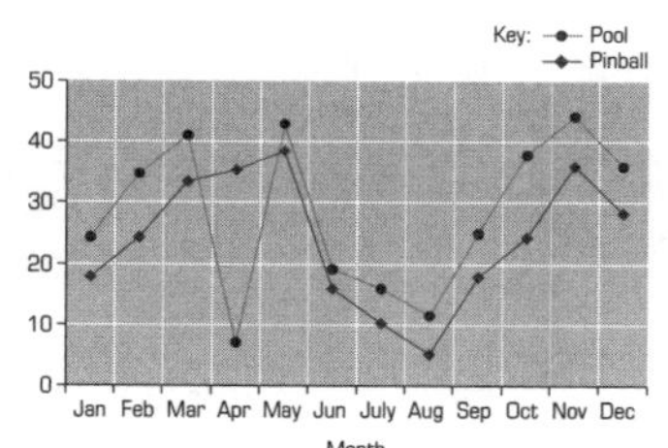

Exercise commentary

The questions assess the objectives on Primary Framework Pages 115 and 117.

Problem solving

Question 3 and the further activity assess Primary Framework Page 77 if students explain reasoning.

Group work

Question 3 is suitable for pairs.

Misconceptions

The interpretation of the charts is quite straightforward for most students. It can be difficult for them to find the total, in particular of a comparative bar chart.
When drawing a comparative bar chart, students must be careful to ensure the bars are the same width and the same distance apart throughout and to use the key.
They can copy the style of question 1.
Encourage a systematic approach of filling in a frequency table to see the data.
The use of scales can cause difficulties. Encourage students to consider the scale before answering questions.
Students should be encouraged to think more deeply about the interpretation of the charts – consistency may be more important than highs or lows.

Links

Scales: Primary Framework Page 95.
Coordinates: Page 109.

Homework

In D3.3HW, students are asked to interpret statistical diagrams.

Answers

1 **a** 2 **b** 5 **c** Wednesday **d** 7A **e** 20

3 **a** Pool was most popular; it was played more times in every month except one.
b April **c** August

D3.4 Describing data using statistics

Mental starter

Don't be mean!

- Ask students to order five numbers and give the middle value: 8, 5, 2, 3, 7.
- Now ask them to add the numbers.
- Then ask them to divide the total by 5.
- Repeat for other sets of numbers.

Useful resources

R1 digit cards for the mental starter.
R11 has a tally chart you can use to produce the modal class table from the student book.
D3.4OHP shows the data from the student book.

Introductory activity

Refer to the mental starter:

- What is the median?
- Ask students to be as specific as possible – the data must first be arranged in order.
- Encourage use of the word average.
- Ask students what they understand by the word average.
- Encourage students to define the mean from the mental starter.

Emphasise that an average is a single value that can be used to represent the data.
Ask whether students know any other measures of average: mode or modal class.
Encourage students to define the mode.

D3.4OHP shows the data from the student book. Use it to discuss the mode of the data. Expect students to think that '99 is the mode as it has the highest snowfall figure.
Emphasise that there is no mode.
Discuss how you could 'produce' a modal value: you need to group the data first (use **R11** of a tally chart). Discuss sensible grouping.
Discuss how to calculate the median and mean of the data.

Encourage students to consider the spread and to use the range.
Discuss why you might need to use both an average and a measure of spread.
You can use the data sets:
2 4 6 8 10 and 4 5 6 7 8 – the average is the same but the spread is different.

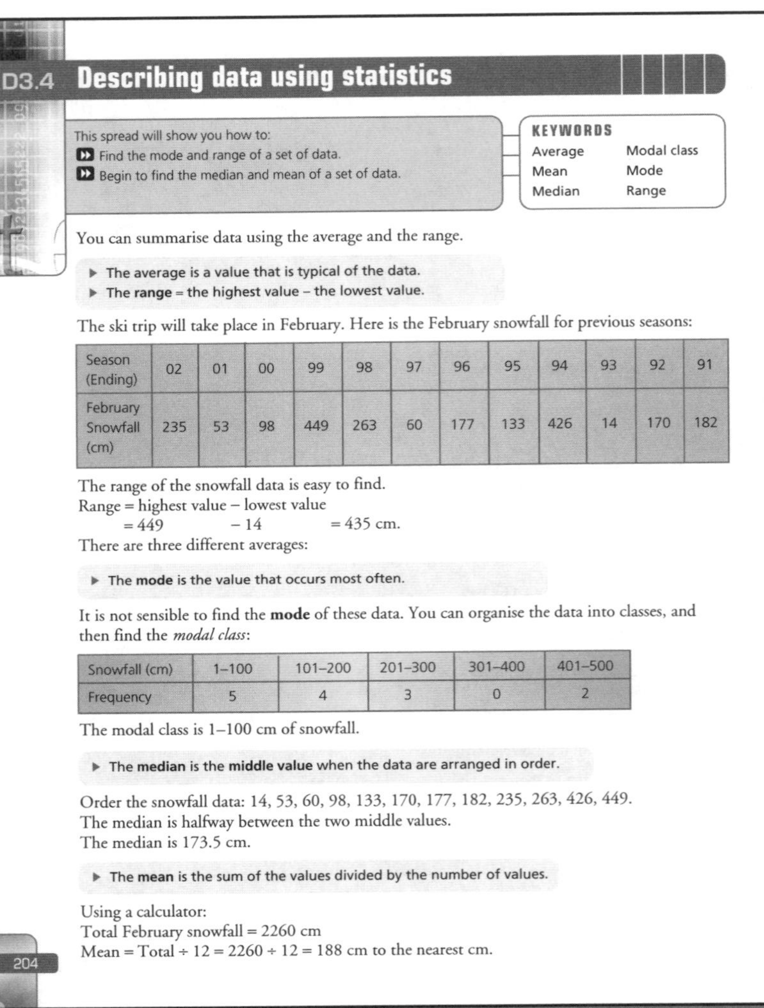

D3.4 **Describing data using statistics**

This spread will show you how to:
- Find the mode and range of a set of data.
- Begin to find the median and mean of a set of data.

KEYWORDS
Average, Mean, Median, Modal class, Mode, Range

You can summarise data using the average and the range.

- The average is a value that is typical of the data.
- The **range** = the highest value – the lowest value.

The ski trip will take place in February. Here is the February snowfall for previous seasons:

Season (Ending)	02	01	00	99	98	97	96	95	94	93	92	91
February Snowfall (cm)	235	53	98	449	263	60	177	133	426	14	170	182

The range of the snowfall data is easy to find.
Range = highest value – lowest value
= 449 – 14 = 435 cm.
There are three different averages:

- The **mode** is the value that occurs most often.

It is not sensible to find the **mode** of these data. You can organise the data into classes, and then find the *modal class*:

Snowfall (cm)	1–100	101–200	201–300	301–400	401–500
Frequency	5	4	3	0	2

The modal class is 1–100 cm of snowfall.

- The **median** is the **middle value** when the data are arranged in order.

Order the snowfall data: 14, 53, 60, 98, 133, 170, 177, 182, 235, 263, 426, 449.
The median is halfway between the two middle values.
The median is 173.5 cm.

- The **mean** is the sum of the values divided by the number of values.

Using a calculator:
Total February snowfall = 2260 cm
Mean = Total ÷ 12 = 2260 ÷ 12 = 188 cm to the nearest cm.

204

Plenary

Discuss which is the best average to use in questions 2 and 3.
Use a number line to illustrate outlying values and emphasise how these can distort a measure of average.

Further activities

Students should find relevant averages typical of the data in their own projects.

Students can find all the averages for each question and discuss the pros and cons of each representation.

Differentiation

Support questions:

- Questions 1 and 2 focus on the mode and range.
- Questions 3–5 focus on all three averages.
- Question 6 focuses on which is the best average to use.

Core tier: focuses on finding the mean, median and mode, including from a table of data.

Exercise D3.4

1 Here are the drinks which a group of students have one lunchtime.

Drink	Number of people
Cola	8
Water	9
Juice	5
Lemonade	4

Use the information in the table to find the **mode**.

2 The table below shows midday temperatures.

Day	Mon	Tue	Wed	Thu	Fri
Temperature (°C)	17	20	21	19	11

Find the **range** of these temperatures.

3 A group of five students measure their heights. Here are their results.

Student	Bob	Jo	Asif	Jen	Kay
Height (cm)	152	137	155	144	149

Arrange the heights in order, and find the **median** height.

4 There are five passengers in a lift. The table below shows the weight (in kg) of each passenger.

Passenger	A	B	C	D	E
Weight (kg)	72	48	51	98	67

a Find the **total** weight of the five passengers.
b Now work out the **mean** weight for the passengers.

5 The table below shows the waiting times for 20 patients at a doctor's surgery.

Waiting time (Minutes)	0–9	10–19	20–29	30–39
Number of patients	4	7	5	4

Find the **modal class** of the waiting times.

6 For the data in question 2, find the **median** and **mean**. Which do you think is the better average to use to describe the average temperature? Explain your answer.

205

Exercise commentary

The questions assess the objective on Primary Framework Page 117.

Problem solving

Question 6 assesses Primary Framework Page 77 if students explain reasoning.

Group work

Question 6 and the further activity are suitable for pairs.

Misconceptions

Students should be encouraged to think about which is the best average to use. Emphasise it should be typical of the data.

Students make various errors when working with averages, in particular:

- Not ordering numbers to find the median.
  Encourage students to always order data whichever average they want to find – ordering the data makes it easier to understand anyway.
- Writing the frequency rather than the category as the mode.
  Emphasise the mode is always part of the original data set.
- Dividing by the highest number when finding the mean.
  Encourage students to start by counting the data values.
- Mixing up the averages.
  Discuss ways to remember as a group.

Links

Ordering: Primary Framework Page 9.
Add several numbers: Page 43.

Homework

In **D3.4HW** students are asked to find an average for the data that they have collected.

Answers

1 Water
2 10 °C
3 137, 144, 149, 152, 155; 149 cm is the median height
4 **a** 336 kg **b** 67.2 kg
5 10–19 minutes
6 Median = 19 °C, mean = 17.6 °C
The median is the best as the mean is affected by the low 11°C.

Mental starter

Above average!

Pose mean problems such as:

- The mean of a set of five data is 6.
  What is the total of the data?
- The mean of a set of five data is 6.
  What must be added to make the mean of the six data 7?

Useful resources

Reuse OHPs from throughout the unit to discuss each of the stages.

D3.5OHP shows the report from the student book.

Introductory activity

Go back to the original question from D3.1.

Discuss and summarise the steps you have been through in the enquiry:

1 Planned data collection:
- Which data to collect
- Where to find it?
- How to collect it?

2 Displayed the data:
- What does the data show?
- How best to display it?
- Which data to compare?

3 Summarised the data:
- What average is typical?
- How wide is the spread?

Emphasise the need to refer to the initial question throughout the enquiry to ensure the data collection, display and analysis is relevant to the problem.

Discuss what happens next.

Emphasise that you put all this information together in a report that describes all the steps in relation to the initial enquiry.

Use **D3.5OHP** to discuss the main features of a report and also whether the report is fair.

- Highlight that you can show all the working out in an appendix so as not to disturb the flow of the report.
- Emphasise that all diagrams should be relevant and not repetitive, and that their main features should be summarised.

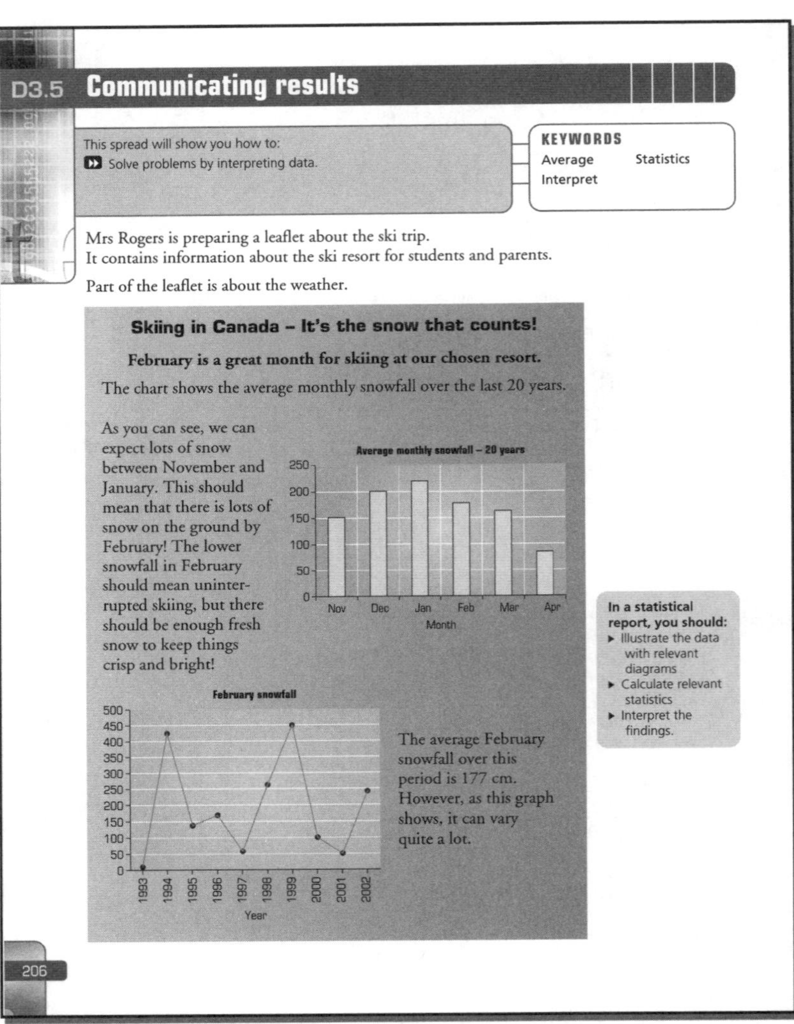

D3.5 Communicating results

This spread will show you how to:
- Solve problems by interpreting data.

KEYWORDS
Average
Interpret
Statistics

Mrs Rogers is preparing a leaflet about the ski trip.
It contains information about the ski resort for students and parents.

Part of the leaflet is about the weather.

Skiing in Canada – It's the snow that counts!

February is a great month for skiing at our chosen resort.

The chart shows the average monthly snowfall over the last 20 years.

As you can see, we can expect lots of snow between November and January. This should mean that there is lots of snow on the ground by February! The lower snowfall in February should mean uninterrupted skiing, but there should be enough fresh snow to keep things crisp and bright!

The average February snowfall over this period is 177 cm. However, as this graph shows, it can vary quite a lot.

In a statistical report, you should:
- Illustrate the data with relevant diagrams
- Calculate relevant statistics
- Interpret the findings.

206

Plenary

- What factors, other than weather, should Mrs Rogers consider in her leaflet?

How could she collect data?

- Discuss the use of statistics by others: lies, damned lies and statistics.

Emphasise that you can collect data to show what you want but that in a good statistical enquiry you would be impartial to the result.

Further activities

Students should summarise their findings in their own projects.
They should be encouraged to criticise the ways they have communicated their results and try to improve each aspect of the project.

D3.2ICT shows how to integrate diagrams into Word documents.

Differentiation

Support questions:

- Question 1 focuses on interpreting simple data.
- Question 2 provides a step by step method for summarising more complex data.
- Question 3 requires students to criticise a summary and reinterpret the findings.

Core tier: focuses on identifying bias in statistical representations.

Exercise D3.5

1 A class has a vote to decide where to go on an end-of-year day trip. Here are the results:

Destination	Wonder Park	Seaside	Animal World
Votes	17	6	8

Write a short report explaining where the class will go.
Use a bar chart to illustrate the results of the vote.

2 Ten students record the number of times they use the Internet one term. Here are their results.

Student	A	B	C	D	E	F	G	H	I	J
Times used	1	4	0	1	2	1	0	4	1	3

Write a short article about the results for a school newsletter. Your article should include:

- A **bar chart** to show the survey results.
- An **average** for the data.
- The **range** of the data.
- Some **conclusions** about what the data show.

3 George has to carry out a survey of 25 customers each year, and send a report to head office.

'How happy are you with our service?'	Very Unhappy	Unhappy	Satisfied	Happy	Delighted
Last Year	6	6	4	2	7
This Year	7	7	3	0	8

Here is part of the data he has gathered.

It's been another great year here at the Camtown branch! Once again, the most common response from our customers was that they were 'delighted' with our service – and we had even more 'delighted' customers than last year.

Here is the start of his report:

a How is his report unfair?

b Write a fairer report, based on the information in the table.

207

Exercise commentary

The questions assess the objective on Primary Framework Page 117.

Problem solving

The questions assess Primary Framework Page 77 when students explain reasoning.

Group work

Question 4 is suitable for paired discussion.

Misconceptions

Effective communication of findings is one of the aspects of statistical project work that students find difficult as it is so open-ended.

Students should be encouraged to explain:

- what they are investigating and why
- how they collected the data
- what conclusions they can reach based on the question they are investigating and, in particular, how the data shows this through relevant charts and averages.

Students should work through the exercise to gain confidence in making summary statements and then apply the techniques in their project summaries.

Links

This aspect of data handling will be used in other areas of the curriculum when students undertake projects.

Homework

In **D3.5HW** students are asked to summarise the findings of their projects.

Answers

1 Wonder Park was the most popular choice.
2 Mean = 1.7, mode = 1, median = 1, range = 4
3 **a** The number of very unhappy and unhappy customers has increased.

Summary

The Year 6 key teaching objective is:

- Solve a problem by extracting and interpreting data in tables, graphs and charts (115, 117).

Plenary activity

Give students a list of eight people's hourly wages:
£5, £4.50, £5, £8, £12, £15, £7.50, £75

Discuss:

- How to describe the data (secondary, discrete).
- How to display the data (bar chart).
- Which is the most appropriate average to use and why (the £75 value shows how the data can be distorted by outlying values so the median is a better measure).

Check out commentary

1 This question may be difficult for students as they have to analyse what the average means.
Emphasise that it is important to think about the most appropriate average to use for the data. Encourage them to order the data before finding the average as this will help them decide which is the most appropriate one to use and it will also help them to find the median correctly.
The outlying values make the median a good average to use.
Many students will also find the mean which can be useful. They should realise that the best method is to use a calculator as there are so many values, but they should check that the mean they find is in the range of the values.

2 Again, open questions like this one can cause students difficulties as they find it hard to make a start.
The list of prompts should help overcome this.
Emphasise that students should be using only relevant diagrams and statistics.
Encourage them to always analyse each one of their findings to ensure they are relevant and then to summarise all these findings in their report.

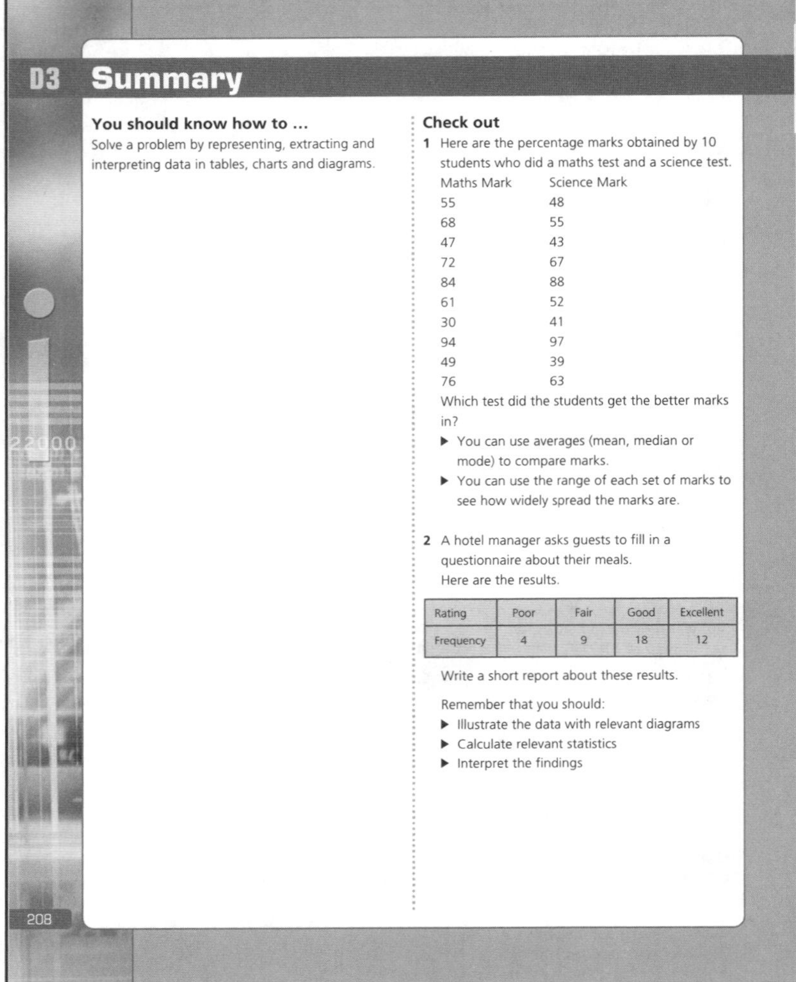

D3 Summary

You should know how to …

Solve a problem by representing, extracting and interpreting data in tables, charts and diagrams.

Check out

1 Here are the percentage marks obtained by 10 students who did a maths test and a science test.

Maths Mark	Science Mark
55	48
68	55
47	43
72	67
84	88
61	52
30	41
94	97
49	39
76	63

Which test did the students get the better marks in?

- You can use averages (mean, median or mode) to compare marks.
- You can use the range of each set of marks to see how widely spread the marks are.

2 A hotel manager asks guests to fill in a questionnaire about their meals.
Here are the results.

Rating	Poor	Fair	Good	Excellent
Frequency	4	9	18	12

Write a short report about these results.

Remember that you should:

- Illustrate the data with relevant diagrams
- Calculate relevant statistics
- Interpret the findings

208

Development

Students will be encouraged to undertake a statistical project in Year 8 in D1.

Links

Students should apply the data handling cycle whenever they undertake a statistical enquiry or experiment/testing.

Mental starters

Objectives covered in this unit:

- Order simple fractions.
- Know pairs of factors of numbers to 100.
- Convert between fractions and decimals.

Resources needed

* means class set needed

Essential:

D4.2OHP – Frequency table example
D4.3OHP – Experiment results

Useful:

R2* – Decimal digit cards
R3* – Fraction cards
R11* (OHP) – Tally chart
D4.1OHP – Equally likely outcomes
Card, tape, scissors

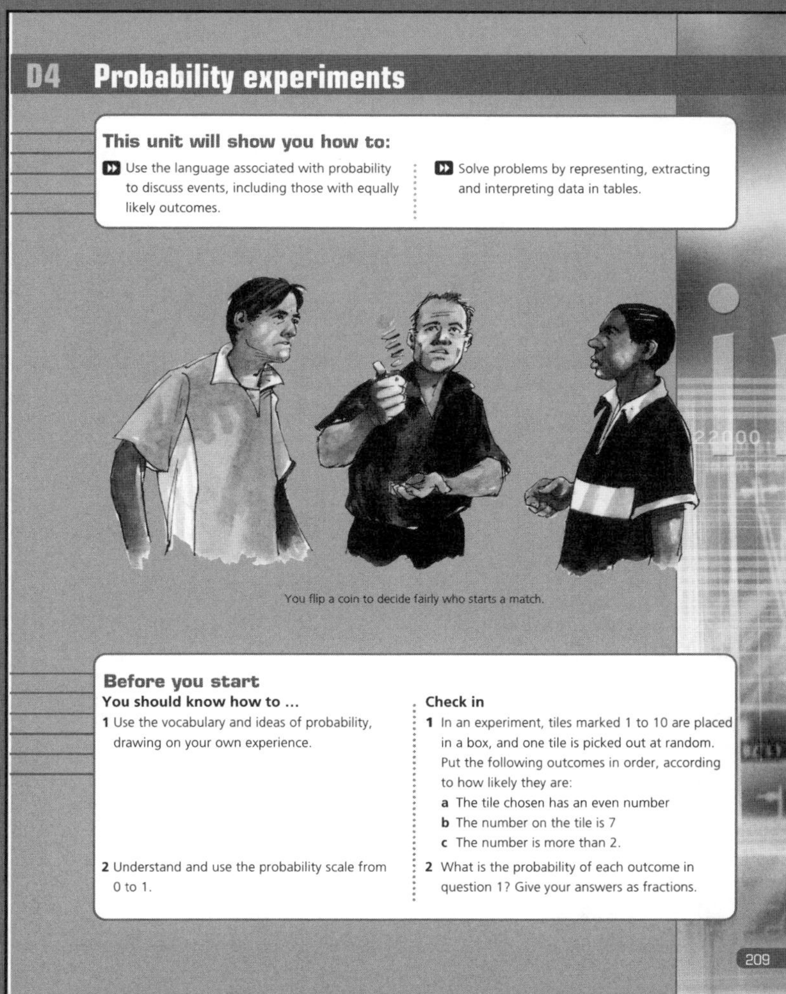

D4 Probability experiments

This unit will show you how to:

- Use the language associated with probability to discuss events, including those with equally likely outcomes.
- Solve problems by representing, extracting and interpreting data in tables.

You flip a coin to decide fairly who starts a match.

Before you start

You should know how to ...	Check in
1 Use the vocabulary and ideas of probability, drawing on your own experience.	1 In an experiment, tiles marked 1 to 10 are placed in a box, and one tile is picked out at random. Put the following outcomes in order, according to how likely they are: **a** The tile chosen has an even number **b** The number on the tile is 7 **c** The number is more than 2.
2 Understand and use the probability scale from 0 to 1.	2 What is the probability of each outcome in question 1? Give your answers as fractions.

209

Unit commentary

Aim of the unit

This unit aims to develop the quantitative approach to probability introduced in D1. Students will explore the relationship between theoretical and experimental probability in more detail.

Introduction

The picture shows a situation that should be unpredictable – the outcome is a matter of luck. Weighting the coin would be unusual but weighting dice or lottery games on purpose or accidentally is quite common. In this unit students will test for fairness.

Framework references

This unit focuses on:

- Year 6 teaching objectives pages: 112, 114, 116
- Problem solving objectives page: 77

The unit provides access to:

- Year 7 teaching objectives pages: 278–284

Check in activity

Discuss where to place various events on a probability line, for example:

- A dog will have kittens.
- A fair dice will show a prime number.
- You will predict the correct outcome of a flip of a coin.
- Your name will be chosen at random from the register.
- You will win the lottery.

Students should justify placements using numbers as appropriate.

Differentiation

Core tier focuses on analysing experimental probabilities to test for fairness and introduces the idea of simulating experiments.

D4.1 Theoretical probability

Mental starter

What's my pair?
List the factors of 72, grouping them in factor pairs.
Start by saying that 1 and 72 are a factor pair because 1 × 72 = 72.
Ask for other factor pairs of 72, and students respond individually.

List them all and ask how many factors 72 has in total.

Useful resources

D4.1OHP illustrates the example in the student book.

Introductory activity

Recap probability from D1.
Discuss the meaning of the word 'probability'. Encourage responses like a measure of chance, or likelihood.

Discuss uncertain events, that is events that could have a variety of outcomes.
Examples could include:

- throwing a dice
- spinning a coin
- predicting tomorrow's weather.

In each case, list the possible outcomes and try to quantify the probability.

Discuss why probability is measured on a scale of 0 to 1.
0 = impossible; 1 = certain
Define the probability of an outcome as the number of ways the outcome can happen divided by the total number of possible outcomes.
Discuss how to write a probability as a fraction or a decimal.

Introduce the use of the formula with the example from the student book, which is illustrated on **D4.1OHP**.
You may need to recap factors and multiples from N5.2.
Explain that the **event** is 'drawing a card at random'. The **outcomes** are the numbers 0 to 10.
Discuss the word '**random**' (without preference).
Emphasise that to calculate the probability of an outcome, you need to list **all** the possible outcomes.

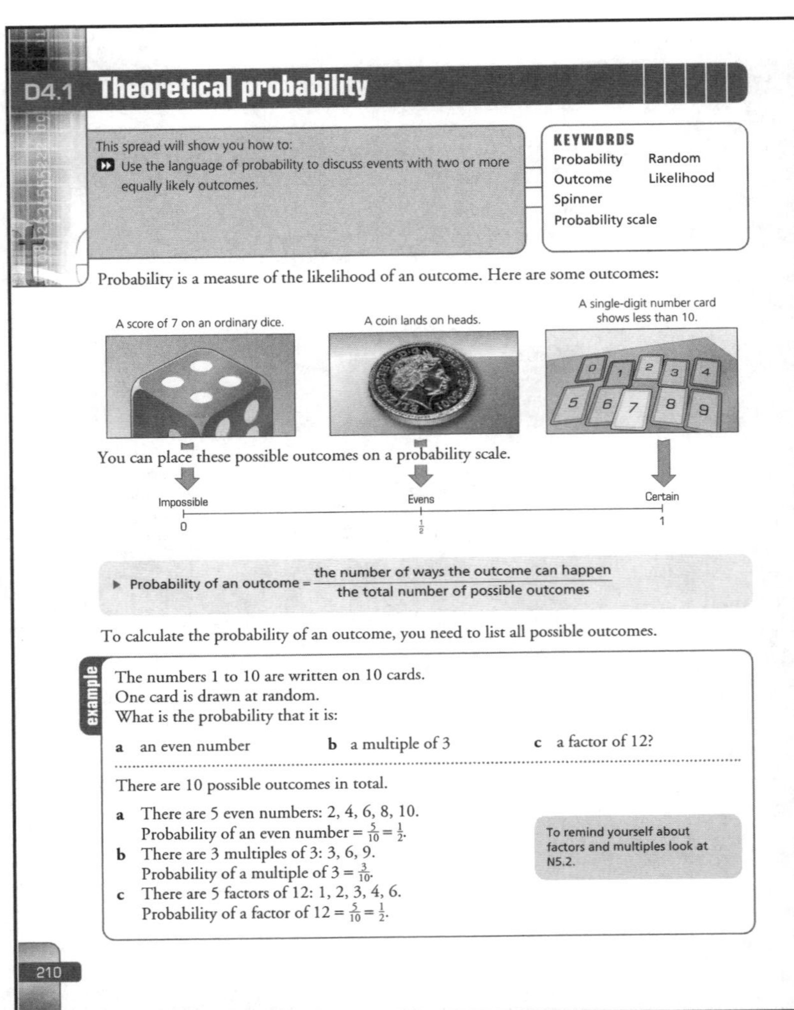

D4.1 Theoretical probability

This spread will show you how to:
- Use the language of probability to discuss events with two or more equally likely outcomes.

KEYWORDS
Probability, Random, Outcome, Likelihood, Spinner, Probability scale

Probability is a measure of the likelihood of an outcome. Here are some outcomes:

A score of 7 on an ordinary dice. — A coin lands on heads. — A single-digit number card shows less than 10.

You can place these possible outcomes on a probability scale.

Impossible 0 — Evens $\frac{1}{2}$ — Certain 1

- Probability of an outcome = $\dfrac{\text{the number of ways the outcome can happen}}{\text{the total number of possible outcomes}}$

To calculate the probability of an outcome, you need to list all possible outcomes.

example

The numbers 1 to 10 are written on 10 cards.
One card is drawn at random.
What is the probability that it is:

a an even number **b** a multiple of 3 **c** a factor of 12?

There are 10 possible outcomes in total.

a There are 5 even numbers: 2, 4, 6, 8, 10.
Probability of an even number = $\frac{5}{10} = \frac{1}{2}$.
b There are 3 multiples of 3: 3, 6, 9.
Probability of a multiple of 3 = $\frac{3}{10}$.
c There are 5 factors of 12: 1, 2, 3, 4, 6.
Probability of a factor of 12 = $\frac{5}{10} = \frac{1}{2}$.

To remind yourself about factors and multiples look at N5.2.

210

Plenary

Discuss questions 1 and 2.
Discuss how can you tell whether outcomes are equally likely or not.

Further activities

Students could label each of the outcomes with a description of its likelihood, choosing from:

- impossible
- very unlikely
- unlikely
- evens
- likely
- very likely
- certain.

Differentiation

Support questions:

- Questions 1 and 2 focus on identifying outcomes.
- Questions 3 and 4 involve finding probabilities based on equally likely outcomes.
- Questions 5 and 6 focus on using a probability scale.

Core tier: focuses on events with a greater number of outcomes.

Exercise D4.1

1 For each of the following situations, say how many possible outcomes there are.

a Kelly rolls an ordinary dice and records the score.
b Pat records whether or not it snows each day.
c Charles puts tickets numbered 1 to 100 in a bag, and then picks one.
d Marcia makes a note of whether or not an elephant walks past her window one morning.

2 For each part of question 1, say whether or not the outcomes are equally likely.
Give reasons for your answers.

3 Mikela writes the letters of her name on a fair 6-sided spinner.
She spins the spinner, and makes a note of the letter touching the table.
What is the probability that the result is:
a M **b** A vowel **c** L or K?

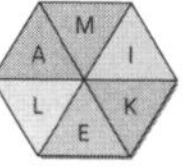

4 Cards numbered 1 to 100 are placed in a box.
What is the probability that a card chosen at random will be:
a 100 **b** An even number
c A number bigger than 20 **d** A number less than 200?
Give your answers as fractions.

5 Mark each of the outcomes from question 4 on a probability scale like this one:

0 — $\frac{1}{2}$ — 1

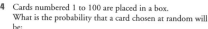

6 The letters of the word ENVELOPE are written on cards, and placed in a bag.
What is the probability that a card chosen at random shows:
a E **b** N **c** A vowel **d** J?
Mark each of these probabilities on a probability scale.

Exercise commentary

The questions assess the objective on Primary Framework Page 113.

Problem solving

Question 2 assesses Primary Framework Page 77.

Group work

Students may discuss placements in questions 5 and 6.

Misconceptions

Many students struggle to realise that outcomes must be equally likely before you can use simple probabilities.
Question 1 is designed to draw this out.
Some students find probability very confusing, especially when they start to describe them with numbers. It is common for students to write the answer to 3b as $\frac{1}{3}$ rather than $\frac{3}{6}$.
This links to describing the fraction of a shape that is shaded where the shaded parts must be of equal size. Emphasise that the denominator describes the total number of outcomes – link back to N2.1.
Students may find question 4 hard to visualise and need to use a 100 square.
In question 7 some students will need to be reminded that all the letters are put into the bag, including repeated letters.

Links

Fractions: Primary Framework Page 23.
Decimals: Page 31.

Homework

D4.1HW provides practice in listing outcomes and calculating probabilities.

Answers

1 **a** 6 **b** 2 **c** 100 **d** 2

2 **a** Equally likely **b** Not equally likely **c** Equally likely **d** Not equally likely

3 **a** $\frac{1}{6}$ **b** $\frac{3}{6} = \frac{1}{2}$ **c** $\frac{2}{6} = \frac{1}{3}$

4 **a** $\frac{1}{100}$ **b** $\frac{50}{100} = \frac{1}{2}$ **c** $\frac{80}{100} = \frac{4}{5}$ **d** $\frac{100}{100} = 1$

6 **a** $\frac{3}{8}$ **b** $\frac{1}{8}$ **c** $\frac{4}{8} = \frac{1}{2}$ **d** 0

D4.2 Experimental probability

Mental starter

Odd one out

List four fractions, three of which are equivalent.

For example, $\frac{6}{42}$, $\frac{3}{21}$, $\mathbf{\frac{7}{48}}$, $\frac{1}{7}$

Students attempt to identify the odd one out (indicated in bold).

List some more sets of four:

$\frac{1}{2}$, $\frac{5}{10}$, $\frac{10}{20}$, $\mathbf{\frac{15}{45}}$ $\quad$ $\frac{3}{7}$, $\frac{12}{28}$, $\mathbf{\frac{9}{24}}$, $\frac{6}{14}$

$\mathbf{\frac{6}{18}}$, $\frac{2}{5}$, $\frac{4}{10}$, $\frac{8}{20}$ $\quad$ $\frac{3}{4}$, $\frac{30}{40}$, $\mathbf{\frac{9}{15}}$, $\frac{12}{16}$

Useful resources

D4.2OHP shows the tally chart from the student book.

R11 has a blank tally chart.

Sheets of card, **tape** and **scissors** for the exercise.

Introductory activity

Recap theoretical probability from the previous lesson.

Emphasise that it is theoretical because it is based on assumptions, namely that:

- You know all possible outcomes.
- You know how likely each outcome is.

If you do not know this information for a particular event, you can work out probabilities by performing a probability experiment.

Discuss the example in the student book.

The tally chart is shown on **D4.2OHP**.

In a probability experiment you:

- observe a set of **trials**, or repetitions of the event (James' event is recording the colour of a car)
- complete a tally chart and calculate frequencies for each outcome (James' outcomes are blue, black, purple...)
- convert the frequencies into experimental probabilities (6 purple cars out of 50 gives a probability of $\frac{6}{50}$, or $\frac{3}{25}$).

Discuss what the formula for experimental probability could be:

Probability of an outcome = number of times the outcome occurs divided by the number of trials in the experiment.

Emphasise that this is only an **estimate.**

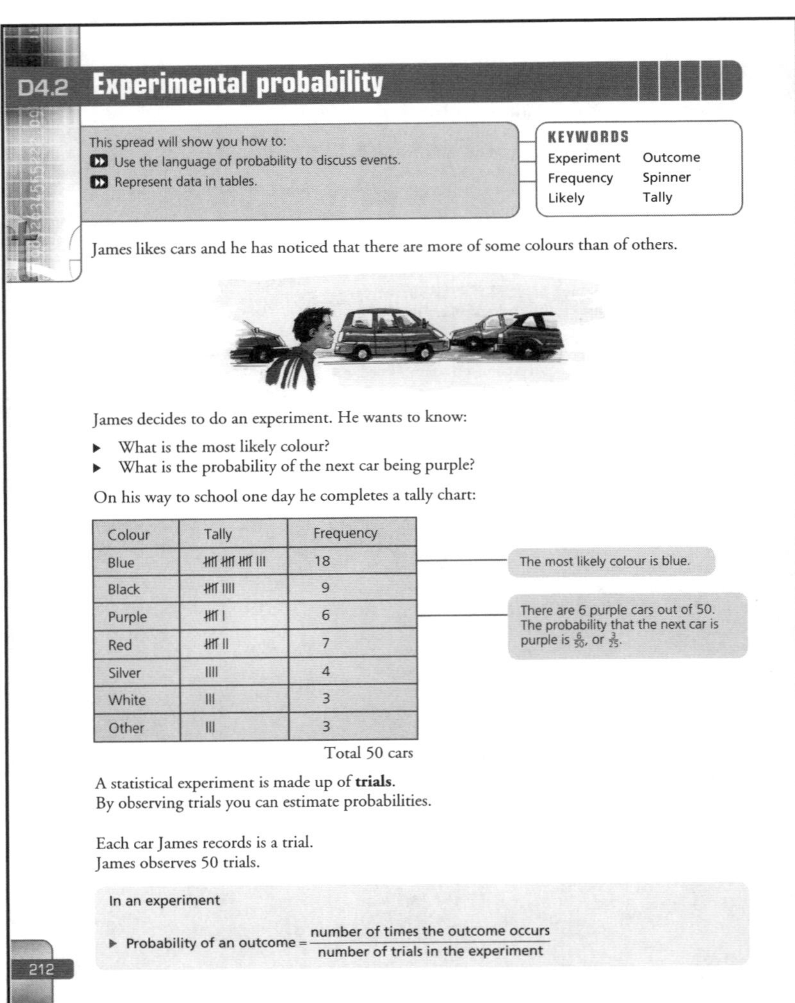

D4.2 **Experimental probability**

This spread will show you how to:
- Use the language of probability to discuss events.
- Represent data in tables.

KEYWORDS
Experiment, Frequency, Likely, Outcome, Spinner, Tally

James likes cars and he has noticed that there are more of some colours than of others.

James decides to do an experiment. He wants to know:

- What is the most likely colour?
- What is the probability of the next car being purple?

On his way to school one day he completes a tally chart:

Colour	Tally	Frequency
Blue	卌 卌 卌 III	18
Black	卌 IIII	9
Purple	卌 I	6
Red	卌 II	7
Silver	IIII	4
White	III	3
Other	III	3

Total 50 cars

The most likely colour is blue.

There are 6 purple cars out of 50. The probability that the next car is purple is $\frac{6}{50}$, or $\frac{3}{25}$.

A statistical experiment is made up of **trials**.
By observing trials you can estimate probabilities.

Each car James records is a trial.
James observes 50 trials.

In an experiment

- Probability of an outcome = $\frac{\text{number of times the outcome occurs}}{\text{number of trials in the experiment}}$

212

Plenary

Discuss the experiment in the exercise.

- Which numbers are more likely to occur, and why?
- What is the estimated probability for each value – do students get similar or very different values for this?
- Why spin the spinner 100 times? Why not just 10, or even once?

Further activities

Students who work quickly should be encouraged to increase the number of trials to say 200 and describe what effect this has on the experimental probabilities.

Differentiation

Support questions:

The differentiation depends on the successful completion of parts of the experiment:

- recording the results in a table
- estimating the probability of each score
- writing a report of the findings.

Core tier: focuses on estimating probabilities from an experiment with unequally likely outcomes.

Exercise D4.2

Experiment

- Make a rectangular spinner from card, using this design.
  You can trace the shape onto card.

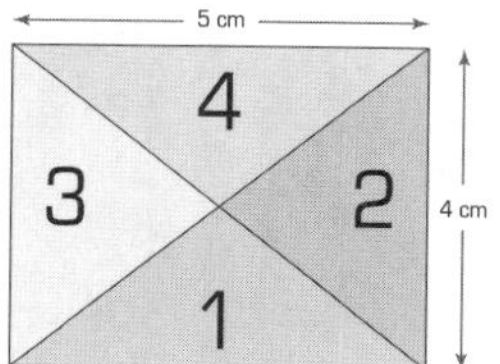

You can use a pencil for the 'spindle';
Use sticky tape to hold it in place, if necessary.
Try to keep everything straight and symmetrical!

- Test your spinner to estimate the probability for each score.
- Spin your spinner 100 times. Record your results in a table like this:

Score	Tally	Frequency
1		
2		
3		
4		

- When you have finished, **work out an estimate of the probability for each score**.
- Write a report of your findings, explaining what you have found out about your spinner.

Exercise commentary

The questions assess the objective on Primary Framework Page 113.

Problem solving

The last part of the experiment assesses Primary Framework Page 77.

Group work

Students should work in pairs or small groups.

Misconceptions

Many students will not realise that the four possible outcomes are not equally likely as the spinner is rectangular rather than square.

Link back to N2.1 and emphasise that the parts are not equal and so neither are the outcomes.

Students may find it hard to write down probabilities from the table.

Encourage them to add a line for the total and emphasise that the probability of an outcome is the frequency/total.

Weaker students may benefit from supportive questioning:

- How many trials?
- How many 2s?
- What fraction are 2s?

Some students will also benefit from having a ready-made spinner.

Links

Fractions: Primary Framework Page 23.
Frequency tables: Page 115.

Homework

In D4.2HW students are asked to evaluate probabilities from given experimental data.

Answers

The exercise is an experiment. There are no unique answers.

D4.3 Comparing experiment with theory

Mental starter

Fraction to decimal

Read out some fractions, such as $\frac{1}{10}$, $\frac{1}{5}$, $\frac{1}{4}$, $\frac{4}{5}$ etc.
Students respond with the decimal equivalent.
They can use decimal digit cards.

Read out some decimals, such as 0.5, 0.75, 0.9, 0.4 etc.
Students respond with the fraction equivalent.
They can use fraction cards.

Useful resources

R2 decimal digit cards for the mental starter activity.
R3 fraction cards for the mental starter activity.
D4.3OHP shows the results from the student book.

Introductory activity

Recap experimental and theoretical probability.
Theoretical probability is calculated by making assumptions. You don't spin any coins or throw any dice.
Experimental probability is calculated by performing an experiment.

Discuss the example of a four-sided spinner, as described in the student book.
Recap the experiment in D4.2, where students made an unfair or 'loaded' spinner.
Discuss what is meant by a fair spinner.
What would the probability of each outcome be? Encourage responses like 'one chance in four', or $\frac{1}{4}$, or 0.25.

Discuss Rob and Maria's results on D4.3OHP.
Address these issues:
- Why do they need 50 trials?
- Why are the experimental probabilities different to the theoretical probabilities?
- With 50 trials, would it be possible to have the frequencies all the same? (No).
- Which is correct – the theoretical or the experimental probability?

(You perform the experiment to test the theory.)
Emphasise that if you increase the number of trials, the experimental probability becomes more accurate.

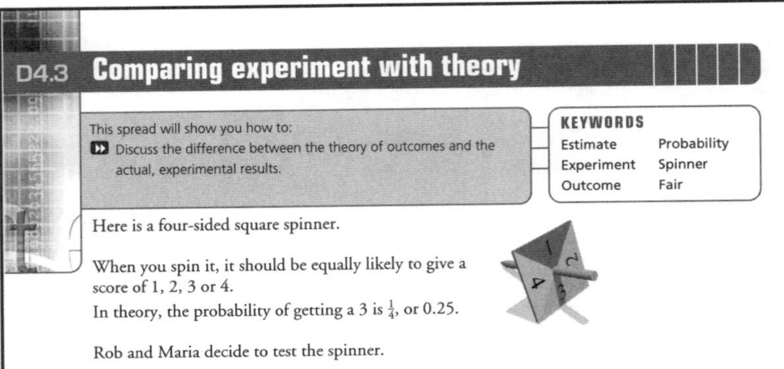

D4.3 **Comparing experiment with theory**

This spread will show you how to:
- Discuss the difference between the theory of outcomes and the actual, experimental results.

KEYWORDS: Estimate, Experiment, Outcome, Probability, Spinner, Fair

Here is a four-sided square spinner.

When you spin it, it should be equally likely to give a score of 1, 2, 3 or 4.
In theory, the probability of getting a 3 is $\frac{1}{4}$, or 0.25.

Rob and Maria decide to test the spinner.
- They spin the spinner and record the score.
- They repeat the experiment 50 times and keep a tally.

Here are their results:

Score	Tally	Frequency
1	卌 卌 III	13
2	卌 卌 卌	15
3	卌 卌	10
4	卌 卌 II	12

From the experiment, Rob and Maria can estimate the probability of getting a 3.

$$\text{Experimental probability} = \frac{\text{number of times the outcome occurs}}{\text{total number of outcomes}}$$
$$= \frac{10}{50}$$
$$= \frac{1}{5} \text{ or } 0.2$$

Compare with the theoretical probability of 0.25.

The two probabilities are similar.

There is no reason to think that the spinner is unfair.

- Theoretical and experimental probabilities should be similar, but are unlikely to be exactly the same.

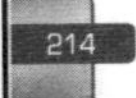

Plenary

Discuss question 4.
How many times does a coin have to come up heads before you start to suspect that it is an unfair coin?

Keep the discussion qualitative, but encourage students to suggest implausible outcomes – for instance, 10 heads in 10 throws.

Further activities

Students can conduct a short experiment based in question 4:
If a single trial consists of spinning a coin four times, how frequently would you expect to get the result 'four of the same'?

Differentiation

Support questions:

- Question 1 focuses on estimating probabilities.
- Questions 2 and 3 focus on how much variation is acceptable before you assume bias.
- Questions 4 and 5 focus on the effect of sample size.

Core tier: focuses on combining experimental results and comparing with theoretical probabilities.

Exercise D4.3

1 Asif spins a spinner 100 times, and gets these results.

Score	1	2	3	4
Frequency	37	28	12	23

Estimate the probability of each score for the spinner.

2 Sara tosses the same coin 100 times. Here are her results:

Outcome	Frequency
Heads	54
Tails	46

Sara says: 'There were more heads than tails, but I still think the coin is probably fair.'
Explain why Sara is correct.

3 Sam rolls a dice 60 times, and gets these results:

Score	1	2	3	4	5	6
Frequency	8	7	14	11	12	8

a Do you think that Sam's dice is fair?
b What should Sam do if he wants to be more certain?

4 Claire tosses a coin four times, and gets 'heads' every time.
She says:

There must be something funny about this coin.
I should be getting as many tails as heads.

Explain why Claire is wrong.

5 Devra is testing a five-sided spinner to see whether it is fair.
She spins the spinner 50 times. Here are her results.

Outcome	Red	Black	Yellow	Green	Blue
Frequency	10	8	13	13	6

Lionel tests the same spinner, but he spins it 500 times.
Here are his results.

Outcome	Red	Black	Yellow	Green	Blue
Frequency	96	112	90	109	94

Do you think the spinner is fair? Explain your answer.

215

Exercse commentary

The questions assess the objective on Primary Framework Page 113.

Problem solving

Questions 2–5 assess Primary Framework Page 77.

Group work

The further activity is suitable for pairs.

Misconceptions

Students often have difficulty with the main focus of this spread.
Experiments will rarely throw up the exact results expected in theory. If they did we would be highly suspicious!
Students own experimental work with coins and dice should help illustrate this.
Discussing the amount of variation to accept before assuming bias can be useful especially if it is based on an actual experiment (coins, dice) so that students can appreciate the amounts involved.
Similarly, students may not appreciate that the more trials performed, the closer to the theory you should get.
Question 5 shows that the more trials, the more significant the results.

Links

Fractions: Primary Framework Page 23.
Frequency tables: Page 115.

Homework

D4.3HW is an experiment involving throwing a dice.

Answers

1 Probability of 1 $\approx \frac{37}{100}$, probability of 2 $\approx \frac{28}{100} = \frac{7}{25}$, probability of 3 $\approx \frac{12}{100} = \frac{3}{25}$, probability of 4 $\approx \frac{23}{100}$
2 The frequencies were close to 50.
3 **a** The dice is probably fair. **b** Roll the dice more times.
4 She needs to toss the coin more times before she can tell.
5 The spinner is probably fair. Each colour occurred roughly the same number of times.

Summary

The Year 6 key teaching objective is:

- Solve a problem by extracting and interpreting data in tables, graphs and charts (115, 117).

Plenary activity

Students imagine the numbers 1 to 20 are in a bag.
Ask them to place these outcomes on a probability scale, justifying placements:

- even number
- prime number
- multiple of 3, 5, 7, 11
- factor of 24, 72, 100
- number less than 100, greater than 23, etc.

Check out commentary

1 Students often find difficulty with the use of fractions in probability, commonly writing answers as whole numbers instead. Encourage students to always think of a probability scale – imagining the scale can help them remember that probabilities are between 0 and 1 as the scale has a definite beginning and end.
Supportive questioning will help:

- How many numbers altogether?
- How many of them are 15?
- What fraction are 15?
- What is the probability of 15?

Students may still find difficulty with part **c** where the answer is 0.
Use the language of probability to emphasise that picking a 3 is impossible so the probability is 0.

2 In part **a** some students find it hard to distinguish between theoretical and experimental probabilities and will believe all three dice are biased as none of the results are perfect.
Carrying out the experiment themselves should help emphasise that they won't always get perfect results. It will also help them get a feel for what is a reasonable amount of variation.
In part **b** students need to realise that the total number of trials is 240 (not 960 or 60) and use that as the denominator of the fraction.

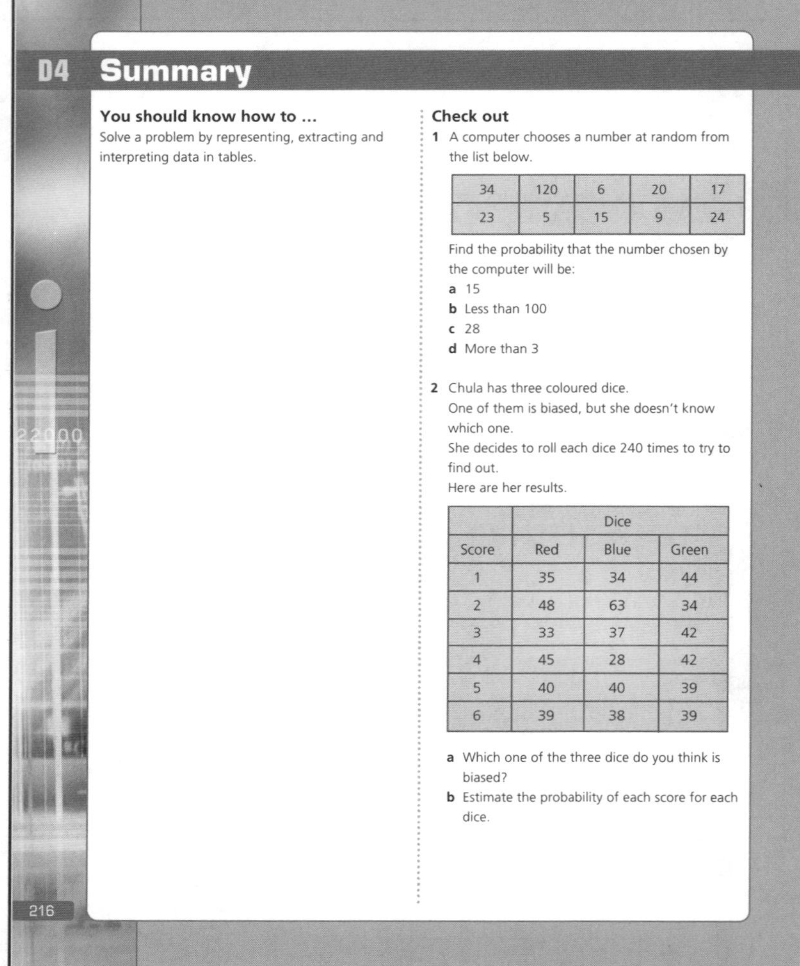

D4 Summary

You should know how to …
Solve a problem by representing, extracting and interpreting data in tables.

Check out

1 A computer chooses a number at random from the list below.

34	120	6	20	17
23	5	15	9	24

Find the probability that the number chosen by the computer will be:
a 15
b Less than 100
c 28
d More than 3

2 Chula has three coloured dice.
One of them is biased, but she doesn't know which one.
She decides to roll each dice 240 times to try to find out.
Here are her results.

	Dice		
Score	Red	Blue	Green
1	35	34	44
2	48	63	34
3	33	37	42
4	45	28	42
5	40	40	39
6	39	38	39

a Which one of the three dice do you think is biased?
b Estimate the probability of each score for each dice.

216

Development

The themes of this unit are developed further in Year 8 in D2.

Links

Probability links to recognising the equivalence between fractions, decimals and percentages in number. The experimental aspect has strong links to testing undertaken in science and technology.

Mental starters

Objectives covered in this unit:

- Count on and back in steps.
- Know complements to 100.
- Recall multiplication and division facts to 10×10.
- Derive answers to calculations.
- Solve equations such as $100 = x + 37$.
- Use the formula for the area of a rectangle.
- Read and plot coordinates in the first quadrant.

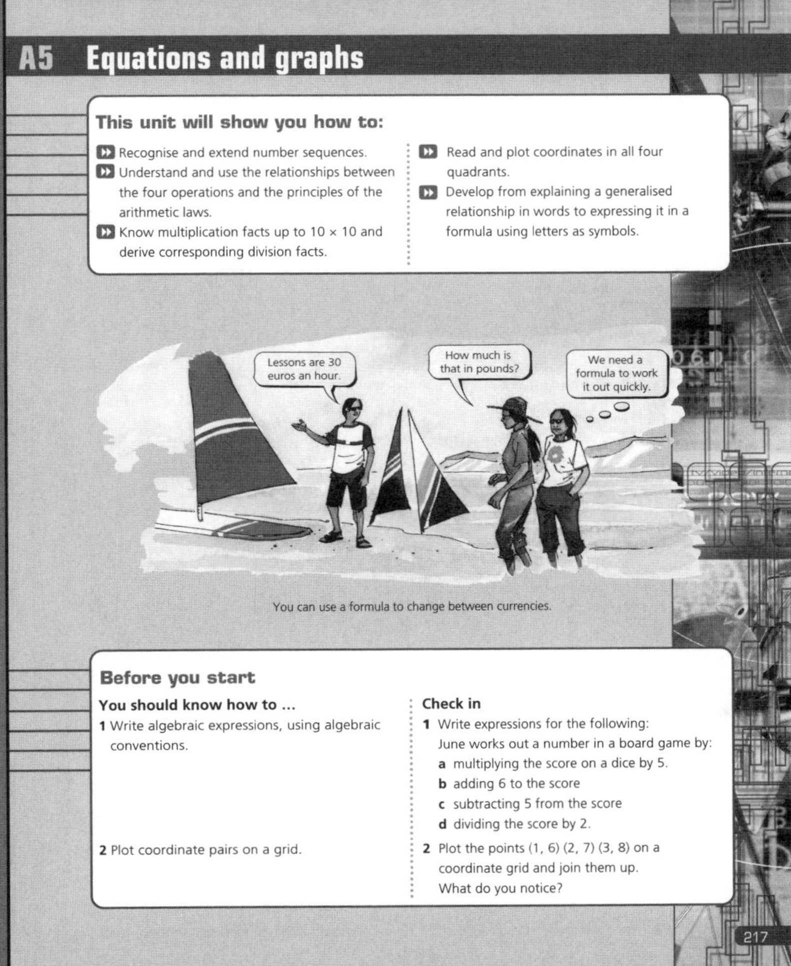

A5 Equations and graphs

This unit will show you how to:

- Recognise and extend number sequences.
- Understand and use the relationships between the four operations and the principles of the arithmetic laws.
- Know multiplication facts up to 10 × 10 and derive corresponding division facts.
- Read and plot coordinates in all four quadrants.
- Develop from explaining a generalised relationship in words to expressing it in a formula using letters as symbols.

Lessons are 30 euros an hour.
How much is that in pounds?
We need a formula to work it out quickly.

You can use a formula to change between currencies.

Before you start

You should know how to ...	Check in
1 Write algebraic expressions, using algebraic conventions.	1 Write expressions for the following: June works out a number in a board game by: **a** multiplying the score on a dice by 5. **b** adding 6 to the score **c** subtracting 5 from the score **d** dividing the score by 2.
2 Plot coordinate pairs on a grid.	2 Plot the points (1, 6) (2, 7) (3, 8) on a coordinate grid and join them up. What do you notice?

Check in activity

Ask simple 'think of a number' type questions and discuss how to write them as expressions:

I think of a number: x and

- add 2: $x + 2$ or
- double it: $2x$ or
- subtract 5: $x - 5$ etc.

Resources needed

* means class set needed

Essential:

R8* (OHP) – Coordinate grid
R9* (OHP) – Axes in one quadrant
A5.4OHP – Matchstick patterns
A5.7OHP – Conversion graph

Useful:

R1* – Digit cards
R7 (OHP) – Function machines
N1.2OHP – Negative number thermometers
A5.8ICT* – Exploring graphs using Omnigraph
Multilink cubes

Unit commentary

Aim of the unit

This unit aims to consolidate the algebra work from the whole book and to consolidate the links between sequences, functions and graphs.

Students will revise the use of letters and graphs to describe relationships, extending to plot graphs in all four quadrants.

Introduction

Discuss when students might need to change from one 'unit' to another, for example changing currency or changing between measurements.

Discuss how this might be made simpler – use a formula or a graph.

Framework references

This unit focuses on:

- Year 6 teaching objectives pages: 17, 53, 55, 59, 109
- Problem solving objectives page: 81

The unit provides access to:

- Year 7 teaching objectives pages: 112, 122, 138, 140, 154, 160, 162, 172, 218

Differentiation

Core tier focuses on expressing relationships using the conventional rules of algebra and considering features of straight-line graphs.

Springboard 7

Pages 395, 491, 492.

A5.1 Solving equations

Mental starter

The answer's 100

- Ask 'think of a number' questions which have an answer of 100.
- Students solve to find the number you are thinking of.

For example, I think of a number and:

- double it (50)
- multiply by 5 (20)
- add 27 (73)
- subtract 17 (83)

Useful resources

Multilink cubes may help solve equations.

Introductory activity

Refer to the mental starter.
Discuss how to write the problems as algebraic expressions – sentences using letters and numbers.

Emphasise the algebraic convention of leaving out the multiplication sign so when x is 3, $2x$ is 6 not 23!

Build up examples into expressions and write them on the board.
Give the expressions a value.
Remind students these are equations.
Discuss methods of solving the equations and emphasise working backwards, or undoing, as a good strategy.
$b + 2 = 6$ so $b = 6 - 2$.

- – undoes + so
- + undoes –

Ask what undoes ×. Use numerical examples and remind students they can write × sums any way round:
$2 \times 3 = 6$ and $6 \div 3 = 2$ or $6 \div 2 = 3$

- ÷ undoes × so
- × undoes ÷

Encourage students to see the equals sign as a balance – like a see-saw.
Work through the book examples.
Students should explain their methods.
Emphasise the process:

- What is the operation?
- How do I undo it without upsetting the balance?

Encourage students to check answers using substitution.

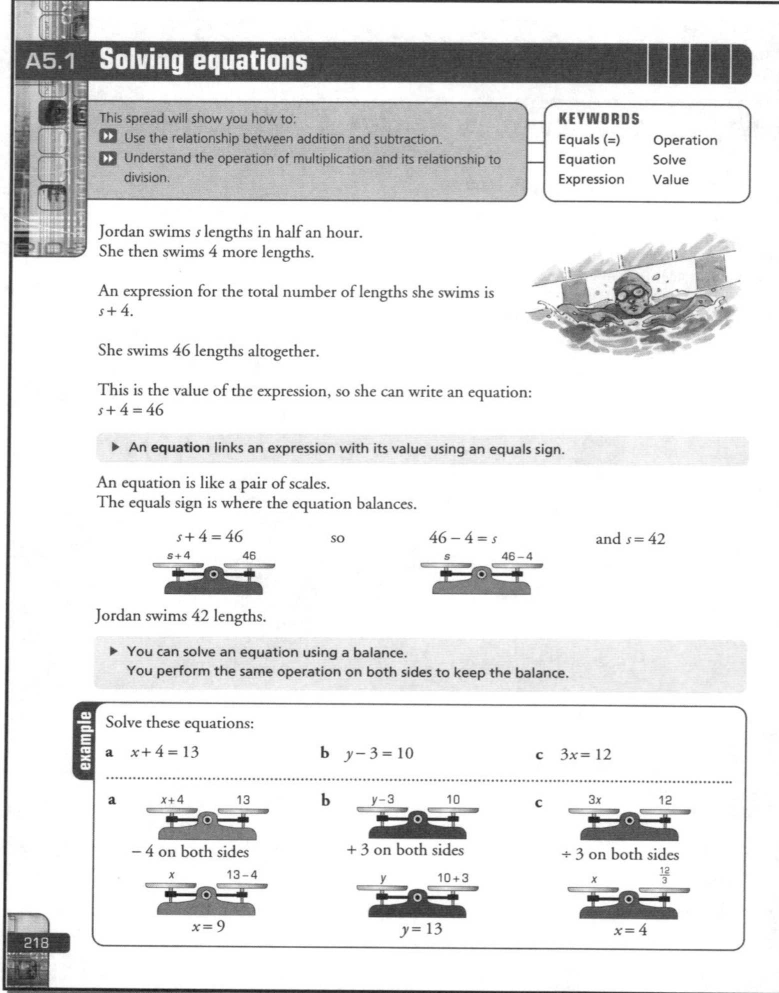

A5.1 **Solving equations**

This spread will show you how to:
- Use the relationship between addition and subtraction.
- Understand the operation of multiplication and its relationship to division.

KEYWORDS
Equals (=) · Operation · Equation · Solve · Expression · Value

Jordan swims s lengths in half an hour.
She then swims 4 more lengths.

An expression for the total number of lengths she swims is $s + 4$.

She swims 46 lengths altogether.

This is the value of the expression, so she can write an equation:
$s + 4 = 46$

- An **equation** links an expression with its value using an equals sign.

An equation is like a pair of scales.
The equals sign is where the equation balances.

$s + 4 = 46$ so $46 - 4 = s$ and $s = 42$

Jordan swims 42 lengths.

- You can solve an equation using a balance.
You perform the same operation on both sides to keep the balance.

example

Solve these equations:

a $x + 4 = 13$ **b** $y - 3 = 10$ **c** $3x = 12$

a – 4 on both sides; $x = 9$
b + 3 on both sides; $y = 13$
c ÷ 3 on both sides; $x = 4$

218

Plenary

Discuss question 4.
Emphasise that $x + x + x + x = 4$ lots of $x = 4x$ and that $4x + 3x = 7x$.
Discuss the difference between an expression and an equation – once the expression is an equation there is a specific value for the unknown.

Further activities

Students can make up sentences to describe the equations in question 1: some dogs were at a show and five more joined, there are now 10 altogether.
They can then work in pairs devising sentences for a partner to write an expression for.

Differentiation

Support questions:

- Question 1 focuses on simple equations involving addition and subtraction. Springboard 7, page 491.
- Questions 2 and 3 focus on using division as the inverse of multiplication to solve equations.
- Question 4 develops the use of equations to solve problems.

Core tier: focuses on solving equations by using inverse operations.

Exercise A5.1

1 Solve each of these equations.

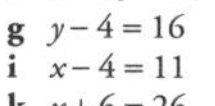

a	$x+5=10$	**b**	$y+12=15$
c	$x+3=9$	**d**	$y+2=8$
e	$x+15=20$	**f**	$y+5=14$
g	$y-4=16$	**h**	$x-5=9$
i	$x-4=11$	**j**	$y-3=17$
k	$x+6=26$	**l**	$y-5=15$

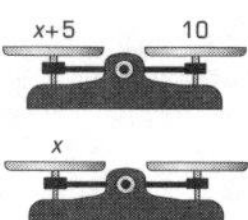

2 Write equations for these sentences then solve them.
The first one is done for you.

a 3 lots of an unknown number make 21.
Let the unknown be n.

$3n=21$
$3\times7=21$
So $n=7$.

b 2 lots of an unknown number make 12
c 4 lots of an unknown number make 32
d 3 lots of an unknown number make 24
e 4 lots of an unknown number make 28
f 3 lots of an unknown number make 33
g 6 lots of an unknown number make 42
h 12 lots of an unknown number make 36
i 10 lots of an unknown number make 90
j 2 lots of an unknown number make 26

3 Solve these equations. Check your solution by multiplying.

a	$4x=12$	**b**	$2y=8$
c	$3x=15$	**d**	$6y=30$
e	$4x=16$	**f**	$3y=18$
g	$6r=24$	**h**	$3m=9$
i	$10n=50$	**j**	$6t=18$
k	$5x=20$	**l**	$7y=28$

4 The diagrams show a square and an equilateral triangle.
The length of all the edges of each shape is x cm.

You find the perimeter of the shapes by adding the lengths of the edges together.

a Write an expression for the total perimeter of the square and the triangle.
b What is x if the total perimeter is 28 cm?

Exercise commentary

The questions assess Primary Framework Pages 43, 53 and 55.

Problem solving
Question 4 assesses Primary Framework Page 81.

Group work
Students would benefit from discussing solutions in pairs.

Misconceptions
Students make many mistakes in solving equations as they find them hard to conceptualise. In particular, they often forget to perform the inverse operation so the answer to question 1a is given as 15.
Use the scales or multilink cubes to help illustrate the need to use the inverse operation to undo the equation.
Encourage students to check their solutions by substitution.
Students forget that $3n$ means 3 times n, or think that if $3n=21$ then $n=21$.
Emphasise that $3n$ means 3 lots of n and encourage students to say the expressions out loud.

Links
Multiplication and division facts: Primary Framework Page 59.

Homework

A5.1HW provides practice at forming and solving equations containing multiples of an unknown quantity.

Answers

1 **a** $x=5$ **b** $y=3$ **c** $x=6$ **d** $y=6$ **e** $x=5$ **f** $y=9$ **g** $y=20$ **h** $x=14$
i $x=15$ **j** $y=20$ **k** $x=20$ **l** $y=20$

2 **b** $2n=12$, $n=6$ **c** $4n=32$, $n=8$ **d** $3n=24$, $n=8$ **e** $4n=28$, $n=7$
f $3n=33$, $n=11$ **g** $6n=42$, $n=7$ **h** $12n=36$, $n=3$
i $10n=90$, $n=9$ **j** $2n=26$, $n=13$

3 **a** $x=3$ **b** $y=4$ **c** $x=5$ **d** $y=5$ **e** $x=4$ **f** $y=6$ **g** $r=4$ **h** $m=3$
i $n=5$ **j** $t=3$ **k** $x=4$ **l** $y=4$

4 **a** $7x$ **b** 4

Mental starter

Area of a rectangle

Draw a 3 × 2 rectangle on the board or OHP – use squared background.

Ask students the name of the shape. Ask what is its area and how to find it – encourage multiplying rather than counting.

Ask for the areas of rectangles with other dimensions.

Useful resources

R1 digit cards for the mental starter.

R9 squared grid on OHP for the mental starter.

Introductory activity

Discuss the word formula/formulae – an equation linking two or more variables.

Refer to the mental starter.
The area of a rectangle is a good example from maths.
Discuss how to write the formula in words.

Emphasise that formulae are used in everyday life, usually using words.

Introduce the mobile phone problem and that you can use a formula to keep on top of your bill.
Ask students:
- Imagine you pay 5p per minute for every call you make. What is the cost of a 10-minute phone call?
- How do you work it out?

Discuss a word formula for the cost of calls.
Emphasise use of the word: per.
This suggests a rate and is the key to the formula.

Introduce an example that includes line rental. Discuss how to build up the formula in words.

Encourage students to think about what aspects of the formula are variable.
Ask them to use the formula to work out bills for various lengths of calls.

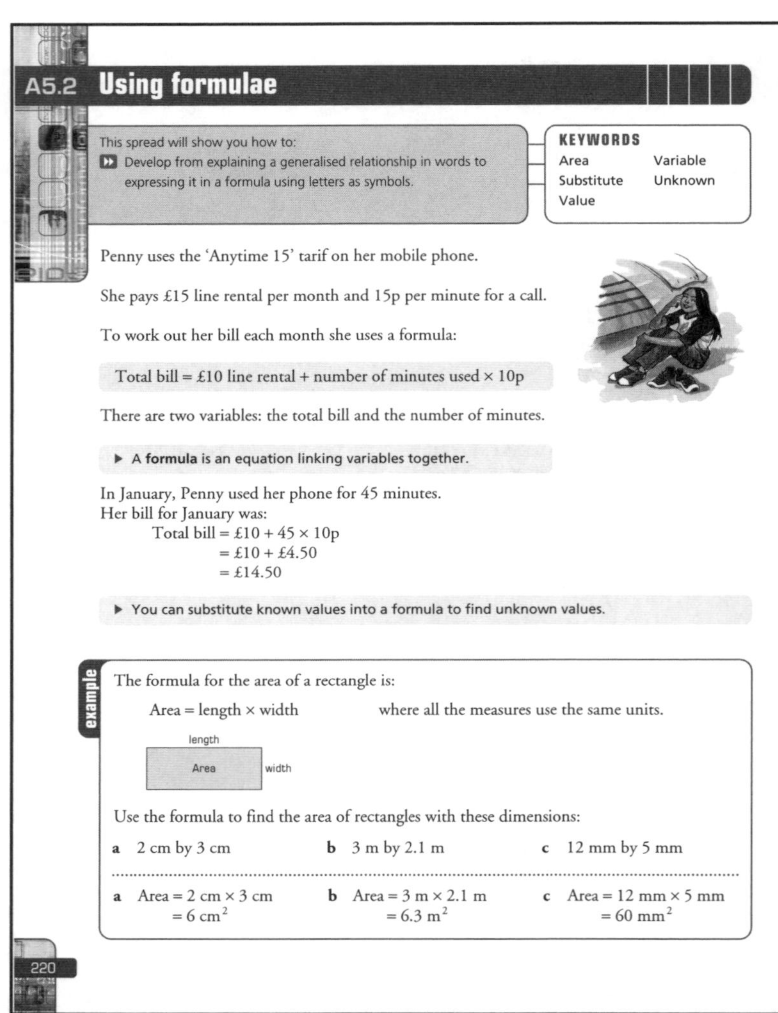

A5.2 **Using formulae**

This spread will show you how to:
- Develop from explaining a generalised relationship in words to expressing it in a formula using letters as symbols.

KEYWORDS
Area, Variable, Substitute, Unknown, Value

Penny uses the 'Anytime 15' tarif on her mobile phone.

She pays £15 line rental per month and 15p per minute for a call.

To work out her bill each month she uses a formula:

Total bill = £10 line rental + number of minutes used × 10p

There are two variables: the total bill and the number of minutes.

- A **formula** is an equation linking variables together.

In January, Penny used her phone for 45 minutes.
Her bill for January was:
Total bill = £10 + 45 × 10p
= £10 + £4.50
= £14.50

- You can substitute known values into a formula to find unknown values.

example

The formula for the area of a rectangle is:

Area = length × width where all the measures use the same units.

Use the formula to find the area of rectangles with these dimensions:

a 2 cm by 3 cm **b** 3 m by 2.1 m **c** 12 mm by 5 mm

a Area = 2 cm × 3 cm = 6 cm^2 **b** Area = 3 m × 2.1 m = 6.3 m^2 **c** Area = 12 mm × 5 mm = 60 mm^2

220

Plenary

Go over question 3.
Discuss the difficulties faced in having one part in £s and the other in ps. Ask questions such as: my bill is £25, how long did I use the phone for?

Further activities

Students can work in pairs to develop formulae for mobile phone tariffs. One student devises the formula and the partner interprets it.

Challenge students to plot the data in question 2 on a graph.

Differentiation

Support questions:

- Question 1 focuses on using a simple formula. Springboard 7, page 492.
- Questions 2 and 3 focus on developing the use of formulae, including working backwards and interpreting terms.
- Question 4 is more complex, involving a few variables.

Core tier: focuses on using formulae expressed algebraically.

Exercise A5.2

1 The formula for the cost of buying packets of crisps is:

Total cost = number of packets bought × 30p

What is the cost of:
a 1 packet
b 2 packets
c 5 packets?

2 Mandy has a Pay as You Go mobile phone.
Her calls cost 20p per minute at any time.
The formula for the cost of her calls is:

Total cost = number of minutes used × 20p

Use the formula to work out the cost of using her phone for:
a 5 minutes
b 10 minutes
c 30 minutes
d 1 hour
e How long would a £5 credit last?

3 Joe uses this formula to work out his mobile phone bill:

Total bill = £20 line rental + number of minutes used × 5p

a How much is Joe's line rental?
Work out Joe's bill when he uses:
b 5 minutes
c 20 minutes
d 12 minutes
e 55 minutes

4 Penny uses a formula to work out the cost of using her land line:

Total cost = number of daytime calls × 50p + number of evening calls × 10p + £10 rental

a How much is a daytime call?
b How much is an evening call?
Use the formula to work out the cost of:
c 5 evening calls and 3 daytime calls
d 20 evening calls and 20 daytime calls

221

Exercise commentary

The questions assess Primary Framework Page 81.

Problem solving
The questions also assess Primary Framework Pages 85 and 87.

Group work
The further activity is suitable for pairs.

Misconceptions
Students just substitute the numbers without thinking, giving the answer to question 2d as 20p and 2e as 100p.
Encourage students to estimate the answer before calculating.
Emphasise that the formula is written using specific units and that they must be followed.
Question 2e shows whether students understand the formula.
In question 3 some students will work from left to right, ignoring the order of operations.
Emphasise that multiplication comes before addition and refer to Bidmas.

Links
Measures: Primary Framework Page 91.
Area: Page 97.

Homework

A5.2HW provides practice at writing and using a word formula in context.

Answers

1 **a** 30p **b** 60p **c** £1.50
2 **a** £1 **b** £2 **c** £6 **d** £12
e 25 minutes
3 **a** £20 **b** £20.25 **c** £21 **d** £20.60
e £22.75
4 **a** 50p **b** 10p **c** £12 **d** £22

A5.3 Formulae using letters

Mental starter

Formula 1!

Write the formula $v = ut$ on the board.
(You may need to remind students there's a hidden × sign.)
You can explain it is a formula used to calculate speed (velocity)!
Give two values – u and t to start with – and ask students to find the third.
Progress to giving v and u other values and asking for t.

Useful resources

R7 contains blank function machines which may help students build up formulae.

Introductory activity

Refer to the mental starter.
Emphasise that t, u and v are all unknown values that can vary and that $v = ut$ is a *formula* linking the variables.

Remind students of the mobile phone problem.
Ask them to give a formula for the cost of the bill each month – start with a pay-as-you-go type problem.
Discuss a simpler way of writing the sentence or formula:
$C = m \times 5\text{p}$ for 5p per minute.

Emphasise that the formula is the same as the word formula but it is quicker to write out so the algebra is like shorthand.

Encourage students to use a key for the shorthand. Discuss why this may be important – so that anyone can understand and use it.

Discuss the line rental problem.
The issues are the same – just the formula is slightly more complex.
Use the formula to work out the number of minutes used given Penny's phone bill.

Discuss other formulae from maths:

- Centimetres in a metre
- Minutes in an hour

These provide a good link back to work on measures in N3.

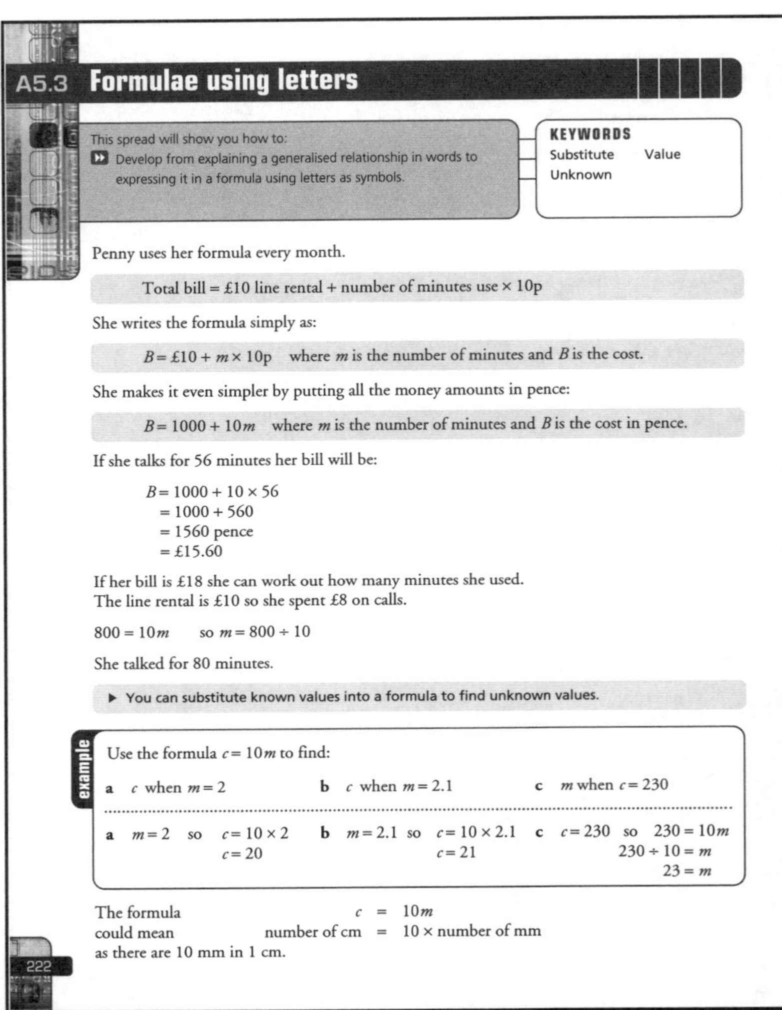

A5.3 Formulae using letters

This spread will show you how to:
- Develop from explaining a generalised relationship in words to expressing it in a formula using letters as symbols.

KEYWORDS
Substitute Value
Unknown

Penny uses her formula every month.

Total bill = £10 line rental + number of minutes use × 10p

She writes the formula simply as:

$B = £10 + m \times 10\text{p}$ where m is the number of minutes and B is the cost.

She makes it even simpler by putting all the money amounts in pence:

$B = 1000 + 10m$ where m is the number of minutes and B is the cost in pence.

If she talks for 56 minutes her bill will be:

$B = 1000 + 10 \times 56$
$= 1000 + 560$
$= 1560$ pence
$= £15.60$

If her bill is £18 she can work out how many minutes she used.
The line rental is £10 so she spent £8 on calls.

$800 = 10m$ so $m = 800 \div 10$

She talked for 80 minutes.

- You can substitute known values into a formula to find unknown values.

example

Use the formula $c = 10m$ to find:

a c when $m = 2$ b c when $m = 2.1$ c m when $c = 230$

a $m = 2$ so $c = 10 \times 2$, $c = 20$
b $m = 2.1$ so $c = 10 \times 2.1$, $c = 21$
c $c = 230$ so $230 = 10m$, $230 \div 10 = m$, $23 = m$

The formula $c = 10m$
could mean number of cm = 10 × number of mm
as there are 10 mm in 1 cm.

222

Plenary

Discuss question 6.
Ask how to use the formula to change centimetres to metres: how many metres are there in 260 cm?
Discuss whether there is an easier way to work out the answer rather than using the formula backwards – use a graph!

Further activities

Students can use their formula from question 1 to work out:

- the cost of using the phone for various lengths of time
- how long she could talk using £2.80 credit.

Challenge students to write the formula in Exercise A5.2 question 4 using letters.

Differentiation

Support questions:

- Questions 1 and 2 focus on writing simple formulae using letters.
- Questions 3–5 focus on writing progressively harder formulae using letters.
- Questions 6 and 7 involve substituting into algebraic formulae.

Core tier: focuses on deriving a formula from context.

Exercise A5.3

1 The formula for Mandy's phone bill is:

Total cost = number of minutes used × 20p

Write her formula using letters.

2 The formula for the cost of buying packets of crisps is:

Total cost = number of packets bought × 30p

Write the formula using letters.

3 The formula for the area of a rectangle is:

Area = length × width

Write the formula using letters.

4 The formula for changing pounds (£) to pence (p) is:

Amount in pence = amount in pounds × 100

Write the formula using letters.

5 Joe uses this formula to work out his mobile phone bill:

Total bill = £20 line rental + number of minutes used × 5p

Write Joe's formula using letters.

6 The formula for changing metres to centimetres is:

Length in centimetres = length in metres × 100

a Write the formula using letters.
b Use the formula to change 3.2 metres to centimetres.

7 This formula links feet and inches:

$i = 12f$

a Work out i when $f = 3$.
b How many inches are there in 3 feet?
c Work out the number of inches in 2.5 feet.

Exercise commentary

The questions assess Primary Framework Page 81.

Problem solving

The questions also assess Primary Framework Pages 85 and 87.

Group work

The further activity is suitable for pairs.

Misconceptions

In the case of formulae, using letters to stand for the object is useful as it helps emphasise what the letter stands for.

It is important though to emphasise that the letter stands for the number of the object rather than for the object itself, so encourage students to take this into account when they give a key for their formula.

Students tend to just substitute the numbers into the formula without stopping to think what the question is asking, hence making mistakes.

Encourage them to estimate the answer first to help them stop and think before calculating.

Links

Measures: Primary Framework Page 91.

Homework

A5.3HW provides practice at using algebraic formulae.

Answers

1 $C = 20n$
2 $C = 30n$
3 $B = 2000 + 5n$
4 $A = lw$
5 Using x for the amount in pence and y for the amount in pounds: $x = 100y$
6 **a** $c = 100m$ **b** 320 cm
7 **a** 36 **b** 36 inches **c** 30 inches

Mental starter

Follow the rule

Give a student a start number: e.g. 2.
Give the class, a rule: e.g. add 3.
Go round the class, each student says the next number in the sequence.
Change the sequence when it gets too large – start to take away 5.
Then change to multiply by 4. Then divide by 2.
At the end the first student says how to get back to the start number.

Useful resources

A5.4OHP shows the matchstick patterns from the student book.

Introductory activity

Refer to the mental starter.
Remind students that a sequence is a series of numbers that follow a rule or pattern.

Introduce the matchstick patterns. They are reproduced on **A5.4OHP**.

Discuss how the sequence grows.
Encourage students to justify their suggestions by referring to the matchstick patterns.
Encourage the rule: add 3 to the last pattern.

Discuss how to write the rule using a formula.

Decide what the variables are that will be linked by the formula – current and next patterns.

Encourage students to start with a word expression using full sentences, and then to simplify it for ease of use.

Discuss how to use the formula to predict future terms of the sequence.
Ask how to find the number of matches in the:
- 6th pattern
- 12th pattern – what other information do you need?

Encourage students to check formulae by drawing.

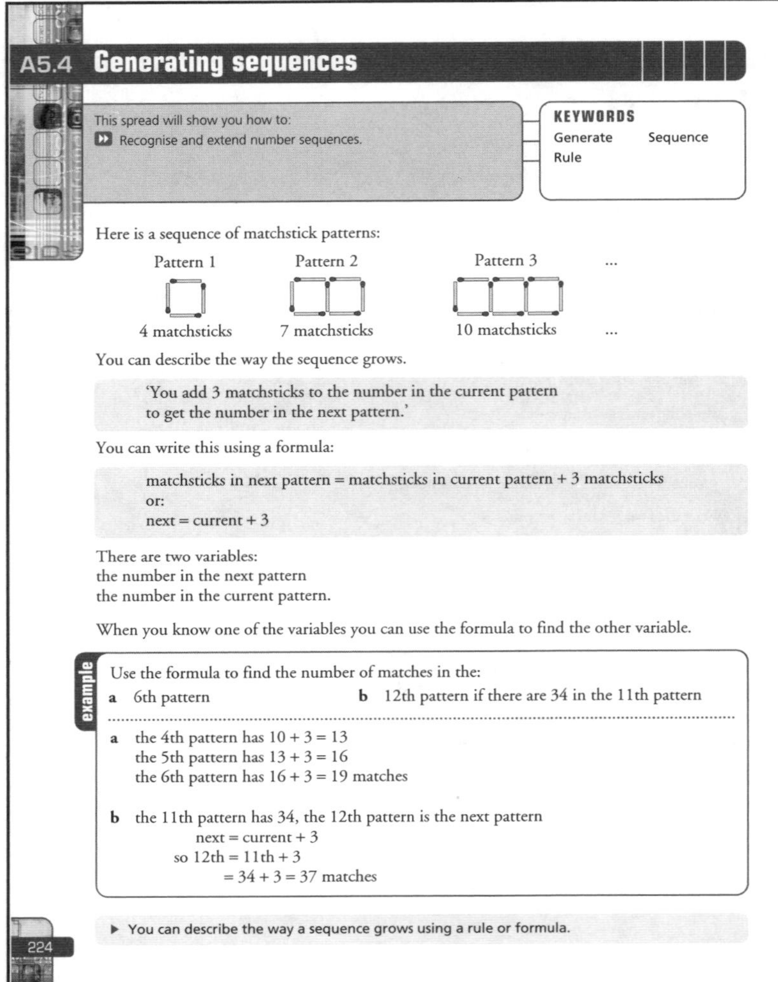

A5.4 Generating sequences

This spread will show you how to:
- Recognise and extend number sequences.

KEYWORDS
Generate
Rule
Sequence

Here is a sequence of matchstick patterns:

Pattern 1	Pattern 2	Pattern 3	...
4 matchsticks	7 matchsticks	10 matchsticks	...

You can describe the way the sequence grows.

'You add 3 matchsticks to the number in the current pattern to get the number in the next pattern.'

You can write this using a formula:

matchsticks in next pattern = matchsticks in current pattern + 3 matchsticks
or:
next = current + 3

There are two variables:
the number in the next pattern
the number in the current pattern.

When you know one of the variables you can use the formula to find the other variable.

example

Use the formula to find the number of matches in the:
a 6th pattern
b 12th pattern if there are 34 in the 11th pattern

a the 4th pattern has $10 + 3 = 13$
the 5th pattern has $13 + 3 = 16$
the 6th pattern has $16 + 3 = 19$ matches

b the 11th pattern has 34, the 12th pattern is the next pattern
next = current + 3
so 12th = 11th + 3
= $34 + 3 = 37$ matches

- You can describe the way a sequence grows using a rule or formula.

224

Plenary

Discuss the use of sequence patterns and diagrams to predict future terms.
Ask students if they know any other ways of predicting future terms.
Encourage them to refer back to the graphing of functions (A3.5) where the graph was such a powerful tool.

Further activities

Challenge students to make up sequence patterns for partners to describe.

Differentiation

Support questions:

- Questions 1a and 2a focus on continuing sequence patterns.
- Questions 1b, 1c, 2b and 2c involve describing the sequence patterns in words.
- Questions 1d and 2d involve using the rule to predict future terms of a sequence.

Core tier: focuses on finding a general position-to-term rule for a sequence.

Exercise A5.4

1 Here is a sequence of matchstick patterns:

Pattern: 1 2 3 4

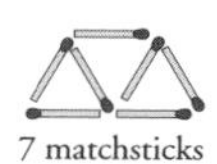
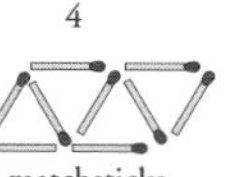

3 matchsticks 5 matchsticks 7 matchsticks 9 matchsticks

a Draw the next two patterns in the sequence.

b Copy and complete this sentence.

> You add ____ matchsticks to the current pattern to get the next pattern.

c Write the sentence as a formula:

> Next pattern = current pattern +

d Use your formula to write down the number of matchsticks in the 7th pattern.
Check your answer by drawing.

2 For this dot pattern:

Pattern: 1 2 3 4

2 dots 4 dots 6 dots 8 dots

a Draw the next two patterns in the sequence.

b Write a sentence to describe how the sequence grows.

c Write the sentence as a formula:

> Next pattern = current pattern +

d Use your formula to write down the number of dots in the 8th pattern.
Check your answer by drawing.

225

Exercise commentary

The questions assess Primary Framework Pages 17 and 81.

Problem solving

The questions assess Primary Framework Page 81.

Group work

The questions are suitable for pairs.

Misconceptions

Students confuse the pattern number with the number of matchsticks.

Emphasise the need to set work out logically and encourage the use of a table to record results or to write findings using complete sentences as in the example on page 224.

Students find a rule to satisfy the first two terms but fail to consider whether it works with further terms, writing the rule in question 2 as ×2.

Encourage students to check the rule with all the terms given and to predict what the next term will be using their rule, verifying by drawing.

Links

Multiples: Primary Framework Page 19.

Homework

A5.4HW provides practice at using a formula to generate a sequence.

Answers

1 **a** 11 matchsticks, 13 matchsticks
  b 2
  c Next pattern = current pattern + 2
  d 15 matchsticks

2 **a** 10 dots, 12 dots
  b You add 2 dots to the current pattern to get the next pattern.
  c Next pattern = current pattern + 2
  d 16 dots

A5.5 Spot the function

Mental starter

What's the rule?

Give students a start number: 15.

Ask questions: add 5, subtract 6, divide by 3, multiply by 2 ...

Students hold up digit cards to show answers.

Then ask the question: 'add'. Students should not be able to do the question as they need to know what to add.

Repeat with divide. Discuss the information needed: divide and by what.

Useful resources

R7 contains function machines – make an OHP.

R1 digit cards for the mental starter.

Introductory activity

Refer to the mental starter.

Write the question function machines – use the machine on R7 (on OHP).

The start number is the input, the answer is the output, the function needs an operation and a number.

Draw ×2 on a function machine.

Show the input 3 – ask for the output.

Show the input 4 – ask for the output.

Discuss what happens to the input numbers to make the output numbers: multiply by 2.

- Write: Input × 2 = output.

Ask students what you call such a sentence – it is a formula as it links two variables.

Discuss how to write the formula more simply: use letters instead of the words.

Encourage students to generalise the input and output values as *x* and *y* to develop a general rule or formula.

Encourage students to remember that you don't use a multiplication sign.

Give examples of inputs and outputs so that there is more than one possible function.

- Ask students for the possible functions in words.
- Give further examples so students can see the exact function.
- Express them using algebra.

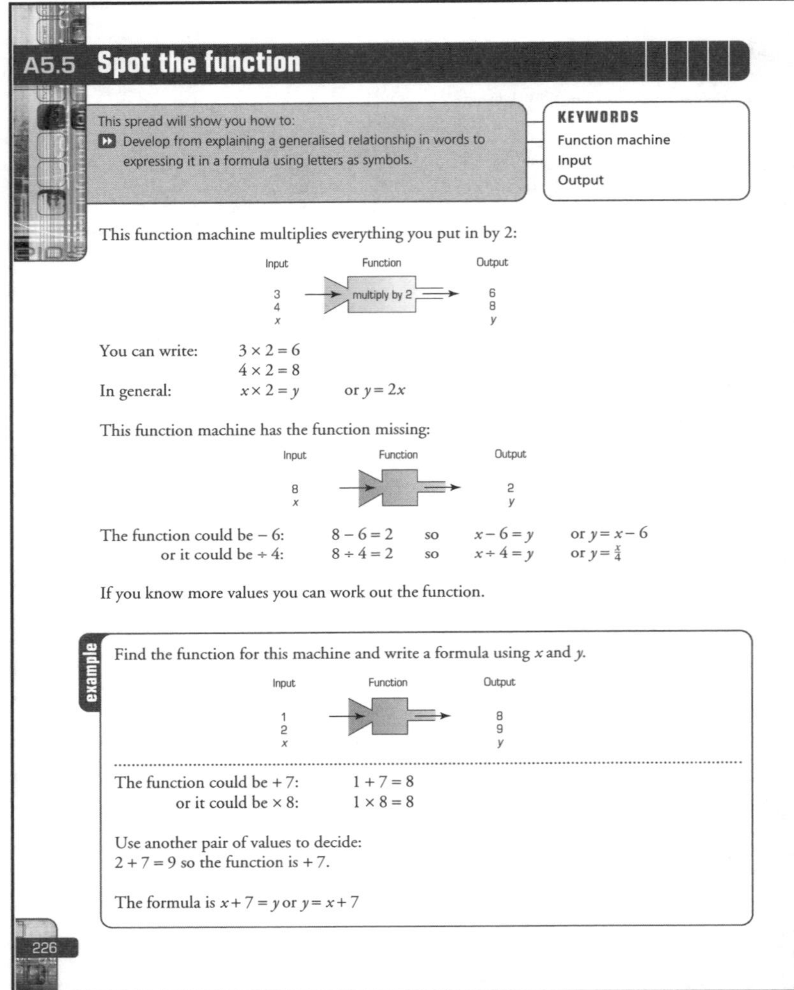

A5.5 Spot the function

This spread will show you how to:

- Develop from explaining a generalised relationship in words to expressing it in a formula using letters as symbols.

KEYWORDS
Function machine
Input
Output

This function machine multiplies everything you put in by 2:

You can write: $3 \times 2 = 6$

$4 \times 2 = 8$

In general: $x \times 2 = y$ or $y = 2x$

This function machine has the function missing:

The function could be – 6: $8 - 6 = 2$ so $x - 6 = y$ or $y = x - 6$

or it could be ÷ 4: $8 \div 4 = 2$ so $x \div 4 = y$ or $y = \frac{x}{4}$

If you know more values you can work out the function.

example

Find the function for this machine and write a formula using *x* and *y*.

The function could be + 7: $1 + 7 = 8$

or it could be × 8: $1 \times 8 = 8$

Use another pair of values to decide:

$2 + 7 = 9$ so the function is + 7.

The formula is $x + 7 = y$ or $y = x + 7$

226

Plenary

What's the input?

Discuss how to find an input value given the output and the function.

Encourage students to formalise their thinking rather than using trial and error.

Set up the formula using algebra and discuss how to undo the function to find the input.

Link back to solving equations in A5.1.

Further activities

Give students a formula and ask them to draw the function machine.
You can challenge able students with double functions.

Differentiation

Support questions:

- Question 1 focuses on using function machines to find the output.
- Question 2 focuses on finding the function.
- Question 3 focuses on expressing the formula using algebra.

Core tier: focuses on using function machines to find a function.

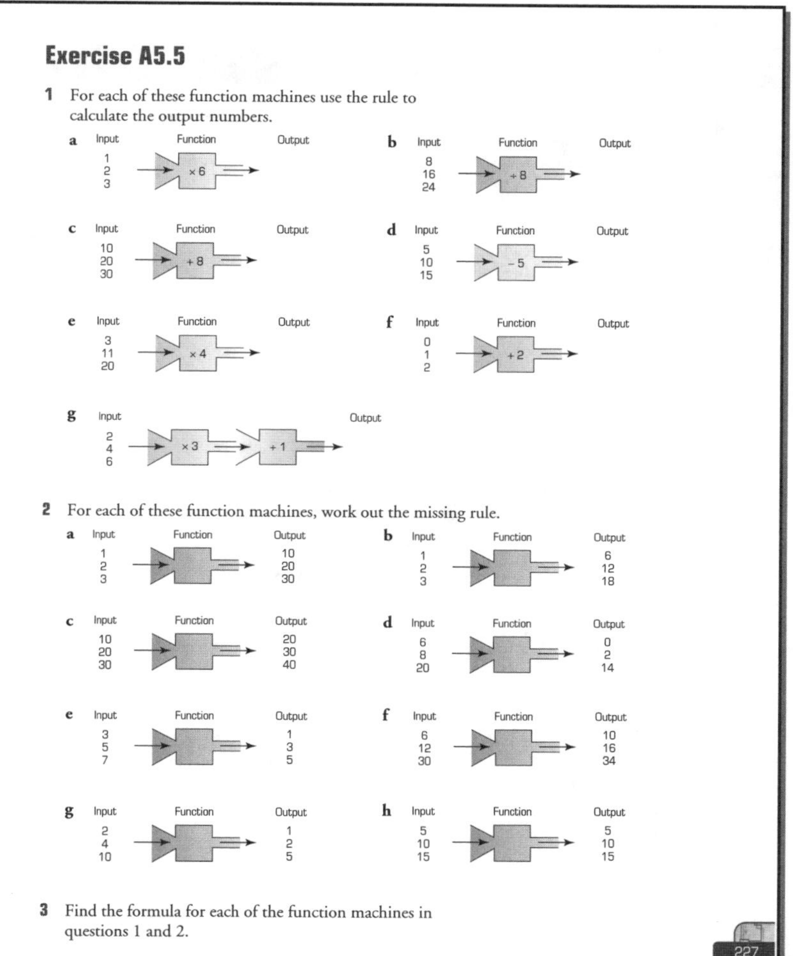

Exercise A5.5

1 For each of these function machines use the rule to calculate the output numbers.

a Input 1, 2, 3 → Function ×6 → Output

b Input 8, 16, 24 → Function ÷8 → Output

c Input 10, 20, 30 → Function +8 → Output

d Input 5, 10, 15 → Function −5 → Output

e Input 3, 11, 20 → Function ×4 → Output

f Input 0, 1, 2 → Function +2 → Output

g Input 2, 4, 6 → ×3 → +1 → Output

2 For each of these function machines, work out the missing rule.

a Input 1, 2, 3 → Function → Output 10, 20, 30

b Input 1, 2, 3 → Function → Output 6, 12, 18

c Input 10, 20, 30 → Function → Output 20, 30, 40

d Input 6, 8, 20 → Function → Output 0, 2, 14

e Input 3, 5, 7 → Function → Output 1, 3, 5

f Input 6, 12, 30 → Function → Output 10, 16, 34

g Input 2, 4, 10 → Function → Output 1, 2, 5

h Input 5, 10, 15 → Function → Output 5, 10, 15

3 Find the formula for each of the function machines in questions 1 and 2.

227

Exercise commentary

The questions assess Primary Framework Page 81.

Problem solving

The questions assess Primary Framework Page 81.

Group work

The further activity is suitable for pairs.

Misconceptions

Most students can successfully input a number into a function machine and many can input the counting numbers.
When there is a string of input numbers some students find it hard to keep track of the information.
Encourage them to work out one output at a time before working on the next input and to write the inputs and outputs on lined paper so that they can keep them together.
Students tend to assume the inputs are always 1, 2, 3 and so can't do the calculations in question 1 and can't find a pattern in question 2.
Emphasise the link between the input and output and encourage students to consider them in pairs.

Links

Multiples: Primary Framework Page 19.
Using coordinates: Page 109.

Homework

A5.5HW is an investigation involving function machines.

Answers

1 **a** 6, 12, 18 **b** 1, 2, 3 **c** 18, 28, 38
d 0, 5, 10 **e** 12, 44, 80 **f** 2, 3, 4 **g** 7, 13, 19

2 **a** ×10 **b** ×6 **c** +10 **d** −6
e −2 **f** +4 **g** ÷2
h +0, −0, ×1 or ÷1

Mental starter

Battle grid

Use **R9** on OHP and label coordinate axes from 0 to 5.

Students can choose any 9 points from the grid and write them down. They should write them on a 3 × 3 grid to make sure they choose 9.

Place a counter or a cross on the grid.

Students cross that one off if they have it in their grid.

Repeat until a student has crossed off all their coordinates.

Useful resources

R7 function machines – make an OHP.

R9 has a blank coordinate grid – make an OHP.

Introductory activity

Build on the the last lesson.

Draw ×2 on a function machine.

Show various input and output values.

The more pairs there are the less easy it is to see which ones go together.

Discuss how to group the input and output values to show they 'belong' to each other.

Encourage all suggestions.

Emphasise the use of a table and encourage students to go one step further and give coordinate pairs.

Discuss what happens to the input numbers to make the output numbers: multiply by 2.

Discuss when else students have come across the rule: multiply by 2.

Lead the discussion to multiples of 2 or even numbers.

Emphasise that the multiples of 2 or the rule 'multiply by 2' produces a pattern or a sequence. You can see this in the table of output values.

Ask students how they would show the pattern made by the input and output pairs of the machine.

Emphasise use of a graph as you have pairs of values.

Plot the input and output pairs.

Emphasise that the pairs must always be written in the same order.

Discuss how to name the graph:

- Input × 2 = output.
- $y = 2x$

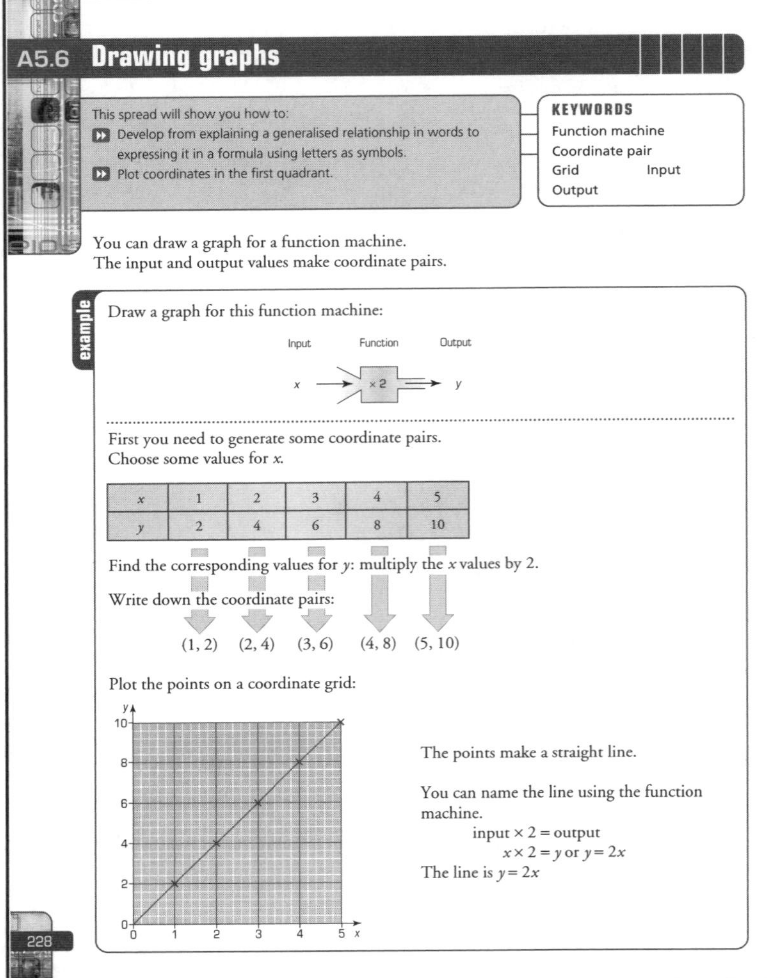
A5.6 Drawing graphs

This spread will show you how to:
Develop from explaining a generalised relationship in words to expressing it in a formula using letters as symbols.
Plot coordinates in the first quadrant.

KEYWORDS
Function machine
Coordinate pair
Grid
Input
Output

You can draw a graph for a function machine.
The input and output values make coordinate pairs.

example
Draw a graph for this function machine:

First you need to generate some coordinate pairs.
Choose some values for x.

x	1	2	3	4	5
y	2	4	6	8	10

Find the corresponding values for y: multiply the x values by 2.

Write down the coordinate pairs:

(1, 2) (2, 4) (3, 6) (4, 8) (5, 10)

Plot the points on a coordinate grid:

The points make a straight line.

You can name the line using the function machine.

input × 2 = output

$x \times 2 = y$ or $y = 2x$

The line is $y = 2x$

228

Plenary

Discuss question 2.

Ask for the coordinate pairs.

Discuss the equation of the line.

Ask what output an input of 1.5 would give.

Emphasise you can check this using the formula.

Further activities

Challenge students to find the formula for the function and graph in question 1.

Differentiation

Support questions:

- Question 1 focuses on drawing a graph of a function machine.
- Questions 2a, 2b, 3a and 3b focus on completing a table of values and drawing a graph.
- Questions 2c and 3c focus on finding the equation of a graph.

Core tier: focuses on plotting points from a mapping diagram.

Exercise A5.6

You will need a coordinate grid for each question.

1 The function machine

Input → ×2 → +1 → Output

generates this table of values:

Input	1	2	3	4
Output	3	5	7	9

a Copy and complete these coordinate pairs:

(1, 3) (2, 5) (3,) (,)

b Plot the pairs on a graph.
Join them to make a straight line.

2 **a** Copy and complete this table of values for the function:

× 3

Input	1	2	3	4
Output			9	

b Plot the coordinate pairs on a graph.
Join them to make a straight line.

c Name the line. Copy and complete:

Input × _______ = output

x × = y

The line is y = _______

3 **a** Copy and complete this table of values for the function:

− 2.

Input	8	7	6	5
Output			4	

b Plot the coordinate pairs on a graph.
Join them to make a straight line.

c Name the line. Copy and complete:

Input _____ _________ = output

x _____ _________ = y

The line is y = _________

229

Exercise commentary

The questions assess Primary Framework Pages 81and 109.

Problem solving

The questions assess Primary Framework Page 81.

Group work

Students may benefit from discussing solutions in pairs.

Misconceptions

Linking the table of values to the coordinates can cause difficulties as student confuse the order of numbers.

Emphasise that you list input then output – i before o.

Some students may not see the link between the input and output values, instead writing the output in the last column of question 2 as 27.

Refer back to the function machine and encourage students to draw one to show the input and output pairs.

Students tend to plot (y, x) instead of (x, y).

Discuss strategies for remembering as a group so good ideas are shared.

Links

Drawing graphs and using frequency tables in data: Primary Framework Pages 115 and 117.

Homework

A5.6HW provides practice at drawing axes in a single quadrant and plotting points in a straight line.

Answers

1 **a** (3, 7), (4, 9)

2 **a** Outputs: 3, 6, 9, 12

c Input × 3 = output, $x \times 3 = y$, $y = 3x$

3 **a** Outputs: 6, 5, 4, 3

c Input −2 = output, $x - 2 = y$, $y = x - 2$

A5.7 Graphs of formulae

Mental starter

× by multiples of 10

- Give students a start number: 15
- Ask them to multiply it by 10: 150
- Ask them to multiply it by 20: 300
- Repeat for other start numbers and other multiples of 10.

Useful resources

R9 has a blank coordinate grid – make an OHP.

A5.7OHP shows the graph from the student book.

Introductory activity

Build on the last lesson.

Discuss how to draw a graph of a function machine:

- Use a table of values
- List input and output values in coordinate pairs
- Draw the graph – join the points

Discuss the rule for a ×2 machine:

- Input × 2 = output or
- $y = 2x$

Emphasise that this is a formula as it links two variables.

Discuss Penny's Pay-as-you-Go mobile phone bill formula:

- Bill = mins used × 5p

Discuss what the variables are – B, m:

- $B = 5m$

Ask why a graph would be useful: it is easy to see any patterns at a glance and to find the Bill for any number of minutes.

Discuss (and work through together) the steps involved in making a graph of the formula:

- Make a table of input (min) and output (Bill) values – discuss max and min values.
- Write down the coordinate pairs.
- Draw coordinate axes – discuss the scale to use – go up in ... ?

Show the graph on **A5.7OHP**.

Discuss how to use the graph to find intermediate values.

Encourage students to mark the coordinates of the point on the line that uses the value.

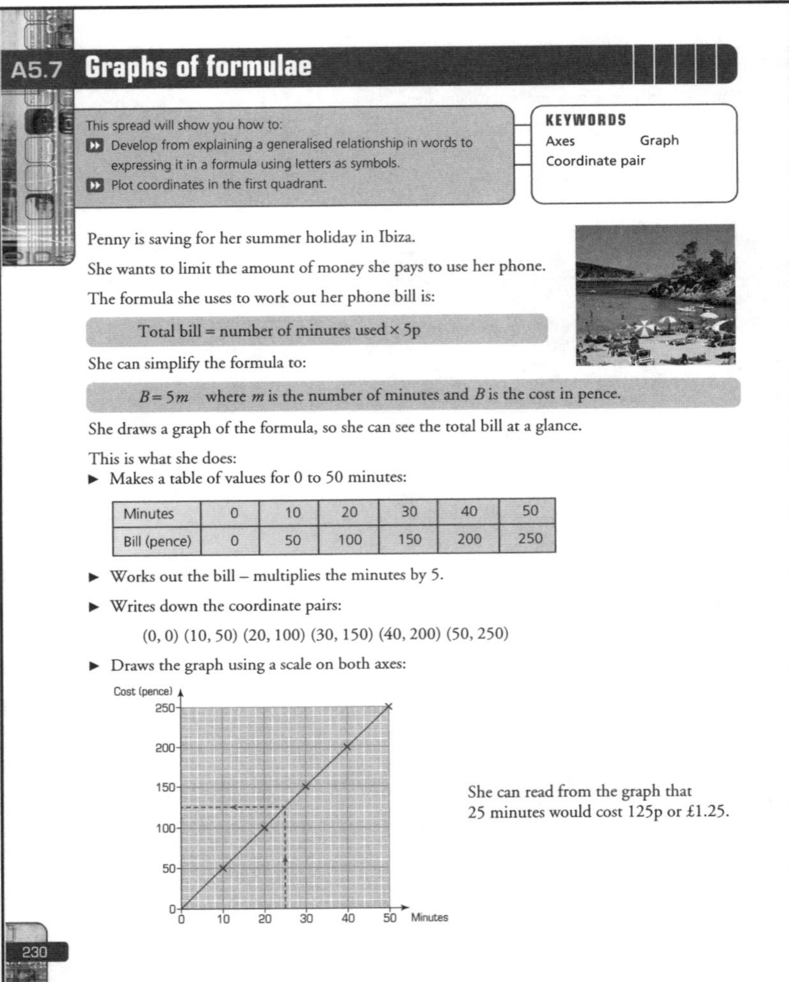

A5.7 **Graphs of formulae**

This spread will show you how to:

- Develop from explaining a generalised relationship in words to expressing it in a formula using letters as symbols.
- Plot coordinates in the first quadrant.

KEYWORDS
Axes
Graph
Coordinate pair

Penny is saving for her summer holiday in Ibiza.

She wants to limit the amount of money she pays to use her phone.

The formula she uses to work out her phone bill is:

Total bill = number of minutes used × 5p

She can simplify the formula to:

$B = 5m$ where m is the number of minutes and B is the cost in pence.

She draws a graph of the formula, so she can see the total bill at a glance.

This is what she does:

- Makes a table of values for 0 to 50 minutes:

Minutes	0	10	20	30	40	50
Bill (pence)	0	50	100	150	200	250

- Works out the bill – multiplies the minutes by 5.
- Writes down the coordinate pairs:

(0, 0) (10, 50) (20, 100) (30, 150) (40, 200) (50, 250)

- Draws the graph using a scale on both axes:

She can read from the graph that 25 minutes would cost 125p or £1.25.

230

Plenary

Discuss question 3.

Work through the steps together:

- fill in the table
- write down the coordinate pairs
- decide on an appropriate scale.

Discuss how to find values from the graph.

Encourage students to mark relevant points.

Further activities

Students can draw the graphs for the formula in Exercise A5.3 question 2. They will need to devise a table of values and plot the points, deciding whether or not it is sensible to join them up.

Challenge students to draw the graph of the formula they found for Exercise A5.3 question 5.

Differentiation

Support questions:

- Question 1 focuses on drawing a graph from a table of values.
- Question 2 focuses on drawing a graph for discrete data and using it to predict other values. Springboard 7, page 395.
- Question 3 focuses on using a graph to find intermediary values.

Core tier: focuses on plotting a straight-line graph from an equation.

Exercise A5.7

You will need a coordinate grid for each question. You can copy the one on page 230.

1 For the formula

$B = 10m$

a Copy and complete this table of values:

M	0	5	10	15	20
B	0			150	

b Write down the coordinate pairs.
Use them to draw the graph of the function.
Join the points to make a straight line.

2 This formula shows the cost of buying packets of crisps:

$C = 30P$ where C = cost in pence and P = number of packets

a Copy and complete this table of values:

P	0	2	4	6	8
C	0			180	

b Write down the coordinate pairs.
c Draw the graph of the formula.
d Explain why it does not make sense to join the points.
e Use the graph to find the cost of 3 packets of crisps.

3 The formula for converting feet to inches is:

$i = 12f$

a Copy and complete this table of values:

f	0	5	10	15	20
i	0	60			

b Plot the graph of $i = 12f$.
Join the points to make a straight line.

Use your graph to find:
c the number of inches in 12.5 feet
d the number of feet in 100 inches

231

Exercise commentary

The questions assess Primary Framework Pages 81and 109.

Problem solving

The questions assess Primary Framework Page 81.

Group work

Students may benefit from discussing solutions to questions 2 and 3 in pairs.

Misconceptions

Use of scales on graphs can be problematic with students counting in 1s regardless.
All the graphs can be drawn on the same axes as those on page 230.
Discuss how to work out the value of each section. It may help to use a number line marked in different scales to discuss where to place a value in just one dimension.
Reading from graphs is often hard for students who try to read off a graph but fail to reach the line.
Emphasise that they are looking for a point on the line. Discuss how to find a point for 3 packets of crisps.

Links

Drawing graphs and using frequency tables in data: Primary Framework Pages 115 and 117. Scales: Page 95.

Homework

A5.7HW provides practice at plotting the graph of a formula in context.

Answers

1 a $B = 0, 50, 100, 150, 200$
  b (0, 0), (5, 50), (10, 100), (15, 150), (20, 200)
2 a $C = 0, 60, 120, 180, 240$
  b (0, 0), (2, 60), (4, 120), (6, 180), (8, 240)
  d You can only buy a whole number of packets of crisps. e 90p
3 a $i = 0, 60, 120, 180, 240$
  b Coordinate pairs: (0, 0), (5, 60), (10, 120), (15, 180), (20, 240)
  c 150 inches d 8.3 feet

Mental starter

Countdown!

Give students a start number: say 12.
Ask them to count on in steps of 2.
Start again. Students count down in steps of 2. Stop when you get to 0.
Start again. Students count down in steps of 5. Carry on past 0.
Repeat with other step sizes.

Useful resources

R9 has a blank coordinate grid – make an OHP.
R8 is a coordinate grid in all four quadrants – copy this for students.
N1.2OHP has a horizontal and vertical thermometer including negative values.

Introductory activity

Refer to the mental starter.
Discuss how to use a number line to show counting on or counting back.
Discuss where to set zero each time.
Start with a vertical number line or a counting stick.
Encourage students to use a horizontal line or a ruler.

Keep the two lines, vertical and horizontal, side by side on the board.
Emphasise that you put two lines together to make coordinate axes.
Discuss how to put the two lines together to make coordinate axes including negative numbers:
You can put any of the numbers together e.g. ($^{-}1$, $^{-}1$) as the origin, but using (0, 0) as the origin makes it easier to count!
Refer back to the Shape work on reflection where four quadrants was introduced: S4.3.

Show students the coordinate grid on **R8**.
Place a counter or a cross on the grid.
Ask for the coordinates of the point.
Start with the first quadrant and discuss what the coordinate pair means – across first then up.
Progress to other quadrants.
Emphasise you move horizontally first.
Across (right) and up are positive directions so across (left) and down are negative.

Give students coordinates and ask volunteers to place the counter.
Discuss the placement.

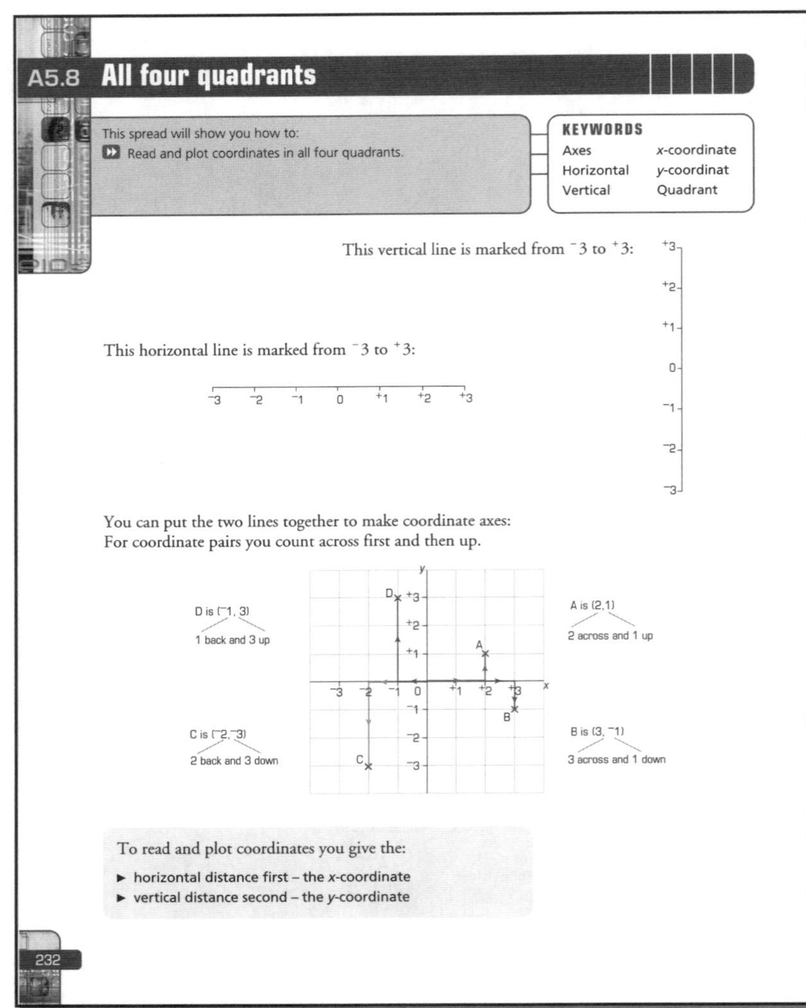

A5.8 All four quadrants

This spread will show you how to:
- Read and plot coordinates in all four quadrants.

KEYWORDS	
Axes	*x*-coordinate
Horizontal	*y*-coordinat
Vertical	Quadrant

This vertical line is marked from $^{-}3$ to $^{+}3$:

This horizontal line is marked from $^{-}3$ to $^{+}3$:

You can put the two lines together to make coordinate axes:
For coordinate pairs you count across first and then up.

To read and plot coordinates you give the:
- horizontal distance first – the *x*-coordinate
- vertical distance second – the *y*-coordinate

232

Plenary

All square!

Use **R8**.
Ask a volunteer to show on the OHP the corners of a square with side length 4 units and centre (0, 0).
There are two possible answers – concentrate on the straightforward one.
Students write down the coordinates of the four vertices.
Discuss the pattern made by the coordinates.
Ask similar questions.

Further activities

In **A5.8ICT** students use Omnigraph to investigate straight-line graphs.

Students can give the coordinates of shapes or words for partners to plot as in question 3.

Differentiation

Support questions:

- Question 1 focuses on reading coordinates.
- Question 2 focuses on plotting coordinates.
- Questions 3 and 4 focus on plotting shapes given the coordinates of their vertices.

Core tier: focuses on graphs of linear functions.

Exercise A5.8

1 Write down the coordinates of each letter marked on this coordinate grid:

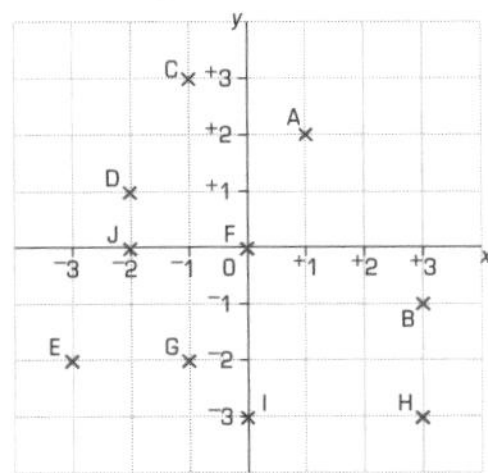

2 Draw *x*- and *y*-axes from $^-10$ to $^+10$.
Plot these points on your coordinate grid.
Mark them with the letter.
Remember you go along the *x*-axis first then the *y*-axis.

A($^-2$, 3)	B(4, $^-6$)	C(0, 0)
D(1, $^-7$)	E($^-3$, $^-4$)	F(5, $^-5$)
G($^-5$, 5)	H(5, 5)	I($^-5$, $^-5$)
J(0, $^-3$)	K($^-6$, 0)	L($^-8$, $^-6$)

3 Plot each of these sets of points on the same grid.
Join each set up as you go.

Set A: (3, 4) (6, 4) (6, 7) (3, 7) (3, 4)

Set B: (5, $^-1$) (3, $^-3$) (5, $^-7$) (7, $^-3$) (5, $^-1$)

Set C: ($^-1$, $^-2$) ($^-1$, $^-5$) ($^-4$, $^-5$) ($^-4$, $^-8$) ($^-2$, $^-8$) ($^-2$, $^-9$) ($^-8$, $^-9$) ($^-8$, $^-8$) ($^-6$, $^-8$) ($^-6$, $^-5$) ($^-9$, $^-5$) ($^-9$, $^-2$) ($^-1$, $^-2$)

Set D: ($^-2$, 8) ($^-2$, 7) ($^-5$, 7) ($^-5$, 5) ($^-7$, 5) ($^-7$, 2) ($^-8$, 2) ($^-8$, 8) ($^-2$, 8)

What shapes do your points make?

4 Plot these points on a coordinate grid:

($^-5$, 5) (5, 5) ($^-5$, $^-5$)

The points form three corners of a square.
Write down the coordinates of the 4th corner.

233

Exercise commentary

The questions assess Primary Framework Page 109.

Problem solving
Question 3 assesses Primary Framework Page 79.

Group work
The further activity is suitable for pairs.

Misconceptions
The use of negative numbers makes using coordinates a lot more difficult for many students.
Emphasise that across then up or horizontal then vertical is still valid.
It may help to practice counting vertically and horizontally separately first – N1.2OHP has a horizontal and vertical thermometer which is a useful visual aid.
Practising counting back beyond zero in steps is also useful.
In question 3 emphasise that the sets of points will make common shapes and so students should be able to see if they make a mistake.

Links
2-D shapes: Primary Framework Page 103.
Negative numbers: Page 15.

Homework

A5.8HW provides practice at reading and plotting coordinates in all four quadrants.

Answers

1 A (1, 2), B (3, $^-1$), C ($^-1$, 3), D ($^-2$, 1), E ($^-3$, $^-2$), F (0, 0), G ($^-1$, $^-2$), H (3, $^-3$), I (0, $^-3$), J ($^-2$, 0)

3 Set A is a square, set B is a kite, set C is a dodecagon, set D is an octagon.

4 (5, $^-5$)

Summary

The Year 6 key teaching objective is:

- Read and plot coordinates in all four quadrants (109).

Plenary activity

Give students the formula $C = 10m$

Discuss what it could mean, for example: cm to mm conversion.

Discuss the easiest way to find unknown values: using the formula or drawing a graph.

The benefit of the graph is that you only need draw it once but if you use the formula you have to reuse it for each value required.

Check out commentary

1 Students need to remember to count across and then up or down to read coordinates. Using the letters of the alphabet (*a* for across etc.) can help. Others find it easier to remember a saying such as 'across the hall and up the stairs'.

Reading and describing points that are on the coordinate axes cause difficulties for many students.

Emphasise that if you are on an axis one of the coordinates is 0.

There is a lot of punctuation involved in writing a series of coordinates. Encourage students to finish off a point before starting on the next one.

2 There are many skills involved in this question and a lot of working involved in each step.

Encourage students to take an ordered approach to the question. First they should input the numbers one at a time to find the output numbers. This is quite a complex task and students may need some supportive questioning to help them complete the table of values.

Emphasise that the input value is the x value and the output is the y value.

To list the coordinate pairs correctly students need to remember that x comes before y. To plot the points correctly they also need to remember that x is across and y is up. It may help if they have a ready-made coordinate grid as on **R9**. To find a value from the graph, encourage students to find where on the line the input is 3.5, then read the output.

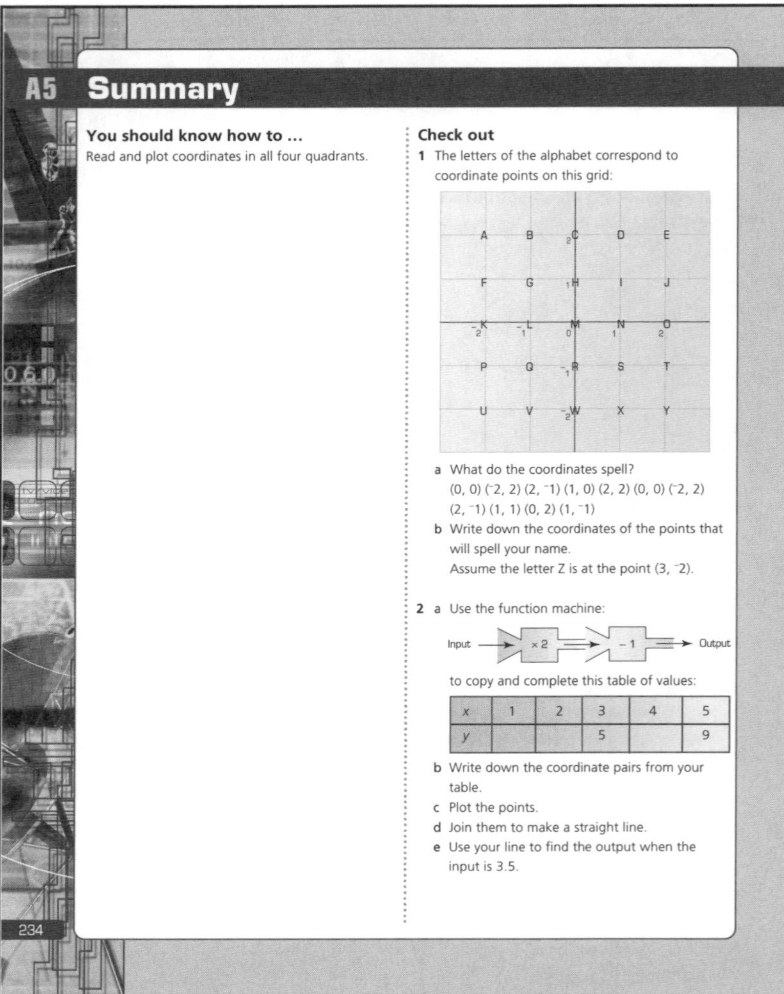

A5 Summary

You should know how to ...

Read and plot coordinates in all four quadrants.

Check out

1 The letters of the alphabet correspond to coordinate points on this grid:

a What do the coordinates spell?
(0, 0) (⁻2, 2) (2, ⁻1) (1, 0) (2, 2) (0, 0) (⁻2, 2) (2, ⁻1) (1, 1) (0, 2) (1, ⁻1)

b Write down the coordinates of the points that will spell your name.
Assume the letter Z is at the point (3, ⁻2).

2 **a** Use the function machine:

to copy and complete this table of values:

x	1	2	3	4	5
y			5		9

b Write down the coordinate pairs from your table.

c Plot the points.

d Join them to make a straight line.

e Use your line to find the output when the input is 3.5.

234

Development

The themes of this unit are developed in A3 in Year 8.

Links

Students draw graphs and describe trends in data handling as well as in other areas of the school curriculum such as science and geography.

Mental starters

Objectives covered in this unit:

- Know complements to 90 and 180.
- Visualise and describe 2-D and 3-D shapes.
- Estimate and order acute and obtuse angles.

Resources needed * means class set needed

Essential:
R14 (OHP) – Special triangles
R15 (OHP) – Special quadrilaterals
R19 (OHP) – Ruler
S5.3OHP – Nets of a closed cube
S5.4OHP* – Various shapes
S5.5OHP – Rotational symmetries
S5.6OHP – Tessellating pattern
Protractors*

Useful:
R1* – Digit cards
R5* – Number ladders
R12 (OHP) – Protractor
S1.4OHP – Net of a cuboid
S3.2OHP – Angle diagrams
S4.1OHP – Letters of the alphabet
S4.1F* – Symmetries in shapes
S5.5ICT* – Polygon symmetries

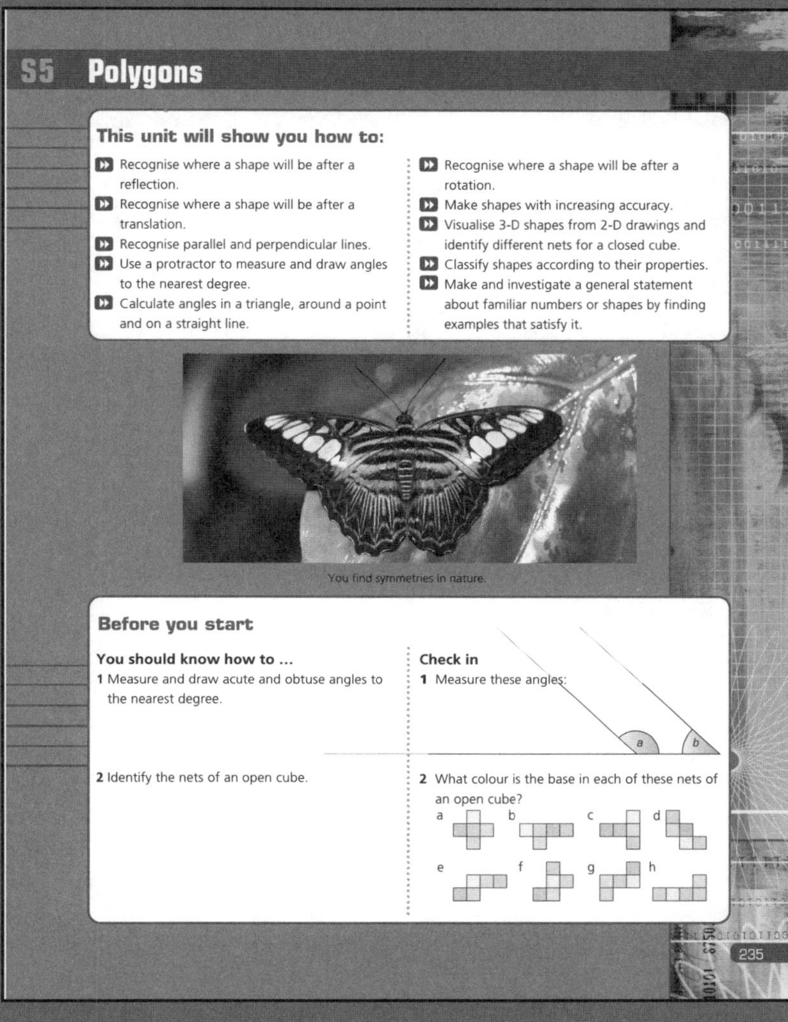

S5 Polygons

This unit will show you how to:

- Recognise where a shape will be after a reflection.
- Recognise where a shape will be after a translation.
- Recognise parallel and perpendicular lines.
- Use a protractor to measure and draw angles to the nearest degree.
- Calculate angles in a triangle, around a point and on a straight line.
- Recognise where a shape will be after a rotation.
- Make shapes with increasing accuracy.
- Visualise 3-D shapes from 2-D drawings and identify different nets for a closed cube.
- Classify shapes according to their properties.
- Make and investigate a general statement about familiar numbers or shapes by finding examples that satisfy it.

You find symmetries in nature.

Before you start

You should know how to …
1 Measure and draw acute and obtuse angles to the nearest degree.
2 Identify the nets of an open cube.

Check in
1 Measure these angles:

2 What colour is the base in each of these nets of an open cube?

235

Unit commentary

Aim of the unit

This unit aims to consolidate the work done in this book on 2-D and 3-D shapes, revising angle facts, drawing and constructing shapes accurately and considering symmetries of shapes. It extends to consider rotational symmetries and tessellations.

Introduction

Discuss why someone might need to draw or construct a shape accurately, either by hand or using ICT. Discuss what facts you would need to know to be able to draw a triangle or a cuboid, and what equipment you would need.

Framework references

This unit focuses on:

- Year 6 teaching objectives pages: 103, 105, 107, 109, 111
- Problem solving objectives page: 81

The unit provides access to:

- Year 7 teaching objectives pages: 180, 182, 186, 188, 198–206, 210, 212, 220, 222

Check in activity

Discuss everyday objects that have symmetry.
List the objects according to whether they are:

- 2-D: triangles, quadrilaterals or
- 3-D: cuboids, prisms, pyramids.

This would give five lists but you can add lists to suit the suggestions made.
Discuss how to describe each list – use geometric properties and encourage use of technical language:

- equal, opposite, parallel, perpendicular, angle, face, edge, vertex, open, closed, symmetry, reflection.

Differentiation

Core tier focuses on constructing 2-D and 3-D shapes and identifying geometric properties of polygons.

Springboard 7

Pages 460, 462, 466, 477.

Mental starter

Acute, obtuse or reflex?

Ask students to hold up digit cards to show an angle that is acute.
Repeat. Include obtuse and reflex angles.
Progress to asking students to sketch and give the size of an acute angle. Then obtuse, then reflex angles.
Students should justify their choice of angle and drawings.
Include 90°, 180° and 360° – discuss the names of these.

Useful resources

R12 – protractor.
S3.2OHP – angle diagrams.
Protractors
R5 number ladders for the plenary.
R1 digit cards for the mental starter.

Introductory activity

Refer to the mental starter.

Ask students how they would draw accurately the angles they estimated.
Emphasise that angle is a measure of turn so it needs special equipment to draw it – a protractor.

Discuss the angle milestones:

- 90° on a corner
- 180° on a straight line
- 360° in a full turn

where the type of angle changes.

Discuss how to find missing angles in a triangle.
Refer back to S3.3 where students checked the angle sum of a triangle by folding.
Encourage them to share strategies for remembering that the sum of angles in a triangle is 180°.

Go over the examples from S3.2OHP or draw new examples on the board.

Use the examples to emphasise that opposite angles are equal.

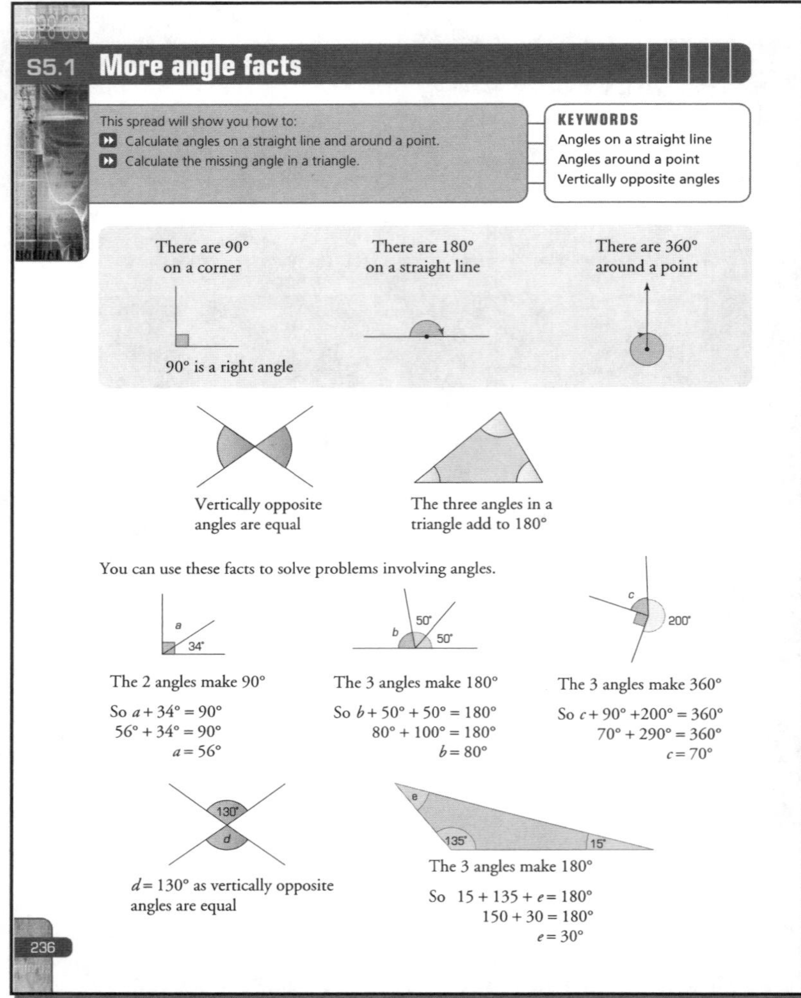

S5.1 More angle facts

This spread will show you how to:
- Calculate angles on a straight line and around a point.
- Calculate the missing angle in a triangle.

KEYWORDS
Angles on a straight line
Angles around a point
Vertically opposite angles

There are 90° on a corner

90° is a right angle

There are 180° on a straight line

There are 360° around a point

Vertically opposite angles are equal

The three angles in a triangle add to 180°

You can use these facts to solve problems involving angles.

The 2 angles make 90°

So $a + 34° = 90°$
$56° + 34° = 90°$
$a = 56°$

The 3 angles make 180°

So $b + 50° + 50° = 180°$
$80° + 100° = 180°$
$b = 80°$

The 3 angles make 360°

So $c + 90° + 200° = 360°$
$70° + 290° = 360°$
$c = 70°$

$d = 130°$ as vertically opposite angles are equal

The 3 angles make 180°

So $15 + 135 + e = 180°$
$150 + 30 = 180°$
$e = 30°$

236

Plenary

Order!

Students use a number ladder as on **R5**.
Roll a dice. The scores stand for these events:

- 1 and 2 = acute angle
- 3 and 4 = obtuse angle
- 5 and 6 = reflex angle.

Students must write down an appropriate angle each time in the ladder, if possible so that the angles are arranged in order of size starting with the smallest.

Further activities

Students devise angle problems as in question 2 for partners to solve. The challenge is to give as little information as possible to describe a unique triangle.

Differentiation

Support questions:

- Question 1 focuses on angles on a straight line and at a point.
- Question 2 focuses on using triangle properties to find missing angles in a triangle. Springboard 7, pages 466, 467.
- Question 3 consists of harder triangle problems including exterior angles.

Core tier: focuses on constructing triangles.

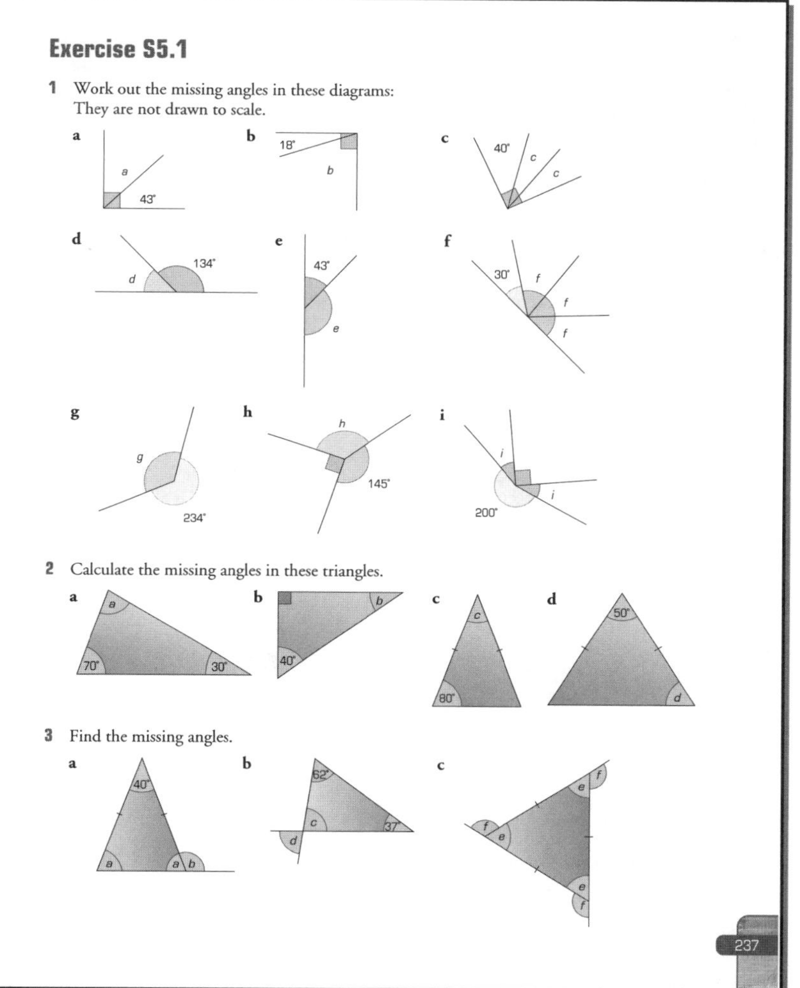

Exercise S5.1

1 Work out the missing angles in these diagrams: They are not drawn to scale.

2 Calculate the missing angles in these triangles.

3 Find the missing angles.

237

Exercise commentary

The questions assess Primary Framework Page 111.

Problem solving

The exercise assesses Primary Framework Page 81 if students generalise.

Group work

The further activity is suitable for pairs.

Misconceptions

Students mix up angle facts.

Emphasise that they only need to remember one fact: angles in a triangle add to 180°, and this can be deduced from visualising an equilateral triangle.

Angles on a straight line can be deduced from a protractor.

In 1c students find $c = 50°$, forgetting to divide by 2.

Encourage students to look back at the question and check whether the answer makes sense. In this case c is obviously smaller than 40°.

Students measure rather than calculate.

Emphasise that while the diagrams give some sense of the relative sizes they are not drawn to scale unless it says so.

Links

2-D shapes: Primary Framework Page 103.

Homework

S5.1HW provides practice at finding missing angles using angle facts.

Answers

1 **a** $a = 47°$ **b** $b = 72°$ **c** $c = 25°$
d $d = 46°$ **e** $e = 137°$ **f** $f = 50°$
g $g = 126°$ **h** $h = 125°$ **i** $i = 35°$

2 **a** 80° **b** 50° **c** 20° **d** 65°

3 **a** $a = 70°$, $b = 110°$
b $c = 81°$, $d = 81°$
c $e = 60°$, $f = 120°$

Mental starter

Target 180

Give a number between 0 and 180. Ask for the complement to 180.

Students can use digit cards or write answers on paper.

Progress to giving two numbers and asking for the third to make the total 180. Keep the numbers relatively simple, e.g. 30 and 100.

Build up to harder numbers such as two lots of 36.

Useful resources

R12 – protractor

Protractors

R1 digit cards

R19 – ruler

Introductory activity

Recall angle facts students know:

- 90° on a corner
- 180° on a straight line and in a triangle
- 360° in a full turn.

Discuss how to recognise a right angle.

Emphasise that a right angle is 90°.

Discuss how to draw a right angle – encourage use of a protractor as the most accurate way (or set square).

Discuss the stages involved in drawing an angle:

- Start with a straight line.
- Fit the protractor scale along it (like a ruler).
- Find the right scale – start from 0.
- Count round the scale.
- Make a mark.
- Join the mark to the right end!

Use acute and obtuse examples.

Sketch the triangle shown in the student book on the board, and label it.

Emphasise it is called a triangle because it has three angles.

Ask what the missing angle is.

Now ask how to work out what the long side (hypotenuse) measures.

You must construct the triangle.

Discuss the steps involved in constructing a triangle:

- Draw a line first – discuss why.
- Construct an angle at each end.
- Be careful which scale you use – discuss why this is important.
- The lines meet at the 3rd vertex.

Emphasise the steps are the same for all triangles.

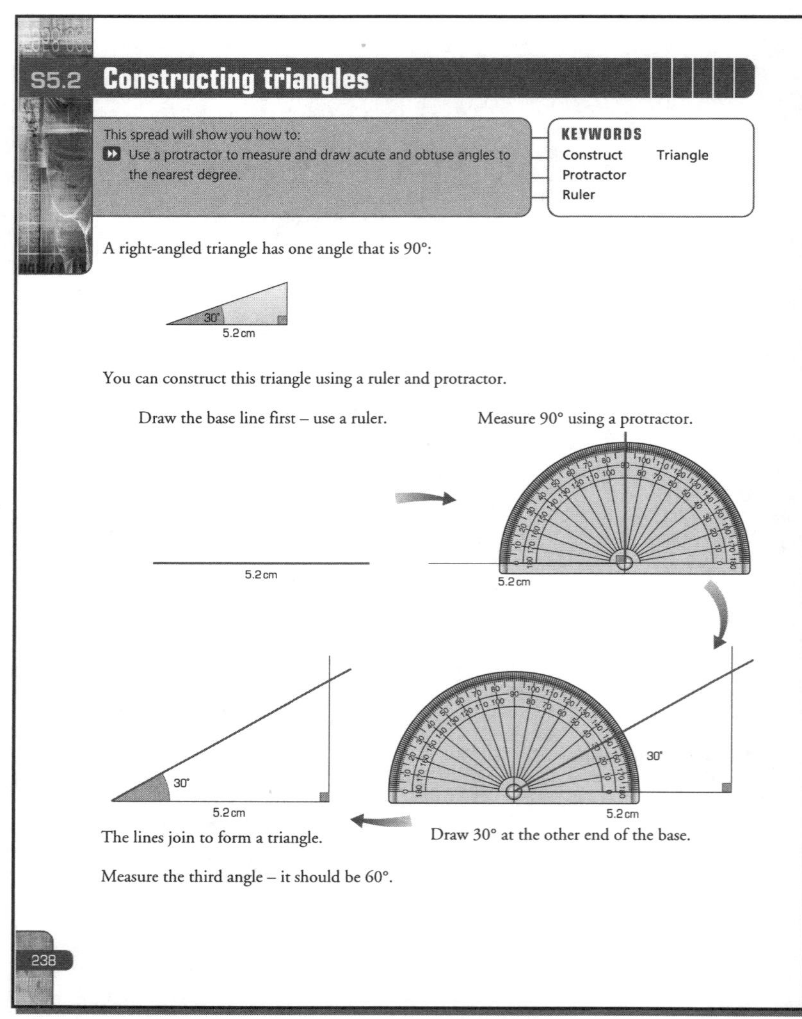

S5.2 Constructing triangles

This spread will show you how to:
- Use a protractor to measure and draw acute and obtuse angles to the nearest degree.

KEYWORDS
Construct
Triangle
Protractor
Ruler

A right-angled triangle has one angle that is 90°:

You can construct this triangle using a ruler and protractor.

Draw the base line first – use a ruler.

Measure 90° using a protractor.

The lines join to form a triangle.

Draw 30° at the other end of the base.

Measure the third angle – it should be 60°.

238

Plenary

Consider question 5 together.

Discuss how to draw the angle at each end of the line.

Emphasise the correct use of scale.

(90° is in the same place on both scales.)

Look at what happens if you use the wrong scale.

Discuss why the triangle would then be impossible.

Emphasise that the interior angles add to 180°.

Further activities

Students could construct a triangle accurately, copy it ten times and fit them all together to make a pattern (tessellation).

Differentiation

Support questions:

- Question 1 focuses on classifying triangles.
- Questions 2 and 3 focus on drawing right-angled triangles. Springboard 7, page 460.
- Questions 4 and 5 focus on constructing triangles from given information. Springboard 7, page 462.

Core tier: focuses on constructing quadrilaterals.

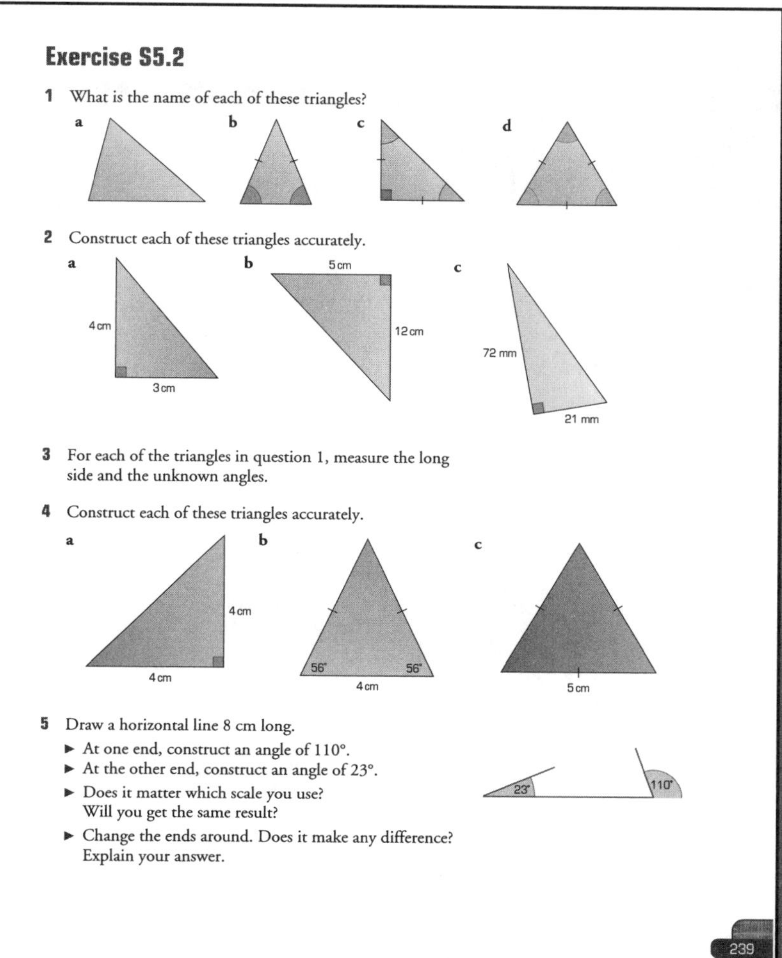

Exercise S5.2
1 What is the name of each of these triangles?
2 Construct each of these triangles accurately.
5 cm
12 cm
4 cm
3 cm
72 mm
21 mm
3 For each of the triangles in question 1, measure the long side and the unknown angles.
4 Construct each of these triangles accurately.
4 cm
4 cm
56°
56°
4 cm
5 cm
5 Draw a horizontal line 8 cm long.
At one end, construct an angle of 110°.
At the other end, construct an angle of 23°.
Does it matter which scale you use? Will you get the same result?
Change the ends around. Does it make any difference? Explain your answer.
23°
110°
239

Exercise commentary

The questions assess Primary Framework Page 111.

Problem solving

Question 4 assesses Primary Framework Page 81 if students generalise.

Group work

The further activity is suitable for pairs.

Misconceptions

Students find the protractor difficult to use and may not place it correctly or use the wrong scale.

To gain confidence and learn how to place the protractor properly, encourage them to place a ruler first, ensuring the end of the line aligns with the zero mark.

Encourage students to estimate the size of the angles first – whether they are acute or obtuse – before constructing so that they can see which scale to use.

Some students will find the angles difficult to measure because of the orientation of the shapes.

Encourage them to turn the page to help and then point out that rotating the protractor is easier!

Links

2-D shapes: Primary Framework Page 103.

Homework

S5.2HW provides practice at constructing triangles. Students will need a protractor.

Answers

1 **a** Scalene **b** Isosceles **c** Right-angled isosceles **d** Equilateral

3 **a** 5 cm, 37°, 53°
b 13 cm, 23°, 67°
c 25 mm, 16°, 74°

5 The result is the same each time.

Mental starter

What shape am I?

Describe 2-D shapes in steps – each step should reveal a new property.

Students hold up cards with the name of the shape on as soon as they know the name. They can change the guess as you give more properties.

- Right-angled triangle: I have 3 sides. I have 3 angles. All my angles are different. One angle is 30°. One angle is 60°. (One angle is 90°.)
- Rectangle: 4 angles, opposite sides equal, parallel, all angles 90°.

Useful resources

S5.3OHP shows some nets of cube.

S1.4OHP shows a 2 × 3 × 4 cuboid and its net.

Introductory activity

Ask students to describe a cube.

Encourage use of terms: faces, edges and vertices. Bring out that the faces are all squares by considering views – what does it look like from the front? side? top?

Discuss the properties of a square – all sides equal in length, all angles equal to 90°.

Discuss how to draw a square.

Emphasise the need to be systematic:

- Use a protractor to measure 90°.
- Measure the length with a ruler.
- Repeat for the next side.

It is easier to use squared paper! – this is fine for the exercise.

Discuss how you would make a cube.

- You can use multilink cubes for whole number lengths.
- You can make a flat shape that will fold up to make the solid.

Define the flat shape as a net.

Illustrate nets using boxes.

Discuss the nets on S5.2OHP.

Encourage students to pair up the sides to make open cubes.

Students should colour the edges to show which ones fit.

This should help them visualise whether it is actually a net.

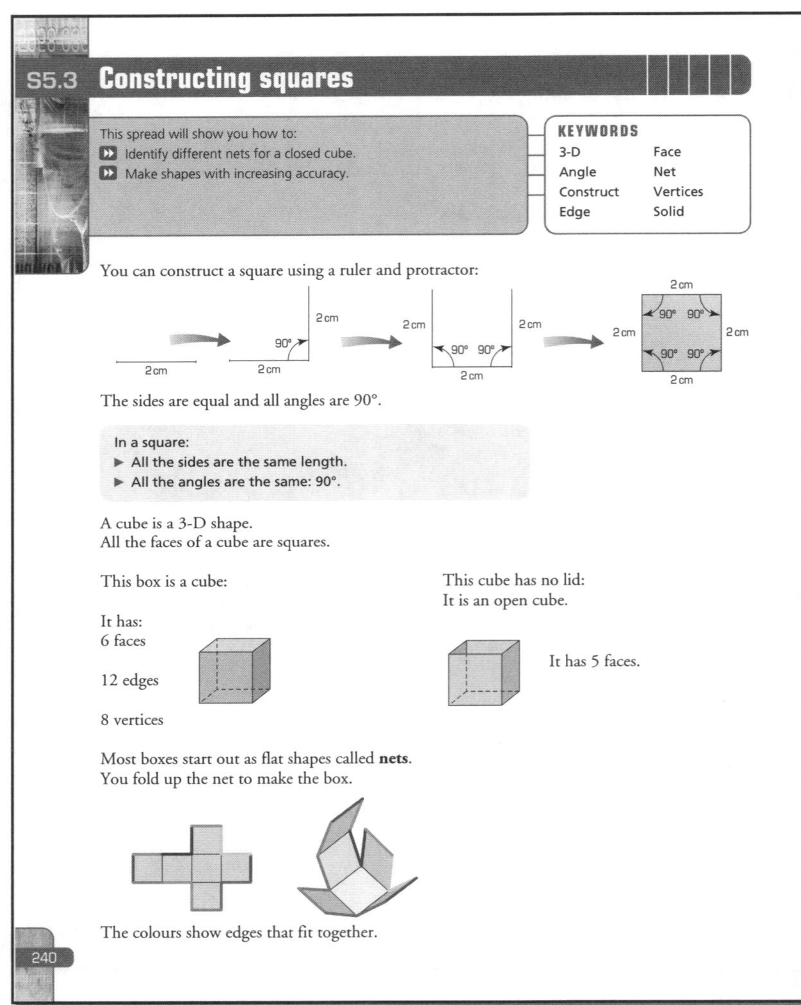

S5.3 Constructing squares

This spread will show you how to:

- Identify different nets for a closed cube.
- Make shapes with increasing accuracy.

KEYWORDS

3-D	Face
Angle	Net
Construct	Vertices
Edge	Solid

You can construct a square using a ruler and protractor:

The sides are equal and all angles are 90°.

In a square:

- All the sides are the same length.
- All the angles are the same: 90°.

A cube is a 3-D shape.
All the faces of a cube are squares.

This box is a cube:

It has:
6 faces

12 edges

8 vertices

This cube has no lid:
It is an open cube.

It has 5 faces.

Most boxes start out as flat shapes called **nets**.
You fold up the net to make the box.

The colours show edges that fit together.

240

Plenary

Discuss which of the nets in question 3 make a closed cube.

Students should justify reasons.

Encourage them to colour in sides in pairs on **S5.3OHP**.

Discuss how to draw the net of a 2 × 3 × 4 cuboid.

S1.4OHP shows a 2 × 3 × 4 cuboid and its net.

Further activities

Challenge students to find the two nets of a tetrahedron.

Able students may construct the nets accurately.

Differentiation

Support questions:

- Question 1 focuses on constructing a square.
- Questions 2 and 3 focus on identifying nets of cubes.
- Questions 4 and 5 focus on constructing nets and trying to minimise the perimeter.

Core tier: focuses on nets of prisms and pyramids.

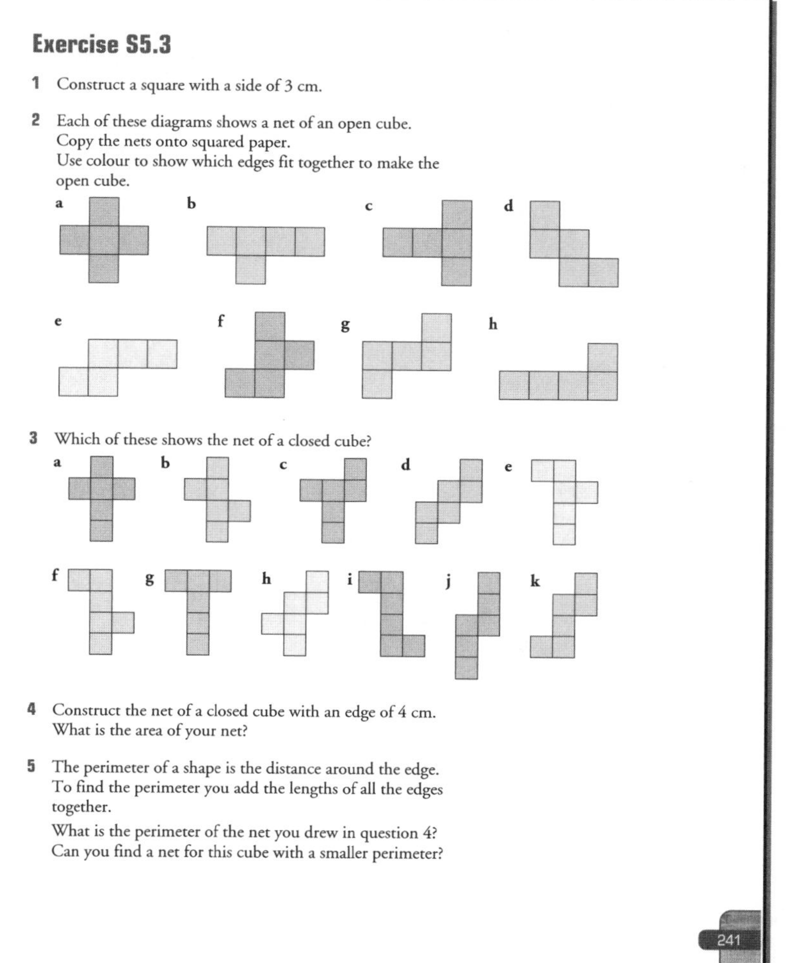

Exercise S5.3

1 Construct a square with a side of 3 cm.

2 Each of these diagrams shows a net of an open cube.
Copy the nets onto squared paper.
Use colour to show which edges fit together to make the open cube.

3 Which of these shows the net of a closed cube?

4 Construct the net of a closed cube with an edge of 4 cm.
What is the area of your net?

5 The perimeter of a shape is the distance around the edge.
To find the perimeter you add the lengths of all the edges together.
What is the perimeter of the net you drew in question 4?
Can you find a net for this cube with a smaller perimeter?

241

Exercise commentary

The questions assess Primary Framework Page 105.

Problem solving

Question 5 assesses Primary Framework Page 81 if students generalise.

Group work

Question 5 and the further activity are suitable for pairs.

Misconceptions

Students find 2-D representations of 3-D shapes difficult to visualise.

Encourage the use of Polydron or similar and ensure students have access to empty boxes so they can see how the net is folded to make up the box.

Some students will need to draw the net on squared paper and fold it up to see if it makes a cube.

In question 5 students may need reminding of the perimeter even though there is a definition in the question.

Students should be encouraged to take a structured approach to this problem.

Links

3-D shapes: Primary Framework Page 103.

Perimeter and area: Page 97.

Homework

In **S5.3HW** students are asked to draw all the possible nets of a cube.

Answers

3 All of them.

4 Area = 96 cm^2

5 All possible nets have perimeter 56 cm.

S5.4 Reflection symmetry

Mental starter

What's my shape?

S4.1OHP shows symmetrical letters. Copy and enlarge the OHP.
Cut out some letters and fold them along a line of symmetry.
Show students each folded letter and where the fold is.
Students say what the letter will be when opened up.

Useful resources

S4.1OHP – symmetrical letters
S5.4OHP has some shapes to discuss – it is useful if students have a copy.
Mirrors
R14 shows special triangles.
R15 shows special quadrilaterals.

Introductory activity

Refer to the mental starter.
Ask students the name for a fold line.
Encourage line of symmetry (mirror line).

Ask how to describe the symmetry of a shape with a line of symmetry – it has reflective symmetry.
Discuss where students use the word 'reflection' – in a mirror.

Define the line of symmetry or fold line as the mirror line.
Emphasise you can use the mirror to:

- check a line of symmetry or
- complete a shape with reflective symmetry.

Show how to check using the letters from the starter.

S5.4OHP has some shapes on to discuss.
Show students the kite.

- Ask if it has any lines of symmetry.
- Students draw in the line.
- Check using a mirror.

Repeat for a parallelogram.
The shape does not have reflective symmetry. This reinforces the need to check with a mirror.
Repeat for the five-pointed star.
This is useful for showing there can be more than one line of symmetry.

Introduce regular shapes: all sides and all angles equal.
Ask students to name the regular triangle and quadrilateral.
Discuss symmetries.

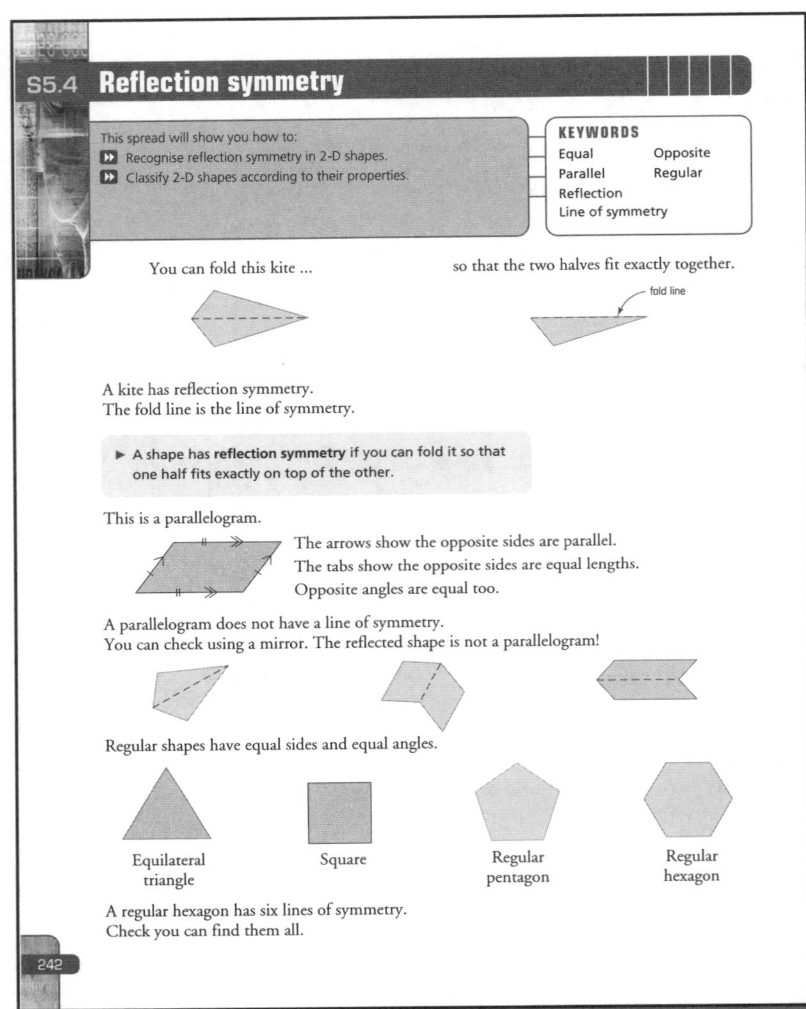

S5.4 Reflection symmetry

This spread will show you how to:

- Recognise reflection symmetry in 2-D shapes.
- Classify 2-D shapes according to their properties.

KEYWORDS
Equal
Opposite
Parallel
Regular
Reflection
Line of symmetry

You can fold this kite ... so that the two halves fit exactly together.

A kite has reflection symmetry.
The fold line is the line of symmetry.

► A shape has **reflection symmetry** if you can fold it so that one half fits exactly on top of the other.

This is a parallelogram.

The arrows show the opposite sides are parallel.
The tabs show the opposite sides are equal lengths.
Opposite angles are equal too.

A parallelogram does not have a line of symmetry.
You can check using a mirror. The reflected shape is not a parallelogram!

Regular shapes have equal sides and equal angles.

Equilateral triangle — Square — Regular pentagon — Regular hexagon

A regular hexagon has six lines of symmetry.
Check you can find them all.

242

Plenary

Discuss answers to questions 3 and 4.

Students give as many shapes as possible for each question.

Discuss whether you can have a quadrilateral with 3 lines of symmetry or a triangle with 2 lines of symmetry.

Further activities

Students could replay the game on **S4.1F** about lines of symmetries in shapes.

Differentiation

Support questions:

- Questions 1 and 2 focus on recognising symmetries of triangles and quadrilaterals.
- Questions 3 and 4 focus on drawing shapes with given symmetry properties.
- Question 5 focuses on symmetries of regular polygons.

Core tier: focuses on geometrical properties of triangles and quadrilaterals.

Exercise S5.4

1 Copy or trace each of these triangles.
Draw in all the lines of symmetry and name each shape.

a **b** **c** **d**

2 Copy or trace each of these quadrilaterals.
Draw in all the lines of symmetry and name each shape.

a **b** **c** **d**

e **f** **g** **h**

3 Draw a triangle with:
a 1 line of symmetry **b** 3 lines of symmetry
Name each shape that you draw.

4 Draw a quadrilateral with:
a 2 lines of symmetry **b** 4 lines of symmetry
c 1 line of symmetry **d** 0 lines of symmetry
Name each shape that you draw.

5 Copy or trace each of these shapes.
Draw in all the lines of symmetry and name each shape.

a **b** **c** **d**

243

Exercise commentary

The questions assess Primary Framework Page 107.

Problem solving
Question 5 assesses Primary Framework Page 81 if students generalise.

Group work
The further activity is suitable for pairs.

Misconceptions
Students find vertical lines of symmetry relatively easy to spot but need more encouragement to find others.
Rotating the page can often help them spot further lines.
Commonly students will find a line of symmetry in a parallelogram and diagonal lines of symmetry in a rectangle.
Encourage the use of a mirror or paper folding to check the lines they have found.

Links
2-D shapes: Primary Framework Page 103.

Homework

S5.4HW contains a table to copy and complete. Students are required to identify shapes and state their number of lines of symmetry.

Answers

1 Number of lines of symmetry: **a** 1 **b** 0 **c** 3 **d** 1
2 Number of lines of symmetry: **a** 2 **b** 0 **c** 1 **d** 1 **e** 4 **f** 2 **g** 0 **h** 1
3 **a** Any isosceles triangle **b** Equilateral triangle
4 **a** Any rectangle or rhombus **b** Square
c Any kite, isosceles trapezium or arrowhead
d Any parallelogram or ordinary quadrilateral
5 **a** 5 lines of symmetry; regular pentagon **b** 1 line of symmetry; pentagon
c No lines of symmetry, trapezium **d** 6 lines of symmetry; 6-pointed star

S5.5 Rotational symmetry

Mental starter

What's my symmetry?
Ask students to name a shape with a given number of lines of symmetry.
For example: 5 lines would be a regular pentagon.
4 lines could be a square or a rhombus.

Useful resources

S5.5OHP shows rotational symmetries.
R15 shows special quadrilaterals to discuss in the plenary.

Introductory activity

Discuss what students understand by the terms rotate and rotation.
A rotation is a turn.

Remind students that you can make a pattern when you rotate a shape.
S5.5OHP has a series of turns of a flag making a pattern.
Ask students to describe the pattern.
Encourage technical terms.
Ask (if you need to) if the pattern looks symmetrical.
Define rotational symmetry – the shape rotates onto itself.

In reflective symmetry the shape reflects onto itself.
Emphasise that the flag pattern has no reflective symmetry.
Show the series of hexagonal patterns on S5.5OHP.
Emphasise that the hexagon is regular.
Discuss its symmetries.

Show students a parallelogram – it looks symmetrical but doesn't have reflective symmetry.
Discuss how to show it has rotational symmetry.

- Put a cross in the centre then turn the shape slowly.
- Students say 'stop' when it looks the same as the start.
- Discuss why you can stop when you get back to the beginning.

Emphasise you can turn the book round in the exercise rather than cut out the shapes.

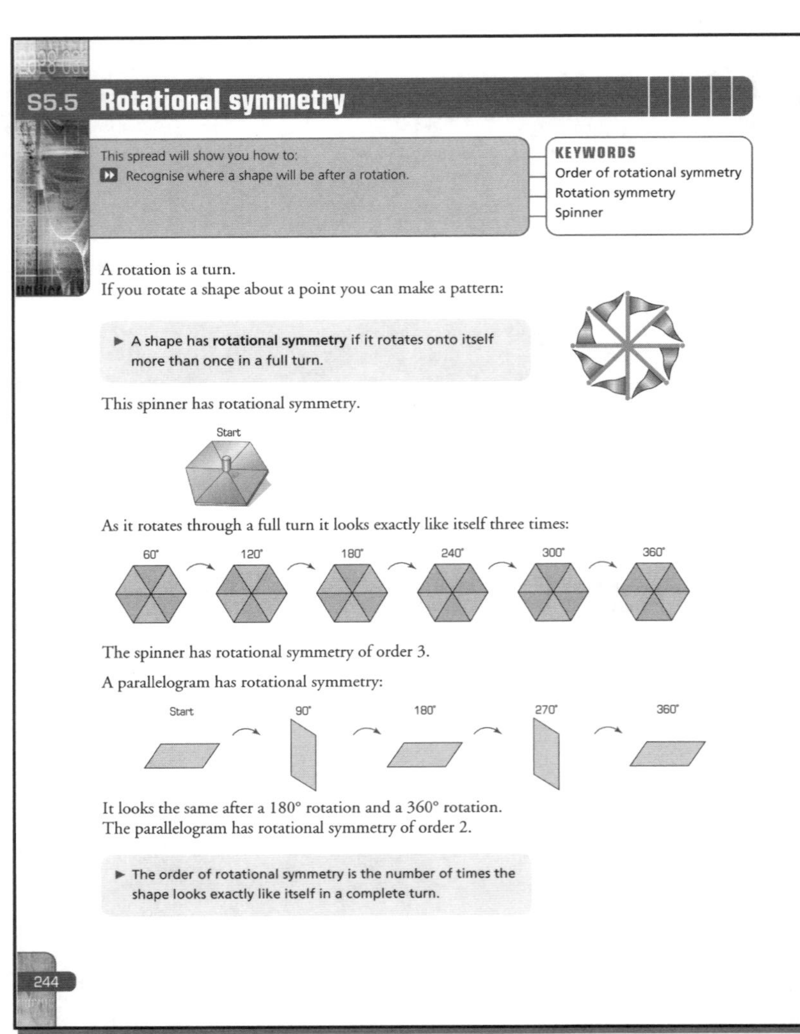

S5.5 **Rotational symmetry**

This spread will show you how to:
- Recognise where a shape will be after a rotation.

KEYWORDS
Order of rotational symmetry
Rotation symmetry
Spinner

A rotation is a turn.
If you rotate a shape about a point you can make a pattern:

- A shape has **rotational symmetry** if it rotates onto itself more than once in a full turn.

This spinner has rotational symmetry.

As it rotates through a full turn it looks exactly like itself three times:

The spinner has rotational symmetry of order 3.

A parallelogram has rotational symmetry:

It looks the same after a 180° rotation and a 360° rotation.
The parallelogram has rotational symmetry of order 2.

- The order of rotational symmetry is the number of times the shape looks exactly like itself in a complete turn.

244

Plenary

Ask questions about the quadrilaterals on **R15**:

- Does it have symmetry?
- What kind of symmetry?
- How many lines?
- How many times does it rotate onto itself?

Or…
Ask students to name shapes with given rotational symmetries.

Further activities

S5.5ICT explores the symmetry of polygons using a geometry package.

Students could replay the game on **S4.1F** about rotational symmetry in shapes.

Students can investigate a general rule for the rotational symmetry of regular polygons using the answers to questions 1, 2, 3, 5 and 9.

Differentiation

Support questions:

- Questions 1–4 focus on recognising rotational symmetries of simple regular polygons.
- Questions 5–17 focus on recognising rotational symmetry in more complex shapes.
- Questions 18 and 19 focus on visualising shapes with rotational symmetry.

Core tier: focuses on geometrical properties of polygons.

Exercise S5.5

Copy each shape and state the order of rotational symmetry.

1 2 3 4

5 6 7 8

9 10 11 12

13 14 15 16

17 Copy these flags.
What is the order of rotational symmetry of each flag?
Draw in any lines of symmetry.

a b c

d e f

18 The year 1961 has rotational symmetry of order 2.
Find four more years between 1000 and this year that also have rotational symmetry of order 2.

19 List the seven capital letters that have rotational symmetry.

245

Exercise commentary

The questions assess Primary Framework Page 111.

Problem solving

Questions 18 and 19 assess Primary Framework Page 79 and the further activity assesses Page 81 if students generalise.

Group work

The further activity is suitable for pairs.

Misconceptions

Some students confuse the different symmetries.

Emphasise that rotation is a turn and that you see a reflection in a mirror.

It can be difficult to visualise the rotational symmetries so it helps if students have cut-outs of the shapes that they can rotate using a pencil point or similar (use S5.5R).

Using tracing paper makes it easiest to see the symmetries. Encourage students to make a mark on the shape so that they can see when they arrive back at the start.

Question 13 may be difficult for some – it has an infinite order!

Links

2-D shapes: Primary Framework Page 103.

Homework

S5.5HW provides practice at recognising rotational symmetry.

Answers

1 3	**2** 8	**3** 5	**4** 2	**5** 4
6 3	**7** 4	**8** 2	**9** 10	**10** 4
11 2	**12** 3	**13** ∞	**14** 5	**15** 2
16 2				

17 All have rotational symmetry order 2. All have 2 lines of symmetry except **d** which has none.

18 1111, 1691, 1001, 1881 **19** H, I, N, O, S, X, Z

Mental starter

It's my turn

Students to sketch shapes with given order of rotational symmetry.
Start with triangles and order 1, 2, 3
then quadrilaterals and order 1, 2, 3, 4.
Discuss any that can't be made.

Useful resources

S5.6OHP – tessellating patterns
R9 – blank squared grid

Introductory activity

Draw the L shape from the student book on an OHP of a squared grid, **R9**.

Discuss the different ways you can move the L shape about on the grid.
Use cut-outs of the L shape to place on the grid or colour in relevant squares.

- Flip the shape over and ask for a description of the move – a reflection
- Turn the shape and ask for a description – rotation

Ask if there are any other ways to move the shape.

- Show a sliding movement – ask how to describe it – a translation.

Define the moves as transformations – they transform where the shape is.

Emphasise that the shape remains constant throughout – so each transformation leaves the shape unchanged but changes the position.

Define the shapes as congruent: exactly the same shape and size.

Ask students if they know the term to use when congruent shapes fit together with no gaps or overlaps – tessellation.

S5.6OHP shows two patterns – one tessellates but the other doesn't. Use these to highlight that if the pattern uses two shapes it is not a tessellation.

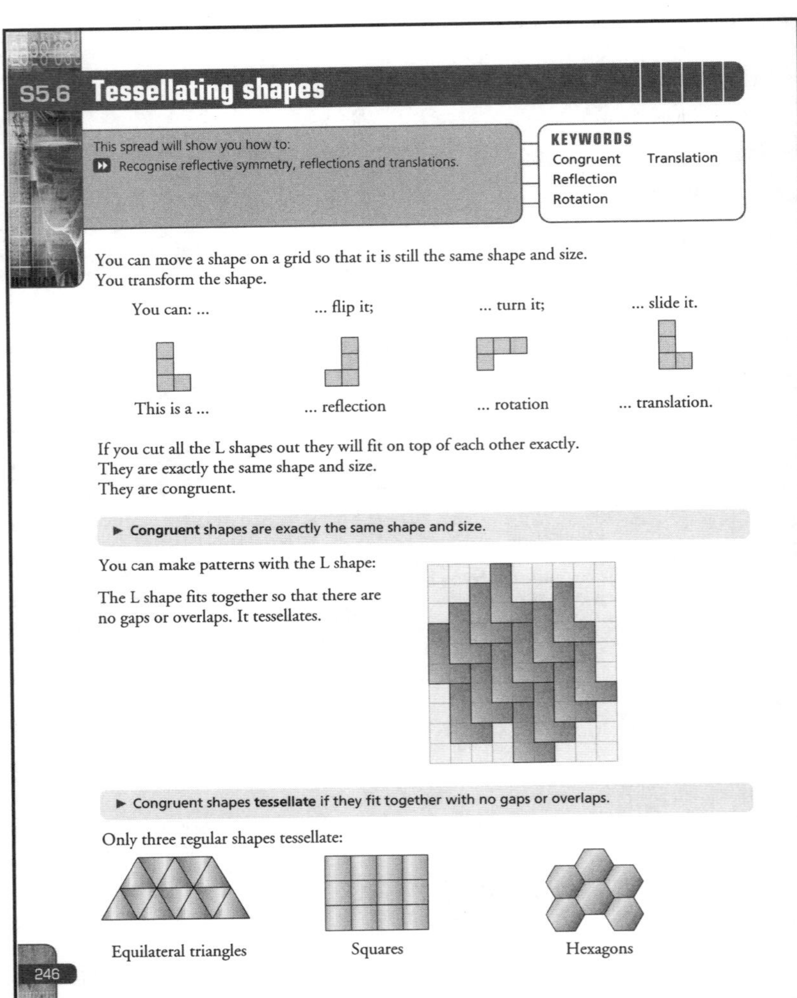
S5.6 Tessellating shapes

This spread will show you how to:
Recognise reflective symmetry, reflections and translations.

KEYWORDS
Congruent
Reflection
Rotation
Translation

You can move a shape on a grid so that it is still the same shape and size.
You transform the shape.

You can: ... ... flip it; ... turn it; ... slide it.

This is a ... ... reflection ... rotation ... translation.

If you cut all the L shapes out they will fit on top of each other exactly.
They are exactly the same shape and size.
They are congruent.

▸ Congruent shapes are exactly the same shape and size.

You can make patterns with the L shape:

The L shape fits together so that there are no gaps or overlaps. It tessellates.

▸ Congruent shapes **tessellate** if they fit together with no gaps or overlaps.

Only three regular shapes tessellate:

Equilateral triangles Squares Hexagons

246

Plenary

Draw an L shape on an OHP of **R9** that is a 3 times enlargement of the L shape in the student book.
Start with a smaller L shape in the bottom left corner and ask students to describe transformations of the shape that will build up to fill the larger L shape.

Further activities

Students can test whether any other regular polygons tessellate. They will need to use cut-out shapes which they can trace from S5.5.

Challenge students to find out which of the 12 pentominoes tessellate. There are copies on **S5.6R**.

Differentiation

Support questions:

- Questions 1–3 focus on simple tessellations.
- Questions 4–10 provide harder tessellations.
- Questions 11 and 12 are difficult questions and students may need to use cut-outs to help them find the tessellations.

Core tier: extends to patterns involving rotated shapes.

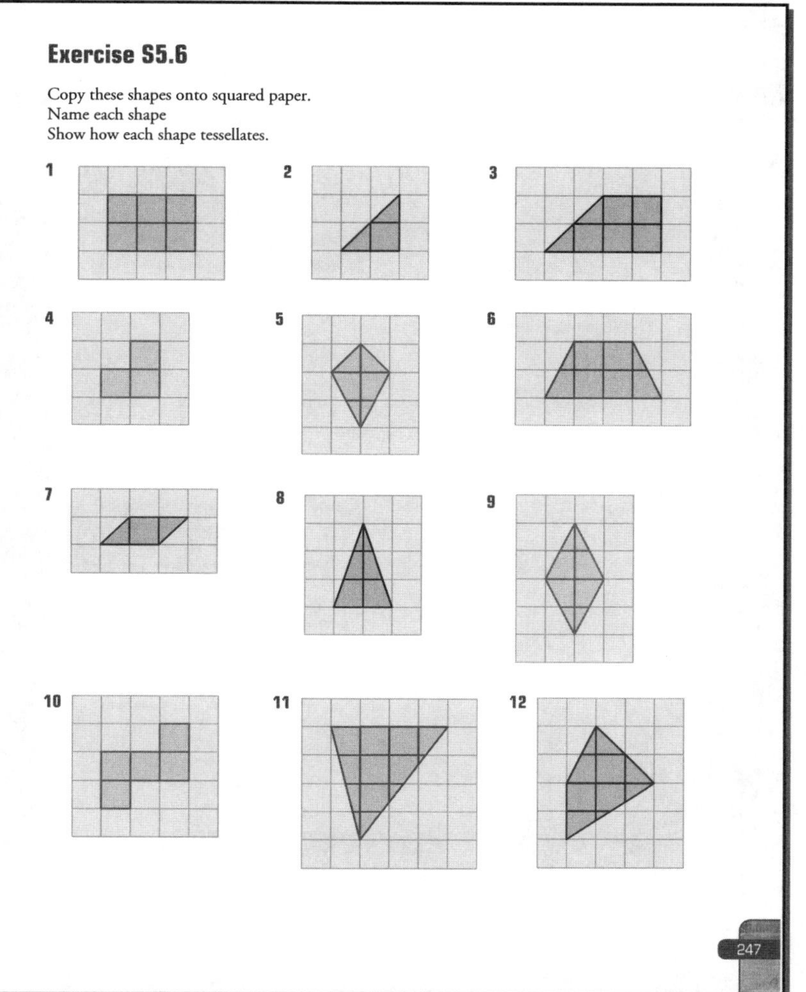

Exercise S5.6
Copy these shapes onto squared paper.
Name each shape
Show how each shape tessellates.
1
2
3
4
5
6
7
8
9
10
11
12
247

Exercise commentary

The questions assess Primary Framework Pages 107 and 111.

Problem solving

The further activity assesses Page 81 if students generalise.

Group work

The further activity is suitable for pairs.

Misconceptions

Students may need to make copies of the shapes to help them see whether or not they tessellate.

Emphasise that the lengths need to fit to avoid the danger of overlaps or gaps.

The answers to questions 11 and 12 may surprise some students and they provide a good basis for discussion as to what properties a shape must have in order for it to stand a chance of tessellating.

Some students fail to see rotations and reflections as possible transformations of a shape, considering translation only for tessellations.

Use real-life examples of tessellating patterns to illustrate that shapes can be transformed in any way that helps them fit.

Links

2-D shapes: Primary Framework Page 103.
Constructing shapes: Page 105.

Homework

S5.6HW is an investigation based on tessellating polygons.

Answers

1	Rectangle	2	Right-angled isosceles triangle
3	Right-angled trapezium	4	Hexagon
5	Kite	6	Isosceles trapezium
7	Parallelogram	8	Isosceles triangle
9	Rhombus	10	Octagon
11	Scalene triangle	12	Irregular quadrilateral

Summary

The unit gives access to the Year 7 key objectives:

- Explain and justify methods and conclusions (Secondary Framework Page 30).
- Know the sum of angles at a point, on a straight line and in a triangle (Secondary Framework Page 182).

Check out commentary

1 It is useful to have copies of the shapes or tracing paper available to help students draw the shapes.
Students will often draw lines of symmetry in a parallelogram and fail to find all the lines in the triangle or pentagon. This question will highlight those students who do not recognise the symmetries of shapes. In particular it is important to note students who cannot identify the lines of symmetry by now and refer back to the work in S4 on reflection in shapes. You could give them S4.1F for more practice.

2 Students may need to draw the nets on squared paper and cut them out to help them decide whether they make nets of cubes.
Encourage them to colour pairs of sides to help them visualise the nets.

3 Most of these statements are true but the justifications for whether they are true or not are fairly challenging for students. It is not vital that students can justify their reasoning at this stage, although the questions do highlight the sort of geometrical facts they should know and so less able students should concentrate on whether the statements are true.
Encourage students to discuss the statements in pairs or small groups.
Allow justifications in the form of drawings but emphasise the use of a counter-example in showing the statement is not true.

Plenary activity

Ask students to describe a kite using its geometric properties.
Draw a kite on an OHP of **R8** (or square dotty paper).
Discuss whether it will tessellate.
Ask students to try to justify answers before attempting to draw any diagrams.
Discuss how the angle properties affect whether a shape will tessellate – the angles must fit around a point.

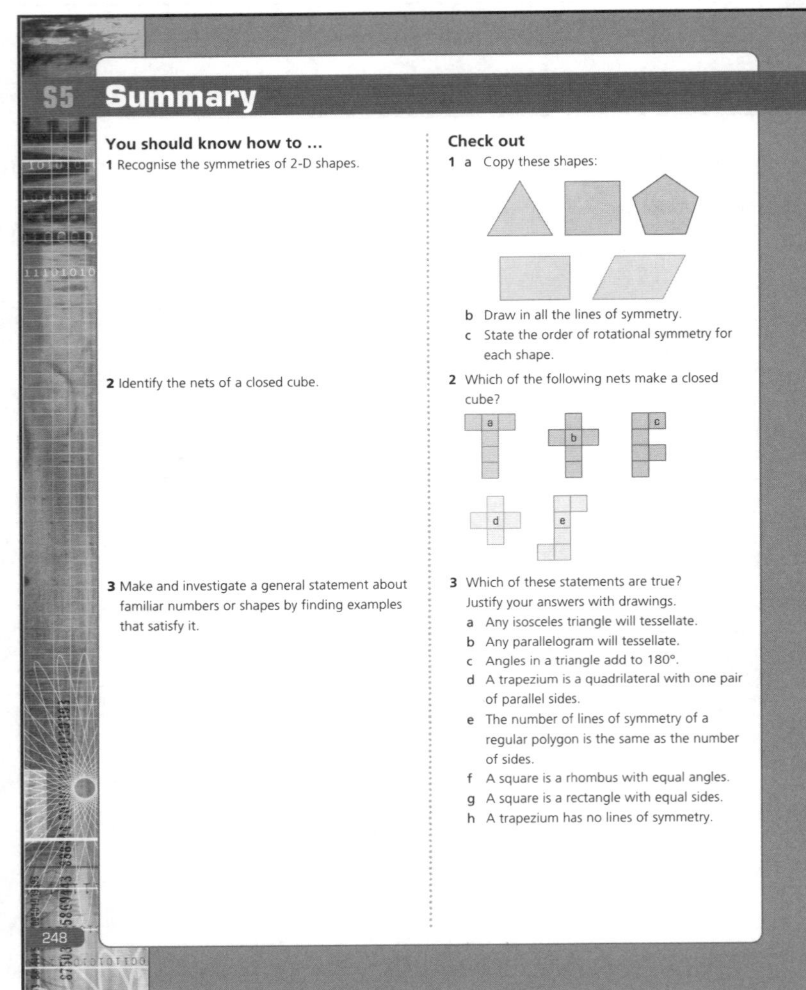

S5 Summary

You should know how to ...	Check out
1 Recognise the symmetries of 2-D shapes.	1 a Copy these shapes: b Draw in all the lines of symmetry. c State the order of rotational symmetry for each shape.
2 Identify the nets of a closed cube.	2 Which of the following nets make a closed cube?
3 Make and investigate a general statement about familiar numbers or shapes by finding examples that satisfy it.	3 Which of these statements are true? Justify your answers with drawings. a Any isosceles triangle will tessellate. b Any parallelogram will tessellate. c Angles in a triangle add to 180°. d A trapezium is a quadrilateral with one pair of parallel sides. e The number of lines of symmetry of a regular polygon is the same as the number of sides. f A square is a rhombus with equal angles. g A square is a rectangle with equal sides. h A trapezium has no lines of symmetry.

Development

The themes of this unit are developed in S1 in Year 8.

Links

Angle and shape properties and constructions are used in product design and analysis in technology.

Glossary

add, addition
N1.3, N1.4

Addition is the sum of two numbers or quantities.

algebra
A2.1, A2.2, A4.3

Algebra is the branch of mathematics where symbols or letters are used to represent numbers.

amount
N1.5, N4.3

Amount means total.

angle: acute, obtuse, right, reflex
S2.1, S3.1, S3.3, S5.1, S5.3

An angle is formed when two straight lines cross or meet each other at a point. The size of an angle is measured by the amount one line has been turned in relation to the other.

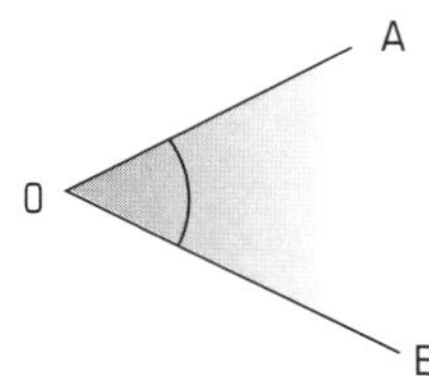

An acute angle is less than 90°.

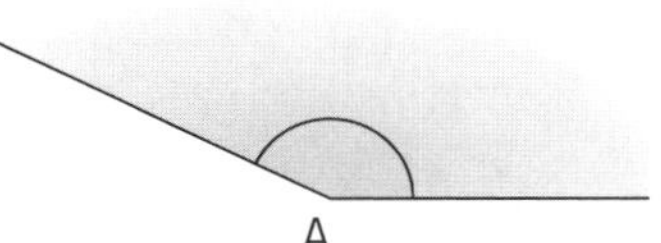

An obtuse angle is more than 90° but less than 180°.

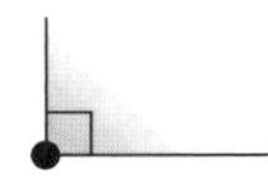

A right angle is a quarter of a turn, or 90°.

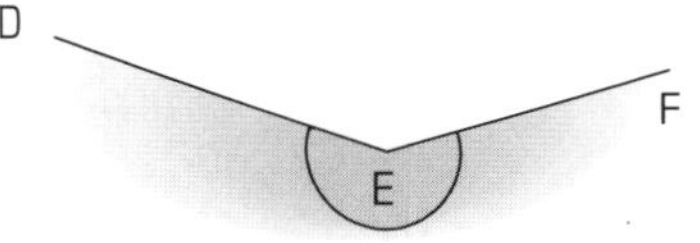

A reflex angle is more than 180° but less than 360°.

angles at a point
S3.2, S5.1

Angles at a point add up to 360°.

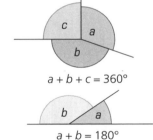

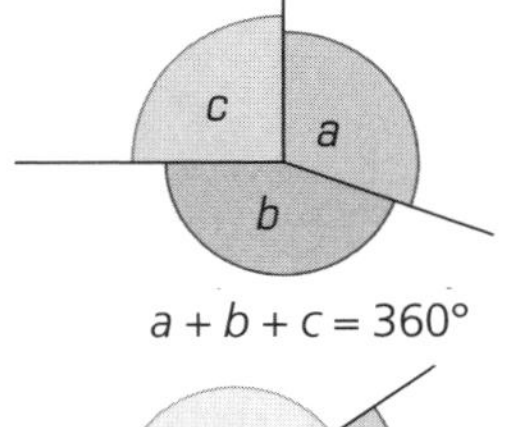

$a + b + c = 360°$

angles on a straight line
S3.2, S3.3, S3.4, S5.1

Angles on a straight line add up to 180°.

b
a

$a + b = 180°$

approximate, approximately
N1.6

An approximate value is a value that is close to the actual value of a number.

area: square millimetre, square centimetre, square metre, square kilometre
S1.1, S1.2, A5.2

The area of a surface is a measure of its size.

average
D1.1, D1.2, D3.4, D3.5

An average is a representative value of a set of data.

axis, axes
A5.7, A5.8

An axis is one of the lines used to locate a point in a coordinate system.

bar chart
D1.3, D2.4, D2.5, D3.2, D3.3

A bar chart is a diagram that uses rectangles of equal width to display data. The frequency is given by the height of the rectangle.

Glossary

bar-line graph
D2.4

A bar-line graph is a diagram that uses lines to display data. The lengths of the lines are proportional to the frequencies.

between
N1.6

Between means in the space bounded by two limits.

brackets
N3.2, N3.8, A4.3

Operations within brackets should be carried out first.

calculate, calculation
N1.3, N1.5

Calculate means work out using a mathematical procedure.

calculator: clear, display, enter, key, memory
N1.6, N3.8, N4.2

You can use a calculator to perform calculations.

cancel
N4.1

A fraction is cancelled down by dividing the numerator and denominator by a common factor.

For example, $\frac{24}{40} = \frac{3}{5}$ (÷ 8 top and bottom)

certain
D1.4

An event that is certain will definitely happen.

chance
D1.4

Chance is the probability of something happening.

compare
N4.5, N5.6

Compare means to assess the similarity of.

congruent
S5.6

Congruent shapes are exactly the same shape and size.

consecutive
A2.3

Consecutive means following on in order.
For example 2, 3 and 4 are consecutive integers.

construct
S3.4, S5.2, S5.3

To construct means to draw a line, angle or shape accurately.

convert
N2.4, N2.6, N3.1, N4.1, N5.7

Convert means to change.

coordinate pair
A3.6, A5.6, A5.7

A coordinate pair is a pair of numbers that give the position of a point on a coordinate grid.
For example, (3, 2) means 3 units across and 2 units up.

coordinates
A3.5, S2.3, S4.3

Coordinates are the numbers that make up a coordinate pair.

data
D1.1, D1.2, D2.4, D3.1

Data are pieces of information.

data collection sheet
D3.1

A data collection sheet is a sheet used to collect data. It is sometimes a list of questions with tick boxes for collecting answers.

decimals, decimal fraction
N1.5, N2.4, N2.6, N4.1, N5.1, N5.4, N5.7

A decimal fraction shows part of a whole represented as tenths, hundredths, thousandths and so on.
For example, 0.65 and 0.3 are decimal fractions.

decimal number
N1.1

A decimal number is a number written using base 10 notation.

decimal place (d.p.)
N3.5, N3.7

Each column after the decimal point is called a decimal place. For example, 0.65 has two decimal places (2 d.p.)

degree (°)
S2.1, S3.1, S3.2, S4.5, S5.1

A degree is a measure of turn. There are 360° in a full turn.

denominator
N2.1, N2.2, N2.3, N5.6, N5.8

The denominator is the bottom number in a fraction. It shows how many parts there are in total.

diagonal
S2.2

A diagonal of a polygon is a line joining any two vertices but not forming a side.

This is a diagonal.

difference
N1.2, N1.4

You find the difference between two amounts by subtracting one from the other.

digit
N1.1, N5.4

A digit is any of the numbers 0, 1, 2, 3, 4, 5, 6, 7, 8, 9.

direction
S4.5

The direction is the orientation of a line in space.

distance
S1.2, S1.3

The distance between two points is the length of the line that joins them.

divide, division
N2.1, N3.1, N3.2, N3.6, N5.3, N5.5, A3.1

Divide (÷) means share equally.

double, halve
N3.3

Double means multiply by two. Halve means divide by two.

draw
S3.4

Draw means create a picture or diagram

edge (of solid)
S3.5, S5.3

An edge is a line along which two faces of a solid meet.

edge

equal (sides, angles)
S3.3, S5.4

Equal sides are the same length. Equal angles are the same size.

equally likely
D1.5

Events are equally likely if they have the same probability.

equals (=)
A2.5, A3.4, A4.1, A5.1

Equals means having exactly the same value or size.

equation
A4.4, A5.1

An equation is a statement linking two expressions that have the same value.

equivalent, equivalence
N2.2, N2.4, N2.5, N2.6, N4.1, N4.2, N4.3, N5.6, N5.7

Equivalent fractions are fractions with the same value.

Glossary

estimate
D4.3, S3.1, N1.4, N1.5, N3.5, N3.7, N3.8, N5.4

An estimate is an approximate answer.

experiment
D1.6, D4.2, D4.3

An experiment is a test or investigation to gather evidence for or against a theory.

expression
A2.2, A2.3, A2.4, A4.1, A4.4, A5.1

An expression is a collection of numbers and symbols linked by operations but not including an equals sign.

face
S3.5, S5.3

A face is a flat surface of a solid.

face

factor
N3.6, N5.2, N5.3, A3.1, A3.2

A factor is a number that divides exactly into another number.
For example, 3 and 7 are factors of 21.

fair
D1.6, D4.3

In a fair experiment there is no bias towards any particular outcome.

fraction
N2.1, N2.2, N2.5, N4.1, N4.2, N4.3, N4.4, N4.5, N5.7, N5.8

A fraction is a way of describing a part of a whole.
For example $\frac{2}{5}$ of the shape shown is red.

frequency
D1.3, D4.2

Frequency is the number of times something occurs.

function
A3.4

A function is a rule.
For example, + 2, − 3, × 4 and ÷ 5 are all functions.

function machine
A3.4, A3.5, A3.6, A5.5, A5.6

A function machine links an input value to an output value by performing a function.

generate
A3.3, A5.4

Generate means produce.

graph
A5.7

A graph is a diagram that shows a relationship between variables.

greater than (>)
N1.1

Greater than means more than.
For example $4 > 3$.

grid
S2.3, A5.6

A grid is a repeated geometrical pattern used as a background to plot coordinate points. It is usually squared.

horizontal
A5.8, S4.3

Horizontal means flat and level with the ground.

hundredth
N1.1

A hundredth is 1 out of 100.
For example 0.05 has 5 hundredths.

image
S4.2

When a shape is reflected, translated or rotated, the new shape is called the image

object

image

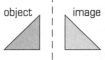

impossible
D1.4

An event is impossible if it definitely cannot happen.

improper fraction
N2.3

An improper fraction is a fraction where the numerator is greater than the denominator. For example, $\frac{8}{5}$ is an improper fraction.

increase, decrease
N1.2, N4.3

Increase means make greater. Decrease means make less.

input, output
A3.4, A3.5, A5.5, A5.6

Input is data fed into a machine or process. Output is the data produced by a machine or process.

integer
N2.5

An integer is a positive or negative whole number (including zero). The integers are: ..., $^{-}3$, $^{-}2$, $^{-}1$, 0, 1, 2, 3, ...

interpret
N3.8, D2.5, D3.3, D3.5, D3.2

You interpret data whenever you make sense of it.

intersect, intersection
S2.2

Two lines intersect at the point, or points, that they cross.

intersection

interval
D2.3

An interval is the size of a class or group in a frequency table.

length: millimetre, centimetre, metre, kilometre; mile, foot, inch
S1.1, S1.2, S1.3, A3.2

Length is a measure of distance. It is often used to describe one dimension of a shape.

less than (<)
N1.1

Less than means smaller than.
For example, 3 is less than 4, or 3 < 4.

likelihood
D4.1

Likelihood is the probability of an event happening.

likely
D1.4, D4.2

An event is likely if it will happen more often than not.

line graph
D3.2, D3.3

A line graph is a set of data points plotted on a graph and joined to show trends.

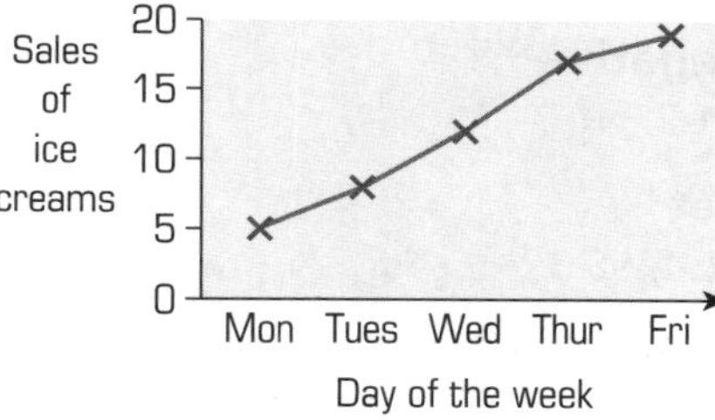

line of symmetry
S4.1, S5.4

A line of symmetry is a line about which a 2-D shape can be folded so that one half of the shape fits exactly on the other half.

line
S3.2, S3.3

A line joins two points and has zero thickness.

mean
D1.2, D3.4

The mean is an average value found by adding all the data values and dividing by the number of pieces of data.

measure
S1.3, S3.1, S3.4

When you measure something you find the size of it.

median
D1.1, D3.4

The median is an average which is the middle value when the data is arranged in size order.

mirror line
S4.1, S4.2, S4.4

A mirror line is a line or axis of symmetry.

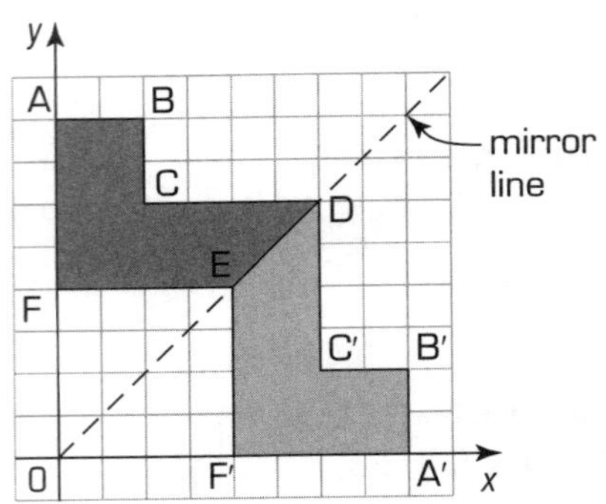

mixed number
N2.3

A mixed number has a whole number part and a fraction part. For example, $3\frac{1}{2}$ is a mixed number.

modal class
D3.4

The modal class is the most commonly occurring class when the data is grouped. It is the class with the highest frequency.

mode
D1.1, D3.4

The mode is an average which is the data value that occurs most often.

multiple
A3.4, A3.5, N3.1, N3.2, N3.6, N5.2, N5.6

A multiple of an integer is the product of that integer and any other. For example, these are multiples of 6: $6 \times 4 = 24$ and $6 \times 12 = 72$.

multiply, multiplication
N3.4, N5.4, N5.5

Multiplication is the operation of combining two numbers or quantities to form a product.

nearest
N1.6, N5.1

Nearest means the closest value.

negative
N1.2, N1.3

A negative number is a number less than zero.

net
S1.4, S5.3

A net is a 2-D arrangement that can be folded to form a solid shape.

numerator
N2.1, N2.2, N2.3, N5.6, N5.8

The numerator is the top number in a fraction. It shows how many parts you are dealing with.

object, image
S4.2

The object is the original shape before a transformation. An image is the same shape after a transformation.

operation
A4.2, A4.3, A5.1, N3.2

An operation is a rule for processing numbers or objects. The basic operations are addition, subtraction, multiplication and division.

opposite (sides, angles)
S2.2, S5.4

Opposite means across from.

The dark side is opposite the dark angle.

order
N1.1, N5.7

To order means to arrange according to size or importance.

order of operations
N3.2

The conventional order of operations is:
brackets first,
then division and multiplication,
then addition and subtraction.

order of rotation symmetry
S5.5

The order of rotation symmetry is the number of times that a shape will fit on to itself during a full turn.

outcome
D1.5, D1.6, D4.1, D4.2, D4.3

An outcome is the result of a trial or experiment.

parallel
S2.2, S5.4

Two lines that always stay the same distance apart are parallel. Parallel lines never cross or meet.

partition; part
N1.4, N3.3, N3.4, N5.3

To partition means to split a number into smaller amounts, or parts. For example, 57 could be split into 50 + 7, or 40 + 17.

percentage (%)
N2.6, N4.1, N4.2, N4.3, N4.4, N5.7, N5.8

A percentage is a fraction expressed as the number of parts per hundred.

perimeter
S1.1, S1.2

The perimeter of a shape is the distance around it. It is the total length of the edges.

perpendicular
S2.2

Two lines are perpendicular to each other if they meet at a right angle.

pie chart
D1.3, D2.4, D2.5, D3.2

A pie chart uses a circle to display data. The angle at the centre of a sector is proportional to the frequency.

place value
N1.1, N3.1

The place value is the value of a digit in a decimal number. For example, in 3.65 the digit 6 has a value of 6 tenths.

point
S3.2, S5.1

A point is a fixed place on a grid or on a shape.

polygon: pentagon, hexagon, octagon

A polygon is a closed shape with three or more straight edges.

A pentagon has five sides.

A hexagon has six sides.

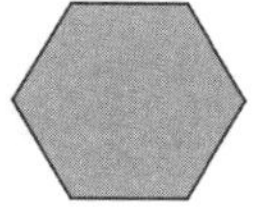

An octagon has eight sides.

positive
N1.2, N1.3

A positive number is greater than zero.

position
S2.3

A position is a place or location.

prime
N5.2, A3.1

A prime number is a number that has exactly two different factors.

probability
D1.4, D1.5, D4.1, D4.3

Probability is a measure of how likely an event is.

probability scale
D1.5, D4.1

A probability scale is a line numbered 0 to 1 or 0% to 100% on which you place an event based on its probability.

proportion
N4.4, N4.5

Proportion compares the size of a part to the size of a whole. You can express a proportion as a fraction, decimal or percentage.

protractor (angle measurer)
S3.1, S3.2, S3.4, S5.1, S5.2

A protractor is an instrument for measuring angles in degrees.

quadrant
A5.8, S4.3

A coordinate grid is divided into four quadrants by the *x*- and *y*-axes.

quadrilateral: kite, parallelogram, rectangle, rhombus, square, trapezium
S2.3, S3.2, S3.3, S5.2, S5.4

A quadrilateral is a polygon with four sides.

rectangle

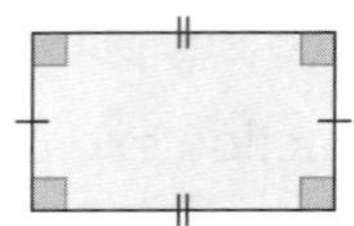

All angles are right angles. Opposite sides equal.

parallelogram

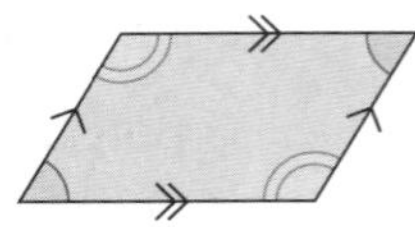

Two pairs of parallel sides.

kite

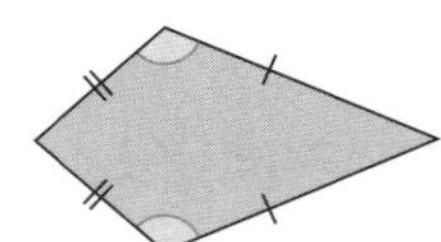

Two pairs of adjacent sides equal. No interior angle greater than 180°.

rhombus

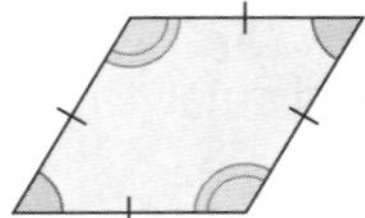

All sides the same length. Opposite angles equal.

square

All sides and angles equal.

trapezium

One pair of parallel sides.

questionnaire
D2.2

A questionnaire is a list of questions used to gather information in a survey.

quotient
N3.6

A quotient is the result of a division.
For example, the quotient of $12 \div 5$ is $2\frac{2}{5}$, or 2.4.

random
D1.5, D4.1

A selection is random if each object or number is equally likely to be chosen.

range
D2.3, D3.4

The range is the difference between the largest and smallest values in a set of data.

ratio
N4.5

Ratio compares the size of one part with the size of another part.

reflect, reflection
S4.2, S4.6, S4.3, S5.6
S4.4, S5.4

A reflection is a transformation in which corresponding points in the object and the image are the same distance from the mirror line.

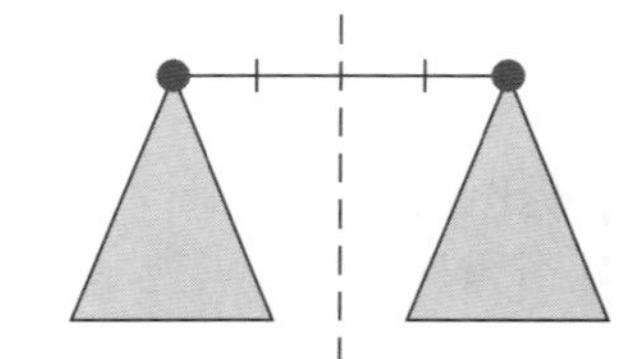

reflection symmetry
S4.1

A shape has reflection symmetry if it has a line of symmetry.

regular
S5.4

A regular polygon has equal sides and equal angles.

relationship
A2.5

A relationship is a link between objects or numbers.

remainder
N3.6, N5.5, A3.1

A remainder is the amount left over when one quantity is exactly divided by another. For example, $9 \div 4 = 2$ remainder 1.

rotate, rotation
S4.5, S4.6, S5.6

A rotation is a transformation in which every point in the object turns through the same angle relative to a fixed point.

rotation symmetry
S5.5

A shape has rotation symmetry if when turned it fits onto itself more than once during a full turn.

roughly
N3.5, N3.7

Roughly means about: 5362 is roughly 5000.

round
N1.6, N3.5, N5.1

You round a number by expressing it to a given degree of accuracy. For example, 639 is 600 to the nearest 100 and 640 to the nearest 10.
To round to one decimal place means to round to the nearest tenth. For example 12.47 is 12.5 to 1 d.p.

rule
A1.2, A2.2, A5.4

A rule describes the link between objects or numbers.
For example, the rule linking 2 and 6 may be +4 or ×3.

ruler
S1.3, S3.4, S5.2

A ruler is an instrument for measuring lengths.

scale
S1.3, N4.2

A scale is a numbered line or dial. The numbers usually increase in sequence.

sequence
A3.3, A5.4

A sequence is a set of numbers or objects that follow a rule.

shape
S4.3, S4.4

A shape is made by a line or lines drawn on a surface, or by putting surfaces together.

side (of 2-D shape)
S3.2

A side is a line segment joining vertices.

simplest form
N2.2, N4.4, N5.6

A fraction (or ratio) is in its simplest form when the numerator and denominator (or parts of the ratio) have no common factors.
For example, $\frac{3}{5}$ is expressed in its simplest form.

simplify
A2.3

To simplify an expression you gather all like terms together into a single term.

solid (3-D) shape: cube, cuboid, prism,
S3.5, S5.3

A solid is a shape formed in three-dimensional space.

cube

six square faces

cuboid

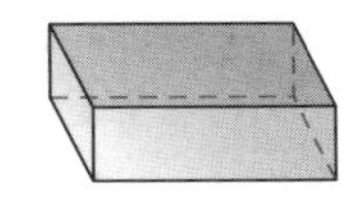

six rectangular faces

prism

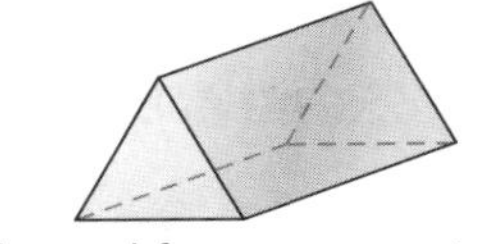

the end faces are constant

solve (an equation)
A5.1

To solve an equation you need to find the value of the variable that will make the equation true.

spin, spinner
D4.1, D4.2, D4.3, S5.5

A spinner is an instrument for creating random outcomes, usually in probability experiments.

square number, squared

If you multiply a number by itself the result is a square number.

A3.2, A3.3 — For example 25 is a square number because $5^2 = 5 \times 5 = 25$.

statistic, statistics
D1.3, D3.5 — Statistics is the collection, display and analysis of information.

straight line
S5.1 — A straight line is the shortest distance between two points

straight-line graph
A3.6 — When coordinate points lie in a straight line they form a straight-line graph. It is the graph of a linear equation.

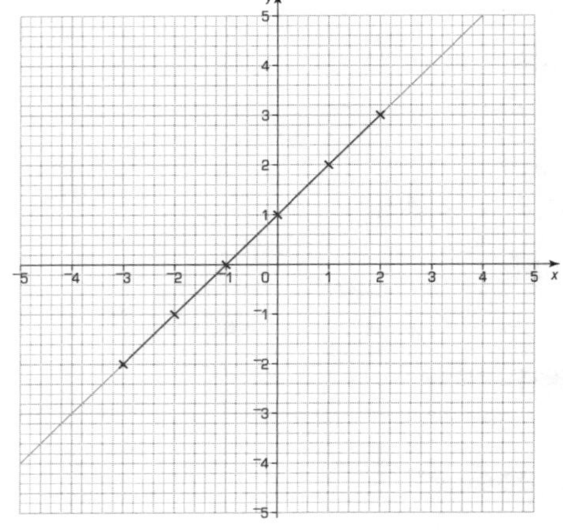

substitute
A2.4, A5.2, A5.3 — When you substitute you replace part of an expression with a value.

subtract, subtraction
N1.3, N1.4, N3.6, N5.5 — Subtraction is the operation that finds the difference in size between two numbers.

sum
N1.5 — The sum is the total and is the result of an addition.

surface, surface area
S1.4 — The surface area of a solid is the total area of its faces.

survey
D2.1, D2.2 — A survey is an investigation to find information.

table
D1.3, D2.3, A3.6, D3.2, A5.7 — A table is an arrangement of information, numbers or letters usually in rows and columns.

tally
D2.3, D1.3, D1.6, D4.2 — You use a tally mark to represent an object when you collect data. Tally marks are usually made in groups of five to make it easier to count them.

temperature: degrees Celsius, degrees Fahrenheit — Temperature is a measure of how hot something is.

tenth
N1.1 — A tenth is 1 out of 10 or $\frac{1}{10}$.
For example 0.5 has 5 tenths.

term
A2.3 — A term is a number or object in a sequence. It is also part of an expression.

three-dimensional (3-D)
S1.4, S3.5, S5.3 — Any solid shape is three-dimensional.

time
S2.1

Time is a measure of duration.
There are:

- 60 seconds in a minute
- 60 minutes in an hour
- 7 days in a week
- 28–31 days in a month
- 365 days in most years

total
N1.5, N3.5

The total is the result of an addition.

transformation
S4.6

A transformation moves a shape from one place to another.

translate, translation
S4.4, S4.6, S5.6

A translation is a transformation in which every point in an object moves the same distance and direction. It is a sliding movement.

triangle: equilateral, isosceles, scalene, right-angled
S2.3, S3.3, S3.4, S5.2

A triangle is a polygon with three sides.

equilateral

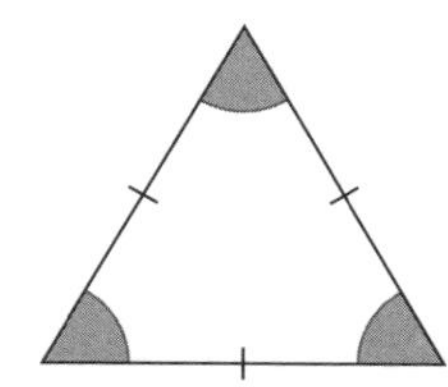

three equal sides

isosceles

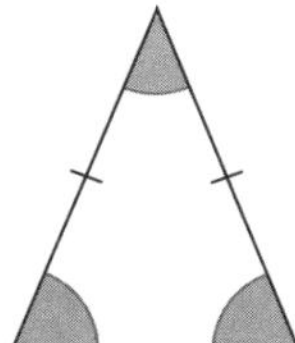

two equal sides

scalene

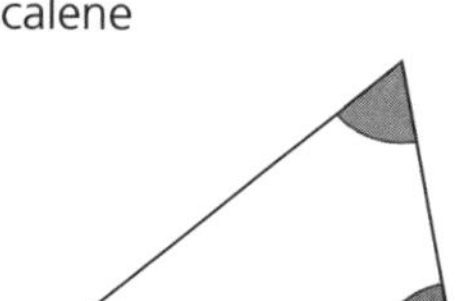

no equal sides

right-angled

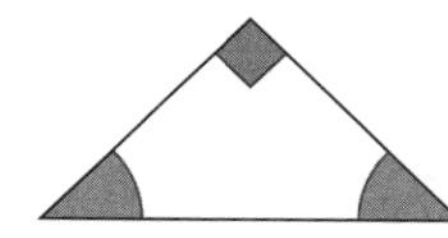

one angle is 90°

triangular number
A3.3

A triangular number is the number of dots in a triangular pattern:
The numbers form the sequence
1, 3, 6, 10, 15, 21, 28 ...

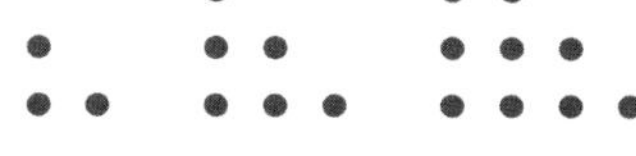

two-dimensional (2-D)
S3.5

A flat shape has two dimensions, length and width or base and height.

unknown
A2.1, A2.2, A2.3, A4.1, A4.2, A4.4, A5.2, A5.3

An unknown is a variable. You can often find its value by solving an equation.

unit
S1.1

A unit is a standard measure or quantity that other quantities can be measured from.

value
A2.2, A2.4, A2.5, A4.1, A4.2, A4.4, A5.1, A5.2, A5.3

The value is the amount an expression or variable is worth.

variable
A2.1, A2.4, A2.5, A4.4, A5.2

A variable is a symbol that can take a range of values.

vertex, vertices
S3.5, S4.3, S5.3

A vertex of a shape is a point at which two or more edges meet.

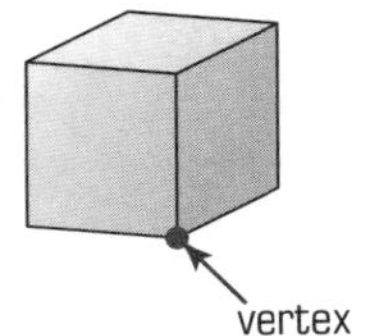

vertical
S4.3, A5.8

Vertical means straight up and down.

vertically opposite angles
S3.3

When two straight lines cross they form two pairs of equal angles called vertically opposite angles.

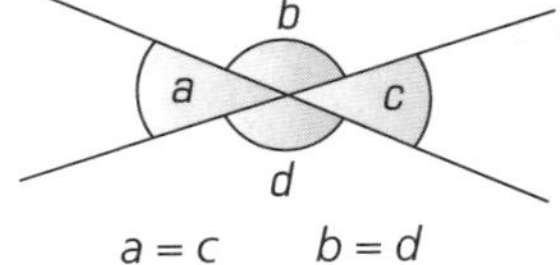

whole number
N2.5

A whole number has no fractional part.

width
S1.1, S1.2, S1.3

Width is a dimension of an object describing how wide it is.

***x*-axis, *y*-axis**
S2.3

On a coordinate grid, the *x*-axis is usually the horizontal axis and the *y*-axis is usually the vertical axis.

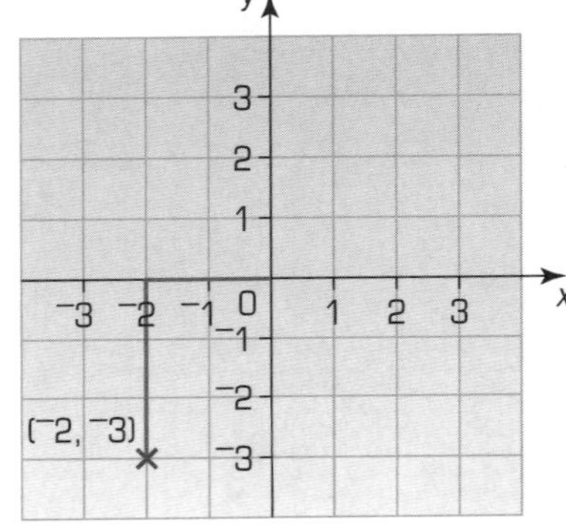

***x*-coordinate, *y*-coordinate**
A5.8

The *x*-coordinate is the distance along the *x*-axis.
The *y*-coordinate is the distance along the *y*-axis.
For example, (⁻2, ⁻3) is ⁻2 along the *x*-axis and ⁻3 along the *y*-axis.

Answers

A1 Check in

1 **a** 2, 5, 8, 11, 14
b 20, 16, 12, 8, 4

2 **a** 20 **b** 9 **c** 20 **d** 7
e 10 **f** 6 **g** 30 **h** 8

3 **a** 4 **b** 5 **c** 7 **d** 6
e 9 **f** 8 **g** 6 **h** 8

A1 Check out

1 **a** 0, 4, 8, 12,16 **b** 1, 2, 4, 8, 16
c 10, 7, 4, 1, $^{-}2$ **d** 15, 21, 27, 33, 39
e First term is 3. Rule is +2
f First term is 20. Rule is −3
g First term is 2. Rule is ×2
h First term is 0. Rule is −1

2 **a** There are *n* dogs in a park.
b There is *x* kg of chocolate eaten each week in the UK.
c *n* people own a skateboard.
d There are *x* fleas on a cat.
e There are *n* fish in the sea.

3 **a** 5
b

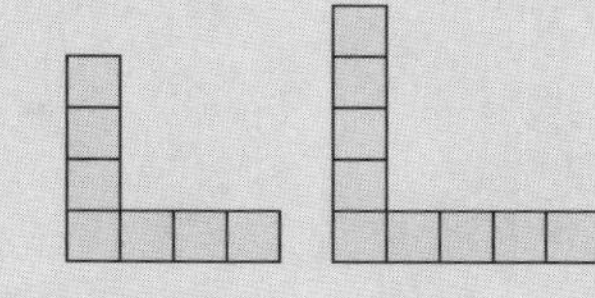

c 11 **d** 39

N1 Check in

1 **a** Forty three
b 87
c 14
d Sixty

2 **a**

0 20
3 5 6 7 11 14 17

3 **a** 40 **b** 25 **c** 19 **d** 63

N1 Check out

1 **a** Three point five six
b Three units
b Six hundredths
b 4

2 **a** 9° C **b** 5° C **c** 9° C **d** $^{-}5$° C

3 **a** 54 **b** 35 **c** £3.50 **d** £5.40
e 339 **f** 2.9

4 **a** 450 **b** 806 **c** 659.7 **d** 438

5 **a** 86 **b** 19 **c** 335 **d** 1350
e 187 **f** 1103 **g** 3679 **h** £3.74
i 283 **j** 439 **k** 3.4 **l** 406

6 1.33 m 1.35 m 1.5 m 1.53 m
1.55 m 2.35 m

S1 Check in

1 9 squares
2 3 cm
3 7

S1 Check out

1 **a** 75 cm^2
b 1 cm × 48 cm
2 cm × 24 cm
3 cm × 16 cm
4 cm × 12 cm
6 cm × 8 cm
2 60 cm^2
3 24 squares

N2 Check in

1 **a** 12 **b** 5 **c** 25 **d** 18
e 7 **f** 42
2 **a** 35 **b** 28 **c** 47 **d** 53
e 48

N2 Check out

1 **a i** $\frac{2}{9}$ **ii** $\frac{4}{9}$ **iii** $\frac{3}{9}$
b i $\frac{7}{20}$ **ii** $\frac{13}{20}$ **iii** $\frac{11}{20}$
iv $\frac{5}{20}$ **v** $\frac{16}{20}$ **vi** $\frac{4}{20}$
c i $\frac{1}{2}$ **ii** $\frac{50}{200}$ **iii** $\frac{25}{200}$ **iv** $\frac{40}{200}$
d i 43 p **ii** 15 cm **iii** 45 cm
iv 4 p **v** 18 p **vi** 36 minutes
2 **a i** $\frac{1}{2}=\frac{7}{14}$ **ii** $\frac{1}{4}=\frac{3}{12}$ **iii** $\frac{2}{3}=\frac{10}{15}$
b i $\frac{3}{6}=\frac{1}{2}$ **ii** $\frac{4}{8}=\frac{1}{2}$ **iii** $\frac{2}{6}=\frac{1}{3}$
iv $\frac{3}{9}=\frac{1}{3}$ **v** $\frac{4}{10}=\frac{2}{5}$
3 **a i** $\frac{3}{7}$ **ii** $\frac{5}{8}$ **iii** $\frac{2}{9}$
iv $\frac{4}{8}$ **v** $\frac{4}{11}$ **vi** $\frac{5}{11}$
b i 0.5 **ii** 0.25 **iii** 0.1
iv 0.75 **v** 0.7 **vi** 0.2
4

30%	0.3	$\frac{3}{10}$
40%	0.4	$\frac{2}{5}$
25%	0.25	$\frac{1}{4}$
7%	0.07	$\frac{7}{100}$

D1 Check in

1 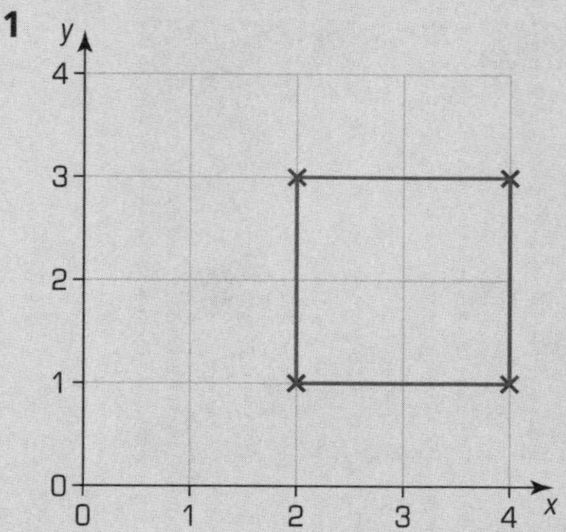

It is a square.

2 A is 5

B is 14

C is 17

D is 22

D1 Check out

1 **a** 17

b 17

c 16.5

d 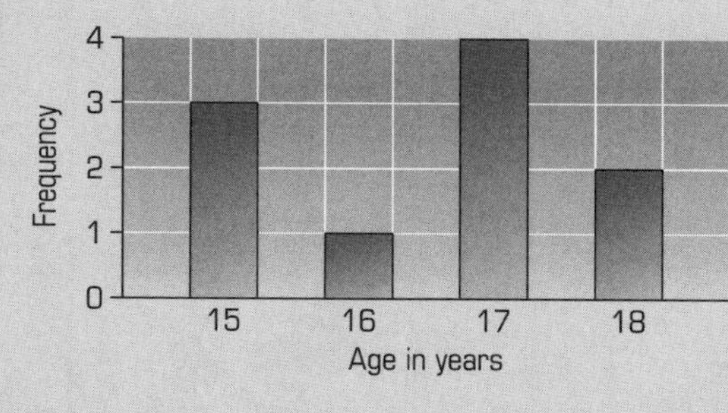

e **i** $\frac{3}{10}$ **ii** $\frac{2}{10}$ or $\frac{1}{5}$ **iii** $\frac{5}{10}$ or $\frac{1}{5}$ **iv** 1

f 

A2 Check in

1 **a**	5	**b**	18
c	5	**d**	8
e	2	**f**	5
g	8	**h**	8
i	9	**j**	15
k	28	**l**	28
m	90	**n**	90
o	11	**p**	11

A2 Check out

1	**a**	$d - 5$	**b**	$n + 2$		
	c	$y + 5$	**d**	$3x$	**e**	$\frac{x}{4}$
2	**a**	$x - 6$	**b**	$y + 3$		
	c	$z + 4$	**d**	$7 - f$		
	e	$4x$	**f**	$7y$		
	g	$\frac{26}{z}$	**h**	$\frac{h}{5}$		
	i	$5y$	**j**	$\frac{12}{x}$		
	k	$8 - x$	**l**	$x - 8$		
3	**a**	$29n$	**b**	$35m$	**c**	my

S2 Check in

1 **a** Clockwise
  b Anticlockwise
  c Anticlockwise
  d Clockwise

2 A = (1, 3)
  B = (4, 2)

S2 Check out

1 and **2**

3 **a** 36 minutes
  b 5 minutes
  c 8 minutes

D2 Check in

1

2 It is Tuesday because it has the highest bar.

D2 Check out

1 **a** 7 students
  b 8 girls
  c The girls were happier overall as more of them rated the meals good or very good.

2 A is true
  B is false – only a quarter of the people were playing either badminton or squash.
  C is true

N3 Check in

1 **a** **i** 56 **ii** 42 **iii** 72 **iv** 44
b **i** 459 **ii** 515 **iii** 485 **iv** 254
2 **a** 21 **b** 8 **c** 36 **d** 40 **e** 5
3 **a** 1979 **b** 158
c 756 **d** 25 290
e 523 **f** 347

N3 Check out

1 **a** 12 **b** 4 **c** 24
d 35 **e** 6 **f** 63
g 8 **h** 300 **i** 6500
j 32 **k** 45 **l** 5.2
2 **a** 17 **b** 13
c 8 **d** 0
e 6 **f** 10
3 **a** 253 **b** 405
c 432 **d** 517
4 **a** 228 stickers
b 900 candles
c 164 boxes
d 400 metres, 84 seconds or 1 minute 24 seconds.

A3 Check in

1 **a** 10 **b** 70
c 7 **d** 5
e 9 **f** 10
2 **a** odd: 15, 2657, 3001, 22 223
even: 12
b 12 pens and 4 books
3 An L shape:

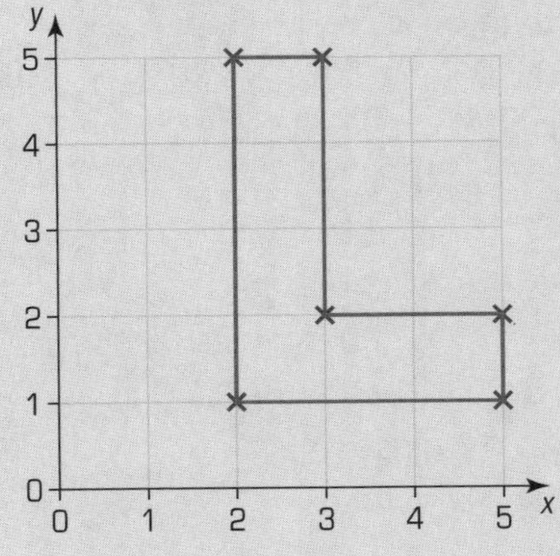

A3 Check out

1 Multiples of 2: 50, 36, 100, 20
Multiples of 3: 36, 231
Multiples of 4: 36, 100, 20
Multiples of 5: 50, 100, 20, 25
Multiples of 10: 50, 100, 20
2 36: 1×36, 2×18, 3×12, 4×9, 6×6
49: 1×49, 7×7
100: 1×100, 2×50, 4×25, 5×20, 10×10
25: 1×25, 5×5
3

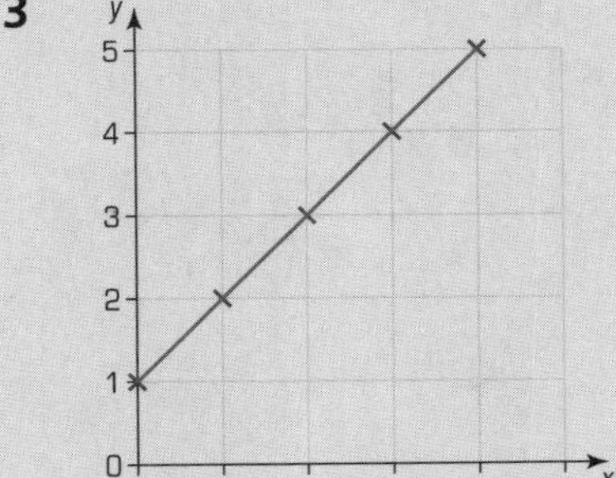

4 **a**

Pattern numbers	1	2	3
Number of matchsticks	4	7	10

b 13 matchsticks

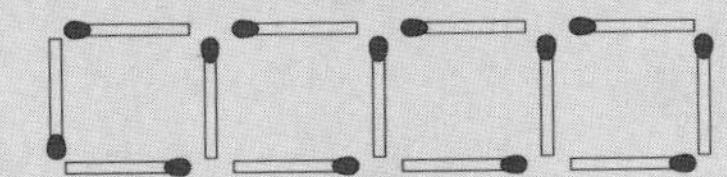

c 61 matchsticks

S3 Check in

1. **a** Equilateral
   b Isosceles
   c Right-angled isosceles
   d Right-angled
   e Scalene

S3 Check out

1. 5 cm
2. **a** $a = 34°$
   b $b = 34°$
3. **a** $c = 112°$
   b $d = 68°$
   c 180°
4. 10 cubes
5. 36 rectangles

N4 Check in

1. **a** 33% **b** 71% **c** 50% **d** 25%
2. $\frac{1}{2} = \frac{4}{8}$, $\frac{2}{20} = \frac{1}{10}$, $\frac{1}{5} = \frac{2}{10}$, $\frac{1}{4} = \frac{3}{12}$, $\frac{3}{9} = \frac{1}{3}$
3. **a** 14 cm **b** 6 minutes
   c 45 cm **d** £15
   e £20 **f** 45 minutes

N4 Check out

1. **a** $\frac{60}{100}$ **b** $\frac{32}{100}$ **c** $\frac{7}{100}$ **d** $\frac{25}{100}$ **e** $\frac{15}{100}$
   f 50% **g** 10% **h** 30% **i** 20% **j** 40%
2. **a** $\frac{3}{5}$ **b** $\frac{8}{25}$ **c** $\frac{7}{100}$ **d** $\frac{1}{4}$ **e** $\frac{3}{20}$
3. **a** £13 **b** £35
   c £12 **d** £36
   e 6 cm **f** 3 minutes
   g 30 cm **h** 60 minutes
4. **a** $\frac{1}{4}$ **b** $\frac{3}{4}$ **c** 1 : 3
5. **a** 18 boys , 12 girls
   b 18 men , 42 women
   c 15 men

A4 Check in

1 a 21 b 54
c 36 d 56
e 6 f 3
g 9 h 10
i 5 j 6
k 36 l 55
m 18 n 24
o 7 p 1.5
q 2 r $\frac{3}{4}$

A4 Check out

1 a $n+5$ b $n-3$
c $n+2$ d $4-n$
e $\frac{n}{2}$ f $\frac{n}{3}$
g $3n$ h $3n+4$
i $5 \times 7 = 35$ so $35 \div 5 = 7$
j $5 \times x = 35$ so $35 \div 5 = x$
k $x = 11$ l $y = 17$
m $x = 6$ n $y = 15$
0 $x = 3$

2 For example:
a The total cost of 12 cans of drink costing 37p each.
b $2 + x$: I have some counters and find two more.
$n - 5$: I have some counters and lose five of them.
$3m$: A plant was m metres tall and is now three times as high.
$\frac{d}{4}$: Four friends share a pizza that costs £d.

S4 Check in

1 TRANSFORMATION
2 a Square
b Rectangle
c Kite
d Isosceles trapezium
e Quadrilateral
f Rhombus
g Parallelogram
h Trapezium

S4 Check out

1 a (0, 0) (0, 3) (3, 3)
b (0, 0) ($^-3$, 0) ($^-3$, $^-3$)
c (1, $^-1$) (1, $^-4$) (4, $^-4$)
2 a Translation: 4 right and 4 down
b Reflection in x axis
c Rotation clockwise through 90°, centre (0, 0)
d Translation: 3 right and 3 up.
e Translation: 4 left and 4 up.
3 These complete shapes have line symmetry:

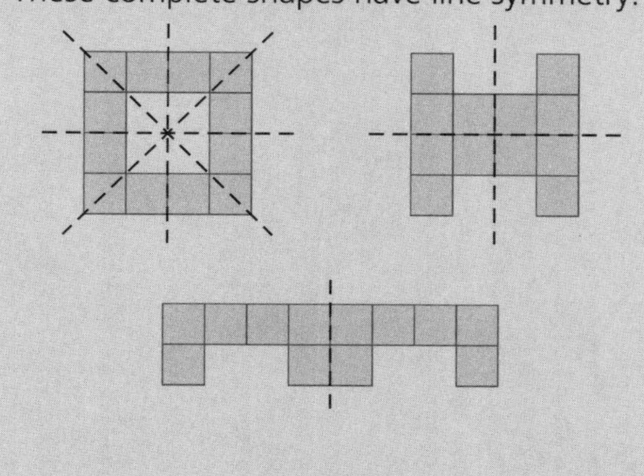

N5 Check in

1 **a** 25 **b** 36 **c** 5 **d** 4 **e** 72 **f** 9
2 **a** 0.5 **b** 0.25 **c** 0.75 **d** 0.1 **e** 0.7 **f** 0.2
3 **a** 31% **b** 63% **c** 7% **d** 50%
e 25% **f** 10% **g** 31% **h** 63%
i 7% **j** 50% **k** 25% **l** 10%
5 **a** 930 ($62 \times 10 = 620$
$62 \times 5 = 310$
so $62 \times 15 = 930$)
b £350: 10% = 200
5% = 100
2.5% = 50
so 17.5% = 350
c 703: $37 \times 20 - 37 \times 1$
d £1.35: 45p × 3
6 **a** $\frac{1}{4}$ **b** $\frac{5}{7}$ **c** $\frac{3}{10}$ **d** $\frac{1}{5}$
e $\frac{3}{5}$ **f** $\frac{2}{5}$ **g** $\frac{7}{20}$ **h** $\frac{3}{20}$

N5 Check out

1 **i** **a** 2730 **b** 2700 **c** 3000
ii **a** 5770 **b** 5800 **c** 6000
iii **a** 570 **b** 600 **c** 1000
iv **a** 330 **b** 300 **c** 0
2 **a** 1452 **b** 5313
c 3105 **d** 11 891
e 56 **f** 68
g 52 **h** 38
3 **a** £32 **b** £4.50
c 5 cm **d** 10 cm
e 2 mins **f** 150 metres
g 70° **h** 3 minutes
i 9 mins **j** 21 cm
4 **a** 5 **b** 15
c 7 **d** 21
e £40 **f** £280
g 60 litres **h** 15 kg
i 24 students **j** 25 students

D3 Check in

1 **a** A: 40, B: 86, C: 150, D: 180, E: 220, F: 275
b A: 40, B: 90, C: 125, D: 160, E: 173
2

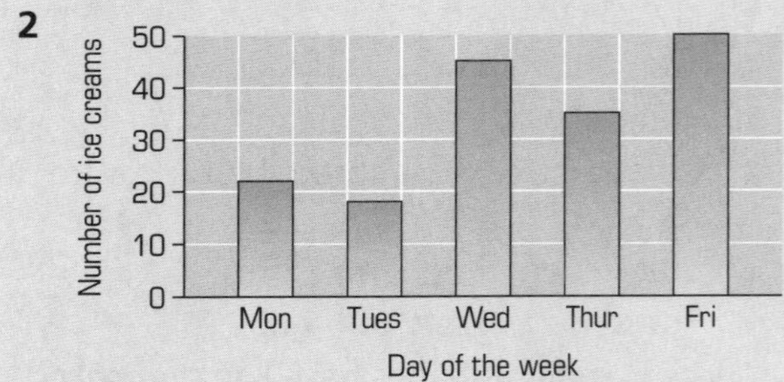

D3 Check out

1 Maths: mean = 63.6%
median = 64.5%
range = 64
Science: mean = 59.3%
median = 53.5%
range = 58

In general students did better in maths. The average score was higher and 7 out of 10 students scored 55 or above in maths compared with 5 out of 10 students in science.

2 Most people, 30 out of 43 or 70% rated the food good or excellent but almost 10% of the respondents found the food poor implying the hotel should improve its standards.

A bar chart would be most suitable to display this data.

D4 Check in

1 **b** **a** **c**

2 **a** = $\frac{1}{2}$ **b** = $\frac{1}{10}$ **c** = $\frac{8}{10}$ or $\frac{4}{5}$

D4 Check out

1 **a** $\frac{1}{10}$ **b** $\frac{9}{10}$ **c** 0 **d** 1

2 **a** The blue dice has widely varying results which suggest there may be bias.

b

	Dice		
Score	Red	Blue	Green
1	$\frac{35}{240}$	$\frac{34}{240}$	$\frac{44}{240}$
2	$\frac{48}{240}$	$\frac{63}{240}$	$\frac{34}{240}$
3	$\frac{33}{240}$	$\frac{37}{240}$	$\frac{42}{240}$
4	$\frac{45}{240}$	$\frac{28}{240}$	$\frac{42}{240}$
5	$\frac{40}{240}$	$\frac{40}{240}$	$\frac{39}{240}$
6	$\frac{39}{240}$	$\frac{38}{240}$	$\frac{39}{240}$

A5 Check in

1 **a** $5d$

b $d + 6$

c $d - 5$

d $\frac{d}{2}$

2

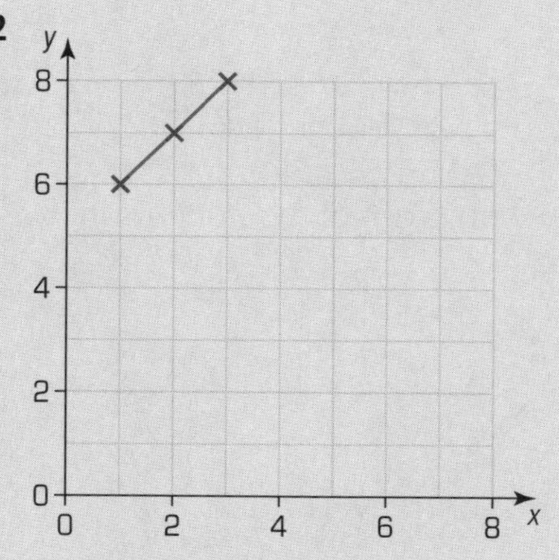

They form a straight line.

A5 Check out

1 **a** MATHEMATICS

b Students own answer.

2 **a**

x	1	2	3	4	5
y	1	3	5	7	9

b (1, 1) (2, 3) (3, 5) (4, 7) (5, 9)

c and **d**

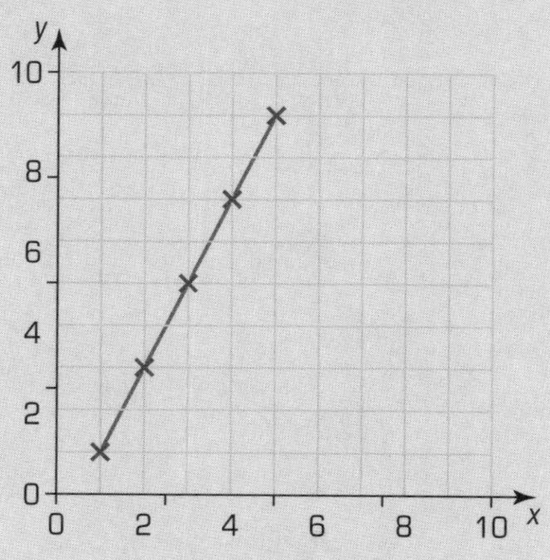

e 6

S5 Check in

1 **a** 136° **b** 44°

2 **a** Blue **b** Green **c** Red **d** Purple
e Pink **f** Yellow **g** Blue **h** Green

S5 Check out

1 **a**

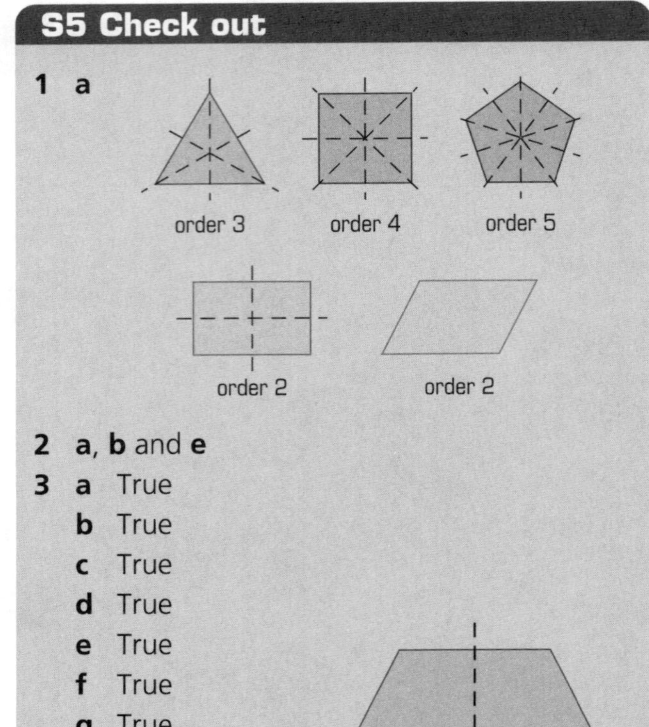

2 **a**, **b** and **e**

3 **a** True
b True
c True
d True
e True
f True
g True
h False

Index

O

P

Q

R

S

Multiplication Table

×	1	2	3	4	5	6	7	8	9	10
1	1	2	3	4	5	6	7	8	9	10
2	2	4	6	8	10	12	14	16	18	20
3	3	6	9	12	15	18	21	24	27	30
4	4	8	12	16	20	24	28	32	36	40
5	5	10	15	20	25	30	35	40	45	50
6	6	12	18	24	30	36	42	48	54	60
7	7	14	21	28	35	42	49	56	63	70
8	8	16	24	32	40	48	56	64	72	80
9	9	18	27	36	45	54	63	72	81	90
10	10	20	30	40	50	60	70	80	90	100